UMass Amherst
Department of Resource Economics

Custom Edition of

Applied Statistics
in Business & Economics
Third Edition

David P. Doane
Oakland University

Lori E. Seward
University of Colorado

Volume 2

Learning Solutions

Boston Burr Ridge, IL Dubuque, IA New York San Francisco St. Louis
Bangkok Bogotá Caracas Lisbon London Madrid
Mexico City Milan New Delhi Seoul Singapore Sydney Taipei Toronto

UMass Amherst
Department of Resource Economics
Custom Edition of
Applied Statistics in Business & Economics, Third Edition
Volume 2

This book is a McGraw-Hill Learning Solutions textbook and contains select material from *Applied Statistics in Business & Economics*, Third Edition by David P. Doane and Lori E. Seward. Copyright © 2011, 2009, 2007 by The McGraw-Hill Companies, Inc. Reprinted with permission of the publisher. Many custom published texts are modified versions or adaptations of our best-selling textbooks. Some adaptations are printed in black and white to keep prices at a minimum, while others are in color.

1 2 3 4 5 6 7 8 9 0 WDD WDD 12 11 10

ISBN-13: 978-0-07-744907-0
ISBN-10: 0-07-744907-X

Learning Solutions Manager: Domenic DiNardo
Production Editor: Jessica Portz
Printer/Binder: Worldcolor

ABOUT THE AUTHORS

David P. Doane

David P. Doane is a professor of quantitative methods in Oakland University's Department of Decision and Information Sciences. He earned his Bachelor of Arts degree in mathematics and economics at the University of Kansas and his PhD from Purdue University's Krannert Graduate School. His research and teaching interests include applied statistics, forecasting, and statistical education. He is corecipient of three National Science Foundation grants to develop software to teach statistics and to create a computer classroom. He is a longtime member of the American Statistical Association and INFORMS, serving in 2002 as president of the Detroit ASA chapter, where he remains on the board. He has consulted with government, health care organizations, and local firms. He has published articles in many academic journals and is the author of *LearningStats* (McGraw-Hill, 2003, 2007) and co-author of *Visual Statistics* (McGraw-Hill, 1997, 2001).

Lori E. Seward

Lori E. Seward is an instructor in the Decisions Sciences Department in the College of Business at the University of Colorado at Denver and Health Sciences Center. She earned her Bachelor of Science and Master of Science degrees in Industrial Engineering at Virginia Tech. After several years working as a reliability and quality engineer in the paper and automotive industries, she earned her PhD from Virginia Tech. She served as the chair of the INFORMS Teachers' Workshop for the annual 2004 meeting. Prior to joining UCDHSC in 2008, Dr. Seward served on the faculty at the Leeds School of Business at the University of Colorado–Boulder for 10 years. Her teaching interests focus on developing pedagogy that uses technology to create a collaborative learning environment in both large undergraduate and MBA statistics courses. Her most recent article was published in *The International Journal of Flexible Manufacturing Systems* (Kluwer Academic Publishers, 2004).

DEDICATION

To Robert Hamilton Doane-Solomon

David

To all my students who challenged me to make statistics relevant to their lives.

Lori

"How often have you heard people/students say about a particular subject, 'I'll never use this in the real world?' I thought statistics was a bit on the 'math-geeky' side at first. Imagine my horror when I saw α, R^2, and correlations on several financial reports at my current job (an intern position at a financial services company). I realized then that I had better try to understand some of this stuff."

—Jill Odette (an introductory statistics student)

As recently as a decade ago our students used to ask us, "**How** do I use statistics?" Today we more often hear, "**Why** should I use statistics?" *Applied Statistics in Business and Economics* has attempted to provide real meaning to the use of statistics in our world by using real business situations and real data and appealing to your need to know *why* rather than just *how*.

With over 50 years of teaching statistics between the two of us, we feel we have something to offer. Seeing how students have changed as the new century unfolds has required us to adapt and seek out better ways of instruction. So we wrote *Applied Statistics in Business and Economics* to meet four distinct objectives.

Objective 1: Communicate the Meaning of Variation in a Business Context Variation exists everywhere in the world around us. Successful businesses know how to measure variation. They also know how to tell when variation should be responded to and when it should be left alone. We'll show how businesses do this.

Objective 2: Use Real Data and Real Business Applications Examples, case studies, and problems are taken from published research or real applications whenever possible. Hypothetical data are used when it seems the best way to illustrate a concept. You can usually tell the difference by examining the footnotes citing the source.

Objective 3: Incorporate Current Statistical Practices and Offer Practical Advice With the increased reliance on computers, statistics practitioners have changed the way they use statistical tools. We'll show the current practices and explain why they are used the way they are. We will also tell you when each technique should *not* be used.

Objective 4: Provide More In-Depth Explanation of the Why and Let the Software Take Care of the How It is critical to understand the importance of communicating with data. Today's computer capabilities make it much easier to summarize and display data than ever before. We demonstrate easily mastered software techniques using the common software available. We also spend a great deal of time on the idea that there are risks in decision making and those risks should be quantified and directly considered in every business decision.

Our experience tells us that students want to be given credit for the experience they bring to the college classroom. We have tried to honor this by choosing examples and exercises set in situations that will draw on students' already vast knowledge of the world and knowledge gained from other classes. Emphasis is on thinking about data, choosing appropriate analytic tools, using computers effectively, and recognizing limitations of statistics.

What's New in This Third Edition?

In this third edition we have listened to you and have made many changes that you asked for. We sought advice from students and faculty who are currently using the textbook, objective reviewers at a variety of colleges and universities, and participants in focus groups on teaching statistics with technology. At the end of this preface is a detailed list of chapter-by-chapter improvements, but here are just a few of them:

- Revised learning objectives mapped to topics within chapter sections.

- Step-by-step instructions on using Excel 2007 for descriptive statistics, histograms, scatter plots, line charts, fitting trends, and editing charts.

- More "practice" exercises and more worked examples in the textbook.

- Sixteen large, real data sets that can be downloaded for class projects.

- Many updated exercises and new skill-focused "business context" exercises.

- Appendix on writing technical business reports and presenting them orally.

- Expanded treatment of business ethics and critical thinking skills.

- Closer compatibility between textbook exercises and Connect online grading.

- Rewritten instructor's manual with step-by-step solutions.

AUTHORS

- New Mini Cases featuring Vail Resorts, Inc., a mountain resort company.

- Consistent notation for random variables and event probabilities.

- Improved flow of normal distribution concepts and matching exercises.

- Restructured material on sampling distributions, estimation, and hypothesis testing.

- Intuitive explanations and illustrations of p-values and steps in hypothesis testing.

- New format for hypotheses in tests of two means or two proportions.

- Moved two-sample confidence intervals to chapter on two-sample hypothesis tests.

- More coverage of covariance and its role in financial analysis.

- More emphasis on interpretation of regression results.

- End of each chapter guides to downloads from the **Online Learning Center** (simulations, demonstrations, tips, and ScreenCam video tutorials for Excel, *MegaStat*, and MINITAB).

Software

Excel is used throughout this book because it is available everywhere. But calculations are illustrated using *MegaStat*, an Excel add-in whose Excel-based menus and spreadsheet format offer more capability than Excel's Data Analysis Tools. MINITAB menus and examples are also included to point out similarities and differences of these tools. To assist students who need extra help or "catch up" work, the text Web site contains tutorials or demonstrations on using Excel, MINITAB, or *MegaStat* for the tasks of each chapter. At the end of each chapter is a list of *LearningStats* demonstrations that illustrate the concepts from the chapter. These demonstrations can be downloaded from the text Web site (**www.mhhe.com/doane3e**).

Math Level

The assumed level of mathematics is pre-calculus, though there are rare references to calculus where it might help the better-trained reader. All but the simplest proofs and derivations are omitted, though key assumptions are stated clearly. The learner is advised what to do when these assumptions are not fulfilled. Worked examples are included for basic calculations, but the textbook does assume that computers will do all calculations after the statistics class is over. Thus, *interpretation* is paramount. End-of-chapter references and suggested Web sites are given so that interested readers can deepen their understanding.

Exercises

Simple practice exercises are placed within each section. End-of-chapter exercises tend to be more integrative or to be embedded in more realistic contexts. The end-of-chapter exercises encourage the learner to try alternative approaches and discuss ambiguities or underlying issues when the statistical tools do not quite "fit" the situation. Some exercises invite miniessays (at least a sentence or two) rather than just quoting a formula. Answers to most odd-numbered exercises are in the back of the book (all answers are in the instructor's manual).

LearningStats

LearningStats is intended to let students explore data and concepts at their own pace, ignoring material they already know and focusing on things that interest them. *LearningStats* includes explanations on topics that are not covered in other software packages, such as how to write effective reports, how to perform calculations, how to make effective charts, or how the bootstrap method works. It also includes some topics that did not appear prominently in the textbook (e.g., stem-and-leaf plots, finite population correction factor, and bootstrap simulation techniques). Instructors can use *LearningStats* PowerPoint presentations in the classroom, but students can also use them for self-instruction. No instructor can "cover everything," but students can be encouraged to explore *LearningStats* data sets and/or demonstrations perhaps with an instructor's guidance, or even as an assigned project.

David P. Doane
Lori E. Seward

HOW ARE CHAPTERS ORGANIZED

Chapter Contents

Each chapter begins with a short list of section topics that are covered in the chapter.

Chapter Learning Objectives

Each chapter includes a list of learning objectives students should be able to attain upon reading and studying the chapter material. Learning objectives give students an overview of what is expected and identify the goals for learning. Learning objectives also appear next to chapter topics in the margins.

Chapter Contents

1.1	What Is Statistics?
1.2	Why Study Statistics?
1.3	Uses of Statistics
1.4	Statistical Challenges
1.5	Critical Thinking

Chapter Learning Objectives

When you finish this chapter you should be able to

LO1 Define statistics and explain some of its uses in business.

LO2 List reasons for a business student to study statistics.

LO3 State the common challenges facing business professionals using statistics.

LO4 List and explain common statistical pitfalls.

Section Exercises

Multiple section exercises are found throughout the chapter so that students can focus on material just learned.

SECTION EXERCISES

Instructions for Exercises 12.21 and 12.22: (a) Perform a regression using MegaStat or Excel. (b) State the null and alternative hypotheses for a two-tailed test for a zero slope. (c) Report the *p*-value and the 95 percent confidence interval for the slope shown in the regression results. (d) Is the slope significantly different from zero? Explain your conclusion.

12.21 College Student Weekly Earnings in Dollars (*n* = 5)
📁 WeekPay

Hours Worked (X)	Weekly Pay (Y)
10	93
15	171
20	204
20	156
35	261

12.22 Phone Hold Time for Concert Tickets in Seconds (*n* = 5)
📁 CallWait

Operators (X)	Wait Time (Y)
4	385
5	335
6	383
7	344
8	288

Mini Cases

Every chapter includes two or three mini cases, which are solved applications. They show and illlustrate the analytical application of specific statistical concepts at a deeper level than the examples.

Mini Case 4.7

Vail Resorts Customer Satisfaction

Figure 4.37 is a matrix showing correlations between several satisfaction variables from a sample of respondents to a Vail Resorts' satisfaction survey. The correlations are all positive, suggesting that greater satisfaction with any one of these criteria tends to be associated with greater satisfaction with the others (positive covariance). The highest correlation (*r* = 0.488) is between *SkiSafe* (attention to skier safety) and *SkiPatV* (Ski Patrol visibility). This makes intuitive sense. When a skier sees a ski patroller, you would expect increased perception that the organization is concerned with skier safety. While many of the correlations seem small, they are all *statistically significant* (as you will learn in Chapter 12).

FIGURE 4.37 Correlation Matrix Skier Satisfaction Variables (*n* = 502)
📁 VailGuestSat

	LiftOps	LiftWait	TrailVar	SnoAmt	GroomT	SkiSafe	SkiPatV
LiftOps	1.000						
LiftWait	0.180	1.000					
TrailVar	0.206	0.128	1.000				
SnoAmt	0.242	0.227	0.373	1.000			
GroomT	0.271	0.251	0.221	0.299	1.000		
SkiSafe	0.306	0.196	0.172	0.200	0.274	1.000	
SkiPatV	0.190	0.207	0.172	0.184	0.149	0.488	1.000

Figures and Tables

Throughout the text, there are hundreds of charts, graphs, tables, and spreadsheets to illustrate statistical concepts being applied. These visuals help stimulate student interest and clarify the text explanations.

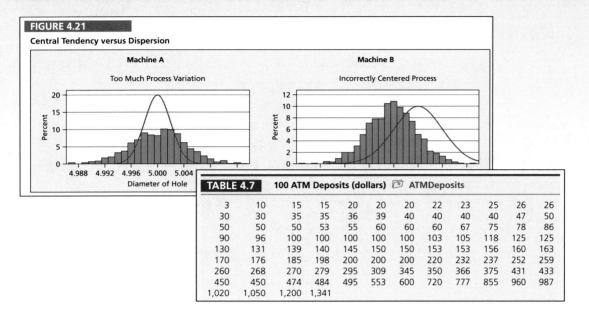

FIGURE 4.21
Central Tendency versus Dispersion

TABLE 4.7   100 ATM Deposits (dollars)   ATMDeposits

3	10	15	15	20	20	20	22	23	25	26	26
30	30	35	35	36	39	40	40	40	40	47	50
50	50	50	53	55	60	60	60	67	75	78	86
90	96	100	100	100	100	100	103	105	118	125	125
130	131	139	140	145	150	150	153	153	156	160	163
170	176	185	198	200	200	200	220	232	237	252	259
260	268	270	279	295	309	345	350	366	375	431	433
450	450	474	484	495	553	600	720	777	855	960	987
1,020	1,050	1,200	1,341								

Examples

Examples of interest to students are taken from published research or real applications to illustrate the statistics concept. For the most part, examples are focused on business but there are also some that are more general and don't require any prerequisite knowledge. And there are some that are based on student projects.

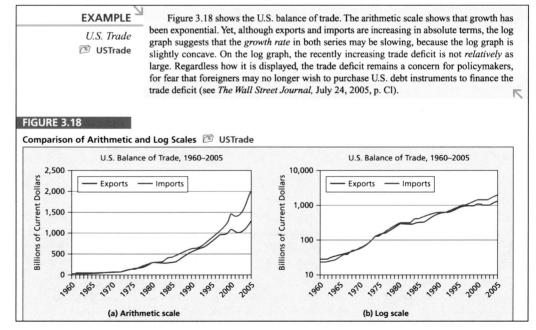

EXAMPLE

U.S. Trade
  USTrade

Figure 3.18 shows the U.S. balance of trade. The arithmetic scale shows that growth has been exponential. Yet, although exports and imports are increasing in absolute terms, the log graph suggests that the *growth rate* in both series may be slowing, because the log graph is slightly concave. On the log graph, the recently increasing trade deficit is not *relatively* as large. Regardless how it is displayed, the trade deficit remains a concern for policymakers, for fear that foreigners may no longer wish to purchase U.S. debt instruments to finance the trade deficit (see *The Wall Street Journal*, July 24, 2005, p. Cl).

FIGURE 3.18

Comparison of Arithmetic and Log Scales   USTrade

Data Set Icon

A data set icon is used throughout the text to identify data sets used in the figures, examples, and exercises that are included on the Online Learning Center (OLC) for the text.

  USTrade

Chapter Summary

Chapter summaries provide an overview of the material covered in the chapter.

CHAPTER SUMMARY For a set of observations on a single numerical variable, a **dot plot** displays the individual data values, while a **frequency distribution** classifies the data into classes called **bins** for a **histogram** of **frequencies** for each bin. The number of bins and their limits are matters left to your judgment, though **Sturges' Rule** offers advice on the number of bins. The **line chart** shows values of one or more **time series** variables plotted against time. A **log scale** is sometimes used in time series charts when data vary by orders of magnitude. The **bar chart** or **column chart** shows a **numerical** data value for each category of an **attribute**. However, a bar chart can also be used for a time series. A **scatter plot** can reveal the association (or lack of association) between two variables X and Y. The **pie chart** (showing a **numerical** data value for each category of an **attribute** if the data values are parts of a whole) is common but should be used with caution. Sometimes a **simple table** is the best visual display. Creating effective visual displays is an acquired skill. Excel offers a wide range of charts from which to choose. Deceptive graphs are found frequently in both media and business presentations, and the consumer should be aware of common errors.

Key Terms

Key terms are highlighted and defined within the text. They are also listed at the ends of chapters, along with chapter page references, to aid in reviewing.

KEY TERMS

arithmetic scale, 79	left-skewed, 71	right-skewed, 71
bar chart, 82	line chart, 77	scatter plot, 86
column chart, 82	logarithmic scale, 79	shape, 59
central tendency, 59	modal class, 71	stacked bar chart, 83
dispersion, 59	ogive, 72	stacked dot plot, 62
dot plot, 61	outlier, 71	Sturges' Rule, 65
frequency distribution, 64	Pareto chart, 82	symmetric, 71
frequency polygon, 72	pie chart, 95	trend line, 89
histogram, 66	pivot table, 92	

Commonly Used Formulas

Some chapters provide a listing of commonly used formulas for the topic under discussion.

Commonly Used Formulas in Descriptive Statistics

Sample mean: $\bar{x} = \dfrac{1}{n} \sum_{i=1}^{n} x_i$

Geometric mean: $G = \sqrt[n]{x_1 x_2 \cdots x_n}$

Range: $R = x_{max} - x_{min}$

Midrange: $\text{Midrange} = \dfrac{x_{min} + x_{max}}{2}$

Sample standard deviation: $s = \sqrt{\dfrac{\sum_{i=1}^{n}(x_i - \bar{x})^2}{n-1}}$

Chapter Review

Each chapter has a list of questions for student self-review or for discussion.

CHAPTER REVIEW

1. (a) What is a dot plot? (b) Why are dot plots attractive? (c) What are their limitations?
2. (a) What is a frequency distribution? (b) What are the steps in creating one?
3. (a) What is a histogram? (b) What does it show?
4. (a) What is a bimodal histogram? (b) Explain the difference between left-skewed, symmetric, and right-skewed histograms. (c) What is an outlier?
5. (a) What is a scatter plot? (b) What do scatter plots reveal? (c) Sketch a scatter plot with a moderate positive correlation. (d) Sketch a scatter plot with a strong negative correlation.

Chapter Exercises

Exercises give students an opportunity to test their understanding of the chapter material. Exercises are included at the ends of sections and at the ends of chapters. Some exercises contain data sets, identified by data set icons. Data sets can be accessed on the Online Learning Center and used to solve problems in the text.

4.75 (a) Choose a data set and prepare a brief, descriptive report. You may use any computer software you wish (e.g., Excel, MegaStat, MINITAB). Include relevant worksheets or graphs in your report. If some questions do not apply to your data set, explain why not. (b) Sort the data. (c) Make a histogram. Describe its shape. (d) Calculate the mean and median. Are the data skewed? (e) Calculate the standard deviation. (f) Standardize the data and check for outliers. (g) Compare the data with the Empirical Rule. Discuss. (h) Calculate the quartiles and interpret them. (i) Make a box plot. Describe its appearance.

DATA SET A   **Advertising Dollars as Percent of Sales in Selected Industries ($n = 30$)** 🖾 Ads

Industry	Percent
Accident and health insurance	0.9
Apparel and other finished products	5.5
Beverages	7.4
⋮	⋮
Steel works and blast furnaces	1.9
Tires and inner tubes	1.8
Wine, brandy, and spirits	11.3

Source: George E. Belch and Michael A. Belch, *Advertising and Promotion*, pp. 219–220. Copyright © 2004 Richard D. Irwin. Used with permission of McGraw-Hill Companies, Inc.

Online Learning Resources

LearningStats, included on the Online Learning Center (OLC; **www.mhhe.com/doane3e**), provides a means for students to explore data and concepts at their own pace. Applications that relate to the material in the chapter are identified by topic at the ends of chapters under Online Learning Resources.

CHAPTER 7   Online Learning Resources

The Online Learning Center (OLC) at www.mhhe.com/doane3e has several *LearningStats* demonstrations to help you understand continuous probability distributions. Your instructor may assign one or more of them, or you may decide to download the ones that sound interesting.

Topic	LearningStats demonstrations
Calculations	🖾 Normal Areas
	🖾 Probability Calculator
Normal approximations	🖾 Evaluating Rules of Thumb
Random data	🖾 Random Continuous Data
	🖾 Visualizing Random Normal Data
Tables	🖾 Table C—Normal Probabilities

Key: 🖾 = Excel

Exam Review Questions

At the end of a group of chapters, students can review the material they covered in those chapters. This provides them with an opportunity to test themselves on their grasp of the material.

EXAM REVIEW QUESTIONS FOR CHAPTERS 5–7

1. Which type of probability (empirical, classical, subjective) is each of the following?
   a. On a given Friday, the probability that Flight 277 to Chicago is on time is 23.7%.
   b. Your chance of going to Disney World next year is 10%.
   c. The chance of rolling a 3 on two dice is 1/18.

2. For the following contingency table, find (a) $P(H \cap T)$; (b) $P(S \mid G)$; (c) $P(S)$

	R	S	T	Row Total
G	10	50	30	90
H	20	50	40	110
Col Total	30	100	70	200

3. If $P(A) = .30$, $P(B) = .70$, and $P(A \cap B) = .25$ are A and B independent events? Explain.

McGraw-Hill Connect™ Business Statistcs

Less Managing. More Teaching. Greater Learning. McGraw-Hill *Connect Business Statistics* is an online assignment and assessment solution that connects students with the tools and resources they'll need to achieve success.

McGraw-Hill *Connect Business Statistics* helps prepare students for their future by enabling faster learning, more efficient studying, and higher retention of knowledge.

McGraw-Hill CONNECT / BUSINESS STATISTICS

Features. *Connect Business Statistics* offers a number of powerful tools and features to make managing assignments easier, so faculty can spend more time teaching. With *Connect Business Statistics*, students can engage with their coursework anytime and anywhere, making the learning process more accessible and efficient. *Connect Business Statistics* offers you the features described below.

Simple Assignment Management. With *Connect Business Statistics*, creating assignments is easier than ever, so you can spend more time teaching and less time managing. The assignment management function enables you to:

- Create and deliver assignments easily with selectable end-of-chapter questions and test bank items.
- Streamline lesson planning, student progress reporting, and assignment grading to make classroom management more efficient than ever.
- Go paperless with the eBook and online submission and grading of student assignments.

Smart Grading. When it comes to studying, time is precious. *Connect Business Statistics* helps students learn more efficiently by providing feedback and practice material when they need it, where they need it. When it comes to teaching, your time also is precious. The grading function enables you to:

- Have assignments scored automatically, giving students immediate feedback on their work and side-by-side comparisons with correct answers.
- Access and review each response; manually change grades or leave comments for students to review.
- Reinforce classroom concepts with practice tests and instant quizzes.

Integration of Excel Data Sets. A convenient feature is the inclusion of an Excel data file link in many problems using data sets in their calculation. This allows students to easily launch into Excel, work the problem, and return to Connect to key in the answer.

Chapter Exercise 5-74

High levels of cockpit noise in an aircraft can damage the hearing of pilots who are exposed to this hazard for many hours. Cockpit noise in a jet aircraft is mostly due to airflow at hundreds of miles per hour. This 3×3 contingency table shows 61 observations of data collected by an airline pilot using a handheld sound meter in a Boeing 727 cockpit. Noise level is defined as "low" (under 88 decibels), "medium" (88 to 91 decibels), or "high" (92 decibels or more). There are three flight phases (climb, cruise, descent).

Cockpit Noise

Noise Level	Flight Phase			Row Total
	Climb(B)	Cruise(C)	Descent(D)	
Low(L)	6	2	6	14
Medium(M)	18	3	8	29
High(H)	1	3	14	18
Column Total	25	8	28	61

Click here for the Excel Data File

(a) Calculate the following probabilities: (Round your answers to 4 decimal places.)

P(B)

P(L)

P(H)

Instructor Library. The *Connect Business Statistics* Instructor Library is your repository for additional resources to improve student engagement in and out of class. You can select and use any asset that enhances your lecture. The *Connect Business Statistics* Instructor Library includes:

- eBook
- PowerPoint presentations
- Test Bank
- Solutions Manual
- Digital Image Library

Student Study Center. The *Connect Business Statistics* Student Study Center is the place for students to access additional resources. The Student Study Center:

- Offers students quick access to lectures, practice materials, eBooks, and more.
- Provides instant practice material and study questions, easily accessible on-the-go.
- Gives students access to the Personalized Learning Plan described below.

Student Progress Tracking. *Connect Business Statistics* keeps instructors informed about how each student, section, and class is performing, allowing for more productive use of lecture and office hours. The progress-tracking function enables you to:

- View scored work immediately and track individual or group performance with assignment and grade reports.
- Access an instant view of student or class performance relative to learning objectives.
- Collect data and generate reports required by many accreditation organizations, such as AACSB.

McGraw-Hill Connect™ Plus Business Statistcs

McGraw-Hill Connect Plus Business Statistics. McGraw-Hill reinvents the textbook learning experience for the modern student with *Connect Plus Business Statistics*. A seamless integration of an eBook and *Connect Business Statistics*, *Connect Plus Business Statistics* provides all of the *Connect Business Statistics* features plus the following:

- An integrated eBook, allowing for anytime, anywhere access to the textbook.
- Dynamic links between the problems or questions you assign to your students and the location in the eBook where that problem or question is covered.
- A powerful search function to pinpoint and connect key concepts in a snap.

In short, *Connect Business Statistics* offers you and your students powerful tools and features that optimize your time and energies, enabling you to focus on course content, teaching, and student learning. *Connect Business Statistics* also offers a wealth of content resources for both instructors and students. This state-of-the-art, thoroughly tested system supports you in preparing students for the world that awaits.

For more information about Connect, go to **www.mcgrawhillconnect.com**, or contact your local McGraw-Hill sales representative.

Tegrity Campus: Lectures 14/7

Tegrity Campus is a service that makes class time available 24/7 by automatically capturing every lecture in a searchable format for students to review when they study and complete assignments. With a simple one-click start-and-stop process, you capture all computer screens and corresponding audio. Students can replay any part of any class with easy-to-use browser-based viewing on a PC or Mac.

McGraw-Hill Tegrity Campus

Educators know that the more students can see, hear, and experience class resources, the better they learn. In fact, studies prove it. With Tegrity Campus, students quickly recall key moments by using Tegrity Campus's unique search feature. This search helps students efficiently find what they need, when they need it, across an entire semester of class recordings. Help turn all your students' study time into learning moments immediately supported by your lecture.

To learn more about Tegrity, watch a 2-minute Flash demo at **http://tegritycampus .mhhe.com**.

Assurance-of-Learning Ready

Many educational institutions today are focused on the notion of *assurance of learning* an important element of some accreditation standards. *Applied Statistics in Business and Economics* is designed specifically to support your assurance-of-learning initiatives with a simple, yet powerful solution.

Each test bank question for *Applied Statistics for Business and Economics* maps to a specific chapter learning outcome/objective listed in the text. You can use our test bank software, EZ Test and EZ Test Online, or *Connect Business Statistics* to easily query for learning outcomes/objectives that directly relate to the learning objectives for your course. You can then use the reporting features of EZ Test to aggregate student results in similar fashion, making the collection and presentation of assurance of learning data simple and easy.

AACSB Statement

The McGraw-Hill Companies is a proud corporate member of AACSB International. Understanding the importance and value of AACSB accreditation, *Applied Statistics in Business and Economics* recognizes the curricula guidelines detailed in the AACSB standards for business accreditation by connecting selected questions in the text and the test bank to the six general knowledge and skill guidelines in the AACSB standards.

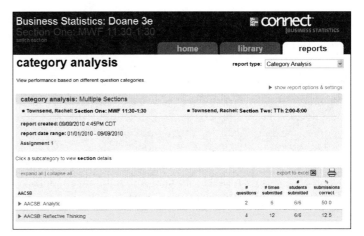

The statements contained in *Applied Statistics in Business and Economics* are provided only as a guide for the users of this textbook. The AACSB leaves content coverage and assessment within the purview of individual schools, the mission of the school, and the faculty. While *Applied Statistics in Business and Economics* and the teaching package make no claim of any specific AACSB qualification or evaluation, we have labeled within *Applied Statistics in Business and Economics* selected questions according to the six general knowledge and skills areas.

McGraw-Hill Customer Care Information

At McGraw-Hill, we understand that getting the most from new technology can be challenging. That's why our services don't stop after you purchase our products. You can e-mail our Product Specialists 24 hours a day to get product-training online. Or you can search our knowledge bank of Frequently Asked Questions on our support Web site. For Customer Support, call **800-331-5094,** e-mail **hmsupport@mcgraw-hill.com,** or visit **www.mhhe.com/support.** One of our Technical Support Analysts will be able to assist you in a timely fashion.

The following software tools are available to assist students in understanding concepts and solving problems.

LearningStats

LearningStats allows students to explore data and concepts at their own pace. It includes demonstrations, simulations, and tutorials that can be downloaded from the Online Learning Center **www.mhhe.com/doane3e.**

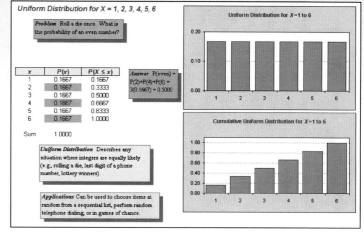

MegaStat® for Excel® (ISBN: 0077395131)

MegaStat is a full-featured Excel add-in that is available with this text. It performs statistical analyses within an Excel workbook. It does basic functions such as descriptive statistics, frequency distributions, and probability calculations as well as hypothesis testing, ANOVA, and regression.

MegaStat output is carefully formatted, and ease-of-use features include Auto Expand for quick data selection and Auto Label detect. Since *MegaStat* is easy to use, students can focus on learning statistics without being distracted by the software. MegaStat is always available from Excel's main menu. Selecting a menu item pops up a dialog box. Regression analysis is shown here. MegaStat works with all recent versions of Excel including Excel 2007.

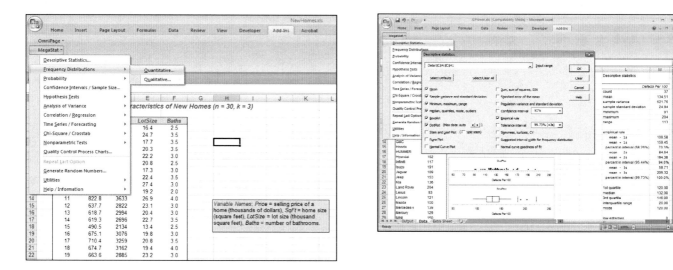

MINITAB® / SPSS® / JMP®

MINITAB® Student Version 14, SPSS® Student Version 17, and JMP Student Edition version 8 are software tools that are available to help students solve the business statistics exercises in the text. Each is available in the student version and can be packaged with any McGraw-Hill business statistics text.

Online Learning Center:
www.mhhe.com/doane3e

The Online Learning Center (OLC) provides the instructor with a complete Instructor's Manual in Word format, the complete Test Bank in both Word files and computerized EZ Test format, Instructor PowerPoint slides, text art files, an introduction to ALEKS®, an introduction to McGraw-Hill Connect™ Business Statistics, access to the eBook, and more.

All test bank questions are available in an EZ Test electronic format. Included are a number of multiple-choice, true–false, and short-answer questions and problems. The answers to all questions are given, along with a rating of the level of difficulty, topic, chapter learning objective, Bloom's taxonomy question type, and AACSB knowledge category.

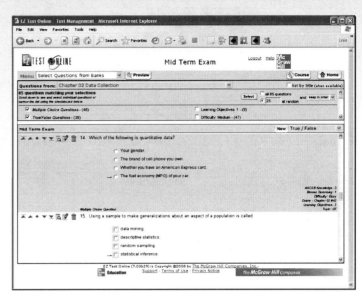

Visual Statistics

Visual Statistics 2.2 by Doane, Mathieson, and Tracy is a package of 21 software programs for teaching and learning statistics concepts. It is unique in that it allows students to learn the concepts through interactive experimentation and visualization. The software and worktext promote active learning through competency-building exercises, individual and team projects, and built-in databases. Over 400 data sets from business settings are included within the package as well as worktext in electronic format. This software is available on the Online Learning Center (OLC) for Doane 3e.

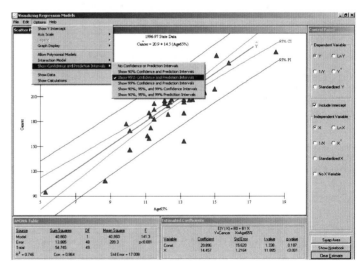

WebCT/Blackboard/eCollege

All of the material in the Online Learning Center is also available in portable WebCT, Blackboard, or e-College content "cartridges" provided free to adopters of this text.

Business Statistics Center (BSC):
www.mhhe.com/bstat/

The BSC contains links to statistical publications and resources, software downloads, learning aids, statistical Web sites and databases, and McGraw-Hill/Irwin product Web sites, and online courses.

CourseSmart CourseSmart (ISBN: 0077321650)

CourseSmart is a new way to find and buy eTextbooks. CourseSmart has the largest selection of eTextbooks available anywhere, offering thousands of the most commonly adopted textbooks from a wide variety of higher education publishers. CourseSmart eTextbooks are available in one standard online reader with full text search, notes and highlighting, and email tools for sharing notes between classmates. Visit **www.CourseSmart.com** for more information on ordering.

Online Learning Center: www.mhhe.com/doane3e

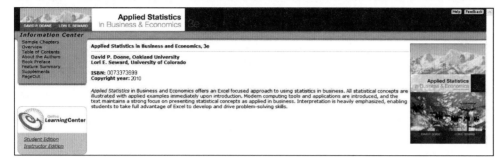

The Online Learning Center (OLC) provides resources for students including quizzes, powerpoint, data sets, screencam tutorials, visual statistics, and learning stats.

Student Study Guide (ISBN: 0077301676)

This supplement has been created to help students master the course content. It highlights the important ideas in the text and provides opportunities for students to review the worked-out solutions, review terms and concepts, and practice. The Study Guide is available through Primis Online at: **www.mhhe.com/primis.** Instructors can order the Study Guide in either print or eBook format for their students.

ALEKS®

ALEKS is an assessment and learning system that provides individualized instruction in Business Statistics. Available from McGraw-Hill/Irwin over the World Wide Web, ALEKS delivers precise assessments of students' knowledge, guides them in the selection of appropriate new study material, and records their progress toward mastery of goals.

ALEKS interacts with students much as a skilled human tutor would, moving between explanation and practice as needed, correcting and analyzing errors, defining terms, and changing topics on request. By accurately assessing their knowledge, ALEKS focuses precisely on what to learn next, helping them master the course content more quickly and easily.

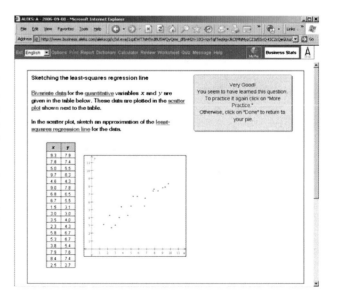

ACKNOWLEDGMENTS

The authors would like to acknowledge some of the many people who have helped with this book. Dorothy Duffy permitted use of the chemistry lab for the experiments on Hershey Kisses, Brach's jelly beans, and Sathers gum drops. Nainan Desai and Robert Edgerton explained the proper use of various kinds of engineering terminology. Thomas W. Lauer and Floyd G. Willoughby permitted quotation of a case study. Richard W. Hartl of Memorial Hospital and Kathryn H. Sheehy of Crittenton Hospital provided data for case studies. Morgan Elliott, Karl Majeske, Robin McCutcheon, Kevin Murphy, John Sase, T. J. Wharton, and Kenneth M. York permitted questionnaires to be administered in their classes. Ian S. Bradbury, Winson Taam, and especially Ron Tracy and Robert Kushler gave generously of their time as expert statistical consultants. Jonathan G. Koomey of E.O. Lawrence Berkeley National Laboratory offered valuable suggestions on visual data presentation.

Mark Isken has reliably provided Excel expertise and has suggested health care applications for examples and case studies. John Seeley and Jeff Whitbey provided regression databases. John Savio and the Michigan State Employees Credit Union provided ATM data. The Siena Research Institute has made its poll results available. The Public Interest Research Group of Michigan (PIRGIM) has generously shared data from its field survey of prescription drug prices.

We owe special thanks to Aaron Kennedy and Dave Boennighausen of Noodles & Company and to Mark Gasta, Anja Wallace, and Clifton Pacaro of Vail Resorts for providing suggestions and access to data for minicases and examples.

We are grateful for the careful proofreading and suggestions offered by students Frances J. Williams, William G. Knapp, John W. Karkowski, Nirmala Ranganathan, Thomas H. Miller, Clara M. Michetti, Fielder S. Lyons, Catherine L. Tatem, Anup D. Karnalkar, Richard G. Taylor, Ian R. Palmer, Rebecca L. Curtiss, Todd R. Keller, Emily Claeys, Tom Selby, and Jun Moon. Dozens of other individuals have provided examples and cases that are cited in the text and *LearningStats* software.

For reviewing the material on quality, we wish to thank Kay Beauregard, Administrative Director at William Beaumont Hospital, and Ellen Barnes and Karry Roberts of Ford Motor Company. Reviewers of the *LearningStats* demonstrations have made numerous suggestions for improvement, which we have tried to incorporate. In particular, we wish to thank Lari H. Arjomand of Clayton College & State University, Richard P. Gebhart of the University of Tulsa, Kieran Mathieson of Oakland University, Vincent F. Melfi of Michigan State University, J. Burdeane Orris of Butler University, Joe Sullivan of Mississippi State University, and Donald L. Westerfield of Webster University.

A special debt of gratitude is due to Carol Rose and Richard Wright for careful copyediting and editorial suggestions, Steve Schuetz for his direction and support, Wanda Zeman for coordinating the project, and Dick Hercher for guiding us at every step, solving problems, and encouraging us along the way. We are grateful to Ardith Baker of Oral Roberts University for her timely and detailed suggestions for improving the manuscript. Thanks to Heather Adams and Charlie Apigian for helping with the Instructor's Manual; Lloyd Jasingh, Morehead State University, for updating the PowerPoint slides; Scott Bailey, Troy University, for creating the quizzes; and Mary Beth Camp, Indiana University, for writing an excellent Study Guide. Special thanks to the accuracy checkers, Scott Bailey, Troy University, Terry Dalton, University of Denver, Don Gren, Salt Lake Community College, Charles Apigian, Middle Tennessee State University, Paul Kuzdrall, Akron University, and David Meyer, Akron University. Gary W. Smith of Florida State University offered many detailed, thoughtful suggestions. Thanks to the many reviewers who provided such valuable feedback including criticism which made the book better, some of whom reviewed several drafts of the manuscript. Any remaining errors or omissions are the authors' responsibility.

Charles Apigian, *Middle Tennessee State University*

Lari H. Arjomand, *Clayton College & State University*

Ardith Baker, *Oral Roberts University*

Kay Ballard, *University of Nebraska-Lincoln*

Bruce Barrett, *University of Alabama*

Mary Beth Camp, *Indiana University—Bloomington*

Timothy Butler, *Wayne State University*

Alan R. Cannon, *University of Texas—Arlington*

Juan Castro, *LeTourneau University*

Alan S. Chesen, *Wright State University*

Chia-Shin Chung, *Cleveland State University*

Susan Cohen, *University of Illinois at Urbana—Champaign*

Teresa Dalton, *University of Denver*

Bernard Dickman, *Hofstra University*

Cassandra DiRienzo, *Elon University*

John Dogbey, *West Virginia University*

Lillian Fok, *University of New Orleans*

James C. Ford, *SAS Institute, North America*

Kent Foster, *Winthrop University*

Ellen Fuller, *Arizona State University*

Richard P. Gebhart, *University of Tulsa*

Robert Gillette, *University of Kentucky—Lexington*

Alicia Grazios, *Temple University*

Betsy Greenberg, *University of Texas—Austin*

Don Gren, *Salt Lake Community College*

Alfred L. Guiffrida, *Kent State University*

Kemal Gursoy, *Long Island University*

Rhonda Hensley, *North Carolina A&T State University*

Mickey A. Hepner, *University of Central Oklahoma*

Johnny C. Ho, *University of Texas—El Paso*

ACKNOWLEDGMENTS

Tom Innis, *University of Cincinnati*

Kishen Iyenger, *University of Colorado—Boulder*

Jerzy Kamburowski, *University of Toledo*

Mark G. Kean, *Boston University*

Belayet Khandoker, *Northeastern University*

Jerry LaCava, *Boise State University*

Carl Lee, *Central Michigan University*

Jun Liu, *Georgia Southern University*

Salvador Martinez, *Weber State University*

Ralph May, *Southwestern Oklahoma State University*

Larry T. McRae, *Appalachian State University*

Mary Ruth McRae, *Appalachian State University*

Glenn Milligan, *The Ohio State University*

Anthony Narsing, *Macon State College*

Robert M. Nauss, *University of Missouri—St. Louis*

Cornelius Nelan, *Quinnipiac University*

Thomas Obremski, *University of Denver*

J. B. Orris, *Butler University*

Jayprakash G. Patankar, *University of Akron*

Dane K. Peterson, *Southwest Missouri State University*

Stephen Pollard, *California State University—Los Angeles*

Michael Polomsky, *Cleveland State University*

Tammy Prater, *Alabama State University*

Priya Rajagopalan, *Purdue University—West Lafayette*

Don R. Robinson, *Illinois State University*

Farhad Saboori, *Albright College*

Sue Schou, *Idaho State University*

Bill Seaver, *University of Tennessee—Knoxville*

Gary W. Smith, *Florida State University*

William E. Stein, *Texas A&M University*

Stanley Stephenson, *Southwest Texas State University*

Joe Sullivan, *Mississippi State University*

Deborah Tesch, *Xavier University*

Patrick Thompson, *University of Florida*

Elzbieta Trybus, *California State University—Northridge*

Geetha Vaidyanathan, *University of North Carolina—Greensboro*

Raja Vatti, *St. Johns University*

Raja P. Velu, *Syracuse University*

Charles Wilf, *Duquesne University*

Janet Wolcutt, *Wichita State University*

Barry Wray, *University of North Carolina—Wilmington*

Jack Yurkiewicz, *Pace University*

Zhen Zhu, *University of Central Oklahoma*

Thanks to the participants in our focus groups and symposia on teaching business statistics in Burr Ridge, LaJolla, Pasadena, Sante Fe, Atlanta, and Las Vegas, who provided so many teaching ideas and insights into their particular students and courses. We hope you will be able to see in the book and the teaching package consideration of those ideas and insights.

Mohammad Ahmadi, *University of Tennessee—Chattanooga*

Sung Ahn, *Washington State University*

Andy Au, *University of Maryland University College*

Mostafa Aminzadeh, *Towson University*

Charlie Apigian, *Middle Tennessee State University*

Scott Bailey, *Troy University*

Michael Bendixen, *Nova Southeastern University*

Imad Benjelloun, *Delaware Valley College*

Carl Bodenschatz, *University of Pittsburgh*

William Borders, *Troy University*

Ted Bos, *University of Alabama—Birmingham*

Dave Bregenzer, *Utah State University*

Scott Callan, *Bentley College*

Greg Cameron, *Brigham Young University—Idaho*

Mary Beth Camp, *Indiana University*

Alan Cannon, *University of Texas—Arlington*

James Carden, *University of Mississippi*

Chris Carolan, *East Carolina University*

Priscilla Chaffe-Stengel, *California State University—Fresno*

Alan Chesen, *Wright State University*

Robert Chi, *California State University—Long Beach*

Chia-Shin Chung, *Cleveland State University*

Susan Cohen, *University of Illinois at Urbana—Champaign*

Susanne Currier, *University of Central Oklahoma*

Nit Dasgupta, *University of Wisconsin—Eau Claire*

Ron Davis, *San Jose State University*

Jay Devore, *California Polytechnic State University*

Joan Donohue, *University of South Carolina*

Brent Eagar, *Utah State University—Logan*

Mike Easley, *University of New Orleans*

Kathy Ernstberger, *Indiana University—Southeast*

Zek Eser, *Eastern Kentucky University*

Soheila Fardanesh, *Towson University*

Gail Gemberling, *University of Texas—Austin*

John Grandzol, *Bloomsburg University of Pennsylvania*

Betsy Greenberg, *University of Texas—Austin*

Don Gren, *Salt Lake City Community College*

Kemal Gursoy, *Long Island University*

Eric Howington, *Valdosta State University*

Ping-Hung Hsieh, *Oregon State University*

ACKNOWLEDGMENTS

Jo Ivester, *St. Edwards University*

Patrick Johanns, *Purdue University—West Lafayette*

Allison Jones-Farmer, *Auburn University*

Jerzy Kamburowski, *University of Toledo*

Mohammad Kazemi, *University of North Carolina—Charlotte*

Belayet Khandoker, *Northeastern University*

Ron Klimberg, *Saint Joseph's University*

Supriya Lahiri, *University of Massachusetts—Lowell*

John Landry, *Metro State College of Denver*

John Lawrence, *California State University—Fullerton*

Andy Liu, *Youngstown State University*

Carol Markowski, *Old Dominion University*

Ed Markowski, *Old Dominion University*

Rutilio Martinez, *University of Northern Colorado*

Salvador Martinez, *Weber State University*

Brad McDonald, *Northern Illinois University*

Elaine McGivern, *Duquesne University*

Herb McGrath, *Bowling Green State University*

Joan McGrory, *Southwest Tennessee Community College—Macon*

Connie McLaren, *Indiana State University—Terre Haute*

Larry McRae, *Appalachian State University*

Edward Melnick, *New York University*

Khosrow Moshirvaziri, *California State University—Long Beach*

Robert Nauss, *University of Missouri—St. Louis*

Gary Newkirk, *Clemson University*

Patrick Noonan, *Emory University*

Quinton Nottingham, *Virginia Polytechnic Institute and State University*

Cliff Nowell, *Weber State University*

Maureen O'Brien, *University of Minnesota—Duluth*

Rene Ordonez, *Southern Oregon University*

Deane Orris, *Butler University*

Edward Pappanastos, *Troy State University*

Norm Pence, *Metropolitan State College of Denver*

Dennis Petruska, *Youngstown State University*

Michael Polomsky, *Cleveland State University*

Janet Pol, *University of Nebraska—Omaha*

Dawn Porter, *University of Southern California—Los Angeles*

B. K. Rai, *University of Massachusetts—Dartmouth*

Priya Rajagopalan, *Purdue University—West Lafayette*

Victor Raj, *Murray State University*

Don Robinson, *Illinois State University*

Anne Royalty, *Indiana University Perdue University—Indianapolis*

David Rubin, *University of North Carolina—Chapel Hill*

Said Said, *East Carolina University*

Abdus Samad, *Utah Valley University*

James Schmidt, *University of Nebraska—Lincoln*

Sue Schou, *Idaho State University*

Pali Sen, *University of North Florida*

Robert Setaputra, *Shippensburg University*

Murali Shanker, *Kent State University*

Sarah Shepler, *Ivy Tech Community College*

Charlie Shi, *Diablo Valley College*

Soheil Sibdari, *University of Massachusetts—Dartmouth*

Harvey Singer, *George Mason University*

Gary Smith, *Florida State University*

Debbie Stiver, *University of Nevada—Reno*

Stanley Taylor, *California State University—Sacramento*

Debbie Tesch, *Xavier University*

Elzbieta Trybus, *California State University—Northridge*

Sue Umashankar, *University of Arizona*

Geetha Vaidyanathan, *University of North Carolina—Greensboro*

Jose Vazquez, *University of Illinois at Urbana—Champaign*

Bill Verdini, *Arizona State University*

Avinash Waikar, *Southeastern Louisiana University*

Rachel Webb, *Portland State University*

Al Webster, *Bradley University*

Jeanne Wendel, *University of Nevada—Reno*

Donald Westerfield, *Webster University*

Kathleen Whitcomb, *University of South Carolina*

Mary Whiteside, *University of Texas—Arlington*

Blake Whitten, *University of Iowa—Iowa City*

Janet Wolcutt, *Wichita State University*

Richard Wollmer, *California State University—Long Beach*

Gary Yoshimoto, *St. Cloud State University*

William Younkin, *University of Miami—Coral Gables*

Zhiwei Zhu, *University of Louisiana—Lafayette*

Many of the following changes were motivated by advice from dozens of reviewers and users of the textbook. We wanted to make chapter material easier for students to understand and to sharpen the focus on essential concepts. Besides hundreds of small edits, five changes were common to all chapters:

- Revised learning objectives, inserted into the margins next to the relevant material.
- More practice problems, more business context exercises, and more intuitive explanations.
- Closer compatibility with *Connect Plus* online homework assignments.

- Updated *Related Readings* and *Web Sources* for students who want to "dive deeper."
- Updated end-of-chapter list of *LearningStats* demonstrations (Online Learning Center downloads) that illustrate key concepts in a way that is impossible in a printed page.

Chapter 1—Overview of Statistics

New MiniCase showing how statistics helped Vail Resorts shape their strategy.

Expanded coverage of ethics and two new ethics mini-projects.

Six new exercises on critical thinking.

Explicit links between the "Eight Statistical Pitfalls" and textbook chapters.

Moved "Writing and Presenting Reports" to Appendix I.

New section "Communicating with Numbers."

Chapter 2—Data Collection

Modified definitions of the key terms and new decision tree for identifying data types.

Ten new exercises on data types, scaling, and sampling.

Six updated exercises, and 13 revised exercises.

Four new or revised figures, two new examples (e.g., Vail Resorts customer survey).

More discussion of random sampling with and without replacement.

New MiniCase "Making Commercials Work Better."

Chapter 3—Describing Data Visually

Much more coverage of Excel chart types, chart tool ribbons, and drop-down menus, with many new Excel 2007 screen shots.

New step-by step instructions for Excel histograms, line charts, scatter plots, and Pivot Tables.

Expanded discussion of Pareto charts with new Vail Resorts MiniCase.

Clarification of equivalent histogram scales using f or f/n or percent $100 f/n$.

Improved coverage of "Deceptive Graphs" and reduced coverage of "novelty" charts.

Nine new exercises on histograms, scatter plots, and Pareto charts (e.g., CEO compensation, housing starts, ski visits, customer complaints, and airline cost per seat mile).

Nine revised or updated exercises.

Chapter 4—Descriptive Statistics

New explanation, visuals, and examples of percentiles and quartiles.

Expanded discussion and examples of boxplots and their business applications.

Revised discussion of outliers, unusual data values, and z-scores.

Six updated Excel 2007 screen shots and four revised MiniCases.

Six new "practice" exercises on central tendency, z-scores, and boxplots.

Six new exercises on Chebychev's Theorem and the Empirical Rule.

Expanded presentation of covariance and correlation.

New MiniCase on correlation in Vail Resorts customer satisfaction surveys.

Five deleted exercises and 26 revised exercises.

Chapter 5—Probability

More discussion and examples of the Law of Large Numbers and probability types.

Eight new exercises on recognizing probability types, independent events, and event probabilities from contingency tables.

Improved visuals and explanations of Bayes' Theorem.

Added Google calculator and Excel functions for factorials and combinations.

Five revised exercises and two new Google and Excel exercises on counting.

Chapter 6—Discrete Distributions

Improved notation for random variables and probabilities of events.

Concise advice on how to recognize binomial and Poisson distributions and events.

Side-by-side presentation of PDF and CDF graphs for pedagogical clarity.

Excel functions for random data.

Two revised exercises.

Two new event definition exercises, three new binomial exercises, and two new Poisson exercises.

Two new approximation exercises, two new geometric exercises, and two new exercises on covariance and sums of random variables.

Five updated Excel 2007 screen shots and new hypergeometric and geometric figures.

Chapter 7—Continuous Distributions

Reorganized and rewritten presentation of normal and inverse normal material.

Improved notation for random variables and event probabilities.

Close matching of section exercises to topics in best pedagogical sequence.

Side-by-side presentation of PDF and CDF graphs.

Six new "practice" exercises on normal probabilities.

Three new "business context" normal exercises.

Two new exercises on solving for μ and σ from given normal area.

Two revised exercises.

New figures, tables, and Excel 2007 screen shots on normal probabilities and their Excel functions.

Combining normal approximations (binomial, Poisson) into one compact section.

Four step-by-step worked examples using normal distribution to solve problems.

Chapter 8—Sampling Distributions and Estimation

Improved graphs and explanations of CLT and related figures.

Substantially reworked section on confidence intervals for μ.

Moved two-sample confidence intervals to Chapter 10.

Revised notation for degrees of freedom to $d.f.$ instead of v (also Appendices D and E).

Three new exercises on the standard error and CLT in business context.

Five new exercises on CLT and how n and σ affect confidence intervals for μ.

Two new Student's t "practice" exercises on confidence intervals for μ.

Two new "practice" exercises on confidence intervals and margin of error for π.

Four new exercises on sample size for estimating μ and π.

Four new Noodles exercises and two new Vail Resorts exercises.

Two new exercises on confidence intervals for σ^2.

Six new Excel 2007 screen shots, five new figures, and two new tables.

Revised 20 exercises and moved four two-sample exercises to Chapter 10.

Chapter 9—One-Sample Hypothesis Tests

New introduction and visualization of hypothesis testing steps.

Extensive rewriting of sections on hypothesis tests and Type I and II error.

New examples of hypothesis tests (right-, left-, and two-tailed tests for μ).

Improved "boxed" explanation of p-values with intuitive visuals and interpretations.

Four new exercises on hypothesis formulation without calculations.

Six new "practice" exercises on z- and t-test statistics, critical values, and p-values.

Three new "business context" t-test exercises.

Three new exercises on hypothesis formulation and Type I error.

Revised notation for degrees of freedom to $d.f.$ instead of v (also Appendices D and E).

New two-tailed power curve examples for μ and π.

Excel functions and Appendix E critical values for confidence interval for σ^2.

Revised three exercises, and updated six Excel 2007 screen shots.

Chapter 10—Two-Sample Hypothesis Tests

Moved confidence intervals for $\mu_1-\mu_2$ and $\pi_1-\pi_2$ from Chapter 8 to Chapter 10.

Rewritten sections on comparing two independent means or proportions.

Revised notation for stating two-sample hypotheses throughout chapter.

Added new step-by-step t-test example from Vail Resorts.

Updated three exercises and added eleven new exercises (e.g., Vail resorts t-test, Vail resorts

rehiring proportions, hospital readmissions, wireless router encryption, Noodles spaghetti sauce, Vail Resorts employee ages, basketball graduation rates).

Revised notation for degrees of freedom to $d.f.$ instead of v (also Appendices D, E, and F).

Updated seven Excel 2007 or MegaStat screen shots.

Chapter 11—Analysis of Variance

Merged last two sections to form new optional section "Higher Order ANOVA Models."

Updated Excel 2007 or MegaStat screen shots.

Notation for Hartley's F_{max} test statistic changed to H to avoid confusion with F test.

Clarified instructions in exercises throughout chapter.

Chapter 12—Simple Regression

New chapter title (formerly called "Bivariate Regression").

Renamed section "Violation of Assumptions" to "Residual Tests" and rewrote it.

Reduced discussion of critical values for r and removed MiniCase "Alumni Giving."

New "boxed text" for some key concepts.

Moved state data correlation matrix example to Chapter 13.

Revised formulas and variable notation throughout the chapter.

New Minicase "Does Per Person Spending Predict Weekly Sales?"

Five new "practice" exercises (interpretation of a regression, calculating residuals, interpreting p-values).

Revised several exercises.

Updated or added 10 new figures and Excel 2007 screen shots throughout chapter.

Chapter 13—Multiple Regression

12 new "practice" regression exercises on interpreting a given regression, calculating F from the ANOVA table, testing coefficients for significance, and interpreting correlations.

New example on foreclosure rates and new exercise data set on foreclosure rates.

New and revised figures and updated screen shots as required.

Revised variable notation and clarified language throughout entire chapter.

Revised equation for R^2_{adj} to emphasize its meaning.

Chapter 14—Time Series Analysis

Four new exercises: aircraft bird strikes, car dealerships, electricity use, snowboards.

Updated data for seven exercises: PepsiCo, JetBlue, new airplane shipments, U.S. federal debt, Boston Marathon, quarterly aviation shipments, Coca Cola.

New Excel 2007 screen shots for five figures.

Forecast error column added to exponential smoothing for MAPE, MAD, and MSE.

Chapter 15—Chi-Square Tests

Added section on test of two proportions as analog to 2×2 chi-square test.

Updated Excel and MegaStat screen shots and added new content for one figure.

Changed notation for degrees of freedom to $d.f.$ instead of v (also Appendix E).

Revised seven exercises and updated notation throughout chapter.

Replaced old Appendix E (chi-square) with new table showing right-tail areas.

Chapter 16—Nonparametric Tests

Updated notation throughout chapter.

Revisions in some explanations and new MegaStat screen shots to match textbook formulas more closely.

Chapter 17—Quality Management

Six updated screen shots for Excel 2007, Minitab, or MegaStat.

Added new MiniCase on Vail Resorts ISO 9001/14001 certification.

Improved discussion of C_p, C_{pk}, and 6σ, 8σ, and 10σ "safety margin" in capability analysis.

Condensed table of pattern assignable causes, and updated notation throughout chapter.

Revised six exercises.

Chapter 18—Simulation

Updated @Risk discussion and references and clarified text throughout chapter.

Updated nine new @Risk and Excel screen shots.

Added new Monte Carlo simulation project and revised eight exercises.

Updated notation throughout chapter.

BRIEF CONTENTS

CONTENTS

CHAPTER SEVENTEEN
Quality Management   714

CHAPTER EIGHTEEN
Simulation (Online Learning Center www.mhhe.com/doane3e)

APPENDIXES

PHOTO CREDITS   808

Applied Statistics

in Business and Economics

Third Edition

CHAPTER 10

Two-Sample Hypothesis Tests

Chapter Learning Objectives

When you finish this chapter you should be able to

LO1 Recognize and perform a test for two means with known σ_1 and σ_2.

LO2 Recognize and perform a test for two means with unknown σ_1 and σ_2.

LO3 Recognize paired data and be able to perform a paired t test.

LO4 Explain the assumptions underlying the two-sample test of means.

LO5 Perform a test to compare two proportions using z.

LO6 Check whether normality may be assumed for two proportions.

LO7 Use Excel to find p-values for two-sample tests using z or t.

LO8 Carry out a test of two variances using the F distribution.

LO9 Construct a confidence interval for $\mu_1 - \mu_2$ or $\pi_1 - \pi_2$.

The logic and applications of hypothesis testing that you learned in Chapter 9 will continue here, but now we consider two-sample tests. The two-sample test is used to make inferences about the two populations from which the samples were drawn. The use of these techniques is widespread in science and engineering as well as social sciences. Drug companies use sophisticated versions called clinical trials to determine the effectiveness of new drugs, agricultural science continually uses these methods to compare yields to improve productivity, and a wide variety of businesses use them to test or compare things.

What Is a Two-Sample Test?

Two-sample tests compare two sample estimates *with each other,* whereas one-sample tests compare a sample estimate with a nonsample benchmark (a claim or prior belief about a population parameter). Here are some actual two-sample tests from this chapter:

Automotive   A new bumper is installed on selected vehicles in a corporate fleet. During a 1-year test period, 12 vehicles with the new bumper were involved in accidents, incurring mean damage of $1,101 with a standard deviation of $696. During the same year, 9 vehicles with the old bumpers were involved in accidents, incurring mean damage of $1,766 with a standard deviation of $838. Did the new bumper significantly reduce damage? Did it reduce variation?

Marketing   At a matinee performance of *X-Men Origins: Wolverine,* a random sample of 25 concession purchases showed a mean of $7.29 with a standard deviation of $3.02. For the evening performance a random sample of 25 concession purchases showed a mean of $7.12 with a standard deviation of $2.14. Is there less variation in the evenings?

Safety   In Dallas, some fire trucks were painted yellow (instead of red) to heighten their visibility. During a test period, the fleet of red fire trucks made 153,348 runs and had 20 accidents, while the fleet of yellow fire trucks made 135,035 runs and had 4 accidents. Is the difference in accident rates significant?

Medicine   Half of a group of 18,882 healthy men with no sign of prostate cancer were given an experimental drug called finasteride, while half were given a placebo, based on a random selection process. Participants underwent annual exams and blood tests. Over the next 7 years, 571 men in the placebo group developed prostate cancer, compared with only 435 in the finasteride group. Is the difference in cancer rates significant?

Education   In a certain college class, 20 randomly chosen students were given a tutorial, while 20 others used a self-study computer simulation. On the same 20-point quiz, the tutorial students' mean score was 16.7 with a standard deviation of 2.5, compared with a mean of 14.5 and a standard deviation of 3.2 for the simulation students. Did the tutorial students do better, or is it just due to chance? Is there any significant difference in the degree of variation in the two groups?

Mini Case	10.1

Early Intervention Saves Lives

Statistics is helping U.S. hospitals prove the value of innovative organizational changes to deal with medical crisis situations. At the Pittsburgh Medical Center, "SWAT teams" were shown to reduce patient mortality by cutting red tape for critically ill patients. They formed a Rapid Response Team (RRT) consisting of a critical care nurse, intensive care therapist, and a respiratory therapist, empowered to make decisions without waiting until the patient's doctor could be paged. Statistics were collected on cardiac arrests for two months before and after the RRT concept was implemented. The sample data revealed more than a 50 percent reduction in total cardiac deaths and a decline in average ICU days after cardiac arrest from 163 days to only 33 days after RRT. These improvements were both *statistically significant* and of *practical importance* because of the medical benefits and the large cost savings in hospital care. Statistics played a similar role at the University of California San Francisco Medical Center in demonstrating the value of a new method of expediting treatment of heart attack emergency patients. (See *The Wall Street Journal,* December 1, 2004, p. D1; and "How Statistics Can Save Failing Hearts," *The New York Times,* March 7, 2007, p. C1.)

Basis of Two-Sample Tests

Two-sample tests are especially useful because they possess a built-in point of comparison. You can think of many situations where two groups are to be compared (e.g., before and after, old and new, experimental and control). Sometimes we don't really care about the actual value of the population parameter, but only whether the parameter is the same for both populations. Usually, the null hypothesis is that both samples were drawn from populations with the same parameter value, but we can also test for a given degree of difference.

The logic of two-sample tests is based on the fact that two samples drawn from the *same population* may yield *different estimates* of a parameter due to chance. For example, exhaust emission tests could yield different results for two vehicles of the same type. Only if the two sample statistics differ by more than the amount attributable to chance can we conclude that the samples came from populations with different parameter values, as illustrated in Figure 10.1.

Test Procedure

The testing procedure is like that of one-sample tests. We state our hypotheses, set up a decision rule, insert the sample statistics, and make a decision. Because the true parameters are unknown, we rely on statistical theory to help us reach a defensible conclusion about our hypotheses. Our decision could be wrong—we could commit a **Type I** or **Type II error**—but at least we can specify our acceptable level of risk of making an error. Larger samples are always

FIGURE 10.1

Same Population or Different?

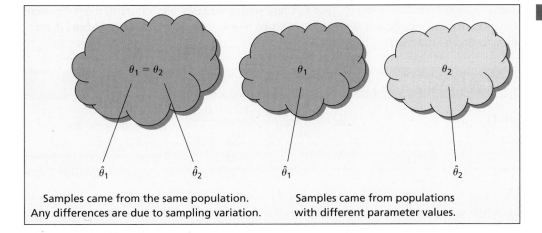

Samples came from the same population. Any differences are due to sampling variation.

Samples came from populations with different parameter values.

desirable because they permit us to reduce the chance of making either a Type I error or Type II error (i.e., increase the power of the test).

10.2 COMPARING TWO MEANS: INDEPENDENT SAMPLES

Comparing two population means is a common business problem. Is there a difference between the average customer purchase at Starbucks on Saturday and Sunday mornings? Is there a difference between the average satisfaction scores from a taste test for two versions of a new menu item at Noodles & Company? Is there a difference between the average age of full-time and part-time seasonal employees at a Vail Resorts ski mountain?

The process of comparing two means starts by stating null and alternative hypotheses, just as we did in Chapter 9. If a company is simply interested in knowing if a difference exists between two populations, they would want to test the null hypothesis $H_0: \mu_1 - \mu_2 = 0$. But there might be situations in which the business would like to know if the difference is equal to some value other than zero, using the null hypothesis $H_0: \mu_1 - \mu_2 = D_0$. For example, we might ask if the difference between the average number of years worked at a Vail Resorts ski mountain for full-time and part-time seasonal employees is greater than two years. In this situation we would formulate the null hypothesis as: $H_0: \mu_1 - \mu_2 = 2$ where $D_0 = 2$ years.

LO1

Recognize and perform a test for two means with known σ_1 and σ_2.

Format of Hypotheses

In this section we will focus on the more common situation of simply comparing two population means. The possible pairs of null and alternative hypotheses are

Left-Tailed Test	*Two-Tailed Test*	*Right-Tailed Test*
$H_0: \mu_1 - \mu_2 \geq 0$	$H_0: \mu_1 - \mu_2 = 0$	$H_0: \mu_1 - \mu_2 \leq 0$
$H_1: \mu_1 - \mu_2 < 0$	$H_1: \mu_1 - \mu_2 \neq 0$	$H_1: \mu_1 - \mu_2 > 0$

LO2

Recognize and perform a test for two means with unknown σ_1 and σ_2.

Test Statistic

The **sample statistic** used to test the parameter $\mu_1 - \mu_2$ is $\bar{X}_1 - \bar{X}_2$ where both $\bar{X}_1$ and $\bar{X}_2$ are calculated from independent random samples taken from normal populations. The **test statistic** will follow the same general format as the z- and t-scores we calculated in Chapter 9. The test statistic is the difference between the sample statistic and the parameter divided by the standard error of the sample statistic. As always, the formula for the test statistic is determined by the sampling distribution of the sample statistic and whether or not we know the population variances.

Case 1: Known Variances For the case where we know the values of the population variances, σ_1^2 and σ_2^2, the test statistic is a z-score. We would use the standard normal distribution to find *p*-values or z_{crit} values.

LO4

Explain the assumptions underlying the two-sample test of means.

Case 1: Known Variances

(10.1)
$$z_{\text{calc}} = \frac{(\bar{x}_1 - \bar{x}_2) - (\mu_1 - \mu_2)}{\sqrt{\dfrac{\sigma_1^2}{n_1} + \dfrac{\sigma_2^2}{n_2}}}$$

Case 2: Unknown Variances but Assumed Equal For the case where we *don't* know the values of the population variances but we have reason to believe they are equal, we would use the Student's t distribution. We would need to rely on sample estimates s_1^2 and s_2^2 for the population variances, σ_1^2 and σ_2^2. By assuming that the population variances are equal, we are allowed to *pool* the sample variances by taking a weighted average of s_1^2 and s_2^2 to calculate an estimate of the common population variance. Weights are assigned to s_1^2 and s_2^2 based on their respective degrees of freedom $(n_1 - 1)$ and $(n_2 - 1)$. Because we are pooling the sample variances, the common variance estimate is called the **pooled variance** and is denoted s_p^2. Case 2 is often called the *pooled* t *test*.

Case 2: Unknown Variances Assumed Equal

(10.2)
$$t_{\text{calc}} = \frac{(\bar{x}_1 - \bar{x}_2) - (\mu_1 - \mu_2)}{\sqrt{\dfrac{s_p^2}{n_1} + \dfrac{s_p^2}{n_2}}} \quad \text{where}$$

$$s_p^2 = \frac{(n_1 - 1)s_1^2 + (n_2 - 1)s_2^2}{n_1 + n_2 - 2} \quad \text{and } d.f. = n_1 + n_2 - 2$$

Case 3: Unknown Variances but Assumed Unequal If the unknown variances σ_1^2 and σ_2^2 are assumed *unequal*, we do not pool the variances. This is a more conservative assumption than Case 2 because we are not assuming equal variances. Under these conditions the distribution of the random variable $\bar{X}_1 - \bar{X}_2$ is no longer certain, a difficulty known at the **Behrens-Fisher problem**. One solution to this problem is the **Welch-Satterthwaite test** which replaces σ_1^2 and σ_2^2 with s_1^2 and s_2^2 in the known variance z formula, but then uses a Student's t test with **Welch's adjusted degrees of freedom**.

Case 3: Unknown Variances Assumed Unequal

(10.3)
$$t_{\text{calc}} = \frac{(\bar{x}_1 - \bar{x}_2) - (\mu_1 - \mu_2)}{\sqrt{\dfrac{s_1^2}{n_1} + \dfrac{s_2^2}{n_2}}} \quad \text{with } d.f. = \frac{\left(\dfrac{s_1^2}{n_1} + \dfrac{s_2^2}{n_2}\right)^2}{\dfrac{\left(\dfrac{s_1^2}{n_1}\right)^2}{n_1 - 1} + \dfrac{\left(\dfrac{s_2^2}{n_2}\right)^2}{n_2 - 1}}$$

Finding Welch's degrees of freedom requires a tedious calculation, but this is easily handled by Excel, MegaStat, or MINITAB. When doing these calculations with a calculator, a conservative quick rule for degrees of freedom is to use $d.f. = \min(n_1 - 1, n_2 - 1)$. If the sample sizes are equal, the value of t_{calc} will be the same as in Case 2, although the degrees of freedom may differ. The formulas for Case 2 and Case 3 will usually yield the same decision about the hypotheses unless the sample sizes and variances differ greatly.

Table 10.1 summarizes the formulas for the test statistic in each of the three cases described above. We have simplified the formulas based on the assumption that we will usually be testing for equal population means. Therefore we have left off the expression $\mu_1 - \mu_2$ because we are assuming it is equal to 0. All of these test statistics presume independent random samples from normal populations, although in practice they are robust to non-normality as long as the samples are not too small and the populations are not too skewed.

TABLE 10.1
Test Statistic for Zero Difference of Means

Case 1	Case 2	Case 3
Known Variances	Unknown Variances, Assumed Equal	Unknown Variances, Assumed Unequal
$z_{calc} = \dfrac{\bar{x}_1 - \bar{x}_2}{\sqrt{\dfrac{\sigma_1^2}{n_1} + \dfrac{\sigma_2^2}{n_2}}}$	$t_{calc} = \dfrac{(\bar{x}_1 - \bar{x}_2)}{\sqrt{\dfrac{s_p^2}{n_1} + \dfrac{s_p^2}{n_2}}}$ where $s_p^2 = \dfrac{(n_1 - 1)s_1^2 + (n_2 - 1)s_2^2}{n_1 + n_2 - 2}$	$t_{calc} = \dfrac{(\bar{x}_1 - \bar{x}_2)}{\sqrt{\dfrac{s_1^2}{n_1} + \dfrac{s_2^2}{n_2}}}$
For critical value, use standard normal distribution	For critical value, use Student's t with $d.f. = n_1 + n_2 - 2$	For critical value, use Student's t with Welch's adjusted degrees of freedom or $\min(n_1 - 1, n_2 - 1)$

The formulas in Table 10.1 require some calculations, but most of the time you will be using a computer. As long as you have raw data (i.e., the original samples of n_1 and n_2 observations) Excel's Data Analysis menu handles all three cases, as shown in Figure 10.2. Both MegaStat and MINITAB also perform these tests and will do so for summarized data as well (i.e., when you have $\bar{x}_1, \bar{x}_2, s_1, s_2$ instead of the n_1 and n_2 data columns).

FIGURE 10.2
Excel's Data Analysis Menu

EXAMPLE

Drug Prices in Two States

The price of prescription drugs is an ongoing national issue in the United States. Zocor is a common prescription cholesterol-reducing drug prescribed for people who are at risk for heart disease. Table 10.2 shows Zocor prices from 15 randomly selected pharmacies in two states. At $\alpha = .05$, is there a difference in the mean for all pharmacies in Colorado and Texas? From the dot plots shown in Figure 10.3, it seems unlikely that there is a significant difference, but we will do a test of means to see whether our intuition is correct.

Step 1: State the Hypotheses
To check for a significant difference without regard for its direction, we choose a two-tailed test. The hypotheses to be tested are

$H_0: \mu_1 - \mu_2 = 0$
$H_1: \mu_1 - \mu_2 \neq 0$

Step 2: Specify the Decision Rule
We will assume equal variances. For the pooled-variance t test, degrees of freedom are $d.f. = n_1 + n_2 - 2 = 16 + 13 - 2 = 27$. From Appendix D we get the two-tail critical value $t = \pm 2.052$. The decision rule is illustrated in Figure 10.4.

TABLE 10.2	Zocor Prices (30-Day Supply) in Two States 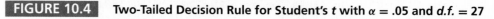 Zocor		
Colorado Pharmacies		**Texas Pharmacies**	
City	*Price ($)*	*City*	*Price ($)*
Alamosa	125.05	Austin	145.32
Avon	137.56	Austin	131.19
Broomfield	142.50	Austin	151.65
Buena Vista	145.95	Austin	141.55
Colorado Springs	117.49	Austin	125.99
Colorado Springs	142.75	Dallas	126.29
Denver	121.99	Dallas	139.19
Denver	117.49	Dallas	156.00
Eaton	141.64	Dallas	137.56
Fort Collins	128.69	Houston	154.10
Gunnison	130.29	Houston	126.41
Pueblo	142.39	Houston	114.00
Pueblo	121.99	Houston	144.99
Pueblo	141.30		
Sterling	153.43		
Walsenburg	133.39		

$$\bar{x}_1 = \$133.994 \qquad \bar{x}_2 = \$138.018$$
$$s_1 = \$11.015 \qquad s_2 = \$12.663$$
$$n_1 = 16 \text{ pharmacies} \qquad n_2 = 13 \text{ pharmacies}$$

Source: Public Research Interest Group (www.pirg.org). Surveyed pharmacies were chosen from the telephone directory in 2004. Data used with permission.

FIGURE 10.3	Zocor Prices from Sampled Pharmacies in Two States

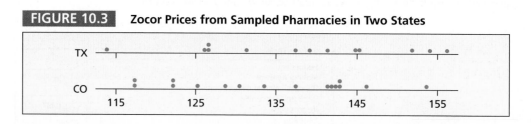

FIGURE 10.4	Two-Tailed Decision Rule for Student's t with $\alpha = .05$ and $d.f. = 27$

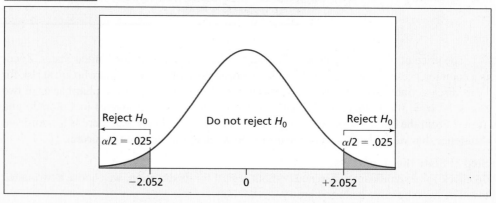

Step 3: Calculate the Test Statistic
The sample statistics are

$$\bar{x}_1 = 133.994 \qquad \bar{x}_2 = 138.018$$
$$s_1 = 11.015 \qquad s_2 = 12.663$$
$$n_1 = 16 \qquad n_2 = 13$$

Because we are assuming equal variances, we use the formulas for Case 2. The pooled variance s_p^2 is

$$s_p^2 = \frac{(n_1 - 1)s_1^2 + (n_2 - 1)s_2^2}{n_1 + n_2 - 2} = \frac{(16 - 1)(11.015)^2 + (13 - 1)(12.663)^2}{16 + 13 - 2} = 138.6737$$

Using s_p^2 the test statistic is

$$t_{calc} = \frac{\bar{x}_1 - \bar{x}_2}{\sqrt{\dfrac{s_p^2}{n_1} + \dfrac{s_p^2}{n_2}}} = \frac{133.994 - 138.018}{\sqrt{\dfrac{138.6737}{16} + \dfrac{138.6737}{13}}} = \frac{-4.024}{4.39708} = -0.915$$

The pooled standard deviation is $s_p = \sqrt{138.6737} = 11.776$. Notice that s_p always lies between s_1 and s_2 (if not, you have an arithmetic error). This is because s_p^2 is a weighted average of s_1^2 and s_2^2.

Step 4: Make the Decision

The test statistic $t_{calc} = -0.915$ does not fall in the rejection region so we cannot reject the hypothesis of equal means. Excel's menu and output are shown in Figure 10.5. Both one-tailed and two-tailed tests are shown.

FIGURE 10.5 **Excel's Data Analysis with Unknown but Equal Variances**

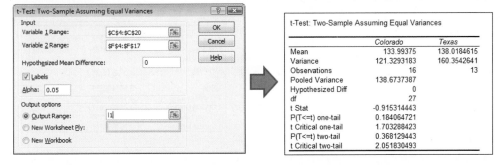

The *p*-value can be calculated using Excel's two-tail function =TDIST(.915,27,2) which gives $p = .3681$. This large *p*-value says that a result this extreme would happen by chance about 37 percent of the time if $\mu_1 = \mu_2$. The difference in sample means seems to be well within the realm of chance.

The sample variances in this example are similar, so the assumption of equal variances is reasonable. But if we instead use the formulas for Case 3 (assuming *unequal* variances) the test statistic is

$$t_{calc} = \frac{\bar{x}_1 - \bar{x}_2}{\sqrt{\dfrac{s_1^2}{n_1} + \dfrac{s_2^2}{n_2}}} = \frac{133.994 - 138.018}{\sqrt{\dfrac{(11.015)^2}{16} + \dfrac{(12.663)^2}{13}}} = \frac{-4.024}{4.4629} = -0.902$$

The formula for degrees of freedom for the Welch-Satterthwaite test is

$$d.f. = \frac{\left[\dfrac{s_1^2}{n_1} + \dfrac{s_2^2}{n_2}\right]^2}{\dfrac{\left(\dfrac{s_1^2}{n_1}\right)^2}{n_1 - 1} + \dfrac{\left(\dfrac{s_2^2}{n_2}\right)^2}{n_2 - 1}} = \frac{\left[\dfrac{(11.015)^2}{16} + \dfrac{(12.663)^2}{13}\right]^2}{\dfrac{\left(\dfrac{(11.015)^2}{16}\right)^2}{16 - 1} + \dfrac{\left(\dfrac{(12.663)^2}{13}\right)^2}{13 - 1}} = 24$$

The degrees of freedom are rounded to the next lower integer, to be conservative.

LO7

Use Excel to find *p*-values for two-sample tests using *z* or *t*.

For the unequal-variance t test with $d.f. = 24$, Appendix D gives the two-tail critical value $t_{.025} = \pm 2.064$. The decision rule is illustrated in Figure 10.6.

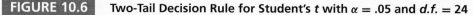

| **FIGURE 10.6** | **Two-Tail Decision Rule for Student's t with $\alpha = .05$ and $d.f. = 24$** |

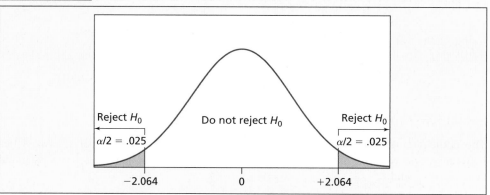

The calculations are best done by computer. Excel's menu and output are shown in Figure 10.7. Both one-tailed and two-tailed tests are shown.

| **FIGURE 10.7** | **Excel's Data Analysis with Unknown and Unequal Variances** |

For the Zocor data, either assumption leads to the same conclusion:

Assumption	Test Statistic	d.f.	Critical Value	Decision
Case 2 (equal variances)	$t_{calc} = -0.915$	27	$t_{.025} = \pm 2.052$	Don't reject
Case 3 (unequal variances)	$t_{calc} = -0.902$	24	$t_{.025} = \pm 2.064$	Don't reject

Which Assumption Is Best?

If the *sample sizes are equal,* the Case 2 and Case 3 test statistics will be identical, although the degrees of freedom may differ. If the *variances are similar,* the two tests usually agree. If you have no information about the population variances, then the best choice is Case 3. The fewer assumptions you make about your populations, the less likely you are to make a mistake in your conclusions. Case 1 (known population variances) is not explored further here because it is so uncommon in business.

Must Sample Sizes Be Equal?

Unequal sample sizes are common, and the formulas still apply. However, there are advantages to equal sample sizes. We avoid unbalanced sample sizes when possible. But many times, we have to take the samples as they come.

Large Samples

For unknown variances, if both samples are large ($n_1 \geq 30$ and $n_2 \geq 30$) and you have reason to think the population isn't badly skewed (look at the histograms or dot plots of the samples), it is common to use formula 10.4 with Appendix C. Although it usually gives results very close to the "proper" t tests, this approach is not conservative (i.e., it may increase Type I risk).

$$z_{\text{calc}} = \frac{\bar{x}_1 - \bar{x}_2}{\sqrt{\dfrac{s_1^2}{n_1} + \dfrac{s_2^2}{n_2}}} \qquad \text{(large samples, symmetric populations)} \qquad \textbf{(10.4)}$$

Caution: Three Issues

Bear in mind three questions when you are comparing two sample means:

- Are the populations skewed? Are there outliers?
- Are the sample sizes large ($n \geq 30$)?
- Is the difference *important* as well as significant?

Skewness or outliers can usually be seen in a histogram or dot plot of each sample. The t tests (Case 2 and Case 3) are probably OK in the face of moderate skewness, especially if the samples are large (e.g., sample sizes of at least 30). Outliers are more serious and might require consultation with a statistician. In such cases, you might ask yourself whether a test of means is appropriate. With small samples or skewed data, the mean may not be a very reliable indicator of central tendency, and your test may lack power. In such situations, it may be better merely to describe the samples, comment on similarities or differences in the data, and skip the formal t-tests.

Regarding importance, note that a small difference in means or proportions could be significant if the sample size is large, because the standard error gets smaller as the sample size gets larger. So, we must separately ask if the difference is *important*. The answer depends on the data magnitude and the consequences to the decision maker. How large must a price differential be to make it worthwhile for a consumer to drive from A to B to save 10 percent on a loaf of bread? A DVD player? A new car? Research suggests, for example, that some cancer victims will travel far and pay much for treatments that offer only small improvement in their chances of survival, because life is so precious. But few consumers compare prices or drive far to save money on a gallon of milk or other items that are unimportant in their overall budget.

Mini Case   10.2

Length of Statistics Articles

Are articles in leading statistics journals getting longer? It appears so, based on a comparison of the June 2000 and June 1990 issues of the *Journal of the American Statistical Association* (*JASA*), shown in Table 10.3.

TABLE 10.3   **Article Length in *JASA***

June 1990 JASA	June 2000 JASA
$\bar{x}_1 = 7.1333$ pages	$\bar{x}_2 = 11.8333$ pages
$s_1 = 1.9250$ pages	$s_2 = 2.5166$ pages
$n_1 = 30$ articles	$n_2 = 12$ articles

Source: *Journal of the American Statistical Association* 85, no. 410, and 95, no. 450.

We will do a left-tailed test at $\alpha = .01$. The hypotheses are

$H_0: \mu_1 - \mu_2 \geq 0$

$H_1: \mu_1 - \mu_2 < 0$

Since the variances are unknown, we will use a t test (both equal and unequal variances) checking the results with Excel. The pooled-variance test (Case 2) requires degrees of freedom $d.f. = n_1 + n_2 - 2 = 30 + 12 - 2 = 40$, yielding a left-tail critical value of $t_{.01} = -2.423$. The estimate of the pooled variance is

$$s_p = \sqrt{\frac{(n_1 - 1)s_1^2 + (n_2 - 1)s_2^2}{n_1 + n_2 - 2}} = \sqrt{\frac{(30 - 1)(1.9250)^2 + (12 - 1)(2.5166)^2}{30 + 12 - 2}}$$

$$= \sqrt{4.428333} = 2.10436$$

The test statistic is $t_{calc} = -6.539$, indicating a very strong rejection of the hypothesis of equal means:

$$t_{calc} = \frac{\bar{x}_1 - \bar{x}_2}{s_p \sqrt{\frac{1}{n_1} + \frac{1}{n_2}}} = \frac{7.1333 - 11.8333}{(2.10436)\sqrt{\frac{1}{30} + \frac{1}{12}}} = \frac{-4.70000}{0.718776} = -6.539$$

Using the Welch-Sattherwaite t test (assuming unequal variances) the test statistic is

$$t_{calc} = \frac{\bar{x}_1 - \bar{x}_2}{\sqrt{\frac{s_1^2}{n_1} + \frac{s_2^2}{n_2}}} = \frac{7.1333 - 11.8333}{\sqrt{\frac{(1.9250)^2}{30} + \frac{(2.5166)^2}{12}}} = \frac{-4.7000}{0.80703} = -5.824$$

The formula for degrees of freedom for the Welch-Satterthwaite test is

$$d.f. = \frac{\left[\frac{s_1^2}{n_1} + \frac{s_2^2}{n_2}\right]^2}{\frac{\left(\frac{s_1^2}{n_1}\right)^2}{n_1 - 1} + \frac{\left(\frac{s_2^2}{n_2}\right)^2}{n_2 - 1}} = \frac{\left[\frac{(1.9250)^2}{30} + \frac{(2.5166)^2}{12}\right]^2}{\frac{\left(\frac{(1.9250)^2}{30}\right)^2}{30 - 1} + \frac{\left(\frac{(2.5166)^2}{12}\right)^2}{12 - 1}} = 16$$

so the critical value is $t_{.01} = -2.583$. If we use the Quick Rule for degrees of freedom, instead of wading through this tedious calculation, we get $d.f. = \min(n_1 - 1 \text{ or } n_2 - 1) = \min(30 - 1 \text{ or } 12 - 1) = 11$ or $t_{.01} = -2.718$, which leads to the same conclusion. Regardless of our assumption about variances, we conclude that articles in *JASA* are getting longer. The decision is clear-cut. Our conviction about the conclusion depends on whether these samples are truly representative of *JASA* articles. This question might be probed further, and more articles could be examined. However, this result seems reasonable *a priori*, due to the growing use of graphics and computer simulation that could lengthen the articles. Is a difference of 4.7 pages of practical importance? Well, editors must find room for articles, so if articles are getting longer, journals must contain more pages or publish fewer articles. A difference of 5 pages over 20 or 30 articles might indeed be important.

SECTION EXERCISES

connect

Hint: Show all formulas and calculations, but use the calculator in *LearningStats* Unit 10 to check your work. Calculate the *p*-values using Excel, and show each Excel formula you used (note that Excel's TDIST function requires that you omit the sign if the test statistic is negative).

10.1 Do a two-sample test for equality of means assuming equal variances. Calculate the *p*-value.

    a. Comparison of GPA for randomly chosen college juniors and seniors: $\bar{x}_1 = 3.05$, $s_1 = .20$, $n_1 = 15$, $\bar{x}_2 = 3.25$, $s_2 = .30$, $n_2 = 15$, $\alpha = .025$, left-tailed test.

    b. Comparison of average commute miles for randomly chosen students at two community colleges: $\bar{x}_1 = 15$, $s_1 = 5$, $n_1 = 22$, $\bar{x}_2 = 18$, $s_2 = 7$, $n_2 = 19$, $\alpha = .05$, two-tailed test.

    c. Comparison of credits at time of graduation for randomly chosen accounting and economics students: $\bar{x}_1 = 139$, $s_1 = 2.8$, $n_1 = 12$, $\bar{x}_2 = 137$, $s_2 = 2.7$, $n_2 = 17$, $\alpha = .05$, right-tailed test.

10.2 Repeat the previous exercise, assuming unequal variances. Calculate the *p*-value using Excel, and show the Excel formula you used.

10.3 Is there a difference in the average number of years' seniority between returning part-time seasonal employees and returning full-time seasonal employees at a Vail Resorts' ski mountain? From a random sample of 191 returning part-time employees, the average seniority, $\bar{x}_1$, was 4.9 years with a standard deviation, s_1, equal to 5.4 years. From a random sample of 833 returning full-time employees, the average seniority, $\bar{x}_2$, was 7.9 years with a standard deviation, s_2, equal to 8.3 years. Assume the population variances are not equal. (a) Test the hypothesis of equal means using $\alpha = .01$. (b) Calculate the *p*-value using Excel.

10.4 The average mpg usage for a 2009 Toyota Prius for a sample of 10 tanks of gas was 45.5 with a standard deviation of 1.8. For a 2009 Honda Insight, the average mpg usage for a sample of 10 tanks of gas was 42.0 with a standard deviation of 2.3. (a) Assuming equal variances, at $\alpha = .01$, is the true mean mpg lower for the Honda Insight? (b) Calculate the *p*-value using Excel.

10.5 When the background music was slow, the mean amount of bar purchases for a sample of 17 restaurant patrons was $30.47 with a standard deviation of $15.10. When the background music was fast, the mean amount of bar purchases for a sample of 14 patrons in the same restaurant was $21.62 with a standard deviation of $9.50. (a) Assuming equal variances, at $\alpha = .01$, is the true mean higher when the music is slow? (b) Calculate the *p*-value using Excel.

10.6 Are women's feet getting bigger? Retailers in the last 20 years have had to increase their stock of larger sizes. Wal-Mart Stores, Inc., and Payless ShoeSource, Inc., have been aggressive in stocking larger sizes, and Nordstrom's reports that its larger sizes typically sell out first. Assuming equal variances, at $\alpha = .025$, do these random shoe size samples of 12 randomly chosen women in each age group show that women's shoe sizes have increased? (See *The Wall Street Journal*, July 17, 2004.) ShoeSize1

| Born in 1980: | 8 | 7.5 | 8.5 | 8.5 | 8 | 7.5 | 9.5 | 7.5 | 8 | 8 | 8.5 | 9 |
| Born in 1960: | 8.5 | 7.5 | 8 | 8 | 7.5 | 7.5 | 7.5 | 8 | 7 | 8 | 7 | 8 |

10.7 Just how "decaffeinated" is decaffeinated coffee? Researchers analyzed 12 samples of two kinds of Starbucks' decaffeinated coffee. The caffeine in a cup of decaffeinated espresso had a mean 9.4 mg with a standard deviation of 3.2 mg, while brewed decaffeinated coffee had a mean of 12.7 mg with a standard deviation of 0.35 mg. Assuming unequal population variances, is there a significant difference in caffeine content between these two beverages at $\alpha = .01$? (Based on McCusker, R. R., *Journal of Analytical Toxicology* 30 [March 2006], pp. 112–114.)

10.3 CONFIDENCE INTERVAL FOR THE DIFFERENCE OF TWO MEANS, $\mu_1 - \mu_2$

There may be occasions when we want to estimate the difference between two unknown population means. The point estimate for $\mu_1 - \mu_2$ is $\bar{X}_1 - \bar{X}_2$, where $\bar{X}_1$ and $\bar{X}_2$ are calculated from independent random samples. We can use a confidence interval estimate to find a range within which the true difference might fall. If the confidence interval for the **difference of two means** includes zero, we could conclude that there is no significant difference in means.

When the population variances are unknown (the usual situation) the procedure for constructing a confidence interval for $\mu_1 - \mu_2$ depends on our assumption about the unknown variances. If both populations are normal and the population variances can be assumed equal, the difference of means follows a Student's *t* distribution with $(n_1 - 1) + (n_2 - 1)$ degrees of freedom. The pooled variance is a weighted average of the sample variances with weights $n_1 - 1$ and $n_2 - 1$ (the respective degrees of freedom for each sample).

Assuming equal variances:

$$(\bar{x}_1 - \bar{x}_2) \pm t_{\alpha/2}\sqrt{\frac{(n_1 - 1)s_1^2 + (n_2 - 1)s_2^2}{n_1 + n_2 - 2}}\sqrt{\frac{1}{n_1} + \frac{1}{n_2}} \quad \text{with } d.f. = (n_1 - 1) + (n_2 - 1)$$

(10.5)

LO9

Construct a confidence interval for $\mu_1 - \mu_2$ or $\pi_1 - \pi_2$.

If the population variances are unknown and are likely to be unequal, we should not pool the variances. A practical alternative is to use the *t* distribution, adding the variances and using *Welch's formula* for the degrees of freedom.

Assuming unequal variances:

(10.6) $\quad (\bar{x}_1 - \bar{x}_2) \pm t_{\alpha/2}\sqrt{\dfrac{s_1^2}{n_1} + \dfrac{s_2^2}{n_2}} \quad$ with $d.f. = \dfrac{\left[s_1^2/n_1 + s_2^2/n_2\right]^2}{\dfrac{\left(s_1^2/n_1\right)^2}{n_1 - 1} + \dfrac{\left(s_2^2/n_2\right)^2}{n_2 - 1}}$

If you wish to avoid the complex algebra of the Welch formula, you can just use degrees of freedom equal to $d.f. = \min(n_1 - 1, n_2 - 1)$. This conservative quick rule allows fewer degrees of freedom than Welch's formula yet generally gives reasonable results. For large samples with similar variances and near-equal sample sizes, the methods give similar results.

EXAMPLE

Marketing Teams

Senior marketing majors were randomly assigned to a virtual team that met only electronically or to a face-to-face team that met in person. Both teams were presented with the task of analyzing eight complex marketing cases. After completing the project, they were asked to respond on a 1–5 Likert scale to this question:

"As compared to other teams, the members got along together."

TABLE 10.4	**Means and Standard Deviations for the Two Marketing Teams**	
Statistic	*Virtual Team*	*Face-to-Face Team*
Sample Mean	$\bar{x}_1 = 2.48$	$\bar{x}_2 = 1.83$
Sample Std. Dev.	$s_1 = 0.76$	$s_2 = 0.82$
Sample Size	$n_1 = 44$	$n_2 = 42$

Source: Roger W. Berry, "The Efficacy of Electronic Communication in the Business School: Marketing Students' Perception of Virtual Teams," *Marketing Education Review* 12, no. 2 (Summer 2002), pp. 73–78. Copyright © 2002. Reprinted with permission, CTC press. All rights reserved.

Table 10.4 shows the means and standard deviations for the two groups. The population variances are unknown, but will be assumed equal (note the similar standard deviations). For a confidence level of 90 percent we use Student's t with $d.f. = 44 + 42 - 2 = 84$. From Appendix D we obtain $t_{.05} = 1.664$ (using 80 degrees of freedom, the next lower value). The confidence interval is

$$(\bar{x}_1 - \bar{x}_2) \pm t\sqrt{\frac{(n_1 - 1)s_1^2 + (n_2 - 1)s_2^2}{n_1 + n_2 - 2}}\sqrt{\frac{1}{n_1} + \frac{1}{n_2}}$$

$$= (2.48 - 1.83) \pm (1.664)\sqrt{\frac{(44 - 1)(0.76)^2 + (42 - 1)(0.82)^2}{44 + 42 - 2}}\sqrt{\frac{1}{44} + \frac{1}{42}}$$

$$= 0.65 \pm 0.284 \quad \text{or} \quad [0.366, 0.934]$$

Since this confidence interval does not include zero, we can say with 90 percent confidence that there is a difference between the means (i.e., the virtual team's mean differs from the face-to-face team's mean).

Because the calculations for the comparison of two sample means are rather complex, it is helpful to use software. Figure 10.8 shows a MINITAB menu that gives the option to assume equal variances or not. If we had not assumed equal variances, the results would be the same in this case because the samples are large and of similar size, and the variances do not differ greatly. But when you have small, unequal sample sizes or unequal variances, the methods can yield different results.

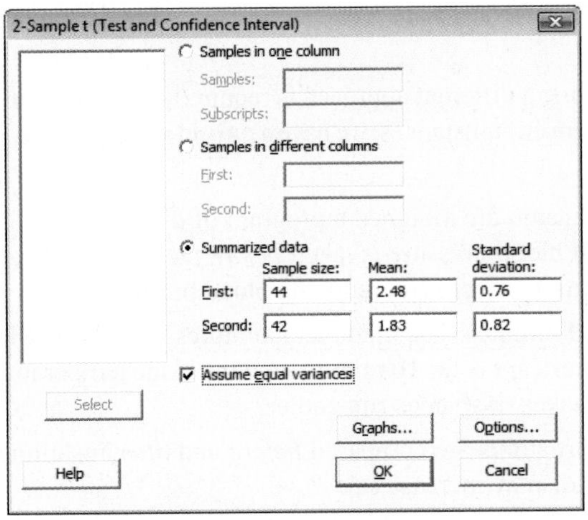

FIGURE 10.8

MINITAB's Menu for Comparing Two Sample Means

```
2-Sample t (Test and Confidence Interval)                          [X]
       C Samples in one column
           Samples: [              ]
           Subscripts: [            ]
       C Samples in different columns
           First: [                 ]
           Second: [                ]
       (•) Summarized data
                    Sample size:   Mean:      Standard deviation:
           First:   [ 44 ]        [ 2.48 ]    [ 0.76 ]
           Second:  [ 42 ]        [ 1.83 ]    [ 0.82 ]
       [✓] Assume equal variances

    [ Select ]
                              [ Graphs... ]   [ Options... ]
    [ Help ]                  [    OK    ]    [ Cancel ]
```

```
Two-Sample T-Test and CI

Sample  N   Mean   StDev  SE Mean
1       44  2.480  0.760   0.11
2       42  1.830  0.820   0.13

Difference = mu (1) - mu (2)
Estimate for difference:  0.650
90% CI for difference:  (0.367, 0.933)
T-Test of difference = 0 (vs not =)
T-Value = 3.81  P-Value = 0.000  DF = 84
Both use Pooled StDev = 0.7899
```

Should Sample Sizes Be Equal?

Many people instinctively try to choose equal sample sizes for tests of means. It is preferable to avoid unbalanced sample sizes, but it is not necessary. Unequal sample sizes are common, and the formulas still apply.

SECTION EXERCISES

connect

10.8 A special bumper was installed on selected vehicles in a large fleet. The dollar cost of body repairs was recorded for all vehicles that were involved in accidents over a 1-year period. Those with the special bumper are the test group and the other vehicles are the control group, shown below. Each "repair incident" is defined as an invoice (which might include more than one separate type of damage).

Statistic	Test Group	Control Group
Mean Damage	$\bar{x}_1 = \$1,101$	$\bar{x}_2 = \$1,766$
Sample Std. Dev.	$s_1 = \$696$	$s_2 = \$838$
Repair Incidents	$n_1 = 12$	$n_2 = 9$

Source: Unpublished study by Thomas W. Lauer and Floyd G. Willoughby.

(a) Construct a 90 percent confidence interval for the true difference of the means assuming equal variances. Show all work clearly. (b) Repeat, using the assumption of unequal variances with either Welch's formula for *d.f.* or the quick rule for degrees of freedom. Did the assumption about variances make a major difference, in your opinion? (c) Construct separate confidence intervals for each mean. Do they overlap? (d) What conclusions can you draw?

10.9 In trials of an experimental Internet-based method of learning statistics, pre-tests and post-tests were given to two groups: traditional instruction (22 students) and Internet-based (17 students). Pre-test scores were not significantly different. On the post-test, the first group (traditional instruction) had a mean score of 8.64 with a standard deviation of 1.88, while the second group (experimental instruction) had a mean score of 8.82 with a standard deviation of 1.70. (a) Construct a 90 percent confidence interval for the true difference of the means assuming equal variances. Show all work clearly. (b) Repeat, using the assumption of unequal variances with either Welch's formula for *d.f.* or the quick rule for degrees of freedom. Did the assumption about variances make a major difference, in your opinion? (c) Construct separate confidence intervals for each mean. Do they overlap? (d) What conclusions can you draw?

10.10 Construct a 95 percent confidence interval for the difference of mean monthly rent paid by undergraduates and graduate students. What do you conclude? 📖 **Rent2**

Undergraduate Student Rents ($n = 10$)

820	780	870	670	800
790	810	680	1,000	730

Graduate Student Rents ($n = 12$)

1,130	920	930	880	780	910
790	840	930	910	860	850

10.4
COMPARING TWO MEANS: PAIRED SAMPLES

LO3

Recognize paired data and be able to perform a paired t test.

Paired Data

When sample data consist of n matched pairs, a different approach is required. If the *same* individuals are observed twice but under different circumstances, we have a **paired comparison**. For example:

- Fifteen retirees with diagnosed hypertension are assigned a program of diet, exercise, and meditation. A baseline measurement of blood pressure is taken *before* the program begins and again *after* 2 months. Was the program effective in reducing blood pressure?

- Ten cutting tools use lubricant A for 10 minutes. The blade temperatures are taken. When the machine has cooled, it is run with lubricant B for 10 minutes and the blade temperatures are again measured. Which lubricant makes the blades run cooler?

- Weekly sales of Snapple at 12 Wal-Mart stores are compared *before* and *after* installing a new eye-catching display. Did the new display increase sales?

Paired data typically come from a *before-after* experiment. If we treat the data as two independent samples, ignoring the *dependence* between the data pairs, the test is less powerful.

Paired t Test

In the **paired t test** we define a new variable $d = X_1 - X_2$ as the *difference* between X_1 and X_2. We usually present the n observed differences in column form:

Obs	X_1	X_2	$d = X_1 - X_2$
1	XXX	XXX	XXX
2	XXX	XXX	XXX
3	XXX	XXX	XXX
. . .	. . .	. . .	. . .
. . .	. . .	. . .	. . .
n	XXX	XXX	XXX

The same sample data could also be presented in row form:

Obs	1	2	3	. . .	. . .	n
X_1	XXX	XXX	XXX	. . .	. . .	XXX
X_2	XXX	XXX	XXX	. . .	. . .	XXX
$d = X_1 - X_2$	XXX	XXX	XXX	. . .	. . .	XXX

The mean $\bar{d}$ and standard deviation s_d of the sample of n differences are calculated with the usual formulas for a mean and standard deviation. We call the mean $\bar{d}$ instead of $\bar{x}$ merely to remind ourselves that we are dealing with *differences*.

(10.7)
$$\bar{d} = \frac{\sum_{i=1}^{n} d_i}{n} \quad \text{(mean of } n \text{ differences)}$$

(10.8)
$$s_d = \sqrt{\sum_{i=1}^{n} \frac{(d_i - \bar{d})^2}{n-1}} \quad \text{(Std. Dev. of } n \text{ differences)}$$

Since the population variance of d is unknown, we will do a paired t test using Student's t with $n - 1$ degrees of freedom to compare the sample mean difference $\bar{d}$ with a hypothesized difference μ_d (usually $\mu_d = 0$). The test statistic is really a one-sample t test, just like those in Chapter 9.

(10.9)
$$t_{\text{calc}} = \frac{\bar{d} - \mu_d}{\frac{s_d}{\sqrt{n}}} \quad \text{(test statistic for \textbf{paired samples})}$$

An insurance company's procedure in settling a claim under $10,000 for fire or water damage to a home owner is to require two estimates for cleanup and repair of structural damage before allowing the insured to proceed with the work. The insurance company compares estimates from two contractors who most frequently handle this type of work in this geographical area. Table 10.5 shows the 10 most recent claims for which damage estimates were provided by both contractors. At the .05 level of significance, is there a difference between the two contractors?

EXAMPLE

Repair Estimates

Repair

TABLE 10.5 Damage Repair Estimates ($) for 10 Claims Repair

Claim	X_1 Contractor A	X_2 Contractor B	$d = X_1 - X_2$ Difference
1. Jones, C.	5,500	6,000	−500
2. Smith, R.	1,000	900	100
3. Xia, Y.	2,500	2,500	0
4. Gallo, J.	7,800	8,300	−500
5. Carson, R.	6,400	6,200	200
6. Petty, M.	8,800	9,400	−600
7. Tracy, L.	600	500	100
8. Barnes, J.	3,300	3,500	−200
9. Rodriguez, J.	4,500	5,200	−700
10. Van Dyke, P.	6,500	6,800	−300

$$\bar{d} = -240.00$$
$$s_d = 327.28$$
$$n = 10$$

Step 1: State the Hypotheses
Since we have no reason to be interested in directionality, we will choose a two-tailed test using these hypotheses:

$H_0: \mu_d = 0$
$H_1: \mu_d \neq 0$

Step 2: Specify the Decision Rule
Our test statistic will follow a Student's t distribution with $d.f. = n - 1 = 10 - 1 = 9$, so from Appendix D with $\alpha = .05$ the two-tail critical value is $t_{.025} = \pm 2.262$, as illustrated in Figure 10.9. The decision rule is

Reject H_0 if $t_{calc} < -2.262$ or if $t_{calc} > +2.262$
Otherwise accept H_0

FIGURE 10.9 Decision Rule for Two-Tailed Paired t Test at $\alpha = .05$

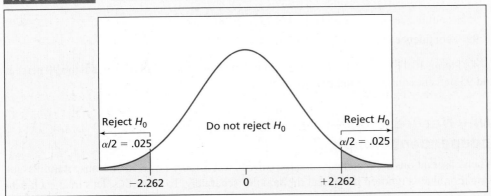

Reject H_0 $\alpha/2 = .025$ Do not reject H_0 Reject H_0 $\alpha/2 = .025$

−2.262   0   +2.262

Step 3: Calculate the Test Statistic

The mean and standard deviation are calculated in the usual way, as shown in Table 10.5, so the test statistic is

$$t_{calc} = \frac{\bar{d} - \mu_d}{\dfrac{s_d}{\sqrt{n}}} = \frac{-240 - 0}{\left(\dfrac{327.28}{\sqrt{10}}\right)} = \frac{-240}{103.495} = -2.319$$

Step 4: Make the Decision

Since $t_{calc} = -2.319$ falls in the left-tail critical region (below -2.262), we reject the null hypothesis, and conclude that there is a significant difference between the two contractors. However, it is a *very* close decision.

Excel's Paired Difference Test

The calculations for our repair estimates example are easy in Excel, as illustrated in Figure 10.10. Excel gives you the option of choosing either a one-tailed or two-tailed test, and also shows the *p*-value. For a two-tailed test, the *p*-value is $p = .0456$, which would barely lead to rejection of the hypothesis of zero difference of means at $\alpha = .05$. The borderline *p*-value reinforces our conclusion that the decision is sensitive to our choice of α. MegaStat and MINITAB also provide a paired *t* test.

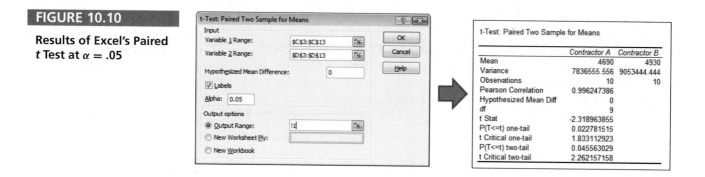

Analogy to Confidence Interval

A two-tailed test for a zero difference is equivalent to asking whether the confidence interval for the true mean difference μ_d includes zero.

(10.10) $$\bar{d} \pm t_{\alpha/2} \frac{s_d}{\sqrt{n}}$$ (confidence interval for difference of paired means)

It depends on the confidence level:

90% confidence ($t_{\alpha/2} = 1.833$): $[-429.72, -50.28]$

95% confidence ($t_{\alpha/2} = 2.262$): $[-474.12, -5.88]$

99% confidence ($t_{\alpha/2} = 3.250$): $[-576.34, +96.34]$

As Figure 10.11 shows, the 99 percent confidence interval includes zero, but the 90 percent and 95 percent confidence intervals do not.

Why Not Treat Paired Data As Independent Samples?

When observations are matched pairs, the paired *t* test is more powerful, because it utilizes information that is ignored if we treat the samples separately. To show this, let's treat each data

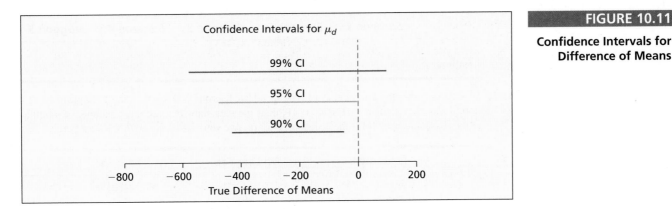

FIGURE 10.11

Confidence Intervals for Difference of Means

column as an **independent sample**. The summary statistics are:

$$\bar{x}_1 = 4{,}690.00 \qquad \bar{x}_2 = 4{,}930.00$$
$$s_1 = 2{,}799.38 \qquad s_2 = 3{,}008.89$$
$$n_1 = 10 \qquad n_2 = 10$$

Assuming equal variances, we get the results shown in Figure 10.12. The *p*-values (one tail or two-tail) are not even close to being significant at the usual α levels. By ignoring the dependence between the samples, we unnecessarily *sacrifice the power of the test*. Therefore, if the two data columns are paired, we should not treat them independently.

FIGURE 10.12

Excel's Paired Sample and Independent Sample *t* Test

Best Test : Paired Samples

t-Test: Paired Two Sample for Means

	Contractor A	Contractor B
Mean	4690	4930
Variance	7836555.556	9053444.444
Observations	10	10
Pearson Correlation	0.996247386	
Hypothesized Mean Diff	0	
df	9	
t Stat	-2.318963855	
P(T<=t) one-tail	0.022781515	
t Critical one-tail	1.833112923	
P(T<=t) two-tail	0.045563029	
t Critical two-tail	2.262157158	

Less Power : Independent Samples

t-Test: Two-Sample Assuming Equal Variances

	Contractor A	Contractor B
Mean	4690	4930
Variance	7836555.556	9053444.444
Observations	10	10
Pooled Variance	8445000	
Hypothesized Mean Differe	0	
df	18	
t Stat	-0.184670029	
P(T<=t) one-tail	0.427776285	
t Critical one-tail	1.734063592	
P(T<=t) two-tail	0.855552569	
t Critical two-tail	2.100922037	

SECTION EXERCISES

connect

10.11 (a) At $\alpha = .05$, does the following sample show that daughters are taller than their mothers? (b) Is the decision close? (c) Why might daughters tend to be taller than their mothers? Why might they not? 📁 **Height**

Family	Daughter's Height (cm)	Mother's Height (cm)
1	167	172
2	166	162
3	176	157
4	171	159
5	165	157
6	181	177
7	173	174

10.12 An experimental surgical procedure is being studied as an alternative to the old method. Both methods are considered safe. Five surgeons perform the operation on two patients matched by age, sex, and other relevant factors, with the results shown. The time to complete the surgery (in minutes) is recorded. (a) At the 5 percent significance level, is the new way faster? State your hypotheses and show all steps clearly. (b) Is the decision close? 📁 **Surgery**

	Surgeon 1	Surgeon 2	Surgeon 3	Surgeon 4	Surgeon 5
Old way	36	55	28	40	62
New way	29	42	30	32	56

10.13 Blockbuster is testing a new policy of waiving all late fees on DVD rentals using a sample of 10 randomly chosen customers. (a) At $\alpha = .10$, does the data show that the mean number of monthly rentals has increased? (b) Is the decision close? (c) Are you convinced? 📠 **DVDRental**

Customer	No Late Fee	Late Fee
1	14	10
2	12	7
3	14	10
4	13	13
5	10	9
6	13	14
7	12	12
8	10	7
9	13	13
10	13	9

10.14 Below is a random sample of shoe sizes for 12 mothers and their daughters. (a) At $\alpha = .01$, does this sample show that women's shoe sizes have increased? State your hypotheses and show all steps clearly. (b) Is the decision close? (c) Are you convinced? (d) Why might shoe sizes change over time? (See *The Wall Street Journal*, July 17, 2004.) 📠 **ShoeSize2**

	1	2	3	4	5	6	7	8	9	10	11	12
Daughter	8	8	7.5	8	9	9	8.5	9	9	8	7	8
Mother	7	7	7.5	8	8.5	8.5	7.5	7.5	6	8	7	7

10.15 A newly installed automatic gate system was being tested to see if the number of failures in 1,000 entry attempts was the same as the number of failures in 1,000 exit attempts. A random sample of eight delivery trucks was selected for data collection. Do these sample results show that there is a significant difference between entry and exit gate failures? Use $\alpha = .01$. 📠 **Gates**

	Truck 1	Truck 2	Truck 3	Truck 4	Truck 5	Truck 6	Truck 7	Truck 8
Entry failures	43	45	53	56	61	51	48	44
Exit failures	48	51	60	58	58	45	55	50

Mini Case   10.3

Detroit's Weight-Loss Contest

Table 10.6 shows the results of a weight-loss contest sponsored by a local newspaper. Participants came from the East Side and West Side, and were encouraged to compete over a 1-month period. At $\alpha = .01$, was there a significant weight loss? The hypotheses are $H_0: \mu_d \geq 0$ and $H_1: \mu_d < 0$.

The test statistic is over nine standard errors from zero, a highly significant difference:

$$t_{calc} = \frac{\bar{d} - 0}{\frac{s_d}{\sqrt{n}}} = \frac{-11.375 - 0}{\frac{4.37516}{\sqrt{12}}} = -9.006$$

Obs	Name	After	Before	Difference
1	Michael M.	202.5	217.0	−14.5
2	Tracy S.	178.0	188.0	−10.0
3	Gregg G.	210.0	225.0	−15.0
4	Boydea P.	157.0	168.0	−11.0
5	Donna I.	169.0	178.0	−9.0
6	Elizabeth C.	173.5	182.0	−8.5
7	Carole K.	163.5	174.5	−11.0
8	Candace G.	153.0	161.5	−8.5
9	Jo Anne M.	170.5	177.5	−7.0
10	Willis B.	336.0	358.5	−22.5
11	Marilyn S.	174.0	181.0	−7.0
12	Tim B.	197.5	210.0	−12.5

TABLE 10.6 Results of Detroit's Weight-Loss Contest WeightLoss

$\bar{d} = -11.375$
$s_d = 4.37516$

Source: *Detroit Free Press*, February 12, 2002, pp. 10H–11H.

Excel's p-value for the paired t test is p-value $= .0000$ for a one-tailed test (a significant result at any α). Therefore, the mean weight loss of 11.375 pounds was *significant* at $\alpha = .01$. Moreover, to most people, a weight loss of 11.375 pounds would also be *important*.

10.5 COMPARING TWO PROPORTIONS

The test for two proportions is the simplest and perhaps most commonly used two-sample test, because percents are ubiquitous. Is the president's approval rating greater, lower, or the same as last month? Is the proportion of satisfied Dell customers greater than Gateway's? Is the annual nursing turnover percentage at Mayo Clinic higher, lower, or the same as Johns Hopkins? To answer such questions, we would compare two sample proportions.

LO5

Perform a test to compare two proportions using z.

Testing for Zero Difference: $\pi_1 - \pi_2 = 0$

Let the true proportions in the two populations be denoted π_1 and π_2. When testing the difference between two proportions, we typically assume the population proportions are equal and set up our hypotheses using the null hypothesis $H_0: \pi_1 - \pi_2 = 0$. This is similar to our approach when testing the difference between two means. The research question will determine the format of our alternative hypothesis. The three possible pairs of hypotheses are

Left-Tailed Test	*Two-Tailed Test*	*Right-Tailed Test*
$H_0: \pi_1 - \pi_2 \geq 0$	$H_0: \pi_1 - \pi_2 = 0$	$H_0: \pi_1 - \pi_2 \leq 0$
$H_1: \pi_1 - \pi_2 < 0$	$H_1: \pi_1 - \pi_2 \neq 0$	$H_1: \pi_1 - \pi_2 > 0$

Sample Proportions

The sample proportion p_1 is a point estimate of π_1, and the sample proportion p_2 is a point estimate of π_2. A "success" is any event of interest (not necessarily something desirable).

$$p_1 = \frac{x_1}{n_1} = \frac{\text{number of "successes" in sample 1}}{\text{number of items in sample 1}} \quad (10.11)$$

$$p_2 = \frac{x_2}{n_2} = \frac{\text{number of "successes" in sample 2}}{\text{number of items in sample 2}} \quad (10.12)$$

Pooled Proportion

If H_0 is true, there is no difference between π_1 and π_2, so the samples can logically be *pooled* or averaged into one "big" sample to estimate the common population proportion:

(10.13) $\quad \bar{p} = \dfrac{x_1 + x_2}{n_1 + n_2} = \dfrac{\text{number of successes in combined samples}}{\text{combined sample size}}$ **(pooled proportion)**

Test Statistic

If the samples are large, the difference of proportions $p_1 - p_2$ may be assumed normally distributed. The *test statistic* is the difference of the sample proportions $p_1 - p_2$ minus the parameter $\pi_1 - \pi_2$ divided by the standard error of the difference $p_1 - p_2$. The standard error is calculated by using the pooled proportion. The general form of the test statistic for testing the difference between two proportions is

(10.14) $\qquad z_{\text{calc}} = \dfrac{(p_1 - p_2) - (\pi_1 - \pi_2)}{\sqrt{\dfrac{\bar{p}(1 - \bar{p})}{n_1} + \dfrac{\bar{p}(1 - \bar{p})}{n_2}}}$

If we are testing the hypothesis that $\pi_1 - \pi_2 = 0$ we can simplify formula 10.14 as shown in formula 10.15.

Test statistic for equality of proportions

(10.15) $\qquad z_{\text{calc}} = \dfrac{p_1 - p_2}{\sqrt{\bar{p}(1 - \bar{p})\left[\dfrac{1}{n_1} + \dfrac{1}{n_2}\right]}}$

EXAMPLE

Active Promoters Vail Resorts

VAILRESORTS·

In order to measure the level of satisfaction with Vail Resorts' Web sites, the Vail Resorts marketing team periodically surveys a random sample of guests and asks them to rate their likelihood of recommending the Web site to a friend or colleague. An *active promoter* is a guest who responds that they are highly likely to recommend the Web site. From a random sample of 2,386 07/08 Vail ski mountain guests there were 2,014 active promoters and from a random sample of 2,309 08/09 Vail ski mountain guests there were 2,048 active promoters. A summary of results from the survey is shown in Table 10.7. At the .01 level of significance, did the proportion of active promoters increase from the 07/08 and 08/09 seasons?

TABLE 10.7 Web Site Satisfaction Survey

Statistic	08/09 Season Guests	07/08 Season Guests
Number of active promoters	$x_1 = 2048$	$x_2 = 2014$
Number of guests surveyed	$n_1 = 2309$	$n_2 = 2386$
Active promoter proportion	$p_1 = \dfrac{2048}{2309} = .8870$	$p_2 = \dfrac{2014}{2386} = .8441$

Step 1: State the Hypotheses

Because Vail Resorts had redesigned their ski mountain Web sites for the 2008/2009 season, they were interested in seeing if the proportion of active promoters had increased. Therefore we will do a right-tailed test for equality of proportions.

$H_0: \pi_1 - \pi_2 \leq 0$
$H_1: \pi_1 - \pi_2 > 0$

Step 2: Specify the Decision Rule

Using $\alpha = .01$ the right-tail critical value is $z_{.01} = 2.326$, which yields the decision rule

Reject H_0 if $z_{\text{calc}} > 2.326$

Otherwise do not reject H_0

The decision rule is illustrated in Figure 10.13. Since Excel uses cumulative left-tail areas, the right-tail critical value $z_{.01} = 2.326$ is obtained using =NORMSINV(.99).

FIGURE 10.13   **Right-Tailed Test for Two Proportions**

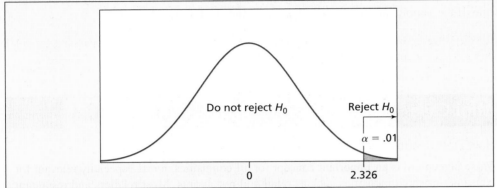

Step 3: Calculate the Test Statistic
The sample proportions indicate that the 08/09 season had a higher proportion of active promoters than the 07/08 season. We assume that $\pi_1 - \pi_2 = 0$ and see if a contradiction stems from this assumption. Assuming that the proportions are equal, we can pool the two samples to obtain a **pooled estimate** of the common proportion by dividing the combined number of active promoters by the combined sample size.

$$\bar{p} = \frac{\bar{x}_1 + \bar{x}_2}{n_1 + n_2} = \frac{2048 + 2014}{2309 + 2386} = \frac{4062}{4695} = .8652, \text{ or } 86.52\%$$

Assuming normality (i.e., large samples) the test statistic is

$$z_{\text{calc}} = \frac{p_1 - p_2}{\sqrt{\bar{p}(1 - \bar{p})\left[\dfrac{1}{n_1} + \dfrac{1}{n_2}\right]}} = \frac{.8870 - .8441}{\sqrt{.8652(1 - .8652)\left[\dfrac{1}{2309} + \dfrac{1}{2386}\right]}} = 4.313$$

Step 4: Make the Decision
If H_0 were true, the test statistic should be near zero. Since the test statistic ($z_{\text{calc}} = 4.313$) exceeds the critical value ($z_{.01} = 2.326$) we reject the null hypothesis and conclude that $\pi_1 - \pi_2 > 0$. If we were to use the p-value approach we would find the p-value by using the function =1−NORMSDIST(4.313) in Excel. This function returns a value so small (.00000807) it is, for all practical purposes, equal to zero. Because the p-value is less than .01 we would reject the null hypothesis.

Whether we use the critical value approach or the p-value approach, we would reject the null hypothesis of equal proportions. In other words, the proportion of 08/09 active promoters (i.e., guests who are highly likely to recommend the Vail ski mountain Web site) is significantly greater than the proportion of 07/08 active promoters. The new Web site design appeared to be attractive to Vail Resorts' guests.

Checking Normality

We have assumed a normal distribution for the statistic $p_1 - p_2$. This assumption can be checked. For a test of two proportions, the criterion for normality is $n\pi \geq 10$ and $n(1 - \pi) \geq 10$ for *each* sample, using each sample proportion in place of π:

$$n_1 p_1 = (2309)(2048/2309) = 2048 \quad n_1(1 - p_1) = (2309)(1 - 2048/2309) = 261$$
$$n_2 p_2 = (2386)(2014/2386) = 2014 \quad n_2(1 - p_2) = (2386)(1 - 2014/2386) = 372$$

The normality requirement is comfortably fulfilled in this case. Ideally, these numbers should exceed 10 by a comfortable margin, as they do in this example. Since the samples are pooled,

LO6

Check whether normality may be assumed for two proportions.

this guarantees that the pooled proportion $(n_1 + n_2)\bar{p} \geq 10$. Note that when using sample data, the sample size rule of thumb is equivalent to requiring that each sample contains at least 10 "successes" and at least 10 "failures."

If sample sizes do not justify the normality assumption, each sample should be treated as a binomial experiment. Unless you have good computational software, this may not be worthwhile. If the samples are small, the test is likely to have low power.

Must Sample Sizes Be Equal?   No. Balanced sample sizes are not necessary. Unequal sample sizes are common, and the formulas still apply.

Mini Case   10.4

How Does Noodles & Company Provide Value to Customers?

Value perception is an important concept for all companies, but is especially relevant for consumer-oriented industries such as retail and restaurants. Most retailers and restaurant concepts periodically make price increases to reflect changes in inflationary items such as cost of goods and labor costs. In 2006, however, Noodles & Company took the opposite approach when it evaluated its value perception through its consumers.

Through rigorous statistical analysis Noodles recognized that a significant percentage of current customers would increase their frequency of visits if the menu items were priced slightly lower. The company evaluated the trade-offs that a price decrease would represent and determined that they would actually be able to increase revenue by reducing price. Despite not advertising this price decrease, the company did in fact see an increase in frequency of visits resulting from the change. To measure the impact, the company statistically evaluated both the increase in frequency as well as customer evaluations of Noodles & Company's value perception. Within a few months, the statistical analysis showed that not only had customer frequency increased by 2–3%, but also that the improved value perception led to an increase in average party size of 2%. Ultimately, the price decrease of roughly 2% led to a total revenue increase of 4–5%.

SECTION EXERCISES

connect

10.16 Find the sample proportions and test statistic for equal proportions. Is the decision close? Find the p-value.

   a. Dissatisfied workers in two companies: $x_1 = 40$, $n_1 = 100$, $x_2 = 30$, $n_2 = 100$, $\alpha = .05$, two-tailed test.

   b. Rooms rented at least a week in advance at two hotels: $x_1 = 24$, $n_1 = 200$, $x_2 = 12$, $n_2 = 50$, $\alpha = .01$, left-tailed test.

   c. Home equity loan default rates in two banks: $x_1 = 36$, $n_1 = 480$, $x_2 = 26$, $n_2 = 520$, $\alpha = .05$, right-tailed test.

10.17 Find the test statistic and do the two-sample test for equality of proportions. Is the decision close?

   a. Repeat buyers at two car dealerships: $p_1 = .30$, $n_1 = 50$, $p_2 = .54$, $n_2 = 50$, $\alpha = .01$, left-tailed test.

   b. Honor roll students in two sororities: $p_1 = .45$, $n_1 = 80$, $p_2 = .25$, $n_2 = 48$, $\alpha = .10$, two-tailed test.

   c. First-time Hawaii visitors at two hotels: $p_1 = .20$, $n_1 = 80$, $p_2 = .32$, $n_2 = 75$, $\alpha = .05$, left-tailed test.

10.18 During the period 1990–1998 there were 46 Atlantic hurricanes, of which 19 struck the United States. During the period 1999–2006 there were 70 hurricanes, of which 45 struck the United States. (a) Does this evidence convince you that the percentage of hurricanes that strike the United States is increasing, at $\alpha = .01$? (b) Can normality be assumed? (Data are from *The New York Times,* August 27, 2006, p. 2WK.)

10.19 In 2006, a sample of 200 in-store shoppers showed that 42 paid by debit card. In 2009, a sample of the same size showed that 62 paid by debit card. (a) Formulate appropriate hypotheses to test whether the percentage of debit card shoppers increased. (b) Carry out the test at $\alpha = .01$. (c) Find the p-value. (d) Test whether normality may be assumed.

10.20 A survey of 100 mayonnaise purchasers showed that 65 were loyal to one brand. For 100 bath soap purchasers, only 53 were loyal to one brand. Perform a two-tailed test comparing the proportion of brand-loyal customers at $\alpha = .05$.

10.21 A 20-minute consumer survey mailed to 500 adults aged 25–34 included a $5 Starbucks gift certificate. The same survey was mailed to 500 adults aged 25–34 without the gift certificate. There were 65 responses from the first group and 45 from the second group. Perform a two-tailed test comparing the response rates (proportions) at $\alpha = .05$.

10.22 Is the water on your airline flight safe to drink? It is not feasible to analyze the water on every flight, so sampling is necessary. In August and September 2004, the Environmental Protection Agency (EPA) found bacterial contamination in water samples from the lavatories and galley water taps on 20 of 158 randomly selected U.S. flights. Alarmed by the data, the EPA ordered sanitation improvements, and then tested water samples again in November and December 2004. In the second sample, bacterial contamination was found in 29 of 169 randomly sampled flights. (a) Use a left-tailed test at $\alpha = .05$ to check whether the percent of all flights with contaminated water was lower in the first sample. (b) Find the *p*-value. (c) Discuss the question of significance versus importance in this specific application. (d) Test whether normality may be assumed. (Data are from *The Wall Street Journal,* November 10, 2004, and January 20, 2005.)

10.23 When tested for compliance with Sarbanes-Oxley requirements for financial records and fraud protection, 14 of 180 publicly traded business services companies failed, compared with 7 of 67 computer hardware, software and telecommunications companies. (a) Is this a statistically significant difference at $\alpha = .05$? (b) Can normality be assumed? (Data are from *The New York Times,* April 27, 2005, p. BU5.)

Testing for Nonzero Difference (Optional)

Testing for equality of π_1 and π_2 is a special case of testing for a specified difference D_0 between the two proportions:

Left-Tailed Test	*Two-Tailed Test*	*Right-Tailed Test*
$H_0: \pi_1 - \pi_2 \geq D_0$	$H_0: \pi_1 - \pi_2 = D_0$	$H_0: \pi_1 - \pi_2 \leq D_0$
$H_1: \pi_1 - \pi_2 < D_0$	$H_1: \pi_1 - \pi_2 \neq D_0$	$H_1: \pi_1 - \pi_2 > D_0$

We have shown how to test for $D_0 = 0$, that is, $\pi_1 = \pi_2$. If the hypothesized difference D_0 is nonzero, we do not pool the sample proportions, but instead use the test statistic shown in formula 10.16.

$$z_{calc} = \frac{p_1 - p_2 - D_0}{\sqrt{\dfrac{p_1(1 - p_1)}{n_1} + \dfrac{p_2(1 - p_2)}{n_2}}} \qquad \text{(test statistic for nonzero difference } D_0\text{)} \qquad \textbf{(10.16)}$$

EXAMPLE

Magazine Ads

A sample of 111 magazine advertisements in *Good Housekeeping* showed 70 that listed a Web site. In *Fortune,* a sample of 145 advertisements showed 131 that listed a Web site. At $\alpha = .025$, does the *Fortune* proportion differ from the *Good Housekeeping* proportion by at least 20 percent? Table 10.8 shows the data.

TABLE 10.8	**Magazine Ads with Web Sites**	
Statistic	**Fortune**	**Good Housekeeping**
Number with Web sites	$x_1 = 131$ with Web site	$x_2 = 70$ with Web site
Number of ads examined	$n_1 = 145$ ads	$n_2 = 111$ ads
Proportion	$p_1 = \dfrac{131}{145} = .90345$	$p_2 = \dfrac{70}{111} = .63063$

Source: Project by MBA students Frank George, Karen Orso, and Lincy Zachariah.

Test Statistic

We will do a right-tailed test for $D_0 = .20$. The hypotheses are

$$H_0: \pi_1 - \pi_2 \leq .20$$
$$H_1: \pi_1 - \pi_2 > .20$$

The test statistic is

$$z_{calc} = \frac{p_1 - p_2 - D_0}{\sqrt{\dfrac{p_1(1 - p_1)}{n_1} + \dfrac{p_2(1 - p_2)}{n_2}}}$$

$$= \frac{.90345 - .63063 - .20}{\sqrt{\dfrac{.90345(1 - .90345)}{145} + \dfrac{.63063(1 - .63063)}{111}}} = 1.401$$

At $\alpha = .025$ the right-tail critical value is $z_{.025} = 1.960$, so the difference of proportions is insufficient to reject the hypothesis that the difference is .20 or less. The decision rule is illustrated in Figure 10.14.

FIGURE 10.14

Right-Tailed Test for Magazine Ads at $\alpha = .025$

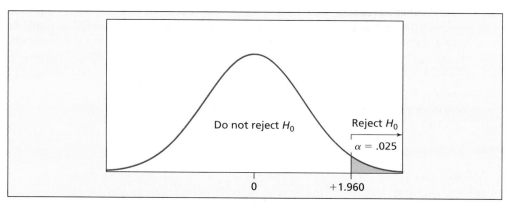

Calculating the *p*-Value

Using the *p*-value approach, we would insert the test statistic $z_{calc} = 1.401$ into Excel's cumulative normal =1-NORMSDIST(1.401) to obtain a right-tail area of .0806 as shown in Figure 10.15. Since the *p*-value >.025, we would not reject H_0. The conclusion is that the difference in proportions is not greater than .20.

FIGURE 10.15

***p*-Value for Magazine Proportions Differing by $D_0 = .20$**

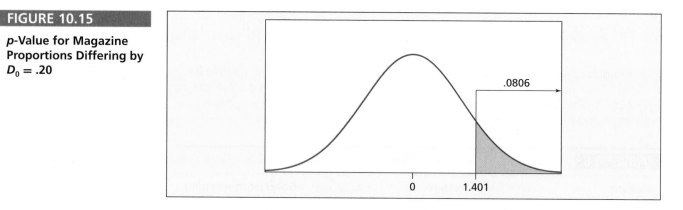

SECTION EXERCISES

connect

Note: Use MINITAB or MegaStat for calculations.

10.24 In 1999, a sample of 200 in-store shoppers showed that 42 paid by debit card. In 2004, a sample of the same size showed that 62 paid by debit card. (a) Formulate appropriate hypotheses to test whether the percentage of debit card shoppers increased by at least 5 percent, using $\alpha = .10$. (b) Find the *p*-value.

10.25 From a telephone log, an executive finds that 36 of 128 incoming telephone calls last week lasted at least 5 minutes. She vows to make an effort to reduce the length of time spent on calls. The phone log for the next week shows that 14 of 96 incoming calls lasted at least 5 minutes. (a) At $\alpha = .05$, has the proportion of 5-minute phone calls declined by at least 10 percent? (b) Find the *p*-value.

10.26 A 30-minute consumer survey mailed to 500 adults aged 25–34 included a $10 gift certificate to Borders. The same survey was mailed to 500 adults aged 25–34 without the gift certificate. There were 185 responses from the first group and 45 from the second group. (a) At $\alpha = .025$, did the gift certificate increase the response rate by at least 20 percent? (b) Find the *p*-value.

Mini Case 10.5

Automated Parking Lot Entry/Exit Gate System

Large universities have many different parking lots. Delivery trucks travel between various buildings all day long to deliver food, mail, and other items. Automated entry/exit gates make travel time much faster for the trucks and cars entering and exiting the different parking lots because the drivers do not have to stop to activate the gate manually. The gate is electronically activated as the truck or car approaches the parking lot.

One large university with two campuses recently negotiated with a company to install a new automated system. One requirement of the contract stated that the proportion of failed gate activations on one campus would be no different from the proportion of failed gate activations on the second campus. (A failed activation was one in which the driver had to manually activate the gate.) The university facilities operations manager designed and conducted a test to establish whether the gate company had violated this requirement of the contract. The university could renegotiate the contract if there was significant evidence showing that the two proportions were different.

The test was set up as a two-tailed test and the hypotheses tested were

$H_0: \pi_1 - \pi_2 = 0$

$H_1: \pi_1 - \pi_2 \neq 0$

Both the university and the gate company agreed on a 5 percent level of significance. Random samples from each campus were collected. The data are shown in Table 10.9.

TABLE 10.9   Proportion of Failed Gate Activations

Statistic	Campus 1	Campus 2
Number of failed activations	$x_1 = 52$	$x_2 = 63$
Sample size (number of entry/exit attempts)	$n_1 = 1{,}000$	$n_2 = 1{,}000$
Proportion	$p_1 = \dfrac{52}{1{,}000} = .052$	$p_2 = \dfrac{63}{1{,}000} = .063$

The pooled proportion is

$$\bar{p} = \frac{x_1 + x_2}{n_1 + n_2} = \frac{52 + 63}{1{,}000 + 1{,}000} = \frac{115}{2{,}000} = .0575$$

The test statistic is

$$z_{calc} = \frac{p_1 - p_2}{\sqrt{\bar{p}(1-\bar{p})\left[\dfrac{1}{n_1} + \dfrac{1}{n_2}\right]}} = \frac{.052 - .063}{\sqrt{.0575(1 - .0575)\left[\dfrac{1}{1{,}000} + \dfrac{1}{1{,}000}\right]}} = -1.057$$

Using the 5 percent level of significance the critical value is $z_{.025} = 1.96$ so it is clear that there is no significant difference between these two proportions. This conclusion is reinforced by Excel's cumulative normal function =NORMSDIST(−1.057) which gives the area to the left of −1.057 as .1453. Because this is a two-tailed test the *p*-value is .2906.

Was it reasonable to assume normality of the test statistic? Yes, the criterion was met.

$$n_1 p_1 = 1,000(52/1,000) = 52 \qquad n_1(1 - p_1) = 1,000(1 - 52/1,000) = 948$$
$$n_2 p_2 = 1,000(63/1,000) = 63 \qquad n_2(1 - p_2) = 1,000(1 - 63/1,000) = 937$$

Based on this sample, the university had no evidence to refute the gate company's claim that the failed activation proportions were the same for each campus.

Source: This case was based on a real contract negotiation between a large western university and a private company. The contract was still being negotiated as of the publication of this text.

10.6 CONFIDENCE INTERVAL FOR THE DIFFERENCE OF TWO PROPORTIONS, $\pi_1 - \pi_2$

A confidence interval for the **difference of two population proportions**, $\pi_1 - \pi_2$, is given by

(10.17)
$$(p_1 - p_2) \pm z_{\alpha/2} \sqrt{\frac{p_1(1 - p_1)}{n_1} + \frac{p_2(1 - p_2)}{n_2}}$$

This formula assumes that both samples are large enough to assume normality. The rule of thumb for assuming normality is that $np \geq 10$ and $n(1 - p) \geq 10$ for each sample.

EXAMPLE

Fire Truck Color

Compared to a traditional red fire truck, does a bright yellow fire truck have a lower accident rate? Proponents of the brighter yellow color argued that its enhanced visibility allowed other traffic to see the trucks and avoid them during fire runs. A frequently cited 4-year study in Dallas, Texas, produced the statistics shown in Table 10.10.

TABLE 10.10	Accident Rate for Dallas Fire Trucks	
Statistic	**Red Fire Trucks**	**Yellow Fire Trucks**
Number of accidents	$x_1 = 20$ accidents	$x_2 = 4$ accidents
Number of fire runs	$n_1 = 153{,}348$ runs	$n_2 = 135{,}035$ runs
Accident rate	$p_1 = \dfrac{20}{153{,}348}$ $= .000130422$	$p_2 = \dfrac{4}{135{,}035}$ $= .000029622$

Source: *The Wall Street Journal*, June 26, 1995, p. B1.

Although $np < 10$ for the second sample, we will use it to illustrate the confidence interval formula. The 95 percent confidence interval for the difference between the proportions is

$$(p_1 - p_2) \pm z_{\alpha/2} \sqrt{\frac{p_1(1 - p_1)}{n_1} + \frac{p_2(1 - p_2)}{n_2}}$$

$$= (.000130422 - .000029622)$$

$$\pm (1.960) \sqrt{\frac{(.000130422)(.999869578)}{153{,}348} + \frac{(.000029622)(.999970378)}{135{,}035}}$$

$$= .0001008 \pm .000064106$$

Since the confidence interval for $\pi_1 - \pi_2$ does not include zero, it appears that the accident rates are significantly different. Should all fire trucks be painted yellow? With such large samples, no one could say that this was a "small sample" fluke. However, both accident rates are quite small to begin with, an argument used by those who favor the traditional red color. A greater problem, the critics say, is that the public has become inured to sirens and flashing lights. As often happens, statistics may play only a small part in the policy decision.

10.27 The American Bankers Association reports that, in a sample of 120 consumer purchases in France, 60 were made with cash, compared with 26 in a sample of 50 consumer purchases in the United States. Construct a 90 percent confidence interval for the difference in proportions. (Data are from *The Wall Street Journal,* July 27, 2004.)

10.28 A study showed that 12 of 24 cell phone users with a headset missed their exit, compared with 3 of 24 talking to a passenger. Construct a 95 percent confidence interval for the difference in proportions. (Data are from *The Wall Street Journal,* September 24, 2004.)

10.29 A survey of 100 cigarette smokers showed that 71 were loyal to one brand, compared to 122 of 200 toothpaste users. Construct a 90 percent confidence interval for the difference in proportions. (Data are from J. Paul Peter and Jerry C. Olson, *Consumer Behavior and Marketing Strategy,* 7th ed. [McGraw-Hill, 2005], p. 97.)

The business statistician knows that comparing the *variances* may be as important as comparing the *means* of two populations. In manufacturing, smaller variation around the mean would indicate a more reliable product. In finance, smaller variation around the mean would indicate less volatility in asset returns. In services, smaller variation around the mean would indicate more consistency in customer treatment. For example, is the *variance* in Ford Mustang assembly times the same this month as last month? Is the *variability* in customer waiting times the same at two Tim Horton's franchises? Is the *variation* the same for customer concession purchases at a movie theater on Friday and Saturday nights?

10.7 COMPARING TWO VARIANCES

LO8

Carry out a test of two variances using the *F* distribution.

Format of Hypotheses

We may test the null hypothesis against a left-tailed, two-tailed, or right-tailed alternative:

Left-Tailed Test	*Two-Tailed Test*	*Right-Tailed Test*
$H_0: \sigma_1^2 \geq \sigma_2^2$	$H_0: \sigma_1^2 = \sigma_2^2$	$H_0: \sigma_1^2 \leq \sigma_2^2$
$H_1: \sigma_1^2 < \sigma_2^2$	$H_1: \sigma_1^2 \neq \sigma_2^2$	$H_1: \sigma_1^2 > \sigma_2^2$

An equivalent way to state these hypotheses is to look at the *ratio* of the two variances. A ratio near 1 would indicate equal variances.

Left-Tailed Test	*Two-Tailed Test*	*Right-Tailed Test*
$H_0: \dfrac{\sigma_1^2}{\sigma_2^2} \geq 1$	$H_0: \dfrac{\sigma_1^2}{\sigma_2^2} = 1$	$H_0: \dfrac{\sigma_1^2}{\sigma_2^2} \leq 1$
$H_1: \dfrac{\sigma_1^2}{\sigma_2^2} < 1$	$H_1: \dfrac{\sigma_1^2}{\sigma_2^2} \neq 1$	$H_1: \dfrac{\sigma_1^2}{\sigma_2^2} > 1$

The *F* Test

In a left-tailed or right-tailed test, we actually test only at the equality, with the understanding that rejection of H_0 would imply rejecting values more extreme. The test statistic is the ratio of the sample variances. Assuming the populations are normal, the test statistic follows the *F* **distribution,** named for Ronald A. Fisher (1890–1962), one of the most famous statisticians of all time.

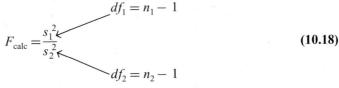

$$F_{\text{calc}} = \frac{s_1^2}{s_2^2} \qquad \begin{aligned} df_1 &= n_1 - 1 \\ df_2 &= n_2 - 1 \end{aligned}$$

(10.18)

If the null hypothesis of equal variances is true, this ratio should be near 1:

$$F_{\text{calc}} \approx 1 \qquad (\text{if } H_0 \text{ is true})$$

If the test statistic *F* is much less than 1 or much greater than 1, we would reject the hypothesis of equal population variances. The numerator s_1^2 has degrees of freedom $df_1 = n_1 - 1$, while the denominator s_2^2 has degrees of freedom $df_2 = n_2 - 1$. The *F* distribution is skewed. Its mean is always greater than 1 and its mode (the "peak" of the distribution) is always less than 1, but both the mean and mode tend to be near 1 for large samples. F cannot be negative, since s_1^2 and s_2^2 cannot be negative.

Critical Values

Critical values for the **F test** are denoted F_L (left tail) and F_R (right tail). The form of the two-tailed F test is shown in Figure 10.16. Notice that the rejection regions are asymmetric. A right-tail critical value F_R may be found from Appendix F using df_1 and df_2 degrees of freedom. It is written

(10.19)
$$F_R = F_{df_1, df_2} \qquad \text{(right-tail critical } F\text{)}$$

To obtain a left-tail critical value F_L we reverse the numerator and denominator degrees of freedom, find the critical value from Appendix F, and take its reciprocal:

(10.20)
$$F_L = \frac{1}{F_{df_2, df_1}} \qquad \text{(left-tail critical } F \text{ with switched } df_1 \text{ and } df_2\text{)}$$

Excel will give F_R using the function $=\text{FINV}(\alpha/2, df_1, df_2)$ or F_L using $=\text{FINV}(1 - \alpha/2, df_1, df_2)$.

FIGURE 10.16

**Critical Values for
Two-Tailed F Test for
Equal Variances**

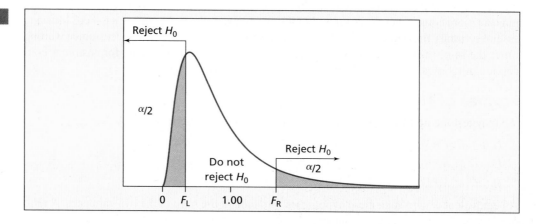

Illustration: Collision Damage

An experimental bumper was designed to reduce damage in low-speed collisions. This bumper was installed on an experimental group of vans in a large fleet, but not on a control group. At the end of a trial period, accident data showed 12 repair incidents (a "repair incident" is a repair invoice) for the experimental vehicles and 9 repair incidents for the control group vehicles. Table 10.11 shows the dollar cost of the repair incidents.

TABLE 10.11

**Repair Cost ($) for
Accident Damage**
📁 **Damage**

Source: Unpublished study by
Floyd G. Willoughby and
Thomas W. Lauer, Oakland University.

Experimental Vehicles	Control Vehicles
1,973	1,185
403	885
509	2,955
2,103	815
1,153	2,852
292	1,217
1,916	1,762
1,602	2,592
1,559	1,632
547	
801	
359	
$\bar{x}_1 = \$1,101.42$	$\bar{x}_2 = \$1,766.11$
$s_1 = \$696.20$	$s_2 = \$837.62$
$n_1 = 12$ incidents	$n_2 = 9$ incidents

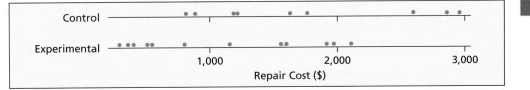

FIGURE 10.17

Dot Plots for Collision Repair Costs
Damage

The same data set could be used to compare either the means or the variances. A dot plot of the two samples, shown in Figure 10.17, suggests that the new bumper may have reduced the *mean* damage. However, the firm was also interested in whether the *variance* in damage had changed. The null hypothesis is that the variances are the same for the control group and the experimental group. We can use the F test to test the hypothesis of equal variances.

Comparison of Variances: Two-Tailed Test

Do the sample variances support the idea of equal variances in the population? We will perform a two-tailed test.

Step 1: State the Hypotheses   For a two-tailed test for equality of variances, the hypotheses are

$$H_0: \sigma_1^2 = \sigma_2^2 \quad \text{or} \quad H_0: \sigma_1^2 / \sigma_2^2 = 1$$
$$H_1: \sigma_1^2 \neq \sigma_2^2 \qquad\quad H_1: \sigma_1^2 / \sigma_2^2 \neq 1$$

Step 2: Specify the Decision Rule   Degrees of freedom for the F test are

Numerator: $df_1 = n_1 - 1 = 12 - 1 = 11$

Denominator: $df_2 = n_2 - 1 = 9 - 1 = 8$

For a two-tailed test, we split the α risk and put $\alpha/2$ in each tail. For $\alpha = .05$ we use Appendix F with $\alpha/2 = .025$. To avoid interpolating, we use the next lower degrees of freedom when the required entry is not found in Appendix F. This conservative practice will not increase the probability of Type I error. For example, since $F_{11,8}$ is not in the table we use $F_{10,8}$, as shown in Figure 10.18.

$$F_R = F_{df_1, df_2} = F_{11,8} \approx F_{10,8} = 4.30 \qquad \text{(right-tail critical value)}$$

FIGURE 10.18

Critical Value for Right-Tail F_R for $\alpha/2 = .025$

CRITICAL VALUES OF $F_{.025}$

This table shows the 2.5 percent right-tail critical values of F for the stated degrees of freedom.

Denominator Degrees of Freedom (df_2)	Numerator Degrees of Freedom (df_1)										
	1	2	3	4	5	6	7	8	9	10	12
1	647.8	799.5	864.2	899.6	921.8	937.1	948.2	956.6	963.3	968.6	976.7
2	38.51	39.00	39.17	39.25	39.30	39.33	39.36	39.37	39.39	39.40	39.41
3	17.44	16.04	15.44	15.10	14.88	14.73	14.62	14.54	14.47	14.42	14.34
4	12.22	10.65	9.98	9.60	9.36	9.20	9.07	8.98	8.90	8.84	8.75
5	10.01	8.43	7.76	7.39	7.15	6.98	6.85	6.76	6.68	6.62	6.52
6	8.81	7.26	6.60	6.23	5.99	5.82	5.70	5.60	5.52	5.46	5.37
7	8.07	6.54	5.89	5.52	5.29	5.12	4.99	4.90	4.82	4.76	4.67
8	7.57	6.06	5.42	5.05	4.82	4.65	4.53	4.43	4.36	4.30	4.20
9	7.21	5.71	5.08	4.72	4.48	4.32	4.20	4.10	4.03	3.96	3.87
10	6.94	5.46	4.83	4.47	4.24	4.07	3.95	3.85	3.78	3.72	3.62
11	6.72	5.26	4.63	4.28	4.04	3.88	3.76	3.66	3.59	3.53	3.43
12	6.55	5.10	4.47	4.12	3.89	3.73	3.61	3.51	3.44	3.37	3.28
13	6.41	4.97	4.35	4.00	3.77	3.60	3.48	3.39	3.31	3.25	3.15
14	6.30	4.86	4.24	3.89	3.66	3.50	3.38	3.29	3.21	3.15	3.05
15	6.20	4.77	4.15	3.80	3.58	3.41	3.29	3.20	3.12	3.06	2.96

FIGURE 10.19

Critical Value for Left-Tail F_L for $\alpha/2 = .025$

CRITICAL VALUES OF $F_{.025}$

This table shows the 2.5 percent right-tail critical values of F for the stated degrees of freedom.

Denominator Degrees of Freedom (df_2)	Numerator Degrees of Freedom (df_1)										
	1	2	3	4	5	6	7	8	9	10	12
1	647.8	799.5	864.2	899.6	921.8	937.1	948.2	956.6	963.3	968.6	976.7
2	38.51	39.00	39.17	39.25	39.30	39.33	39.36	39.37	39.39	39.40	39.41
3	17.44	16.04	15.44	15.10	14.88	14.73	14.62	14.54	14.47	14.42	14.34
4	12.22	10.65	9.98	9.60	9.36	9.20	9.07	8.98	8.90	8.84	8.75
5	10.01	8.43	7.76	7.39	7.15	6.98	6.85	6.76	6.68	6.62	6.52
6	8.81	7.26	6.60	6.23	5.99	5.82	5.70	5.60	5.52	5.46	5.37
7	8.07	6.54	5.89	5.52	5.29	5.12	4.99	4.90	4.82	4.76	4.67
8	7.57	6.06	5.42	5.05	4.82	4.65	4.53	4.43	4.36	4.30	4.20
9	7.21	5.71	5.08	4.72	4.48	4.32	4.20	4.10	4.03	3.96	3.87
10	6.94	5.46	4.83	4.47	4.24	4.07	3.95	3.85	3.78	3.72	3.62
11	6.72	5.26	4.63	4.28	4.04	3.88	3.76	3.66	3.59	3.53	3.43
12	6.55	5.10	4.47	4.12	3.89	3.73	3.61	3.51	3.44	3.37	3.28
13	6.41	4.97	4.35	4.00	3.77	3.60	3.48	3.39	3.31	3.25	3.15
14	6.30	4.86	4.24	3.89	3.66	3.50	3.38	3.29	3.21	3.15	3.05
15	6.20	4.77	4.15	3.80	3.58	3.41	3.29	3.20	3.12	3.06	2.96

FIGURE 10.20

Two-Tailed F Test at $\alpha = .05$

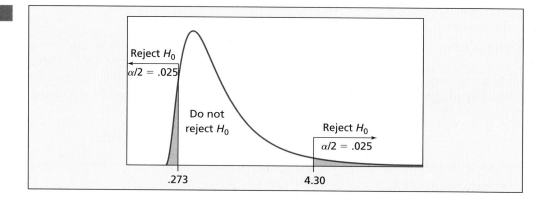

Alternatively, we could use Excel to get F_R=FINV(.025,11,8)=4.243 and F_L=FINV(.975,11,8) =0.273. To find the left-tail critical value we reverse the numerator and denominator degrees of freedom, find the critical value from Appendix F, and take its reciprocal, as shown in Figure 10.19. (Excel's function=FINV returns a *right-tail* area.)

$$F_L = \frac{1}{F_{df_2, df_1}} = \frac{1}{F_{8,11}} = \frac{1}{3.66} = 0.273 \qquad \text{(left-tail critical value)}$$

As shown in Figure 10.20, the two-tailed decision rule is

Reject H_0 if $F_{calc} < 0.273$ or if $F_{calc} > 4.30$

Otherwise do not reject H_0

Step 3: Calculate the Test Statistic   The test statistic is

$$F_{calc} = \frac{s_1^2}{s_2^2} = \frac{(696.20)^2}{(837.62)^2} = 0.691$$

Step 4: Make the Decision   Since $F_{calc} = 0.691$, we cannot reject the hypothesis of equal variances in a two-tailed test at $\alpha = .05$. In other words, the ratio of the sample variances does not differ significantly from 1. Because Excel's function = FDIST gives a *right-tail* area, the function you use for the *p*-value will depend on the value of F_{calc}:

If $F_{calc} > 1$ Two-tailed *p*-value is $=2*FDIST(F_{calc}, df_1, df_2)$
If $F_{calc} < 1$ Two-tailed *p*-value is $=2*FDIST(1/F_{calc}, df_2, df_1)$

For the bumper data, $F_{calc} = 0.691$ so Excel's two-tailed *p*-value is $=2*FDIST((1/0.691),8,11) = .5575$.

Folded *F* Test

We can make the two-tailed test for equal variances into a right-tailed test, so it is easier to look up the critical values in Appendix F. This method requires that we put the *larger observed variance* in the numerator, and then look up the critical value for $\alpha/2$ instead of the chosen α. The test statistic for the folded *F* test is.

$$F_{calc} = \frac{s^2_{larger}}{s^2_{smaller}}$$ (10.21)

The larger variance goes in the numerator and the smaller variance in the denominator. *"Larger" refers to the variance (not to the sample size)*. But the hypotheses are the same as for a two-tailed test:

$H_0: \sigma_1^2/\sigma_2^2 = 1$

$H_1: \sigma_1^2/\sigma_2^2 \neq 1$

For the bumper data, the second sample variance ($s_2^2 = 837.62$) is larger than the first sample variance ($s_1^2 = 696.20$) so the folded *F* test statistic is

$$F_{calc} = \frac{s^2_{larger}}{s^2_{smaller}} = \frac{s_2^2}{s_1^2} = \frac{(837.62)^2}{(696.20)^2} = 1.448$$

We must be careful that the degrees of freedom match the variances in the modified *F* statistic. In this case, the second sample variance is larger (it goes in the numerator) so we must reverse the degrees of freedom:

Numerator: $n_2 - 1 = 9 - 1 = 8$

Denominator: $n_1 - 1 = 12 - 1 = 11$

Now we look up the critical value for $F_{8, 11}$ in Appendix F using $\alpha/2 = .05/2 = .025$:

$$F_{.025} = 3.66$$

Since the test statistic $F_{calc} = 1.448$ does not exceed the critical value $F_{.025} = 3.66$, we cannot reject the hypothesis of equal variances. This is the same conclusion that we reached in the two-tailed test. Since $F_{calc} > 1$, Excel's two-tailed *p*-value is $=2*FDIST(1.448,8,11) = .5569$ which is the same as in the previous result except for rounding. Anytime you want a two-tailed *F* test, you may use the folded *F* test if you think it is easier.

Comparison of Variances: One-Tailed Test

In this case, the firm was interested in knowing whether the new bumper had *reduced* the variance in collision damage cost, so the consultant was asked to do a left-tailed test.

Step 1: State the Hypotheses   The hypotheses for a left-tailed test are

$H_0: \sigma_1^2/\sigma_2^2 \geq 1$

$H_1: \sigma_1^2/\sigma_2^2 < 1$

Step 2: Specify the Decision Rule   Degrees of freedom for the *F* test are the same as for a two-tailed test (the hypothesis doesn't affect the degrees of freedom):

Numerator: $df_1 = n_1 - 1 = 12 - 1 = 11$

Denominator: $df_2 = n_2 - 1 = 9 - 1 = 8$

However, now the entire $\alpha = .05$ goes in the left tail. We reverse the degrees of freedom and find the left-tail critical value from Appendix F as the reciprocal of the table value, as illustrated in Figures 10.21 and 10.22. Notice that the asymmetry of the F distribution causes the left-tail area to be compressed in the horizontal direction.

$$F_L = \frac{1}{F_{df_2, df_1}} = \frac{1}{F_{8,11}} = \frac{1}{2.95} = 0.339 \qquad \text{(left-tail critical value)}$$

The decision rule is

Reject H_0 if $F_{\text{calc}} < 0.339$

Otherwise do not reject H_0

Step 3: Calculate the Test Statistic   The test statistic is the same as for a two-tailed test (the hypothesis doesn't affect the test statistic):

$$F_{\text{calc}} = \frac{s_1^2}{s_2^2} = \frac{(696.20)^2}{(837.62)^2} = 0.691$$

Step 4: Make the Decision   Since the test statistic $F = 0.691$ is not in the critical region, we cannot reject the hypothesis of equal variances in a one-tailed test. The bumpers did not significantly decrease the variance in collision repair cost.

FIGURE 10.21

Right-Tail F_R for $\alpha = .05$

CRITICAL VALUES OF $F_{.05}$

This table shows the 5 percent right-tail critical values of F for the stated degrees of freedom.

Denominator Degrees of Freedom (df_2)	Numerator Degrees of Freedom (df_1)										
	1	2	3	4	5	6	7	8	9	10	12
1	161.4	199.5	215.7	224.6	230.2	234.0	236.8	238.9	240.5	241.9	243.9
2	18.51	19.00	19.16	19.25	19.30	19.33	19.35	19.37	19.38	19.40	19.41
3	10.13	9.55	9.28	9.12	9.01	8.94	8.89	8.85	8.81	8.79	8.74
4	7.71	6.94	6.59	6.39	6.26	6.16	6.09	6.04	6.00	5.96	5.91
5	6.61	5.79	5.41	5.19	5.05	4.95	4.88	4.82	4.77	4.74	4.68
6	5.99	5.14	4.76	4.53	4.39	4.28	4.21	4.15	4.10	4.06	4.00
7	5.59	4.74	4.35	4.12	3.97	3.87	3.79	3.73	3.68	3.64	3.57
8	5.32	4.46	4.07	3.84	3.69	3.58	3.50	3.44	3.39	3.35	3.28
9	5.12	4.26	3.86	3.63	3.48	3.37	3.29	3.23	3.18	3.14	3.07
10	4.96	4.10	3.71	3.48	3.33	3.22	3.14	3.07	3.02	2.98	2.91
11	4.84	3.98	3.59	3.36	3.20	3.09	3.01	2.95	2.90	2.85	2.79
12	4.75	3.89	3.49	3.26	3.11	3.00	2.91	2.85	2.80	2.75	2.69
13	4.67	3.81	3.41	3.18	3.03	2.92	2.83	2.77	2.71	2.67	2.60
14	4.60	3.74	3.34	3.11	2.96	2.85	2.76	2.70	2.65	2.60	2.53
15	4.54	3.68	3.29	3.06	2.90	2.79	2.71	2.64	2.59	2.54	2.48

FIGURE 10.22

Left-Tail F_L for $\alpha = .05$

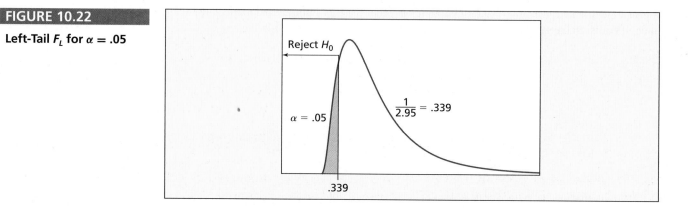

Reject H_0

$\frac{1}{2.95} = .339$

$\alpha = .05$

.339

Excel's *F* Test

Excel makes it quite easy to do the *F* test for variances. Figure 10.23 shows Excel's left-tailed test. One advantage of using Excel is that you also get a *p*-value. For the bumper data, the large *p*-value of .279 indicates that we would face a Type I error risk of about 28 percent if we were to reject H_0. In other words, a sample variance ratio as extreme as $F = 0.691$ would occur by chance about 28 percent of the time if the population variances were in fact equal. The sample evidence does not indicate that the variances differ.

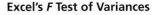

FIGURE 10.23

Excel's *F* Test of Variances

Assumptions of the *F* Test

The *F* test assumes that the populations being sampled are normal. Unfortunately, the test is rather sensitive to non-normality of the sampled populations. Alternative tests are available, but they tend to be rather complex and nonintuitive. MINITAB reports both the *F* test and a robust alternative known as *Levene's test* along with their *p*-values. As long as you know how to interpret a *p*-value, you really don't need to know the details of Levene's test. An attractive feature of MINITAB's *F* test is its graphical display of a confidence interval for each population standard deviation, shown in Figure 10.24. If you are concerned about non-normality, you can test each sample for non-normality by using a probability plot, although these samples are a bit small for normality tests.

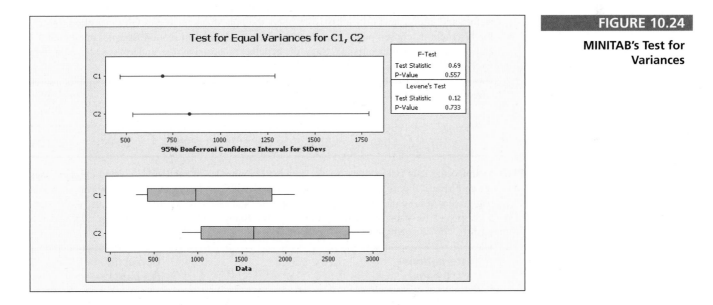

FIGURE 10.24

MINITAB's Test for Variances

Significance versus Importance

The test of means showed a mean difference of $665 per repair incident. That is large enough that it might be important. The incremental cost per vehicle of the new bumper would have to be compared with the present discounted value of the expected annual savings per vehicle over its useful life. In a large fleet of vehicles, the payback period could be calculated. Most firms require that a change pay for itself in a fairly short period of time. *Importance* is a question to be answered ultimately by financial experts, not statisticians.

SECTION EXERCISES

connect

Hint: Use Excel or MegaStat.

10.30 Which samples show unequal variances? Use $\alpha = .10$ in all tests. Show the critical values and degrees of freedom clearly and illustrate the decision rule.

a. $s_1 = 10.2$, $n_1 = 22$, $s_2 = 6.4$, $n_2 = 16$, two-tailed test
b. $s_1 = 0.89$, $n_1 = 25$, $s_2 = 0.67$, $n_2 = 18$, right-tailed test
c. $s_1 = 124$, $n_1 = 12$, $s_2 = 260$, $n_2 = 10$, left-tailed test

10.31 Which samples show unequal variances? Use $\alpha = .05$ in all tests. Show the critical values and degrees of freedom clearly and illustrate the decision rule.

a. $s_1 = 5.1$, $n_1 = 11$, $s_2 = 3.2$, $n_2 = 8$, two-tailed test
b. $s_1 = 221$, $n_1 = 8$, $s_2 = 445$, $n_2 = 8$, left-tailed test
c. $s_1 = 67$, $n_1 = 10$, $s_2 = 15$, $n_2 = 13$, right-tailed test

10.32 Researchers at the Mayo Clinic have studied the effect of sound levels on patient healing and have found a significant association (louder hospital ambient sound level is associated with slower postsurgical healing). Based on the Mayo Clinic's experience, Ardmore Hospital installed a new vinyl flooring that is supposed to reduce the mean sound level (decibels) in the hospital corridors. The sound level is measured at five randomly selected times in the main corridor. (a) At $\alpha = .05$, has the mean been reduced? Show the hypotheses, decision rule, and test statistic. (b) At $\alpha = .05$, has the variance changed? Show the hypotheses, decision rule, and test statistic. (See *Detroit Free Press*, February 2, 2004, p. 8H.) 📷 **Decibels**

New Flooring	Old Flooring
42	48
41	51
40	44
37	48
44	52

10.33 A manufacturing process drills holes in sheet metal that are supposed to be .5000 cm in diameter. Before and after a new drill press is installed, the hole diameter is carefully measured (in cm) for 12 randomly chosen parts. At $\alpha = .05$, do these independent random samples prove that the new process has smaller variance? Show the hypotheses, decision rule, and test statistic. *Hint:* Use Excel =FINV(1-α, v_1, v_2) to get F_L. 📷 **Diameter**

New drill:	.5005	.5010	.5024	.4988	.4997	.4995
	.4976	.5042	.5014	.4995	.4988	.4992
Old drill:	.5052	.5053	.4947	.4907	.5031	.4923
	.5040	.5035	.5061	.4956	.5035	.4962

10.34 Examine the data below showing the weights (in pounds) of randomly selected checked bags for an airline's flights on the same day. (a) At $\alpha = .05$, is the mean weight of an international bag greater? Show the hypotheses, decision rule, and test statistic. (b) At $\alpha = .05$, is the variance greater for bags on an international flight? Show the hypotheses, decision rule, and test statistic. 📷 **Luggage**

International (10 bags)		Domestic (15 bags)		
39	47	29	37	43
54	48	36	33	42
46	28	33	29	32
39	54	34	43	35
69	62	38	39	39

A **two-sample test** compares samples with each other rather than comparing with a benchmark, as in a one-sample test. For **independent samples,** the comparison of means generally utilizes the Student's t distribution, because the population variances are almost always unknown. If the unknown variances are **assumed equal,** we use a **pooled variance** estimate and **add the degrees of freedom.** If the unknown variances are **assumed unequal,** we do not pool the variances and we reduce the degrees of freedom by using **Welch's formula.** The test statistic is the difference of means divided by their standard error. For tests of means or proportions, **equal sample sizes** are desirable, but not necessary. The *t* **test for paired samples** uses the differences of n paired observations, thereby being a **one-sample** *t* **test.** For two proportions, the samples may be **pooled** if the population proportions are assumed equal, and the test statistic is the difference of proportions divided by the standard error, the square root of the sum of the sample variances. For proportions, **normality** may be assumed if both samples are large, that is, if they each contain at least 10 successes and 10 failures. The *F* **test** for equality of **two variances** is named after Sir Ronald Fisher. Its test statistic is the **ratio** of the sample variances. We want to see if the ratio differs significantly from 1. The F table shows critical values based on both **numerator** and **denominator** degrees of freedom.

Behrens-Fisher
   problem, *394*
difference of two
   means, *401*
difference of two population
   proportions, *416*
F distribution, *417*
F test, *418*

independent sample, *407*
paired comparison, *404*
paired samples, *404*
paired *t* test, *404*
pooled estimate, *411*
pooled proportion, *410*
pooled variance, *394*
p-values, *394*

sample statistic, *393*
test statistic, *393*
two-sample tests, *391*
Type I error, *392*
Type II error, *392*
Welch-Satterthwaite test, *394*
Welch's adjusted degrees of
   freedom, *394*

Commonly Used Formulas in Two-Sample Hypothesis Tests

Test Statistic (Difference of Means, Equal Variances):

$$t_{\text{calc}} = \frac{\bar{x}_1 - \bar{x}_2}{\sqrt{\dfrac{s_p^2}{n_1} + \dfrac{s_p^2}{n_2}}}, \text{ with } d.f. = n_1 + n_2 - 2 \text{ and } s_p^2 = \frac{(n_1 - 1)s_1^2 + (n_2 - 1)s_2^2}{n_1 + n_2 - 2}$$

Test Statistic (Difference of Means, Unequal Variances):

$$t_{\text{calc}} = \frac{\bar{x}_1 - \bar{x}_2}{\sqrt{\dfrac{s_1^2}{n_1} + \dfrac{s_2^2}{n_2}}}, \text{ with } d.f. = \frac{\left[s_1^2/n_1 + s_2^2/n_2\right]^2}{\dfrac{\left(s_1^2/n_1\right)^2}{n_1 - 1} + \dfrac{\left(s_2^2/n_2\right)^2}{n_2 - 1}}$$

Confidence Interval for $\mu_1 - \mu_2$:

$$(\bar{x}_1 - \bar{x}_2) \pm t_{\alpha/2}\sqrt{\frac{s_1^2}{n_1} + \frac{s_2^2}{n_2}}, \text{ with } d.f. = \frac{\left(\dfrac{s_1^2}{n_1} + \dfrac{s_2^2}{n_2}\right)^2}{\dfrac{\left(\dfrac{s_1^2}{n_1}\right)^2}{n_1 - 1} + \dfrac{\left(\dfrac{s_2^2}{n_2}\right)^2}{n_2 - 1}}$$

Test Statistic (Paired Differences): $t_{\text{calc}} = \dfrac{\bar{d} - \mu_d}{\dfrac{s_d}{\sqrt{n}}}$, with $d.f. = n - 1$

Test Statistic (Equality of Proportions): $z_{\text{calc}} = \dfrac{p_1 - p_2}{\sqrt{\bar{p}(1 - \bar{p})\left[\dfrac{1}{n_1} + \dfrac{1}{n_2}\right]}}$, with $\bar{p} = \dfrac{x_1 + x_2}{n_1 + n_2}$

Confidence Interval for $\pi_1 - \pi_2$: $(p_1 - p_2) \pm z_{\alpha/2}\sqrt{\dfrac{p_1(1 - p_1)}{n_1} + \dfrac{p_2(1 - p_2)}{n_2}}$

Test Statistic (Two Variances): $F_{\text{calc}} = \dfrac{s_1^2}{s_2^2}$, with $df_1 = n_1 - 1$, $df_2 = n_2 - 1$

CHAPTER REVIEW

1. (a) Explain why two samples from the same population could appear different. (b) Why do we say that two-sample tests have a built-in point of reference?

2. (a) In a two-sample test of proportions, what is a pooled proportion? (b) Why is the test for normality important for a two-sample test of proportions? (c) What is the criterion for assuming normality of the test statistic?

3. (a) Is it necessary that sample sizes be equal for a two-sample test of proportions? Is it desirable? (b) Explain the analogy between overlapping confidence intervals and testing for equality of two proportions.

4. List the three cases for a test comparing two means. Explain carefully how they differ.

5. Consider *Case 1* (known variances) in the test comparing two means. (a) Why is *Case 1* unusual and not used very often? (b) What distribution is used for the test statistic? (c) Write the formula for the test statistic.

6. Consider *Case 2* (unknown but equal variances) in the test comparing two means. (a) What distribution is used for the test statistic? (b) State the degrees of freedom used in this test. (c) Write the formula for the pooled variance and interpret it. (d) Write the formula for the test statistic.

7. Consider *Case 3* (unknown and unequal variances) in the test comparing two means. (a) What complication arises in degrees of freedom for *Case 3?* (b) What distribution is used for the test statistic? (c) Write the formula for the test statistic.

8. (a) Is it ever acceptable to use a normal distribution in a test of means with unknown variances? (b) If we assume normality, what is gained? What is lost?

9. Why is it a good idea to use a computer program like Excel to do tests of means?

10. (a) Explain why the paired *t* test for dependent samples is really a one-sample test. (b) State the degrees of freedom for the paired *t* test. (c) Why not treat two paired samples as if they were independent?

11. Explain how a difference in means could be statistically *significant* but not *important*.

12. (a) Why do we use an *F* test? (b) Where did it get its name? (c) When two population variances are equal, what value would you expect of the *F* test statistic?

13. (a) In an *F* test for two variances, explain how to obtain left- and right-tail critical values. (b) What are the assumptions underlying the *F* test?

CHAPTER EXERCISES

connect

Note: For tests on two proportions, two means, or two variances it is a good idea to check your work by using MINITAB, MegaStat, or the *LearningStats* two-sample calculators in Unit 10.

10.35 The top food snacks consumed by adults aged 18–54 are gum, chocolate candy, fresh fruit, potato chips, breath mints/candy, ice cream, nuts, cookies, bars, yogurt, and crackers. Out of a random sample of 25 men, 15 ranked fresh fruit in their top five snack choices. Out of a random sample of 32 women, 22 ranked fresh fruit in their top five snack choices. Is there a difference in the proportion of men and women who rank fresh fruit in their top five list of snacks? (a) State the hypotheses and a decision rule for $\alpha = .10$. (b) Calculate the sample proportions. (c) Find the test statistic and its *p*-value. What is your conclusion? (d) Is normality assured? (Data are from The NPD Group press release, "Fruit #1 Snack Food Consumed by Kids," June 16, 2005.)

10.36 In an early home game, an NBA team made 70.21 percent of their 94 free throw attempts. In one of their last home games, the team had a free throw percentage equal to 76.4 percent out of 89 attempts. (a) Do basketball teams improve their free throw percentage as their season progresses? Test the hypothesis of equal free throw percentages, treating the early season and late season games as random samples. Use a level of significance of .10. (b) Use Excel to calculate the *p*-value and interpret it. (See *The New York Times,* March 3, 2009.)

10.37 Do a larger proportion of college students than young children eat cereal? Researchers surveyed both age groups to find the answer. The results are shown in the table below. (a) State the hypotheses used to answer the question. (b) Using $\alpha = .05$, state the decision rule and sketch it. (c) Find the sample proportions and *z* statistic. (d) Make a decision. (e) Find the *p*-value and interpret it. (f) Is the normality assumption fulfilled? Explain.

Statistic	College Students (ages 18–25)	Young Children (ages 6–11)
Number who eat cereal	$x_1 = 833$	$x_2 = 692$
Number surveyed	$n_1 = 850$	$n_2 = 740$

10.38 A 2005 study found that 202 women held board seats out of a total of 1,195 seats in the Fortune 100 companies. A 2003 study found that 779 women held board seats out of a total of 5,727 seats in the Fortune 500 companies. Treating these as random samples (since board seat assignments change often), can we conclude that Fortune 100 companies have a greater proportion of women board members than the Fortune 500? (a) State the hypotheses. (b) Calculate the sample proportions. (c) Find the test statistic and its *p*-value. What is your conclusion at $\alpha = .05$? (d) If statistically significant, can you suggest factors that might explain the increase? (Data are from *The 2003 Catalyst Census of Women Board Directors of the Fortune 500,* and "Women and Minorities on Fortune 100 Boards," *The Alliance for Board Diversity,* May 17, 2005.)

10.39 A study of the Fortune 100 board of director members showed that there were 36 minority women holding board seats out of 202 total female board members. There were 142 minority men holding board seats out of 993 total male board members. (a) Treating the findings from this study as samples, calculate the sample proportions. (b) Find the test statistic and its *p*-value. (c) At the 5 percent level of significance, is there a difference in the percentage of minority women board directors and minority men board directors? (Data are from "Women and Minorities on Fortune 100 Boards," *The Alliance for Board Diversity,* May 17, 2005.)

10.40 To test his hypothesis that students who finish an exam first get better grades, a professor kept track of the order in which papers were handed in. Of the first 25 papers, 10 received a B or better compared with 8 of the last 24 papers handed in. Is the first group better, at $\alpha = .10$? (a) State your hypotheses and obtain a test statistic and *p*-value. Interpret the results. (b) Are the samples large enough to assure normality? (c) Make an argument that early-finishers should do better. Then make the opposite argument. Which is more convincing?

10.41 How many full-page advertisements are found in a magazine? In an October issue of *Muscle and Fitness,* there were 252 ads, of which 97 were full-page. For the same month, the magazine *Glamour* had 342 ads, of which 167 were full-page. (a) Is the difference significant at $\alpha = .01$? (b) Find the *p*-value. (c) Is normality assured? (d) Based on what you know of these magazines, why might the proportions of full-page ads differ? (Data are from a project by MBA students Amy DeGuire and Don Finney.)

10.42 In Utica, Michigan, 205 of 226 school buses passed the annual safety inspection. In Detroit, Michigan, only 151 of 296 buses passed the inspection. (a) State the hypotheses for a right-tailed test. (b) Obtain a test statistic and *p*-value. (c) Is normality assured? (d) If *significant,* is the difference also large enough to be *important?* (Data are from *Detroit Free Press,* August 19, 2000, p. 8A.)

10.43 After John F. Kennedy, Jr., was killed in an airplane crash at night, a survey was taken, asking whether a noninstrument-rated pilot should be allowed to fly at night. Of 409 New York State residents, 61 said yes. Of 70 aviation experts who were asked the same question, 40 said yes. (a) At $\alpha = .01$, did a larger proportion of experts say yes compared with the general public, or is the difference within the realm of chance? (b) Find the *p*-value and interpret it. (b) Is normality assured? (Data are from www.siena.edu/sri.)

10.44 A ski company in Vail owns two ski shops, one on the east side and one on the west side. Sales data showed that at the eastern location there were 56 pairs of large gloves sold out of 304 total pairs sold. At the western location there were 145 pairs of large gloves sold out of 562 total pairs sold. (a) Calculate the sample proportion of large gloves for each location. (b) At $\alpha = .05$, is there a significant difference in the proportion of large gloves sold? (c) Can you suggest any reasons why a difference might exist? (*Note:* Problem is based on actual sales data).

10.45 Does hormone replacement therapy (HRT) cause breast cancer? Researchers studied women ages 50 to 79 who used either HRT or a dummy pill over a 5-year period. Of the 8,304 HRT women, 245 cancers were reported, compared with 185 cancers for the 8,304 women who got the dummy pill. Assume that the participants were randomly assigned to two equal groups. (a) State the hypotheses for a one-tailed test to see if HRT was associated with increased cancer risk. (b) Obtain a test statistic and *p*-value. Interpret the results. (c) Is normality assured? (d) Is the difference large enough to be important? Explain. (e) What else would you need to know to assess this research? (Data are from *www.cbsnews.com,* accessed June 25, 2003.)

10.46 Vail Resorts tracks the proportion of seasonal employees who are rehired each season. Rehiring a seasonal employee is beneficial in many ways including lowering the costs incurred during the hiring process such as training costs. A random sample of 833 full-time and 386 part-time seasonal employees from 2009 showed that the proportion of full-time rehires was .5214 and the proportion of part-time rehires was .4887. (a) Is there a significant difference in the proportion of rehires between the full-time and part-time seasonal employees? Use an $\alpha = .10$ for the level of significance. (b) Use Excel to calculate the *p*-value. Was your decision close?

VAILRESORTS

10.47 Does a "follow-up reminder" increase the renewal rate on a magazine subscription? A magazine sent out 760 subscription renewal notices (without a reminder) and got 703 renewals. As an experiment, they sent out 240 subscription renewal notices (with a reminder) and got 228 renewals. (a) At $\alpha = .05$, was the renewal rate higher in the experimental group? (b) Can normality be assumed?

10.48 A study revealed that the 30-day readmission rate was 31.4 percent for 370 patients who received after-hospital care instructions (e.g., how to take their medications) compared to a readmission rate of 45.1 percent for 368 patients who did not receive such information. (a) Set up the hypotheses to see whether the admissions rate was lower for those who received the information. (b) Find the *p*-value for the test. (c) What is your conclusion at $\alpha = .05$? At $\alpha = .01$? (Source: U.S. Department of Health and Human Services, *AHRQ Research Activities*, no. 343, March 2009, pp. 1–2.)

10.49 In a marketing class, 44 student members of virtual (Internet) project teams (group 1) and 42 members of face-to-face project teams (group 2) were asked to respond on a 1–5 scale to the question: "As compared to other teams, the members helped each other." For group 1 the mean was 2.73 with a standard deviation of 0.97, while for group 2 the mean was 1.90 with a standard deviation of 0.91. At $\alpha = .01$, is the virtual team mean significantly higher? (Data are from Roger W. Berry, *Marketing Education Review* 12, no. 2 [2002], pp. 73–78.)

10.50 In San Francisco, a sample of 3,106 wireless routers showed that 40.12 percent used encryption (to prevent hackers from intercepting information). In Seattle, a sample of 3,013 wireless routers showed that 25.99 percent used encryption. (a) Set up hypotheses to test whether or not the population proportion of encryption is higher in San Francisco than Seattle. (b) Test the hypotheses at $\alpha = .05$. (Source: www.pnas.org/cgi/doi/10.1073/pnas.0811973106, Vol. 106, No. 5, February 3, 2009, pp. 1318–23.)

10.51 U.S. Vice President Dick Cheney received a lot of publicity after his fourth heart attack. A portable defibrillator was surgically implanted in his chest to deliver an electric shock to restore his heart rhythm whenever another attack was threatening. Researchers at the University of Rochester (NY) Medical Center implanted defibrillators in 742 patients after a heart attack and compared them with 490 similar patients without the implant. Over the next 2 years, 98 of those without defibrillators had died, compared with 104 of those with defibrillators. (a) State the hypotheses for a one-tailed test to see if the defibrillators reduced the death rate. (b) Obtain a test statistic and *p*-value. (c) Is normality assured? (d) Why might such devices not be widely implanted in heart attack patients? (Data are from *Science News* 161 [April 27, 2002], p. 270.)

10.52 In 2009 Noodles & Company introduced spaghetti and meatballs to their menu. Before putting on the menu they performed taste tests to determine the best tasting spaghetti sauce. Random samples of 70 tasters were asked to rate their satisfaction with two different sauces on a scale of 1–10 with 10 being the highest. Was there a significant difference in satisfaction scores between the two sauces? (a) Perform a two-tailed test for the difference in two independent means using the summary data in the table below. Assume equal population variances and state your conclusion using $\alpha = .05$. (b) What if Noodles & Company had used only one set of tasters to test the sauces? Perform a two-tailed paired difference test using the data in the file Spaghetti.xls. State your conclusion using $\alpha = .05$. (c) Compare the results in parts (a) and (b). Which test had lower power?

Satisfaction Scores for Spaghetti Sauce 🖻 **Spaghetti**

Statistic	Sauce #1	Sauce #2
Mean satisfaction score	6.857	7.243
Sample standard deviation	1.497	1.209
Sample size	70	70

10.53 Has the cost to outsource a standard employee background check changed from 2008 to 2009? A random sample of 10 companies in spring 2008 showed a sample average of $105 with a sample standard deviation equal to $32. A random sample of 10 different companies in spring 2009 resulted in a sample average of $75 with a sample standard deviation equal to $45. (a) Conduct a hypothesis test to test the difference in sample means with a level of significance equal to .05. Assume the population variances are not equal. (b) Discuss why a paired sample design might have made more sense in this case.

10.54 From her firm's computer telephone log, an executive found that the mean length of 64 telephone calls during July was 4.48 minutes with a standard deviation of 5.87 minutes. She vowed to make an effort to reduce the length of calls. The August phone log showed 48 telephone calls whose mean was 2.396 minutes with a standard deviation of 2.018 minutes. (a) State the hypotheses for a right-tailed test. (b) Obtain a test statistic and p-value assuming unequal variances. Interpret these results using $\alpha = .01$. (c) Why might the sample data *not* follow a normal, bell-shaped curve? If not, how might this affect your conclusions?

10.55 An experimental bumper was designed to reduce damage in low-speed collisions. This bumper was installed on an experimental group of vans in a large fleet, but not on a control group. At the end of a trial period, accident data showed 12 repair incidents for the experimental group and 9 repair incidents for the control group. Vehicle downtime (in days per repair incident) is shown below. At $\alpha = .05$, did the new bumper reduce downtime? (a) Make stacked dot plots of the data (a sketch is OK). (b) State the hypotheses. (c) State the decision rule and sketch it. (d) Find the test statistic. (e) Make a decision. (f) Find the p-value and interpret it. (g) Do you think the difference is large enough to be important? Explain. (Data are from an unpublished study by Floyd G. Willoughby and Thomas W. Lauer, Oakland University). 📨 **DownTime**

> New bumper (12 repair incidents): 9, 2, 5, 12, 5, 4, 7, 5, 11, 3, 7, 1
>
> Control group (9 repair incidents): 7, 5, 7, 4, 18, 4, 8, 14, 13

10.56 Medicare spending per patient in different U.S. metropolitan areas may differ. Based on the sample data below, is the average spending in the northern region significantly less than the average spending in the southern region at the 1 percent level? (a) State the hypotheses and decision rule. (b) Find the test statistic assuming unequal variances. (c) State your conclusion. Is this a strong conclusion? (d) Can you suggest reasons why a difference might exist? (See *The New Yorker* [May 30, 2005], p. 38.)

Medicare Spending per Patient (adjusted for age, sex, and race)

Statistic	Northern Region	Southern Region
Sample mean	$3,123	$8,456
Sample standard deviation	$1,546	$3,678
Sample size	14 patients	16 patients

10.57 In a 15-day survey of air pollution in two European capitals, the mean particulate count (micrograms per cubic meter) in Athens was 39.5 with a standard deviation of 3.75, while in London the mean was 31.5 with a standard deviation of 2.25. (a) Assuming equal population variances, does this evidence convince you that the mean particulate count is higher in Athens, at $\alpha = .05$? (b) Are the variances equal or not, at $\alpha = .05$? (Based on *The Economist* 383, no. 8514 [February 3, 2007], p. 58.)

10.58 One group of accounting students took a distance learning class, while another group took the same course in a traditional classroom. At $\alpha = .10$, is there a significant difference in the mean scores listed below? (a) State the hypotheses. (b) State the decision rule and sketch it. (c) Find the test statistic. (d) Make a decision. (e) Use Excel to find the p-value and interpret it.

Exam Scores for Accounting Students

Statistic	Distance	Classroom
Mean scores	$\bar{x}_1 = 9.1$	$\bar{x}_2 = 10.3$
Sample std. dev.	$s_1 = 2.4$	$s_2 = 2.5$
Number of students	$n_1 = 20$	$n_2 = 20$

10.59 Do male and female school superintendents earn the same pay? Salaries for 20 males and 17 females in a certain metropolitan area are shown below. At $\alpha = .01$, were the mean superintendent salaries greater for men than for women? (a) Make stacked dot plots of the sample data (a sketch will do). (b) State the hypotheses. (c) State the decision rule and sketch it. (d) Find the test statistic. (e) Make a decision. (f) Estimate the p-value and interpret it. (g) If statistically significant, do you think the difference is large enough to be important? Explain. 📨 **Paycheck**

School Superintendent Pay

Men (n = 20)		Women (n = 17)	
114,000	121,421	94,675	96,000
115,024	112,187	123,484	112,455
115,598	110,160	99,703	120,118
108,400	128,322	86,000	124,163
109,900	128,041	108,000	76,340
120,352	125,462	94,940	89,600
118,000	113,611	83,933	91,993
108,209	123,814	102,181	
110,000	111,280	86,840	
151,008	112,280	85,000	

10.60 The average take-out order size for Ashoka Curry House restaurant is shown. Assuming equal variances, at $\alpha = .05$, is there a significant difference in the order sizes? (a) State the hypotheses. (b) State the decision rule and sketch it. (c) Find the test statistic. (d) Make a decision. (e) Use Excel to find the p-value and interpret it.

Customer Order Size

Statistic	Friday Night	Saturday Night
Mean order size	$\bar{x}_1 = 22.32$	$\bar{x}_2 = 25.56$
Standard deviation	$s_1 = 4.35$	$s_2 = 6.16$
Number of orders	$n_1 = 13$	$n_2 = 18$

10.61 Cash withdrawals (in multiples of $20) at an on-campus ATM for a random sample of 30 Fridays and 30 Mondays are shown following. At $\alpha = .01$, is there a difference in the mean ATM withdrawal on Monday and Friday? (a) Make stacked dot plots of the data (a sketch is OK). (b) State the hypotheses. (c) State the decision rule and sketch it. (d) Find the test statistic. (e) Make a decision. (f) Find the p-value and interpret it. 📂 **ATM**

Randomly Chosen ATM Withdrawals ($)

Friday			Monday		
250	10	10	40	30	10
20	10	30	100	70	370
110	20	10	20	20	10
40	20	40	30	50	30
70	10	10	200	20	40
20	20	400	20	30	20
10	20	10	10	20	100
50	20	10	30	40	20
100	20	20	50	10	20
20	60	70	60	10	20

10.62 A sample of 25 concession stand purchases at the May 12 matinee of *Xmen Origins: Wolverine* showed a mean purchase of $7.29 with a standard deviation of $3.02. For the May 18 evening showing of the same movie, for a sample of 25 purchases the mean was $7.12 with a standard deviation of $2.14. The means appear to be very close, but not the variances. At $\alpha = .05$, is there a difference in variances? Show all steps clearly, including an illustration of the decision rule.

10.63 A ski company in Vail owns two ski shops, one on the west side and one on the east side of Vail. Is there a difference in daily average goggle sales between the two stores? Assume equal variances. (a) State the hypotheses for a two-tailed test. (b) State the decision rule for a level of significance equal to 5 percent and sketch it. (c) Find the test statistic and state your conclusion.

Sales Data for Ski Goggles

Statistic	East Side Shop	West Side Shop
Mean sales	$328	$435
Sample std. dev.	$104	$147
Sample size	28 days	29 days

10.64 A ski company in Vail owns two ski shops, one on the west side and one on the east side of Vail. Ski hat sales data (in dollars) for a random sample of 5 Saturdays during the 2004 season showed the following results. Is there a significant difference in sales dollars of hats between the west side and east side stores at the 5 percent level of significance? (a) State the hypotheses. (b) State the decision rule and sketch it. (c) Find the test statistic and state your conclusion. 📷 **Hats**

Saturday Sales Data ($) for Ski Hats

Saturday	East Side Shop	West Side Shop
1	548	523
2	493	721
3	609	695
4	567	510
5	432	532

10.65 Emergency room arrivals in a large hospital showed the statistics below for 2 months. At $\alpha = .05$, has the variance changed? Show all steps clearly, including an illustration of the decision rule.

Statistic	October	November
Mean arrivals	177.0323	171.7333
Standard deviation	13.48205	15.4271
Days	31	30

10.66 Here are heart rates for a sample of 30 students before and after a class break. At $\alpha = .05$, was there a significant difference in the mean heart rate? (a) State the hypotheses. (b) State the decision rule and sketch it. (c) Find the test statistic. (d) Make a decision. (e) Estimate the p-value and interpret it. 📷 **HeartRate**

Heart Rate before and after Class Break

Student	Before	After	Student	Before	After
1	60	62	16	70	64
2	70	76	17	69	66
3	77	78	18	64	69
4	80	83	19	70	73
5	82	82	20	59	58
6	82	83	21	62	65
7	41	66	22	66	68
8	65	63	23	81	77
9	58	60	24	56	57
10	50	54	25	64	62
11	82	93	26	78	79
12	56	55	27	75	74
13	71	67	28	66	67
14	67	68	29	59	63
15	66	75	30	98	82

Note: Thanks to colleague Gene Fliedner for having his evening students take their own pulses before and after the 10-minute class break.

10.67 A certain company will purchase the house of any employee who is transferred out of state and will handle all details of reselling the house. The purchase price is based on two assessments, one assessor being chosen by the employee and one by the company. Based on the sample of eight assessments shown, do the two assessors agree? Use the .01 level of significance, state hypotheses clearly, and show all steps. 📁 **HomeValue**

Assessments of Eight Homes ($ thousands)

Assessed By	Home 1	Home 2	Home 3	Home 4	Home 5	Home 6	Home 7	Home 8
Company	328	350	455	278	290	285	535	745
Employee	318	345	470	285	310	280	525	765

10.68 Nine homes are chosen at random from real estate listings in two suburban neighborhoods, and the square footage of each home is noted following. At the .10 level of significance, is there a difference between the sizes of homes in the two neighborhoods? State your hypotheses and show all steps clearly. 📁 **HomeSize**

Size of Homes in Two Subdivisions

Subdivision				Square Footage				
Greenwood	2,320	2,450	2,270	2,200	2,850	2,150	2,400	2,800	2,430
Pinewood	2,850	2,560	2,300	2,100	2,750	2,450	2,550	2,750	3,150

10.69 Two labs produce 1280 × 1024 LCD displays. At random, records are examined for 12 independently chosen hours of production in each lab, and the number of bad pixels per thousand displays is recorded. (a) Assuming equal variances, at the .01 level of significance, is there a difference in the defect rate between the two labs? State your hypotheses and show all steps clearly. (b) At the .01 level of significance, can you reject the hypothesis of equal variances? State your hypotheses and show all steps clearly.

Defects in Randomly Inspected LCD Displays 📁 **LCDDefects**

Lab A   422, 319, 326, 410, 393, 368, 497, 381, 515, 472, 423, 355

Lab B   497, 421, 408, 375, 410, 489, 389, 418, 447, 429, 404, 477

10.70 A cognitive retraining clinic assists outpatient victims of head injury, anoxia, or other conditions that result in cognitive impairment. Each incoming patient is evaluated to establish an appropriate treatment program and estimated length of stay. To see if the evaluation teams are consistent, 12 randomly chosen patients are separately evaluated by two expert teams (*A* and *B*) as shown. At the .10 level of significance, are the evaluator teams consistent in their estimates? State your hypotheses and show all steps clearly. 📁 **LengthStay**

Estimated Length of Stay in Weeks

Team	Patient											
	1	2	3	4	5	6	7	8	9	10	11	12
A	24	24	52	30	40	30	18	30	18	40	24	12
B	24	20	52	36	36	36	24	36	16	52	24	16

10.71 Rates of return (annualized) in two investment portfolios are compared over the last 12 quarters. They are considered similar in safety, but portfolio *B* is advertised as being "less volatile." (a) At $\alpha = .025$, does the sample show that portfolio *A* has significantly greater variance in rates of return than portfolio *B*? (b) At $\alpha = .025$, is there a significant difference in the means? 📁 **Portfolio**

Portfolio A	Portfolio B	Portfolio A	Portfolio B
5.23	8.96	7.89	7.68
10.91	8.60	9.82	7.62
12.49	7.61	9.62	8.71
4.17	6.60	4.93	8.97
5.54	7.77	11.66	7.71
8.68	7.06	11.49	9.91

10.72 Is there a difference between the variance in ages for full-time seasonal employees and part-time   VAILRESORTS
seasonal employees at Vail Resorts? A sample of 62 full-time employees had an $s_1^2 = 265.69$. A
sample of 78 part-time employees had an $s_2^2 = 190.44$. (a) Test for equal variances with $\alpha = .05$.
(b) If you were to then test for equal mean ages between the two groups would you use the pooled
t statistic for the test statistic? Why or why not?

10.73 A survey of 100 mayonnaise purchasers showed that 65 were loyal to one brand. For 100 bath soap
purchasers, only 53 were loyal to one brand. Form a 95 percent confidence interval for the difference of proportions. Does it include zero?

10.74 A 20-minute consumer survey mailed to 500 adults aged 25–34 included a $5 Starbucks gift cer-
tificate. The same survey was mailed to 500 adults aged 25–34 without the gift certificate. There
were 65 responses from the first group and 45 from the second group. Form a 95 percent confidence interval for the difference of proportions. Does it include zero?

10.75 One group of accounting students used simulation programs, while another group received a tutorial. Scores on an exam were compared. (a) Construct a 90 percent confidence interval for the
true difference in mean scores, explaining any assumptions that are necessary. (b) Do you think
the learning methods have significantly different results? Explain.

Statistic	Simulation	Tutorial
Mean score	$\bar{x}_1 = 9.1$	$\bar{x}_2 = 10.3$
Sample std. dev.	$s_1 = 2.4$	$s_2 = 2.5$
Number of students	$n_1 = 20$	$n_2 = 20$

10.76 Advertisers fear that users of DVD recorders will "fast forward" past commercials when they
watch a recorded program. Sky, the leading British pay television company, told their advertisers
that this effect might be offset because DVD users watch more TV. A sample of 15 DVD users
showed a daily mean screen time of 2 hours and 26 minutes with a standard deviation of 14 minutes,
compared with a daily mean of 2 hours and 7 minutes with a standard deviation of 12 minutes for
a sample of 15 non-DVD users. (a) Construct a 95 percent confidence interval for the difference
in mean TV watching. Would this sample support Sky's claim (i.e., is zero within the confidence
interval for the mean difference)? (b) Discuss any assumptions that are needed. (See *The New York
Times*, January 8, 2007, p. C2.)

10.77 In preliminary tests of a vaccine that may help smokers quit by reducing the "rush" from tobacco,
64 subjects who wanted to quit smoking were given either a placebo or the vaccine. Of the 32 in
the placebo group, only 3 quit smoking for 30 days (the U.S. Food and Drug Administration's criterion for smoking cessation) compared with 11 of the vaccine group. (a) Assuming equal sample sizes, find the 95 percent confidence interval for the difference in proportions. What does it
suggest? (b) Why is the sample size a problem here? (See *Science News*, February 10, 2007,
p. 91).

10.78 Do positive emotions reduce susceptibility to colds? Healthy volunteers were divided into two
groups based on their emotional profiles and each group was exposed to rhinovirus (the common
cold). Of those who reported mostly positive emotions, 14 of 50 developed cold symptoms, compared with 23 of 56 who reported mostly negative emotions. (a) Find the 95 percent confidence interval for the difference in proportions. What does it suggest? (b) Is the criterion for normality met?

10.79 Are the graduation rates for male college basketball players different from all male student athletes?
A random sample of 20 Division I colleges and universities from 2008 is shown in the table below.

(a) Form a 95 percent confidence interval for μ_d, the mean difference between graduation rates for male basketball players and all student athletes. (b) Would you conclude that there is a difference?

2008 Graduation Rates for Male College Basketball Players 📁 **GradRates**

School	Male Basketball Student Athletes	All Male Student Athletes	School	Male Basketball Student Athletes	All Male Student Athletes
Arizona	20	49	Notre Dame	100	98
Baylor	44	75	Oregon	58	71
Butler	92	92	Portland State	17	31
Clemson	29	76	San Diego	53	69
Duke	89	96	Stanford	67	96
Georgetown	70	94	Texas	31	64
Indiana	62	75	Texas-Arlington	57	64
Kansas State	67	76	UNLV	29	56
Marquette	100	95	Washington State	33	64
Michigan State	60	75	West Virginia	41	66

Source: www.ncaa.org

DO-IT-YOURSELF

10.80 Count the number of two-door vehicles among 50 vehicles from a college or university student parking lot. Use any sampling method you like (e.g., the first 50 you see). Do the same for a grocery store that is not very close to the college or university. At $\alpha = .10$, is there a significant difference in the proportion of two-door vehicles in these two locations? (a) State the hypotheses. (b) State the decision rule and sketch it. (c) Find the sample proportions and z test statistic. (d) Make a decision. (e) Find the p-value and interpret it. (f) Is the normality assumption fulfilled? Explain.

10.81 Choose 40 words at random from this book (use a systematic sampling method, such as every fifth word on every tenth page). Then do the same for a novel of your choice. List the words and count the syllables in each. Find the mean and standard deviation. Is there a significant difference in the number of syllables at the .05 level? If so, is the difference important, as well as significant? To whom, and why? Show all work carefully.

10.82 Choose 100 words at random from this book (use a systematic sampling method, such as every tenth word on every fifth page). Then do the same for a novel of your choice. List the words and count the syllables in each. For each sample, find the proportion of words with more than three syllables. Is there a significant difference in the mean number of syllables at the .05 level? How does this analysis differ from the preceding exercise?

RELATED READING

Best, D. J., and J. C. W. Rayner. "Welch's Approximate Solution for the Behrens-Fisher Problem." *Technometrics* 29 (1987), pp. 205–10.

Payton, Mark E.; Matthew H. Greenstone; and Nathan Schenker. "Overlapping Confidence Intervals or Standard Error Intervals: What Do They Mean in terms of Statistical Significance?" *Journal of Insect Science* 3, no. 34 (October 2003), pp. 1–6.

Posten, H. O. "Robustness of the Two-Sample *t*-Test under Violations of the Homogeneity of Variance Assumption, Part II." *Communications in Statistics—Theory and Methods* 21 (1995), pp. 2169–84.

Scheffé, H. "Practical Solutions of the Behrens-Fisher Problem." *Journal of the American Statistical Association* 65 (1970), pp. 1501–08.

Shoemaker, Lewis F. "Fixing the *F* Test for Equal Variances." *The American Statistician* 57, no. 2 (May 2003), pp. 105–14.

Wang, Y. "Probabilities of the Type I Errors of the Welch Tests for the Behrens-Fisher Problem." *Journal of the American Statistical Association* 66 (1971), pp. 605–08.

CHAPTER 10 Online Learning Resources

The Online Learning Center (OLC) at www.mhhe.com/doane3e has several *LearningStats* demonstrations to help you understand two-sample hypothesis tests. Your instructor may assign one or more of them, or you may decide to download the ones that sound interesting.

Topic	LearningStats Demonstrations
Common hypothesis tests	☒ Calculator for Two Means
	☒ Calculator for Two Proportions
Simulations	☒ Two-Sample Bootstrap
Tables	☒ Appendix F—*F* Distribution

Key: ☒ = Excel

EXAM REVIEW QUESTIONS FOR CHAPTERS 8–10

1. Which statement is *not* correct? Explain.

   a. the sample data $x_1, x_2, \ldots, x_n$ will be approximately normal if the sample size n is large.
   b. for a skewed population, the distribution of $\bar{X}$ is approximately normal if n is large.
   c. the expected value of $\bar{X}$ is equal to the true mean μ even if the population is skewed.

2. Match each statement to the correct property of an estimator (unbiased, consistent, efficient):

   a. The estimator "collapses" on the true parameter as n increases.
   b. The estimator has a relatively small variance.
   c. The expected value of the estimator is the true parameter.

3. Concerning confidence intervals, which statement is *most nearly* correct? Why not the others?

   a. We should use z instead of t when n is large.
   b. We use the Student's t distribution when σ is unknown.
   c. Using the Student's t distribution instead of z narrows the confidence interval.

4. A sample of 9 customers in the "quick" lane in a supermarket showed a mean purchase of $14.75 with a standard deviation of $2.10. (a) Find the 95 percent confidence interval for the true mean. (b) Why should you use t instead of z in this case?

5. A sample of 200 customers at a supermarket showed that 28 used a debit card to pay for their purchases. (a) Find the 95 percent confidence interval for the population proportion. (b) Why is it OK to assume normality in this case? (c) What sample size would be needed to estimate the population proportion with 90 percent confidence and an error of $\pm .03$?

6. Which statement is *incorrect*? Explain.

   a. If $p = .50$ and $n = 100$ the estimated standard error of the sample proportion is .05.
   b. In a sample size calculation for estimating π it is conservative to assume $\pi = .50$.
   c. If $n = 250$ and $p = .07$ it is not safe to assume normality in a confidence interval for π.

7. Given $H_0: \mu \geq 18$ and $H_1: \mu < 18$, we would commit Type I error if we

   a. conclude that $\mu \geq 18$ when the truth is that $\mu < 18$.
   b. conclude that $\mu < 18$ when the truth is that $\mu \geq 18$.
   c. fail to reject $\mu \geq 18$ when the truth is that $\mu < 18$.

8. Which is the correct z value for a two-tailed test at $\alpha = .05$?

   a. $z = \pm 1.645$ b. $z = \pm 1.960$ c. $z = \pm 2.326$

9. The process that produces Sonora Bars (a type of candy) is intended to produce bars with a mean weight of 56 gm. The process standard deviation is known to be 0.77 gm. A random sample of 49 candy bars yields a mean weight of 55.82 gm. (a) State the hypotheses to test whether the mean is smaller than it is supposed to be. (b) What is the test statistic? (c) At $\alpha = .05$, what is the critical value for this test? (d) What is your conclusion?

10. A sample of 16 ATM transactions shows a mean transaction time of 67 seconds with a standard deviation of 12 seconds. (a) State the hypotheses to test whether the mean transaction time exceeds 60 seconds. (b) Find the test statistic. (c) At $\alpha = .025$, what is the critical value for this test? (d) What is your conclusion?

11. Which statement is *correct*? Why not the others?

   a. The level of significance α is the probability of committing Type I error.
   b. As the sample size increases, critical values of $t_{.05}$ increase, gradually approaching $z_{.05}$.
   c. When σ is unknown, it is conservative to use $z_{.05}$ instead of $t_{.05}$ in a hypothesis test for μ.

12. Last month, 85 percent of the visitors to the Sonora Candy Factory made a purchase in the on-site candy shop after taking the factory tour. This month, a random sample of 500 such visitors showed that 435 purchased candy after the tour. The manager said "Good, the percentage of candy-buyers has risen significantly." (a) At $\alpha = .05$, do you agree? (b) Why is it acceptable to assume normality in this test?

13. Weights of 12 randomly-chosen Sonora Bars (a type of candy) from assembly line 1 had a mean weight of 56.25 gm with a standard deviation of 0.65 gm, while the weights of 12 randomly-chosen Sonora Bars from assembly line 2 had a mean weight of 56.75 gm with a standard deviation of 0.55 gm. (a) Find the test statistic to test whether or not the mean population weights are the same for both assembly lines (i.e., that the difference is due to random variation). (b) State the critical value for $\alpha = .05$ and degrees of freedom that you are using. (c) State your conclusion.

14. In a random sample of 200 Colorado residents, 150 had skied at least once last winter. A similar sample of 200 Utah residents revealed that 140 had skied at least once last winter. At $\alpha = .025$, is the percentage significantly greater in Colorado? Explain fully and show calculations.

15. Five students in a large lecture class compared their scores on two exams. "Looks like the class mean was higher on the second exam," Bob said. (a) What kind of test would you use? (b) At $\alpha = .10$, what is the critical value? (c) Do you agree with Bob? Explain.

	Bill	Mary	Sam	Sarah	Megan
Exam 1	75	85	90	65	86
Exam 2	86	81	90	71	89

16. Which statement is *not* correct concerning a *p*-value? Explain.

    a. *Ceteris paribus,* a larger *p*-value makes it more likely that H_0 will be rejected.
    b. The *p*-value shows the risk of Type I error if we reject H_0 when H_0 is true.
    c. In making a decision, we compare the *p*-value with the desired level of significance α.

17. Given $n_1 = 8$, $s_1 = 14$, $n_2 = 12$, $s_2 = 7$. (a) Find the test statistic for a test for equal population variances. (b) At $\alpha = .05$ in a two-tailed test, state the critical value and degrees of freedom.

CHAPTER 11

Analysis of Variance

Chapter Learning Objectives

When you finish this chapter you should be able to

LO1 Use basic ANOVA terminology correctly.

LO2 Recognize from data format when one-factor ANOVA is appropriate.

LO3 Interpret sums of squares and calculations in an ANOVA table.

LO4 Use Excel or other software for ANOVA calculations.

LO5 Use a table or Excel to find critical values for the F distribution.

LO6 Explain the assumptions of ANOVA and why they are important.

LO7 Understand and perform Tukey's test for paired means.

LO8 Use Hartley's test for equal variances in c treatment groups.

LO9 Recognize from data format when two-factor ANOVA is needed.

LO10 Interpret main effects and interaction effects in two-factor ANOVA.

LO11 Recognize the need for experimental design and GLM (optional).

You have already learned to compare the means of two samples. In this chapter, you will learn to compare more than two means *simultaneously* and how to trace sources of variation to potential explanatory factors by using **analysis of variance** (commonly referred to as **ANOVA**). Proper *experimental design* can make efficient use of limited data to draw the strongest possible inferences. Although analysis of variance has a relatively short history, it is one of the richest and most thoroughly explored fields of statistics. Originally developed by the English statistician Ronald A. Fisher (1890–1962) in connection with agricultural research (factors affecting crop growth), it was quickly applied in biology and medicine. Because of its versatility, it is now used in engineering, psychology, marketing, and many other areas. In this chapter, we will only illustrate a few kinds of problems where ANOVA may be utilized (see Related Reading if you need to go further).

The Goal: Explaining Variation

Analysis of variance seeks to identify *sources of variation* in a numerical *dependent* variable Y (the **response variable**). Variation in the response variable about its mean either is **explained** by one or more categorical *independent* variables (the **factors**) or is **unexplained** (random error):

$$\begin{array}{ccc} \text{Variation in } Y & = & \text{Explained Variation} & + & \text{Unexplained Variation} \\ \text{(around its mean)} & & \text{(due to factors)} & & \text{(random error)} \end{array}$$

ANOVA is a *comparison of means*. Each possible value of a factor or combination of factors is a **treatment**. Sample observations within each treatment are viewed as coming from populations with possibly different means. We test whether each factor has a significant effect on Y, and sometimes we test for interaction between factors. The test uses the F distribution, which was introduced in Chapter 10. ANOVA can handle any number of factors, but the researcher often is interested only in a few. Also, data collection costs may impose practical limits on the number of factors or treatments we can choose. This chapter concentrates on ANOVA models with one or two factors, although more complex models are briefly mentioned at the end of the chapter.

Illustration: Manufacturing Defect Rates

Figure 11.1 shows a dot plot of daily defect rates for automotive computer chips manufactured at four plant locations. Samples of 10 days' production were taken at each plant. Are the observed differences in the plants' sample mean defect rates merely due to random variation? Or are the observed differences between the plants' defect rates too great to be attributed to chance? This is the kind of question that ANOVA is designed to answer.

FIGURE 11.1

Chip defect rates at four plants. The treatment means are significantly different ($p = .02$). Note that the confidence interval for Lee's Bluff falls to the right of the dotted vertical line, which represents the overall mean.

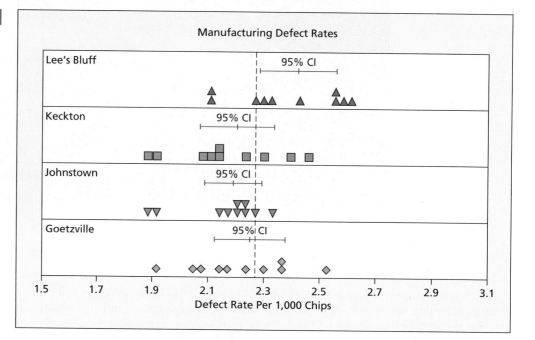

A simple way to state the ANOVA hypothesis is

H_0: $\mu_1 = \mu_2 = \mu_3 = \mu_4$ (mean defect rates are the same at all four plants)

H_1: Not all the means are equal (at least one mean differs from the others)

If we cannot reject H_0, then we conclude that the observations within each treatment or group actually have a common mean μ (represented by a dashed line in Figure 11.1). This one-factor ANOVA model may be visualized as in Figure 11.2.

FIGURE 11.2

ANOVA Model for Chip Defect Rate

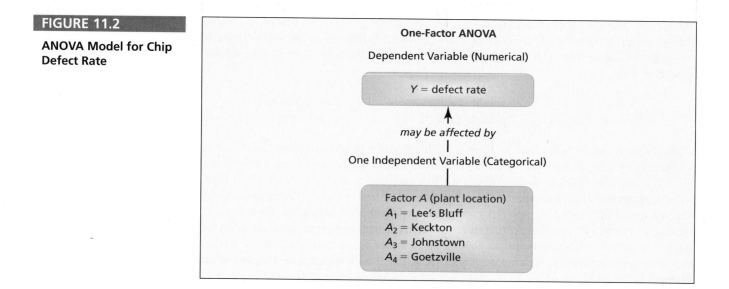

Illustration: Hospital Length of Stay

To allocate resources and fixed costs correctly, hospital management needs to test whether a patient's length of a stay (LOS) depends on the diagnostic-related group (DRG) code and the patient's age group. Consider the case of a bone fracture. LOS is a *numerical* response variable (measured in hours). The hospital organizes the data by using five diagnostic codes for type of fracture (facial, radius or ulna, hip or femur, other lower extremity, all other) and three age groups (under 18, 18 to 64, 65 and over). Although patient age is a numerical variable, it is coded into three categories based on stages of bone growth. Figure 11.3 illustrates two possible ANOVA models (one-factor or two-factor). We could also test for **interaction** between factors, as you will see later on.

One factor: Length of stay $= f$(Type of Fracture)

Two factors: Length of stay $= f$(Type of Fracture, Age Group)

FIGURE 11.3

ANOVA Models for Hospital Length of Stay

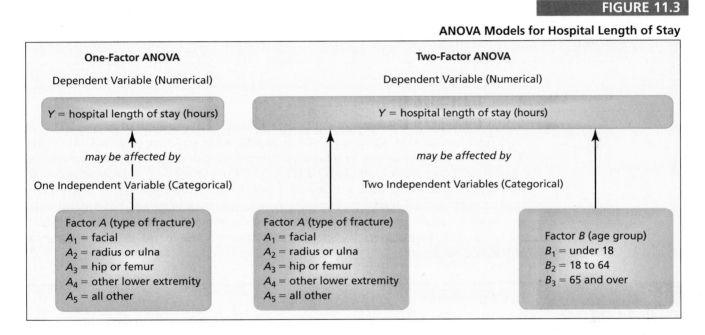

Illustration: Automobile Painting

Paint quality is a major concern of car makers. A key characteristic of paint is its viscosity, a continuous *numerical* variable. Viscosity is to be tested for dependence on application temperature (low, medium, high) and/or the supplier of the paint (Sasnak Inc., Etaoin Ltd., or Shrdlu Inc.). Although temperature is a numerical variable, it has been coded into *categories* that represent the test conditions of the experiment. Figure 11.4 illustrates two potential ANOVA models:

One factor: Viscosity $= f$(temperature)

Two factors: Viscosity $= f$(temperature, supplier)

ANOVA Assumptions

Analysis of variance assumes that the

- Observations on Y are independent.
- Populations being sampled are normal.
- Populations being sampled have equal variances.

Fortunately, ANOVA is somewhat robust to departures from the normality and equal variance assumptions. Later in this chapter, you will see tests for equal variances and normality.

LO6

Explain the assumptions of ANOVA and why they are important.

FIGURE 11.4

Several ANOVA Models for Paint Viscosity

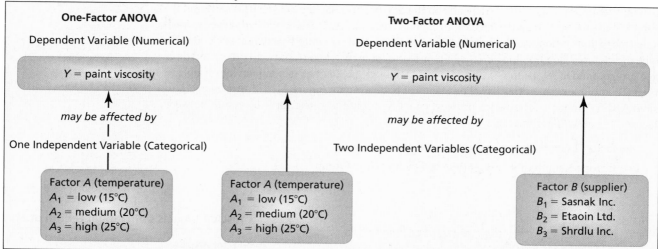

ANOVA Calculations

ANOVA calculations usually are too tedious to do by calculator, so after we choose an ANOVA model and collect the data, we rely on software (e.g., Excel, MegaStat, MINITAB, SPSS) to do the calculations. In some applications (accounting, finance, human resources, marketing) large samples can easily be taken from existing records, while in others (engineering, manufacturing, computer systems) experimental data collection is so expensive that small samples are used. Large samples increase the power of the test, but power also depends on the degree of variation in Y. Lowest power would be in small samples with high variation in Y, and conversely. Specialized software is needed to calculate power for ANOVA experiments.

11.2

ONE-FACTOR ANOVA (COMPLETELY RANDOMIZED MODEL)

Data Format

If we are only interested in comparing the means of c groups (*treatments* or *factor levels*), we have a **one-factor ANOVA.*** This is by far the most common ANOVA model that covers many business problems. The one-factor ANOVA is usually viewed as a comparison between several columns of data, although the data could also be presented in rows. Table 11.1 illustrates the data format for a one-factor ANOVA with c treatments, denoted $A_1, A_2, \ldots, A_c$. The group means are $\bar{y}_1, \bar{y}_2, \ldots, \bar{y}_c$.

TABLE 11.1

Format of One-Factor ANOVA Data

One-Factor ANOVA: Data in Columns

A_1	A_2	...	A_c
y_{11}	y_{12}	...	y_{1c}
y_{21}	y_{22}	...	y_{2c}
y_{31}	y_{32}	...	y_{3c}
...	...	...	...
etc.	etc.	...	etc.
n_1 obs.	n_2 obs.	...	n_c obs.
$\bar{y}_1$	$\bar{y}_2$	...	$\bar{y}_c$

One-Factor ANOVA: Data in Rows

A_1	y_{11}	y_{21}	y_{31}	...	etc.	n_1 obs.	$\bar{y}_1$
A_2	y_{12}	y_{22}	y_{32}	...	etc.	n_2 obs.	$\bar{y}_2$
...				...		...	...
A_c	y_{1c}	y_{2c}	y_{3c}	...	etc.	n_c obs.	$\bar{y}_c$

*If subjects (or individuals) are assigned randomly to treatments, then we call this the *completely randomized model.*

Within each treatment j we have n_j observations on Y. Sample sizes within each treatment do *not* need to be equal, although there are advantages to having balanced sample sizes. Equal sample size (1) ensures that each treatment contributes equally to the analysis; (2) reduces problems arising from violations of the assumptions (e.g., nonindependent Y values, unequal variances or nonidentical distributions within treatments, or non-normality of Y); and (3) increases the power of the test (i.e., the ability of the test to detect differences in treatment means). The total number of observations is the sum of the sample sizes for each treatment:

$$n = n_1 + n_2 + \cdots + n_c \tag{11.1}$$

Hypotheses to Be Tested

The question of interest is whether the mean of Y varies from treatment to treatment. The hypotheses to be tested are

H_0: $\mu_1 = \mu_2 = \cdots = \mu_c$ (all the treatment means are equal)

H_1: Not all the means are equal (at least one pair of treatment means differs)

Since one-factor ANOVA is a generalization of the test for equality of two means, why not just compare all possible pairs of means by using repeated two-sample t tests (as in Chapter 10)? Consider our experiment comparing the four manufacturing plant average defect rates. To compare pairs of plant averages we would have to perform six different t tests. If each t test has a Type I error probability equal to .05, then the probability that at least one of those tests results in a Type I error is $1 - (.95)^6 = .2649$. ANOVA tests all the means *simultaneously* and therefore does not inflate our Type I error.

One-Factor ANOVA as a Linear Model

An equivalent way to express the one-factor model is to say that observations in treatment j came from a population with a common mean (μ) plus a treatment effect (A_j) plus random error (ε_{ij}):

$$y_{ij} = \mu + A_j + \varepsilon_{ij} \qquad j = 1, 2, \ldots, c \quad \text{and} \quad i = 1, 2, \ldots, n_j \tag{11.2}$$

The random error is assumed to be normally distributed with zero mean and the same variance for all treatments. If we are interested only in what happens to the response for the particular *levels* of the factor that were selected (a **fixed-effects model**), then the hypotheses to be tested are

H_0: $A_1 = A_2 = \cdots = A_c = 0$ (all treatment effects are zero)

H_1: Not all A_j are zero (some treatment effects are nonzero)

If the null hypothesis is true ($A_j = 0$ for all j), then knowing that an observation x came from treatment j does not help explain the variation in Y and the ANOVA model collapses to

$$y_{ij} = \mu + \varepsilon_{ij} \tag{11.3}$$

Group Means

The *mean of each group* is calculated in the usual way by summing the observations in the treatment and dividing by the sample size:

$$\bar{y}_j = \frac{1}{n_j} \sum_{i=1}^{n_j} y_{ij} \tag{11.4}$$

The *overall sample mean* or *grand mean* $\bar{y}$ can be calculated either by summing *all* the observations and dividing by n or by taking a weighted average of the c sample means:

$$\bar{y} = \frac{1}{n} \sum_{j=1}^{c} \sum_{i=1}^{n_j} y_{ij} = \frac{1}{n} \sum_{j=1}^{c} n_j \, \bar{y}_j \tag{11.5}$$

Partitioned Sum of Squares

To understand the logic of ANOVA, consider that for a given observation y_{ij} the following relationship must hold (on the right-hand side we just add and subtract $\bar{y}_j$):

$$\text{(11.6)} \qquad (y_{ij} - \bar{y}) = (\bar{y}_j - \bar{y}) + (y_{ij} - \bar{y}_j)$$

This says that any deviation of an observation from the grand mean $\bar{y}$ may be expressed in two parts: the deviation of the column mean ($\bar{y}_j$) from the grand mean ($\bar{y}$), or *between* treatments, and the deviation of the observation (y_{ij}) from its own column mean ($\bar{y}_j$), or *within* treatments. We can show that this relationship also holds for *sums* of squared deviations, yielding the **partitioned sum of squares**:

$$\text{(11.7)} \qquad \sum_{j=1}^{c}\sum_{i=1}^{n_j}(y_{ij} - \bar{y})^2 = \sum_{j=1}^{c}n_j(\bar{y}_j - \bar{y})^2 + \sum_{j=1}^{c}\sum_{i=1}^{n_j}(y_{ij} - \bar{y}_j)^2$$

This important relationship may be expressed simply as

$$\text{(11.8)} \qquad SST = SSA + SSE \qquad \text{(partitioned sum of squares)}$$

Partitioned Sum of Squares

Sum of Squares Total (*SST*)	=	Sum of Squares between Treatments (*SSA*)	+	Sum of Squares within Treatments (*SSE*)
		↑ Explained by Factor *A*		↑ Unexplained Random Error

If the treatment means do not differ greatly from the grand mean, *SSA* will be small and *SSE* will be large (and conversely). The sums *SSA* and *SSE* may be used to test the hypothesis that the treatment means differ from the grand mean. However, we first divide each sum of squares by its *degrees of freedom* (to adjust for group sizes). The *F test statistic* is the ratio of the resulting **mean squares**. These calculations can be arranged in a worksheet like Table 11.2.

TABLE 11.2

One-Factor ANOVA Table

LO3

Interpret sums of squares and calculations in an ANOVA table.

Source of Variation	Sum of Squares	Degrees of Freedom	Mean Square	F Statistic
Treatment (between groups)	$SSA = \sum_{j=1}^{c} n_j(\bar{y}_j - \bar{y})^2$	$c - 1$	$MSA = \dfrac{SSA}{c-1}$	$F = \dfrac{MSA}{MSE}$
Error (within groups)	$SSE = \sum_{j=1}^{c}\sum_{i=1}^{n_j}(y_{ij} - \bar{y}_j)^2$	$n - c$	$MSE = \dfrac{SSE}{n-c}$	
Total	$SST = \sum_{j=1}^{c}\sum_{i=1}^{n_j}(y_{ij} - \bar{y})^2$	$n - 1$		

The ANOVA calculations are mathematically simple but involve tedious sums. These calculations are almost always done on a computer.* For example, Excel's one-factor ANOVA menu using Data Analysis is shown in Figure 11.5. MegaStat uses a similar menu.

---

*Detailed step-by-step examples of all ANOVA calculations can be found in the case studies in *LearningStats* Unit 11.

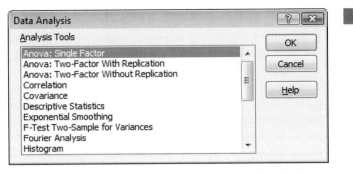

FIGURE 11.5

Excel's ANOVA Menu

Test Statistic

At the beginning of this chapter we described the variation in Y as consisting of explained variation and unexplained variation. To test whether the independent variable explains a significant proportion of the variation in Y, we need to compare the explained (due to treatments) and unexplained (due to error) variation. Recall that the F distribution describes the *ratio of two variances*. Therefore it makes sense that the ANOVA test statistic is the F *test statistic*. The F statistic is the ratio of the variance due to treatments to the variance due to error. *MSA* is the mean square due to treatments and *MSE* is the mean square within treatments. Formula 11.9 shows the F statistic and its degrees of freedom.

$$\text{Explained} \longrightarrow MSA \qquad F = \frac{MSA}{MSE} = \frac{\left(\dfrac{SSA}{c-1}\right)}{\left(\dfrac{SSE}{n-c}\right)} \quad \begin{array}{l} \longleftarrow df_1 = c - 1 \text{ (numerator)} \\[2em] \longleftarrow df_2 = n - c \text{ (denominator)} \end{array}$$

$$\text{Unexplained} \longrightarrow \qquad\qquad\qquad\qquad\qquad\qquad\qquad\qquad \tag{11.9}$$

The test statistic $F = MSA/MSE$ cannot be negative (it's based on sums of squares—see Table 11.2). The F test for equal treatment means is always a right-tailed test because it is the ratio of explained to unexplained variance. If there is little difference among treatments, we would expect *MSA* to be near zero because the treatment means $\bar{y}_j$ would be near the overall mean $\bar{y}$. Thus, when F is near zero we would not expect to reject the hypothesis of equal group means. The larger the F statistic, the more we are inclined to reject the hypothesis of equal means. But how large must F be to convince us that the means differ? Just as with a z test or a t test, we need a *decision rule*.

Decision Rule

The F distribution is a right-skewed distribution that starts at zero (F cannot be negative since variances are sums of squares) and has no upper limit (since the variances could be of any magnitude). For ANOVA, the F test is a right-tailed test. For a given level of significance α, we can use Appendix F to obtain the right-tail critical value of F. Alternatively, we can use Excel's function =FINV(α,df$_1$,df$_2$). The decision rule is illustrated in Figure 11.6. This critical value is denoted F_{df_1, df_2} or $F_{c-1, n-c}$.

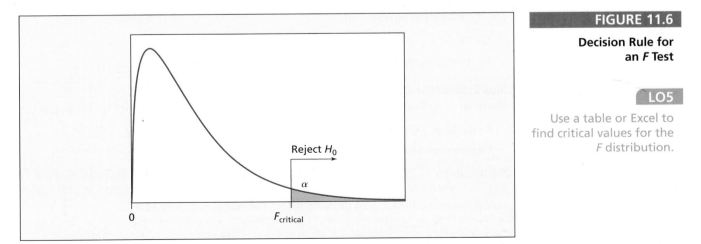

FIGURE 11.6

Decision Rule for an *F* Test

LO5

Use a table or Excel to find critical values for the *F* distribution.

EXAMPLE

Carton Packing

A cosmetics manufacturer's regional distribution center has four workstations that are responsible for packing cartons for shipment to small retailers. Each workstation is staffed by two workers. The task involves assembling each order, placing it in a shipping carton, inserting packing material, taping the carton, and placing a computer-generated shipping label on each carton. Generally, each station can pack 200 cartons a day, and often more. However, there is variability, due to differences in orders, labels, and cartons. Table 11.3 shows the number of cartons packed per day during a recent week. Is the variation among stations within the range attributable to chance, or do these samples indicate actual differences in the means?

TABLE 11.3	**Number of Cartons Packed** 🖻 Cartons			
	Station 1	*Station 2*	*Station 3*	*Station 4*
	236	238	220	241
	250	239	236	233
	252	262	232	212
	233	247	243	231
	239	246	213	213
Sum	1,210	1,232	1,144	1,130
Mean	242.0	246.4	228.8	226.0
St. Dev.	8.515	9.607	12.153	12.884
n	5	5	5	5

As a preliminary step, we plot the data (Figure 11.7) to check for any time pattern and just to visualize the data. We see some potential differences in means, but no obvious time pattern (otherwise we would have to consider observation order as a second factor). We proceed with the hypothesis test.

FIGURE 11.7 **Plot of the Data**

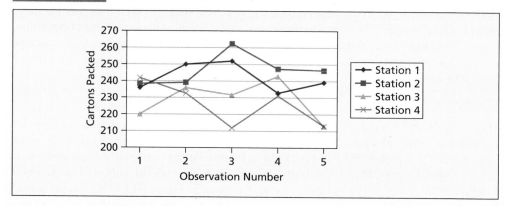

Step 1: State the Hypotheses
The hypotheses to be tested are

$H_0: \mu_1 = \mu_2 = \mu_3 = \mu_4$ (the means are the same)

H_1: Not all the means are equal (at least one mean is different)

Step 2: State the Decision Rule
There are $c = 4$ groups and $n = 20$ observations, so degrees of freedom for the F test are

Numerator: $df_1 = c - 1 = 4 - 1 = 3$ (between treatments, factor)

Denominator: $df_2 = n - c = 20 - 4 = 16$ (within treatments, error)

We will use $\alpha = .05$ for the test. The 5 percent right-tail critical value from Appendix F is $F_{3,16} = 3.24$. Instead of Appendix F we could use Excel's function =FINV(0.05,3,16) which yields $F_{.05} = 3.238872$. This decision rule is illustrated in Figure 11.8.

FIGURE 11.8

F Test Using $\alpha = .05$ with $F_{3,16}$

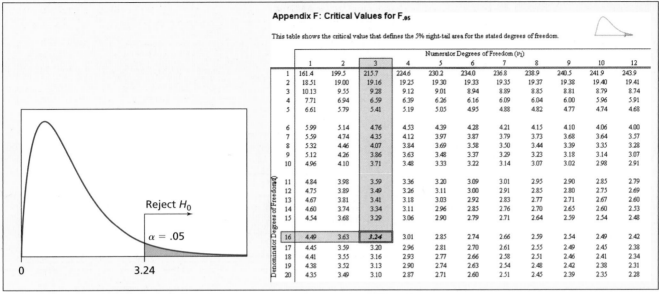

Step 3: Perform the Calculations

Using Excel for the calculations, we obtain the results shown in Figure 11.9. You can specify the desired level of significance (Excel's default is $\alpha = .05$). Note that Excel labels *SSA* "between groups" and *SSE* "within groups." This is an intuitive and attractive way to describe the variation.

LO5

Use a table or Excel to find critical values for the *F* distribution.

FIGURE 11.9 **Excel's One-Factor ANOVA Results** 📂 **Cartons**

Anova: Single Factor

SUMMARY

Groups	Count	Sum	Average	Variance
Station 1	5	1210	242	72.5
Station 2	5	1232	246.4	92.3
Station 3	5	1144	228.8	147.7
Station 4	5	1130	226	166

ANOVA

Source of Variation	SS	df	MS	F	P-value	F crit
Between Groups	1479.2	3	493.0667	4.121769	0.024124	3.238872
Within Groups	1914	16	119.625			
Total	3393.2	19				

LO4

Use Excel or other software for ANOVA calculations.

Step 4: Make the Decision

Since the test statistic $F = 4.12$ exceeds the critical value $F_{.05} = 3.24$, we can reject the hypothesis of equal means. Since Excel gives the *p*-value, you don't actually need Excel's critical value. The *p*-value ($p = .024124$) is less than the level of significance ($\alpha = .05$) which confirms that we should reject the hypothesis of equal treatment means. For comparison, Figure 11.10 shows MegaStat's ANOVA table for the same data. The results are the same, although MegaStat rounds things off, highlights significant *p*-values, and gives standard deviations instead of variances for each treatment.

FIGURE 11.10 **MegaStat's One-Factor ANOVA Results** 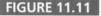 **Cartons**

One factor ANOVA

Mean	n	Std. Dev	
242.0	5	8.51	Station 1
246.4	5	9.61	Station 2
228.8	5	12.15	Station 3
226.0	5	12.88	Station 4
235.8	20	13.36	Total

ANOVA table

Source	SS	df	MS	F	p-value
Treatment	1,479.20	3	493.067	4.12	.0241
Error	1,914.00	16	119.625		
Total	3,393.20	19			

MegaStat provides additional insights by showing a dot plot of observations by group, shown in Figure 11.11. The display includes group means (shown as short horizontal tick marks) and the overall mean (shown as a dashed line). The dot plot suggests that stations 3 and 4 have means below the overall mean, while stations 1 and 2 are above the overall mean.

FIGURE 11.11 **Dot Plot of Four Samples** 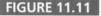 **Cartons**

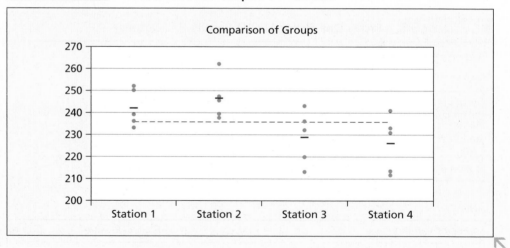

Using MINITAB

MINITAB's output, shown in Figure 11.12, is the same as Excel's except that MINITAB rounds off the results and displays a confidence interval for each group mean, an attractive feature.* In our carton example, the confidence intervals overlap, except possibly stations 2 and 4. But comparing pairs of confidence intervals is not quite the same as what an ANOVA test does, since ANOVA seeks to compare *all* the group means *simultaneously*.

---

*MINITAB and most other statistical packages prefer the data in *stacked* format. Each variable has its own column (e.g., column one contains all the *Y* values, while column two contains group labels like "Station 1"). MINITAB will convert *unstacked* data to *stacked* data for one-factor ANOVA, but not for other ANOVA models.

FIGURE 11.12

MINITAB's One-Factor ANOVA

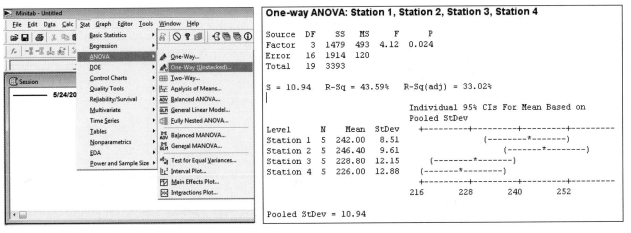

Instructions: For each data set: (a) State the hypotheses. (b) Use Excel's Data Analysis (or MegaStat or MINITAB) to perform the one-factor ANOVA, using $\alpha = .05$. (c) State your conclusion about the population means. Was the decision close? (d) Interpret the *p*-value carefully. (e) Include a plot of the data for each group if you are using MegaStat, and confidence intervals for the group means if you are using MINITAB. What do the plots show?

SECTION EXERCISES

connect

11.1 Scrap rates per thousand (parts whose defects cannot be reworked) are compared for 5 randomly selected days at three plants. Does the data show a significant difference in mean scrap rates? 📁 **ScrapRate**

Scrap Rate (Per Thousand Units)		
Plant A	*Plant B*	*Plant C*
11.4	11.1	10.2
12.5	14.1	9.5
10.1	16.8	9.0
13.8	13.2	13.3
13.7	14.6	5.9

11.2 One particular morning, the length of time spent in the examination rooms is recorded for each patient seen by each physician at an orthopedic clinic. Does the data show a significant difference in mean times? 📁 **Physicians**

Time in Examination Rooms (minutes)			
Physician 1	*Physician 2*	*Physician 3*	*Physician 4*
34	33	17	28
25	35	30	33
27	31	30	31
31	31	26	27
26	42	32	32
34	33	28	33
21		26	40
		29	

11.3 Semester GPAs are compared for seven randomly chosen students in each class level at Oxnard University. Does the data show a significant difference in mean GPAs? 📂 **GPA1**

GPA for Randomly Selected Students in Four Business Majors

Accounting	Finance	Human Resources	Marketing
2.48	3.16	2.93	3.54
2.19	3.01	2.89	3.71
2.62	3.07	3.48	2.94
3.15	2.88	3.33	3.46
3.56	3.33	3.53	3.50
2.53	2.87	2.95	3.25
3.31	2.85	3.58	3.20

11.4 Sales of *People* magazine are compared over a 5-week period at four Borders outlets in Chicago. Does the data show a significant difference in mean weekly sales? 📂 **Magazines**

Weekly Sales

Store 1	Store 2	Store 3	Store 4
102	97	89	100
106	77	91	116
105	82	75	87
115	80	106	102
112	101	94	100

11.3
MULTIPLE COMPARISONS

Tukey's Test

Besides performing an *F* test to compare the *c* means *simultaneously,* we also could ask whether *pairs* of means differ. You might expect to do a *t* test for two independent means (Chapter 10), or check whether there is overlap in the confidence intervals for each group's mean. But the null hypothesis in ANOVA is that *all* the means are the same, so to maintain the desired overall probability of Type I error, we need to create a *simultaneous confidence interval* for the difference of means based on the *pooled* variances for all *c* groups at once and then see which pairs exclude zero. For *c* groups, there are $c(c-1)/2$ distinct pairs of means to be compared.

Several **multiple comparison** tests are available. Their logic is similar. We will discuss only one, called **Tukey's studentized range test** (sometimes called the *HSD* or "honestly significant difference" test). It has good power and is widely used. We will refer to it as *Tukey's test,* named for statistician John Wilder Tukey (1915–2000). This test is available in most statistical packages (but not in Excel's Data Analysis). It is a two-tailed test for equality of paired means from *c* groups compared simultaneously and is a natural follow-up when the results of the one-factor ANOVA test show a significant difference in at least one mean. The hypotheses to compare group *j* with group *k* are

$H_0: \mu_j = \mu_k$

$H_1: \mu_j \neq \mu_k$

The decision rule is

(11.10)
$$\text{Reject } H_0 \text{ if } T_{\text{calc}} = \frac{|\bar{y}_j - \bar{y}_k|}{\sqrt{MSE\left[\dfrac{1}{n_j} + \dfrac{1}{n_k}\right]}} > T_{c,n-c}$$

where $T_{c,n-c}$ is a critical value of the *Tukey test statistic* T_{calc} for the desired level of significance. Table 11.4 shows 5 percent critical values of $T_{c,n-c}$. If the desired degrees of freedom cannot be found, we could interpolate or better yet rely on a computer package like MegaStat to provide the exact critical value. We take *MSE* directly from the ANOVA calculations (see Table 11.2). The MSE is the *pooled variance* for all c samples combined (rather than pooling just two sample variances as in Chapter 10).

n − c	Number of Groups (c)								
	2	**3**	**4**	**5**	**6**	**7**	**8**	**9**	**10**
5	2.57	3.26	3.69	4.01	4.27	4.48	4.66	4.81	4.95
6	2.45	3.07	3.46	3.75	3.98	4.17	4.33	4.47	4.59
7	2.37	2.95	3.31	3.58	3.79	3.96	4.11	4.24	4.36
8	2.31	2.86	3.20	3.46	3.66	3.82	3.96	4.08	4.19
9	2.26	2.79	3.12	3.36	3.55	3.71	3.84	3.96	4.06
10	2.23	2.74	3.06	3.29	3.47	3.62	3.75	3.86	3.96
15	2.13	2.60	2.88	3.09	3.25	3.38	3.49	3.59	3.68
20	2.09	2.53	2.80	2.99	3.14	3.27	3.37	3.46	3.54
30	2.04	2.47	2.72	2.90	3.04	3.16	3.25	3.34	3.41
40	2.02	2.43	2.68	2.86	2.99	3.10	3.20	3.28	3.35
60	2.00	2.40	2.64	2.81	2.94	3.05	3.14	3.22	3.29
120	1.98	2.37	2.61	2.77	2.90	3.00	3.09	3.16	3.22
∞	1.96	2.34	2.57	2.73	2.85	2.95	3.03	3.10	3.16

TABLE 11.4

Five Percent Critical Values of Tukey Test Statistic*

*Table shows studentized range divided by $\sqrt{2}$ to obtain $T_{c,n-c}$. See R. E. Lund and J. R. Lund, "Probabilities and Upper Quantiles for the Studentized Range," *Applied Statistics* 32 (1983), pp. 204–210.

We will illustrate the Tukey test for the carton-packing data. We assume that a one-factor ANOVA has already been performed and the results showed that at least one mean was significantly different. We will use the *MSE* from the ANOVA. For the carton-packing data there are 4 groups and 20 observations, so $c = 4$ and $n - c = 20 - 4 = 16$. From Table 11.4 we must interpolate between $T_{4,15} = 2.88$ and $T_{4,20} = 2.80$ to get $T_{4,16} = 2.86$. The decision rule for any pair of means is therefore

$$\text{Reject } H_0 \text{ if } T_{calc} = \frac{|\bar{y}_j - \bar{y}_k|}{\sqrt{MSE\left[\frac{1}{n_j} + \frac{1}{n_k}\right]}} > 2.86$$

There may be a different decision rule for every pair of stations unless the sample sizes n_j and n_k are identical (in our example, the group sizes are the same). For example, to compare groups 2 and 4 the test statistic is

$$T_{calc} = \frac{|\bar{y}_2 - \bar{y}_4|}{\sqrt{MSE\left[\frac{1}{n_2} + \frac{1}{n_4}\right]}} = \frac{|246.4 - 226.0|}{\sqrt{119.625\left[\frac{1}{5} + \frac{1}{5}\right]}} = 2.95$$

Since $T_{calc} = 2.95$ exceeds 2.86, we reject the hypothesis of equal means for station 2 and station 4. We conclude that there is a significant difference between the mean output of stations 2 and 4. A similar test must be performed for every possible pair of means.

All six possible comparisons of means are shown in Figure 11.13. Only stations 2 and 4 differ at $\alpha = .05$. However, if we use the independent sample *t* test (as in Chapter 10) shown in the lower table, we obtain two p-values smaller than $\alpha = .05$ (stations 1, 4 and stations 2, 3) and one that is below $\alpha = .01$ (stations 2, 4). This demonstrates that a *simultaneous* Tukey *T* test is not the same as comparing individual pairs of means. As noted in Section 11.2, using multiple independent *t* tests results in a greater probability of making a Type I error. An attractive feature of MegaStat's Tukey test is that it highlights significant results using color-coding for $\alpha = .05$ and $\alpha = .01$, as seen in Figure 11.13.

Tukey simultaneous comparison *t*-values (d.f. = 16)

		Station 4 226.0	Station 3 228.8	Station 1 242.0	Station 2 246.4
Station 4	226.0				
Station 3	228.8	0.40			
Station 1	242.0	2.31	1.91		
Station 2	246.4	2.95	2.54	0.64	

critical values for experimentwise error rate:
0.05	2.86
0.01	3.67

p-values for pairwise *t*-tests

		Station 4 226.0	Station 3 228.8	Station 1 242.0	Station 2 246.4
Station 4	226.0				
Station 3	228.8	.6910			
Station 1	242.0	.0344	.0745		
Station 2	246.4	.0094	.0217	.5337	

Instructions: Use MegaStat, MINITAB, or another software package to perform Tukey's test for significant pairwise differences. Perform the test using both the 5 percent and 1 percent levels of significance.

11.5 Refer to Exercise 11.1. Which pairs of mean scrap rates differ significantly (3 plants)? 🗇 **ScrapRate**

11.6 Refer to Exercise 11.2. Which pairs of mean examination times differ significantly (4 physicians)? 🗇 **Physicians**

11.7 Refer to Exercise 11.3. Which pairs of mean GPAs differ significantly (4 majors)? 🗇 **GPA1**

11.8 Refer to Exercise 11.4. Which pairs of mean weekly sales differ significantly (4 stores)? 🗇 **Magazines**

11.4
TESTS FOR HOMOGENEITY OF VARIANCES

ANOVA Assumptions

Analysis of variance assumes that observations on the response variable are from normally distributed populations that have the same variance. We have noted that few populations meet these requirements perfectly and unless the sample is quite large, a test for normality is impractical. However, we can easily test the assumption of **homogeneous** (equal) **variances**. Although the one-factor ANOVA test is only slightly affected by inequality of variance when group sizes are equal or nearly so, it is still a good idea to test this assumption. In general, surprisingly large differences in variances must exist to conclude that the population variances are unequal.

Hartley's Test

If we had only two groups, we could use the *F* test you learned in Chapter 10 to compare the variances. But for *c* groups, a more general test is required. One such test is **Hartley's test**, named for statistician H. O. Hartley (1912–1980). The hypotheses are

$H_0: \sigma_1^2 = \sigma_2^2 = \cdots = \sigma_c^2$ (equal variances)

$H_1:$ The σ_j^2 are not all equal (unequal variances)

Hartley's test statistic is the ratio of the largest sample variance to the smallest sample variance:

$$H_{calc} = \frac{s^2_{max}}{s^2_{min}} \qquad (11.11)$$

The decision rule is:

Reject H_0 if $H_{calc} > H_{critical}$

Critical values of $H_{critical}$ may be found in Table 11.5 using degrees of freedom given by

Numerator: $df_1 = c$

Denominator: $df_2 = \dfrac{n}{c} - 1$

where n is the total number of observations. This test assumes equal group sizes, so df_2 would be an integer. For group sizes that are not drastically unequal, this procedure will still be approximately correct, using the next lower integer if df_2 is not an integer.

	Numerator df_1								
Denominator df_2	**2**	**3**	**4**	**5**	**6**	**7**	**8**	**9**	**10**
2	39.0	87.5	142	202	266	333	403	475	550
3	15.4	27.8	39.2	50.7	62.0	72.9	83.5	93.9	104
4	9.60	15.5	20.6	25.2	29.5	33.6	37.5	41.1	44.6
5	7.15	10.8	13.7	16.3	18.7	20.8	22.9	24.7	26.5
6	5.82	8.38	10.4	12.1	13.7	15.0	16.3	17.5	18.6
7	4.99	6.94	8.44	9.7	10.8	11.8	12.7	13.5	14.3
8	4.43	6.00	7.18	8.12	9.03	9.78	10.5	11.1	11.7
9	4.03	5.34	6.31	7.11	7.80	8.41	8.95	9.45	9.91
10	3.72	4.85	5.67	6.34	6.92	7.42	7.87	8.28	8.66
12	3.28	4.16	4.79	5.30	5.72	6.09	6.42	6.72	7.00
15	2.86	3.54	4.01	4.37	4.68	4.95	5.19	5.40	5.59
20	2.46	2.95	3.29	3.54	3.76	3.94	4.10	4.24	4.37
30	2.07	2.40	2.61	2.78	2.91	3.02	3.12	3.21	3.29
60	1.67	1.85	1.96	2.04	2.11	2.17	2.22	2.26	2.30
∞	1.00	1.00	1.00	1.00	1.00	1.00	1.00	1.00	1.00

TABLE 11.5

Critical 5 Percent Values of Hartley's $H = s^2_{max}/s^2_{min}$

Source: E. S. Pearson and H. O. Hartley, *Biometrika Tables for Statisticians*, 3rd. ed. (Oxford University Press, 1970), p. 202. Copyright © 1970 Oxford University Press. Used with permission.

Using the carton-packing data in Table 11.3, there are 4 groups and 20 total observations, so we have

Numerator: $df_1 = c = 4$

Denominator: $df_2 = n/c - 1 = 20/4 - 1 = 5 - 1 = 4$

From Table 11.5 we choose the critical value $H_{critical} = 20.6$ using $df_1 = 4$ and $df_2 = 4$. The sample statistics (from Excel) for our workstations are

EXAMPLE

Carton Packing: Tukey Test 🖳 **Cartons**

Work Station	**n**	**Mean**	**Variance**
Station 1	15	242.0	72.5
Station 2	17	246.4	92.3
Station 3	15	228.8	147.7
Station 4	12	226.0	166.0

The test statistic is

$$H_{calc} = \frac{s^2_{max}}{s^2_{min}} = \frac{166.0}{72.5} = 2.29$$

In this case, we cannot reject the hypothesis of equal variances. Indeed, Table 11.5 makes it clear that unless the sample size is very large, the variance ratio would have to be quite large to reject the hypothesis of equal population variances. If Hartley's test is significant, we prefer an alternative* to one-factor ANOVA, which does not require this assumption.

Levene's Test

LO6

Explain the assumptions of ANOVA and why they are important.

Hartley's test relies on the assumption of normality in the populations from which the sample observations are drawn. A more robust alternative is **Levene's test,** which does not assume a normal distribution. This test requires a computer package. It is not necessary to discuss the computational procedure except to say that Levene's test is based on the distances of the observations from their sample *medians* rather than their sample *means*. As long as you know how to interpret a p-value, Levene's test is easy to use. Figure 11.14 shows MINITAB's output for the test of homogeneity of variance for the carton-packing data using Levene's test, with the added attraction of confidence intervals for each population standard deviation. Since the confidence intervals overlap and the p-value (.823) is large, we cannot reject the hypothesis of equal population variances. This confirms that the one-factor ANOVA procedure was appropriate for the carton-packing data.

FIGURE 11.14

MINITAB's Equal-Variance Test Cartons

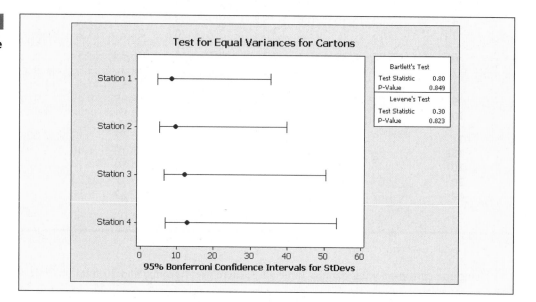

SECTION EXERCISES

connect

Instructions: For each data set, use Hartley's test to test the hypothesis of equal variances, using the 5 percent table of critical values from this section and the largest and smallest sample variances from your previous ANOVA. Alternatively, if you have access to MINITAB or another software package, perform Levene's test for equal group variances, discuss the *p*-value, and interpret the graphical display of confidence intervals for standard deviations.

11.9   Refer to Exercise 11.1. Are the population variances the same for scrap rates (3 plants)? **ScrapRate**

11.10   Refer to Exercise 11.2. Are the population variances the same for examination times (4 physicians)? **Physicians**

11.11   Refer to Exercise 11.3. Are the population variances the same for the GPAs (4 majors)? **GPA1**

11.12   Refer to Exercise 11.4. Are the population variances the same for weekly sales (4 stores)? **Magazines**

*For one-factor ANOVA, we could use the nonparametric *Kruskal-Wallis* test described in Chapter 16.

Mini Case 11.1

Hospital Emergency Arrivals

To plan its staffing schedule, a large urban hospital examined the number of arrivals per day over a 3-month period, as shown in Table 11.6. Each day has 13 observations except Tuesday, which has 14. Data are shown in rows rather than in columns to make a more compact table.

TABLE 11.6	Number of Emergency Arrivals by Day of the Week	 Emergency

Mon	188	175	208	176	179	184	191	194	174	191	198	213	217	
Tue	174	167	165	164	169	164	150	175	178	164	202	175	191	180
Wed	177	169	180	173	182	181	168	165	174	175	174	177	182	
Thu	170	164	190	169	164	170	153	150	156	173	177	183	208	
Fri	177	167	172	185	185	170	170	193	212	171	175	177	209	
Sat	162	184	173	175	144	170	163	157	181	185	199	203	198	
Sun	182	176	183	228	148	178	175	174	188	179	220	207	193	

We perform a one-factor ANOVA to test the model *Arrivals = f(Weekday)*. The single factor (*Weekday*) has 7 treatments. The Excel results, shown in Figure 11.15, indicate that *Weekday* does have a significant effect on *Arrivals,* since the test statistic $F = 3.257$ exceeds the 5 percent critical value $F_{6,85} = 2.207$. The p-value (.006) indicates that a test statistic this large would arise by chance only about 6 times in 1,000 samples if the hypothesis of equal daily means were true.

FIGURE 11.15

One-Factor ANOVA for Emergency Arrivals and Sample Plot

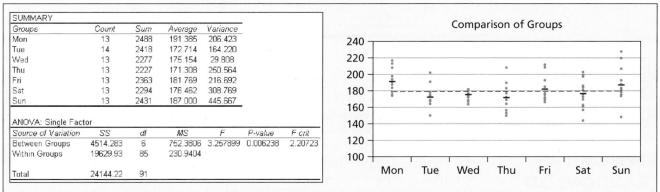

The Tukey multiple comparison test (Figure 11.16) shows that the only pairs of *significantly different* means at $\alpha = .05$ are (*Mon, Tue*) and (*Mon, Thu*). In testing for equal variances, we

FIGURE 11.16	MegaStat's Tukey Test for $\mu_j - \mu_k$

Tukey simultaneous comparison *t*-values (d.f. = 84)

		Thu 171.3	Tue 172.2	Wed 175.2	Sat 176.5	Fri 181.8	Sun 187.0	Mon 191.4
Thu	171.3							
Tue	172.2	0.14						
Wed	175.2	0.64	0.50					
Sat	176.5	0.86	0.72	0.22				
Fri	181.8	1.75	1.61	1.10	0.89			
Sun	187.0	2.62	2.48	1.98	1.76	0.87		
Mon	191.4	3.35	3.21	2.71	2.49	1.61	0.73	

critical values for experimentwise error rate:
        0.05   3.03
        0.01   3.59

get conflicting conclusions, depending on which test we use. Hartley's test gives $H_{calc} = (445.667)/(29.808) = 14.95$, which exceeds the critical value $H_{7,12} = 6.09$ (note that *Wed* has a *very* small variance). But Levene's test for homogeneity of variances (Figure 11.17) has a *p*-value of .221, which at $\alpha = .05$ does not allow us to reject the equal-variance assumption that underlies the ANOVA test. When it is available, we prefer Levene's test because it does not depend on the assumption of normality.

FIGURE 11.17　MINITAB Test for Equal Variances 🖼 Emergency

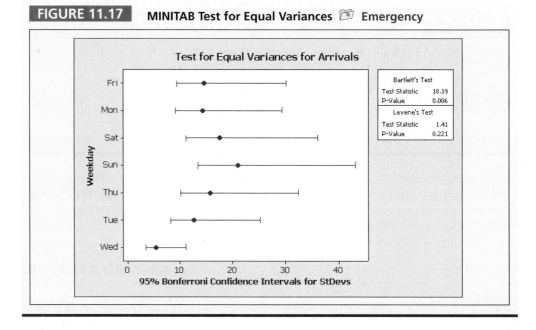

11.5
TWO-FACTOR ANOVA WITHOUT REPLICATION (RANDOMIZED BLOCK MODEL)

Data Format

Suppose that two factors *A* and *B* may affect *Y*. One way to visualize this is to imagine a data matrix with *r* rows and *c* columns. Each row is a level of factor *A*, while each column is a level of factor *B*. Initially, we will consider the case where all levels of both factors occur, and each cell contains only one observation. In this **two-factor ANOVA without replication** (or *non-repeated measures design*) each factor combination is observed exactly once. The mean of *Y* can be computed either across the rows or down the columns, as shown in Table 11.7. The grand mean $\bar{y}$ is the sum of all data values divided by the sample size *rc*.

TABLE 11.7

Format of Two-Factor ANOVA Data Set without Replication

Levels of Factor A	Levels of Factor B				Row Mean
	B_1	B_2	...	B_c	
A_1	y_{11}	y_{12}	...	y_{1c}	$\bar{y}_{1.}$
A_2	y_{21}	y_{22}	...	y_{2c}	$\bar{y}_{2.}$
...	...	...	...	...	...
A_r	y_{r1}	y_{r2}	...	y_{rc}	$\bar{y}_{r.}$
Col Mean	$\bar{y}_{.1}$	$\bar{y}_{.2}$	...	$\bar{y}_{.c}$	$\bar{y}$

For example, *Y* might be computer chip defects per thousand for three different deposition techniques (A_1, A_2, A_3) on four different types of silicon substrate (B_1, B_2, B_3, B_4) yielding a table with $3 \times 4 = 12$ cells. Each factor combination is a *treatment*. With only one observation per treatment, no interaction between the two factors is included.*

*There are not enough degrees of freedom to estimate an interaction unless the experiment is replicated.

Two-Factor ANOVA Model

Expressed in linear form, the two-factor ANOVA model is

$$y_{jk} = \mu + A_j + B_k + \varepsilon_{jk} \tag{11.12}$$

where

y_{jk} = observed data value in row j and column k

μ = common mean for all treatments

A_j = effect of row factor A ($j = 1, 2, \ldots, r$)

B_k = effect of column factor B ($k = 1, 2, \ldots, c$)

ε_{jk} = random error

The random error is assumed to be normally distributed with zero mean and the same variance for all treatments.

Hypotheses to Be Tested

If we are interested only in what happens to the response for the particular levels of the factors that were selected (a *fixed-effects model*) then the hypotheses to be tested are

LO10

Interpret main effects and interaction effects in two-factor ANOVA.

Factor A

H_0: $A_1 = A_2 = \cdots = A_r = 0$ (row means are the same)

H_1: Not all the A_j are equal to zero (row means differ)

Factor B

H_0: $B_1 = B_2 = \cdots = B_c = 0$ (column means are the same)

H_1: Not all the B_k are equal to zero (column means differ)

If we are unable to reject either null hypothesis, all variation in Y is just a random disturbance around the mean μ:

$$y_{jk} = \mu + \varepsilon_{jk} \tag{11.13}$$

Randomized Block Model

LO9

Recognize from data format when two-factor ANOVA is needed.

A special terminology is used when only one factor is of research interest and the other factor is merely used to control for potential confounding influences. In this case, the two-factor ANOVA model with one observation per cell is sometimes called the **randomized block model**. In the randomized block model, it is customary to call the column effects *treatments* (as in one-factor ANOVA to signify that they are the effect of interest) while the row effects are called *blocks*.* For example, a North Dakota agribusiness might want to study the effect of four kinds of fertilizer (F_1, F_2, F_3, F_4) in promoting wheat growth (Y) on three soil types (S_1, S_2, S_3). To control for the effects of soil type, we could define three blocks (rows) each containing one soil type, as shown in Table 11.8. Subjects within each block (soil type) would be randomly assigned to the treatments (fertilizer).

TABLE 11.8

Format of Randomized Block Experiment: Two Factors

Block (Soil Type)	Treatment (Fertilizer)			
	F_1	F_2	F_3	F_4
S_1				
S_2				
S_3				

*In principle, either rows or columns could be the blocking factor, but it is customary to put the blocking factor in rows.

A randomized block model looks like a two-factor ANOVA and is computed exactly like a two-factor ANOVA. However, its interpretation by the researcher may resemble a one-factor ANOVA since only the column effects (treatments) are of interest. The blocks exist only to reduce variance. The effect of the blocks will show up in the hypothesis test, but is of no interest to the researcher as a separate factor. In short, the difference between a randomized block model and a standard two-way ANOVA model lies in the mind of the researcher. Since calculations for a randomized block design are identical to the two-factor ANOVA with one observation per cell, we will not call the row factor a "block" and the column factor a "treatment." Instead, we just call them *factor A* and *factor B*. Interpretation of the factors is not a mathematical issue. If only the column effect is of interest, you may call the column effect the "treatment."

Format of Calculation of Nonreplicated Two-Factor ANOVA

Calculations for the unreplicated two-factor ANOVA may be arranged as in Table 11.9. Degrees of freedom sum to $n - 1$. For a data set with r rows and c columns, notice that $n = rc$. The total sum of squares shown in Table 11.9 has three components:

(11.14)
$$SST = SSA + SSB + SSE$$

where

$SST = $ total sum of squared deviations about the mean

$SSA = $ between rows sum of squares (effect of factor A)

$SSB = $ between columns sum of squares (effect of factor B)

$SSE = $ error sum of squares (residual variation)

LO3

Interpret sums of squares and calculations in an ANOVA table.

SSE is a measure of unexplained variation. If SSE is relatively high, we would fail to reject the null hypothesis that the factor effects do not differ significantly from zero. Conversely, if SSE is relatively small, it is a sign that at least one factor is a relevant predictor of Y, and we would expect either SSA or SSB (or both) to be relatively large. Before doing the F test, each sum of squares must be divided by its degrees of freedom to obtain the *mean square*. Calculations are almost always done by a computer. For details of two-factor calculation methods see *LearningStats* Unit 11. There are case studies for each ANOVA.

TABLE 11.9	**Format of Two-Factor ANOVA with One Observation Per Cell**			
Source of Variation	*Sum of Squares*	*Degrees of Freedom*	*Mean Square*	*F Ratio*
Factor A (row effect)	$SSA = c \sum_{j=1}^{r} (\bar{y}_{j.} - \bar{y})^2$	$r - 1$	$MSA = \dfrac{SSA}{r - 1}$	$F_A = \dfrac{MSA}{MSE}$
Factor B (column effect)	$SSB = r \sum_{k=1}^{c} (\bar{y}_{.k} - \bar{y})^2$	$c - 1$	$MSB = \dfrac{SSB}{c - 1}$	$F_B = \dfrac{MSB}{MSE}$
Error	$SSE = \sum_{j=1}^{r} \sum_{k=1}^{c} (y_{jk} - \bar{y}_{j.} - \bar{y}_{.k} + \bar{y})^2$	$(r - 1)(c - 1)$	$MSE = \dfrac{SSE}{(c - 1)(r - 1)}$	
Total	$SST = \sum_{j=1}^{c} \sum_{k=1}^{r} (y_{jk} - \bar{y})^2$	$rc - 1$		

Drivers expect a car to have good acceleration. A driver is coasting on the highway, with his foot off the accelerator. He steps on the gas to speed up. What is the peak acceleration to a final speed of 80 mph? Tests were carried out on one vehicle at 4 different initial speeds (10, 25, 40, 55 mph) and three different levels of rotation of accelerator pedal (5, 8, 10 degrees). The acceleration results are shown in Table 11.10. Does this sample show that the two experimental factors (pedal rotation, initial speed) are significant predictors of acceleration? Bear in mind that a different sample could yield different results; this is an *unreplicated* experiment.

EXAMPLE

Vehicle Acceleration

TABLE 11.10   **Maximum Acceleration Under Test Conditions** 📁 **Acceleration**

Pedal Rotation	Initial Speed			
	10 mph	**25 mph**	**40 mph**	**55 mph**
5 degrees	0.35	0.19	0.14	0.10
8 degrees	0.37	0.28	0.19	0.19
10 degrees	0.42	0.30	0.29	0.23

Note: Maximum acceleration is measured as a fraction of acceleration due to gravity (32 ft./sec.^{2}).

Step 1: State the Hypotheses

It is helpful to assign short, descriptive variable names to each factor. The general form of the model is

$$Acceleration = f(PedalRotation, InitialSpeed)$$

Stated as a linear model:

$$y_{jk} = \mu + A_j + B_k + \varepsilon_{jk}$$

The hypotheses are

Factor A (PedalRotation)

$H_0: A_1 = A_2 = A_3 = 0$ (pedal rotation has no effect)

$H_1:$ Not all the A_j are equal to zero

Factor B (InitialSpeed)

$H_0: B_1 = B_2 = B_3 = B_4 = 0$ (initial speed has no effect)

$H_1:$ Not all the B_k are equal to zero

Step 2: State the Decision Rule

Each F test may require a different right-tail critical value because the numerator degrees of freedom depend on the number of factor levels, while denominator degrees of freedom (error *SSE*) are the same for all three tests:

Factor A: $df_1 = r - 1 = 3 - 1 = 2$ ($r = 3$ pedal rotations)

Factor B: $df_1 = c - 1 = 4 - 1 = 3$ ($c = 4$ initial speeds)

Error: $df_2 = (r - 1)(c - 1) = (3 - 1)(4 - 1) = 6$

From Appendix F, the 5 percent critical values in a right-tailed test (all ANOVA tests are right-tailed tests) are

$F_{2,6} = 5.14$ for factor A

$F_{3,6} = 4.76$ for factor B

We will reject the null hypothesis (no factor effect) if the F test statistic exceeds the critical value.

LO4

Use Excel or other software for ANOVA calculations.

Step 3: Perform the Calculations

Calculations are done by using Excel's Data Analysis. The menu and results are shown in Figure 11.18. There is a table of means and variances, followed by the ANOVA table.

FIGURE 11.18

Excel's ANOVA: Two-Factor Without Replication 📄 **Acceleration**

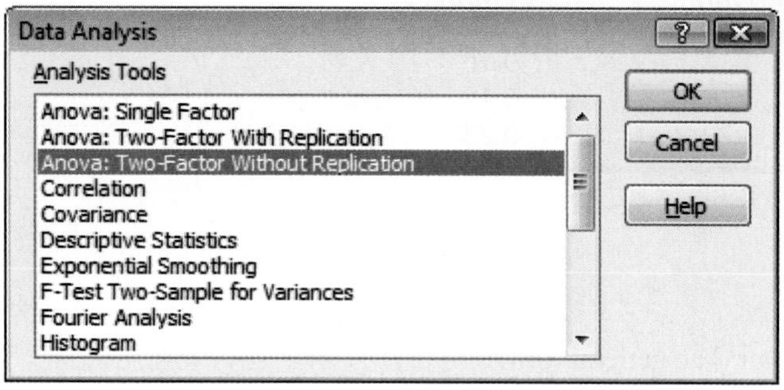

Anova: Two-Factor Without Replication

SUMMARY	Count	Sum	Average	Variance
5 degrees	4	0.78	0.1950	0.0120
8 degrees	4	1.03	0.2575	0.0074
10 degrees	4	1.24	0.3100	0.0063
10 mph	3	1.14	0.3800	0.0013
25 mph	3	0.77	0.2567	0.0034
40 mph	3	0.62	0.2067	0.0058
55 mph	3	0.52	0.1733	0.0044

ANOVA

Source of Variation	SS	df	MS	F	P-value	F crit
Rows	0.026517	2	0.013258	22.83732	0.001565	5.143253
Columns	0.073892	3	0.024631	42.42584	0.000196	4.757063
Error	0.003483	6	0.000581			
Total	0.103892	11				

Data Analysis

Analysis Tools

Anova: Single Factor
Anova: Two-Factor With Replication
Anova: Two-Factor Without Replication
Correlation
Covariance
Descriptive Statistics
Exponential Smoothing
F-Test Two-Sample for Variances
Fourier Analysis
Histogram

OK   Cancel   Help

Step 4: Make the Decision

Since $F_A = 22.84$ (rows) exceeds $F_{2,6} = 5.14$, we see that factor A (pedal rotation) has a significant effect on acceleration. The p-value for pedal rotation is very small ($p = .001565$), which says that the F statistic is not due to chance. Similarly, $F_B = 42.43$ exceeds $F_{3,6} = 4.76$, so we see that factor B (initial speed) also has a significant effect on acceleration. Its tiny p-value (.000196) is unlikely to be a chance result. In short, we conclude that

- Acceleration is significantly affected by pedal rotation ($p = .001565$).

- Acceleration is significantly affected by initial speed ($p = .000196$).

The p-values suggest that initial speed is a more significant predictor than pedal rotation, although both are highly significant. These results conform to your own experience. Maximum acceleration ("pushing you back in your seat") from a low speed or standing stop is greater than when you are driving down the freeway, and of course the harder you press the accelerator pedal, the faster you will accelerate. In fact, you might think of the pedal rotation as a blocking factor since its relationship to acceleration is tautological and of little research interest. Nonetheless, omitting pedal rotation and using a one-factor model would not be a correct model specification. Further, the engineers who did this experiment were actually interested in both effects.

Using MegaStat

Figure 11.19 shows MegaStat's dot plot and ANOVA table. The dot plot shows the column factor (presumed to be the factor of research interest) on the horizontal axis, while the row factor (presumed to be a blocking factor) is only used to define the line graphs. MegaStat rounds its ANOVA results more than Excel and highlights significant p-values. MegaStat does not provide critical F values, which are basically redundant since you have the p-values.

FIGURE 11.19

MegaStat's Two-Factor ANOVA (Randomized Block Model) 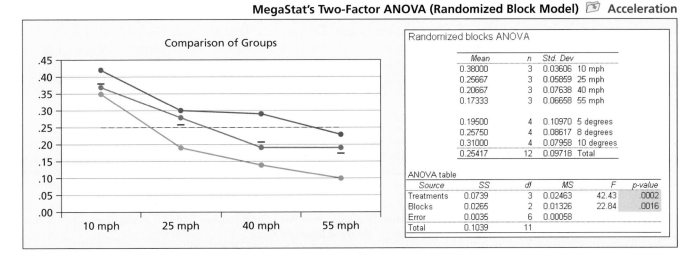 Acceleration

Multiple Comparisons

Figure 11.20 shows MegaStat's Tukey simultaneous comparisons of the treatment pairs using a pooled variance. There are also *p*-values for corresponding independent two-sample *t* tests. However, MegaStat presents Tukey comparisons *only for the column factor* (the row factor is presumed merely to be a blocking factor). For this data, the Tukey tests and independent sample *t* tests agree on all comparisons except for 25 mph versus 40 mph. (The *t* test shows a significant difference between 25 mph and 40 mph at the .05 level of significance.) Both tests show no significant difference in acceleration between 40 mph and 55 mph.

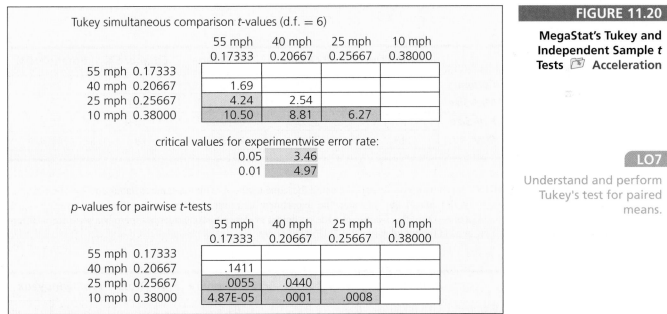

FIGURE 11.20

MegaStat's Tukey and Independent Sample *t* Tests 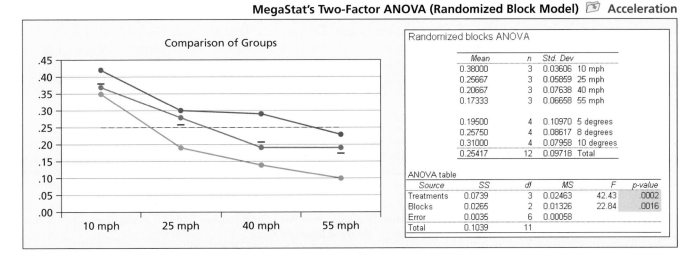 Acceleration

LO7

Understand and perform Tukey's test for paired means.

Limitations of Two-Factor ANOVA without Replication

When replication is impossible or extremely expensive, two-factor ANOVA without replication must suffice. For example, crash-testing of automobiles to estimate collision damage is very costly. However, whenever possible, there is a strong incentive to replicate the experiment to add power to the tests. Would different results have been obtained if the car had been tested not once but several times at each speed? Or if several different cars had been tested? For testing acceleration, there would seem to be no major cost impediment to replication except the time and effort required to take the measurements. Of course, it could be argued that if the measurements of acceleration were careful and precise the first time, replication would be a waste of time. And yet, some random variation is found in any experiment. These are matters to ponder. But two-factor ANOVA *with replication* does offer advantages, as you will see.

SECTION EXERCISES

connect

Instructions: For each data set: (a) State the hypotheses. If you are viewing this data set as a randomized block, which is the blocking factor, and why? (b) Use Excel's Data Analysis (or MegaStat or MINITAB) to perform the two-factor ANOVA without replication, using $\alpha = .05$. (c) State your conclusions about the treatment means. (d) Interpret the p-values carefully. (e) Include a plot of the data for each group if you are using MegaStat, or individual value plots if you are using MINITAB. What do the plots show?

11.13 Concerned about Friday absenteeism, management examined absenteeism rates for the last three Fridays in four assembly plants. Does this sample provide sufficient evidence to conclude that there is a significant difference in treatment means? 🖾 **Absences**

	Plant 1	Plant 2	Plant 3	Plant 4
March 4	19	18	27	22
March 11	22	20	32	27
March 18	20	16	28	26

11.14 Engineers are testing company fleet vehicle fuel economy (miles per gallon) performance by using different types of fuel. One vehicle of each size is tested. Does this sample provide sufficient evidence to conclude that there is a significant difference in treatment means? 🖾 **MPG2**

	87 Octane	89 Octane	91 Octane	Ethanol 5%	Ethanol 10%
Compact	27.2	30.0	30.3	26.8	25.8
Mid-Size	23.0	25.6	28.6	26.6	23.3
Full-Size	21.4	22.5	22.2	18.9	20.8
SUV	18.7	24.1	22.1	18.7	17.4

11.15 Five statistics professors are using the same textbook with the same syllabus and common exams. At the end of the semester, the department committee on instruction looked at average exam scores. Does this sample provide sufficient evidence to conclude that there is a significant difference in treatment means? 🖾 **ExamScores**

	Prof. Argand	Prof. Blague	Prof. Clagmire	Prof. Dross	Prof. Ennuyeux
Exam 1	80.9	72.3	84.9	81.2	70.9
Exam 2	75.5	74.6	78.7	76.5	70.3
Exam 3	79.0	76.0	79.6	75.0	73.7
Final	69.9	78.0	77.8	74.1	73.9

11.16 A beer distributor is comparing quarterly sales of Coors Light (number of six-packs sold) at three convenience stores. Does this sample provide sufficient evidence to conclude that there is a significant difference in treatment means? 🖾 **BeerSales**

	Store 1	Store 2	Store 3
Qtr 1	1,521	1,298	1,708
Qtr 2	1,396	1,492	1,382
Qtr 3	1,178	1,052	1,132
Qtr 4	1,730	1,659	1,851

Mini Case

Automobile Interior Noise Level

Most consumers prefer quieter cars. Table 11.11 shows interior noise level for five vehicles selected from tests performed by a popular magazine. Noise level (in decibels) was measured at idle, at 60 miles per hour, and under hard acceleration from 0 to 60 mph. For reference, 60 dB is a normal conversation, 75 dB is a typical vacuum cleaner, 85 dB is city traffic, 90 dB is a typical hair dryer, and 110 dB is a chain saw. Two questions may be asked: (1) Does noise level vary significantly among the vehicles? (2) Does noise level vary significantly with speed? If you wish to think of this as a randomized block experiment, the column variable (*vehicle type*) is the research question, while the row variable (*speed*) is the blocking factor.

TABLE 11.11 **Interior Noise Levels in Five Randomly Selected Vehicles**
NoiseLevel

Speed	Chrysler 300M	BMW 528i Sport Wagon	Ford Explorer Sport Trac	Chevy Malibu LS	Subaru Outback H6-3.0
Idle	41	45	44	45	46
60 mph	65	67	66	66	76
0–60 mph	76	72	76	77	64

Source: *Popular Science* 254–258 (selected issues).

Note: Data are a random sample to be used for educational purposes only and should not be viewed as a guide to vehicle performance.

The general form of the model is *NoiseLevel = f(CarSpeed, CarType)*. Degrees of freedom for *CarSpeed* (rows) will be $r - 1 = 3 - 1 = 2$, while degrees of freedom for *CarType* (columns) will be $c - 1 = 5 - 1 = 4$. Denominator degrees of freedom will be the same for both factors since *SSE* has degrees of freedom $(r - 1)(c - 1) = (3 - 1)(5 - 1) = 8$. Excel's ANOVA results and MegaStat's dot plot are shown in Figure 11.21.

FIGURE 11.21

Results of Two-Factor ANOVA Without Replication for Car Noise

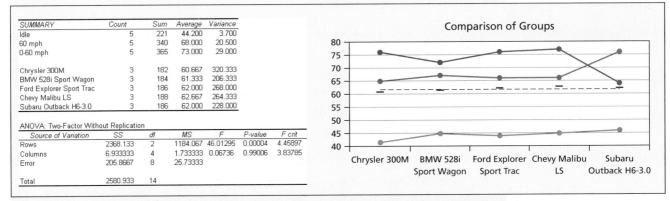

Since $F = 46.01$ exceeds $F_{2,8} = 4.46$, we see that *CarSpeed* (row factor) does have a highly significant effect on noise level. Its very small *p*-value ($p = .00004$) is unlikely to be a chance result. But *CarType* (column factor) has no significant effect on noise level since $F = 0.07$ does not exceed $F_{4,8} = 3.84$. The *p*-value for *CarType* ($p = .99006$) says that its F statistic could easily have arisen by chance. In short, we conclude that

- Interior noise *is* significantly affected by car speed ($p = .00004$).
- Interior noise *is not* significantly affected by car type ($p = .9901$).

We do not bother with Tukey multiple comparisons of means since we know that car type has no significant effect on noise level (the research hypothesis) and the effect of initial speed is of less research interest (a blocking factor).

11.6

TWO-FACTOR ANOVA WITH REPLICATION (FULL FACTORIAL MODEL)

What Does Replication Accomplish?

In a two-factor model, suppose that each factor combination is observed *m* times. With multiple observations within each cell, we can do more detailed statistical tests. With an equal number of observations in each cell (*balanced data*), we have a two-factor ANOVA model *with* **replication**. Replication allows us to test not only the factors' **main effects** but also an **interaction effect**. This model is often called the **full factorial** model. In linear model format it may be written

(11.15)
$$y_{ijk} = \mu + A_j + B_k + AB_{jk} + \varepsilon_{ijk}$$

where

LO1

Use basic ANOVA terminology correctly.

y_{ijk} = observation *i* for row *j* and column *k* ($i = 1, 2, \ldots, m$)

μ = common mean for all treatments

A_j = effect attributed to factor *A* in row *j* ($j = 1, 2, \ldots, r$)

B_k = effect attributed to factor *B* in column *k* ($k = 1, 2, \ldots, c$)

AB_{jk} = effect attributed to interaction between factors *A* and *B*

ε_{ijk} = random error (normally distributed, zero mean, same variance for all treatments)

Interaction effects can be important. For example, an agribusiness researcher might postulate that corn yield is related to seed type (*A*), soil type (*B*), interaction between seed type and soil type (*AB*), or all three. In the absence of any factor effects, all variation about the mean μ is purely random.

Format of Hypotheses

For a fixed-effects ANOVA model, the hypotheses that could be tested in the two-factor ANOVA model with replicated observations are

LO10

Interpret main effects and interaction effects in two-factor ANOVA.

Factor A: Row Effect

H_0: $A_1 = A_2 = \cdots = A_r = 0$ (row means are the same)

H_1: Not all the A_j are equal to zero (row means differ)

Factor B: Column Effect

H_0: $B_1 = B_2 = \cdots = B_c = 0$ (column means are the same)

H_1: Not all the B_k are equal to zero (column means differ)

Interaction Effect

H_0: All the AB_{jk} are equal to zero (there is no interaction effect)

H_1: Not all AB_{jk} are equal to zero (there is an interaction effect)

If none of the proposed factors has anything to do with Y, then the model collapses to

$$y_{ijk} = \mu + \varepsilon_{ijk} \qquad\qquad \textbf{(11.16)}$$

Format of Data

Table 11.12 shows the format of a data set with two factors and a balanced (equal) number of observations per treatment (each row/column intersection is a treatment). To avoid needless subscripts, the m observations in each treatment are represented simply as yyy. Except for the replication within cells, the format is the same as the unreplicated two-factor ANOVA.

	Levels of Factor B				
Levels of Factor A	B_1	B_2	$\ldots$	B_c	**Row Mean**
A_1	yyy yyy $\ldots$ yyy	yyy yyy $\ldots$ yyy	$\ldots$ $\ldots$ $\ldots$ $\ldots$	yyy yyy $\ldots$ yyy	$\bar{y}_{1.}$
A_2	yyy yyy $\ldots$ yyy	yyy yyy $\ldots$ yyy	$\ldots$ $\ldots$ $\ldots$ $\ldots$	yyy yyy $\ldots$ yyy	$\bar{y}_{2.}$
$\ldots$	$\ldots$	$\ldots$	$\ldots$	$\ldots$	$\ldots$
A_r	yyy yyy $\ldots$ yyy	yyy yyy $\ldots$ yyy	$\ldots$ $\ldots$ $\ldots$ $\ldots$	yyy yyy $\ldots$ yyy	$\bar{y}_{r.}$
Col Mean	$\bar{y}_{.1}$	$\bar{y}_{.2}$	$\ldots$	$\bar{y}_{.c}$	$\bar{y}$

TABLE 11.12

Data Format of Replicated Two-Factor ANOVA

LO9

Recognize from data format when two-factor ANOVA is needed.

Sources of Variation

There are now three F tests that could be performed: one for each main effect (factors A and B) and a third F test for interaction. The total sum of squares is partitioned into four components:

$$SST = SSA + SSB + SSI + SSE \qquad\qquad \textbf{(11.17)}$$

where

> $SST =$ total sum of squared deviations about the mean
>
> $SSA =$ between rows sum of squares (effect of factor A)
>
> $SSB =$ between columns sum of squares (effect of factor B)
>
> $SSI =$ interaction sum of squares (effect of AB)
>
> $SSE =$ error sum of squares (residual variation)

For an experiment with r rows, c columns, and m replications per treatment, the sums of squares and ANOVA calculations may be presented in a table, shown in Table 11.13.

If SSE is relatively high, we expect that we would fail to reject H_0 for the various hypotheses. Conversely, if SSE is relatively small, it is likely that at least one of the factors (row effect, column effect, or interaction) is a relevant predictor of Y. Before doing the F test, each sum of squares must be divided by its degrees of freedom to obtain its *mean square*. Degrees of freedom sum to $n - 1$ (note that $n = rcm$).

TABLE 11.13	Two-Factor ANOVA with Replication			
Source of Variation	**Sum of Squares**	**Degrees of Freedom**	**Mean Square**	**F Ratio**
Factor A (row effect)	$SSA = cm \sum_{j=1}^{r} (\bar{y}_{j.} - \bar{y})^2$	$r - 1$	$MSA = \dfrac{SSA}{r-1}$	$F_A = \dfrac{MSA}{MSE}$
Factor B (column effect)	$SSB = rm \sum_{k=1}^{c} (\bar{y}_{.k} - \bar{y})^2$	$c - 1$	$MSB = \dfrac{SSB}{c-1}$	$F_B = \dfrac{MSB}{MSE}$
Interaction $(A \times B)$	$SSI = m \sum_{j=1}^{r} \sum_{k=1}^{c} (\bar{y}_{jk} - \bar{y}_{j.} - \bar{y}_{.k} + \bar{y})^2$	$(r-1)(c-1)$	$MSI = \dfrac{SSI}{(r-1)(c-1)}$	$F_I = \dfrac{MSI}{MSE}$
Error	$SSE = \sum_{i=1}^{m} \sum_{j=1}^{r} \sum_{k=1}^{c} (y_{ijk} - \bar{y}_{jk})^2$	$rc(m-1)$	$MSE = \dfrac{SSE}{rc(m-1)}$	
Total	$SST = \sum_{i=1}^{m} \sum_{j=1}^{r} \sum_{k=1}^{c} (y_{ijk} - \bar{y})^2$	$rcm - 1$		

EXAMPLE

Delivery Time

A health maintenance organization orders weekly medical supplies for its four clinics from five different suppliers. Delivery times (in days) for 4 recent weeks are shown in Table 11.14.

LO3

Interpret sums of squares and calculations in an ANOVA table.

TABLE 11.14	Delivery Times (in days) 🖼 Deliveries				
	Supplier 1	**Supplier 2**	**Supplier 3**	**Supplier 4**	**Supplier 5**
Clinic A	8	14	10	8	17
	8	9	15	7	12
	10	14	10	13	9
	13	11	7	10	10
Clinic B	13	9	12	6	15
	14	9	10	10	12
	12	7	10	12	12
	13	8	11	8	10
Clinic C	11	8	12	10	14
	10	9	10	11	13
	12	11	13	7	10
	14	12	10	10	12
Clinic D	7	8	7	8	14
	10	13	5	5	13
	10	9	6	11	8
	13	12	5	4	11

Using short variable names, the two-factor ANOVA model has the general form

$$DeliveryTime = f(Clinic, Supplier, Clinic \times Supplier)$$

The effects are assumed additive. The linear model is

$$y_{ijk} = \mu + A_j + B_k + AB_{jk} + \varepsilon_{ijk}$$

Step 1: State the Hypotheses
The hypotheses are

Factor *A*: Row Effect (*Clinic*)

H_0: $A_1 = A_2 = \cdots = A_r = 0$ (clinic means are the same)
H_1: Not all the A_j are equal to zero (clinic means differ)

Factor *B*: Column Effect (*Supplier*)

H_0: $B_1 = B_2 = \cdots = B_c = 0$ (supplier means are the same)
H_1: Not all the B_k are equal to zero (supplier means differ)

Interaction Effect (*Clinic* × *Supplier*)

H_0: All the AB_{jk} are equal to zero (there is no interaction effect)
H_1: Not all AB_{jk} are equal to zero (there is an interaction effect)

LO10

Interpret main effects and interaction effects in two-factor ANOVA.

Step 2: State the Decision Rule
Each *F* test may require a different right-tail critical value because the numerator degrees of freedom depend on the number of factor levels, while denominator degrees of freedom (error *SSE*) are the same for all three tests:

Factor A: $df_1 = r - 1 = 4 - 1 = 3$ ($r = 4$ clinics)
Factor B: $df_1 = c - 1 = 5 - 1 = 4$ ($c = 5$ suppliers)
Interaction (AB): $df_1 = (r - 1)(c - 1) = (4 - 1)(5 - 1) = 12$
Error $df_2 = rc(m - 1) = 4 \times 5 \times (4 - 1) = 60$

Excel provides the right-tail *F* critical values for $\alpha = .05$, which we can verify using Appendix F:

$F_{3,60} = 2.76$ for Factor *A*
$F_{4,60} = 2.53$ for Factor *B*
$F_{12,60} = 1.92$ for Factor *AB*

We reject the null hypothesis if an *F* test statistic exceeds its critical value.

LO5

Use a table or Excel to find critical values for the *F* distribution.

Step 3: Perform the Calculations
Excel provides tables of row and column sums and means (not shown here because they are lengthy). The ANOVA table in Figure 11.22 summarizes the partitioning of variation into its component sums of squares, degrees of freedom, mean squares, *F* test statistics, *p*-values, and critical *F*-values for $\alpha = .05$.

FIGURE 11.22

Excel's Two-Factor ANOVA with Replication **Deliveries**

Data Analysis

Analysis Tools

- Anova: Single Factor
- Anova: Two-Factor With Replication
- Anova: Two-Factor Without Replication
- Correlation
- Covariance
- Descriptive Statistics
- Exponential Smoothing
- F-Test Two-Sample for Variances
- Fourier Analysis
- Histogram

OK
Cancel
Help

ANOVA

Source of Variation	SS	df	MS	F	P-value	F crit
Sample	51.350	3	17.1167	3.434783	0.022424	2.758078
Columns	104.425	4	26.1063	5.238712	0.001097	2.525215
Interaction	102.775	12	8.5646	1.718645	0.085176	1.917396
Within	299.000	60	4.9833			
Total	557.550	79				

LO4

Use Excel or other software for ANOVA calculations.

Step 4: Make the Decision
For the row variable (*Clinic*) the test statistic $F = 3.435$ and its *p*-value ($p = .0224$) lead us to conclude that the mean delivery times among clinics are not the same at $\alpha = .05$. For the

column variable (*Supplier*) the test statistic $F = 5.239$ and its *p*-value ($p = .0011$) lead us to conclude that the mean delivery times from suppliers are not the same at $\alpha = .05$. For the interaction effect, the test statistic $F = 1.719$ and its *p*-value ($p = .0852$) lack significance at $\alpha = .05$. The *p*-values permit a more flexible interpretation since α need not be specified in advance. In summary:

Variable	p-Value	Interpretation
Clinic	.0224	Clinic means differ (significant at $\alpha = .05$)
Supplier	.0011	Supplier means differ (significant at $\alpha = .01$)
Clinic×Supplier	.0852	Weak interaction effect (significant at $\alpha = .10$)

Using MegaStat

MegaStat's two-factor ANOVA results, shown in Figure 11.23, are similar to Excel's except that the table of treatment means is more compact, the results are rounded, and significant *p*-values are highlighted (bright yellow for $\alpha = .01$, light green for $\alpha = .05$).

FIGURE 11.23

MegaStat's Two-Factor ANOVA 🖭 Deliveries

Two factor ANOVA

Means: Factor 2

		Supplier 1	Supplier 2	Supplier 3	Supplier 4	Supplier 5	
	Clinic A	9.8	12.0	10.5	9.5	12.0	10.8
Factor 1	Clinic B	13.0	8.3	10.8	9.0	12.3	10.7
	Clinic C	11.8	10.0	11.3	9.5	12.3	11.0
	Clinic D	10.0	10.5	5.8	7.0	11.5	9.0
		11.1	10.2	9.6	8.8	12.0	10.3

ANOVA table

Source	SS	df	MS	F	p-value
Factor 1	51.35	3	17.117	3.43	.0224
Factor 2	104.43	4	26.106	5.24	.0011
Interaction	102.78	12	8.565	1.72	.0852
Error	299.00	60	4.983		
Total	557.56	79			

Interaction Effect

The statistical test for interaction is just like any other *F* test. But you might still wonder, What *is* an interaction, anyway? You may be familiar with the idea of drug interaction. If you consume a few ounces of vodka, it has an effect on you. If you take an allergy pill, it has an effect on you. But if you combine the two, the effect may be different (and possibly dangerous) compared with using either drug by itself. That is why many medications carry a warning like "Avoid alcohol while using this medication."

To visualize an interaction, we plot the treatment means for one factor against the levels of the other factor. Within each factor level, we connect the means. In the absence of an interaction, the lines will be roughly parallel or will tend to move in the same direction at the same time. If there is a strong interaction, the lines will have differing slopes and will tend to cross one another.

Figure 11.24 illustrates several possible situations, using a hypothetical two-factor ANOVA model in which factor *A* has three levels and factor *B* has two levels. For the delivery time example, a significant *interaction effect* would mean that suppliers have different mean delivery times for different clinics. However, Figure 11.25 shows that, while the interaction plot lines do cross, there is no consistent pattern, and the lines tend to be parallel more than crossing. The visual indications of interaction are, therefore, weak for the delivery time data. This conclusion is consistent with the interaction *p*-value ($p = .085$) for the *F* test of $A \times B$.

FIGURE 11.24

Possible Interaction Patterns

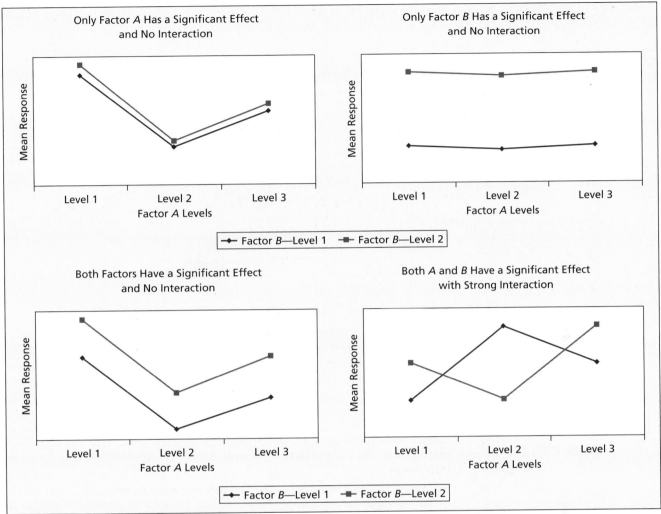

FIGURE 11.25

Interaction Plots from MegaStat   Deliveries

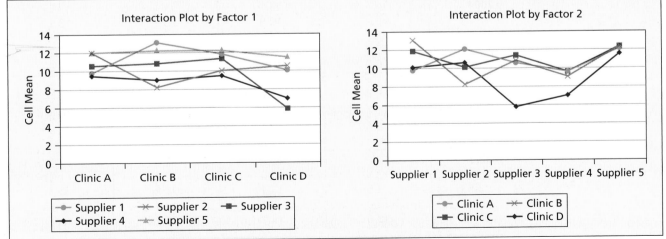

LO7

Understand and perform Tukey's test for paired means.

Tukey Tests of Pairs of Means

MegaStat's Tukey comparisons, shown in Figure 11.26, reveal significant differences at $\alpha = .05$ between clinics *C*, *D* and between suppliers (1, 4) and (3, 5). At $\alpha = .01$ there is also a significant difference in means between one pair of suppliers (4, 5).

FIGURE 11.26

MegaStat Table of Tukey Comparisons Deliveries

Tukey simultaneous comparison *t*-values (d.f. = 60)

		Clinic D	Clinic B	Clinic A	Clinic C
		9.0	10.7	10.8	11.0
Clinic D	9.0				
Clinic B	10.7	2.41			
Clinic A	10.8	2.55	0.14		
Clinic C	11.0	2.83	0.42	0.28	

critical values for experimentwise error rate:

0.05	2.64
0.01	3.25

Tukey simultaneous comparison *t*-values (d.f. = 60)

		Supplier 4	Supplier 3	Supplier 2	Supplier 1	Supplier 5
		8.8	9.6	10.2	11.1	12.0
Supplier 4	8.8					
Supplier 3	9.6	1.03				
Supplier 2	10.2	1.82	0.79			
Supplier 1	11.1	3.01	1.98	1.19		
Supplier 5	12.0	4.12	3.09	2.30	1.11	

critical values for experimentwise error rate:

0.05	2.81
0.01	3.41

Significance versus Importance

MegaStat's table of means (Figure 11.23) allows us to explore these differences further and to assess the question of *importance* as well as *significance*. The largest differences in means between clinics or suppliers are about 2 days. Such a small difference might be unimportant most of the time. However, if their inventory is low, a 2-day difference could be important.

SECTION EXERCISES

connect

Instructions: For each data set: (a) State the hypotheses. (b) Use Excel's Data Analysis (or MegaStat or MINITAB) to perform the two-factor ANOVA with replication, using $\alpha = .05$. (c) State your conclusions about the main effects and interaction effects. (d) Interpret the *p*-values carefully. (e) Create interaction plots and interpret them.

11.17 A small independent stock broker has created four sector portfolios for her clients. Each portfolio always has five stocks that may change from year to year. The volatility (coefficient of variation) of each stock is recorded for each year. Are the main effects significant? Is there an interaction? **Volatility**

	Stock Portfolio Type			
Year	*Health*	*Energy*	*Retail*	*Leisure*
2004	14.5	23.0	19.4	17.6
	18.4	19.9	20.7	18.1
	13.7	24.5	18.5	16.1
	15.9	24.2	15.5	23.2
	16.2	19.4	17.7	17.6
2005	21.6	22.1	21.4	25.5
	25.6	31.6	26.5	24.1
	21.4	22.4	21.5	25.9
	26.6	31.3	22.8	25.5
	19.0	32.5	27.4	26.3
2006	12.6	12.8	22.0	12.9
	13.5	14.4	17.1	11.1
	13.5	13.1	24.8	4.9
	13.0	8.1	13.4	13.3
	13.6	14.7	22.2	12.7

11.18 Oxnard Petro, Ltd., has three interdisciplinary project development teams that function on an on-going basis. Team members rotate from time to time. Every 4 months (three times a year) each department head rates the performance of each project team (using a 0 to 100 scale, where 100 is the best rating). Are the main effects significant? Is there an interaction? 📁 **Ratings**

Year	Marketing	Engineering	Finance
2004	90	69	96
	84	72	86
	80	78	86
2005	72	73	89
	83	77	87
	82	81	93
2006	92	84	91
	87	75	85
	87	80	78

11.19 A market research firm is testing consumer reaction to a new shampoo on four age groups in four regions. There are five consumers in each test panel. Each consumer completes a 10-question product satisfaction instrument with a 5-point scale (5 is the highest rating) and the average score is recorded. Are the main effects significant? Is there an interaction? 📁 **Satisfaction**

	Northeast	Southeast	Midwest	West
Youth (under 18)	3.9	3.9	3.6	3.9
	4.0	4.2	3.9	4.4
	3.7	4.4	3.9	4.0
	4.1	4.1	3.7	4.1
	4.3	4.0	3.3	3.9
College (18–25)	4.0	3.8	3.6	3.8
	4.0	3.7	4.1	3.8
	3.7	3.7	3.8	3.6
	3.8	3.6	3.9	3.6
	3.8	3.7	4.0	4.1
Adult (26–64)	3.2	3.5	3.5	3.8
	3.8	3.3	3.8	3.6
	3.7	3.4	3.8	3.4
	3.4	3.5	4.0	3.7
	3.4	3.4	3.7	3.1
Senior (65+)	3.4	3.6	3.3	3.4
	2.9	3.4	3.3	3.2
	3.6	3.6	3.1	3.5
	3.7	3.6	3.1	3.3
	3.5	3.4	3.1	3.4

11.20 Oxnard Petro, Ltd., has three suppliers of catalysts. Orders are placed with each supplier every 15 working days, or about once every 3 weeks. The delivery time (days) is recorded for each order over 1 year. Are the main effects significant? Is there an interaction? 📁 **Deliveries2**

	Supplier 1	Supplier 2	Supplier 3
Qtr 1	12 15 11 11	10 13 11 9	16 13 14 14
Qtr 2	13 11 13 12	10 10 13 11	14 11 12 12
Qtr 3	12 8 8 13	11 9 8 6	13 8 13 6
Qtr 4	8 10 13 11	8 10 10 10	11 11 10 11

Mini Case   11.3

Turbine Engine Thrust

Engineers testing turbofan aircraft engines wanted to know if oil pressure and turbine temperature are related to engine thrust (pounds). They chose four levels for each factor and observed each combination five times, using the two-factor replicated ANOVA model $Thrust = f(OilPres, TurbTemp, OilPres \times TurbTemp)$. The test data are shown in Table 11.15.

TABLE 11.15   Turbofan Engine Thrust Test Results 🗁 Turbines

	Turbine Temperature			
Oil Pressure	**T1**	**T2**	**T3**	**T4**
P1	1,945.0 1,933.0 1,942.4 1,948.0 1,930.0	1,942.3 1,931.7 1,946.0 1,959.0 1,939.9	1,934.2 1,930.0 1,944.0 1,941.0 1,942.0	1,916.7 1,943.0 1,948.8 1,928.0 1,946.0
P2	1,939.4 1,952.8 1,940.0 1,948.0 1,925.0	1,922.0 1,936.8 1,928.0 1,930.7 1,939.0	1,950.6 1,947.9 1,950.0 1,922.0 1,918.0	1,929.6 1,930.0 1,934.0 1,923.0 1,914.0
P3	1,932.0 1,955.0 1,949.7 1,933.0 1,936.5	1,939.0 1,932.0 1,933.1 1,952.0 1,943.0	1,952.0 1,963.0 1,923.0 1,965.0 1,944.0	1,960.4 1,946.0 1,931.0 1,949.0 1,906.0
P4	1,960.2 1,909.3 1,950.0 1,920.0 1,964.9	1,937.0 1,941.0 1,928.2 1,938.9 1,919.0	1,940.0 1,984.0 1,971.0 1,930.0 1,944.0	1,924.0 1,906.0 1,925.8 1,923.0 1,916.7

Source: Research project by three engineering students enrolled in an MBA program. Data are disguised.

The ANOVA results in Figure 11.27 indicate that only turbine temperature is significantly related to thrust. The table of means suggests that, because mean thrust varies only over a tiny range, the effect may not be very important. The lack of interaction is revealed by the nearly parallel **interaction plots**. Levene's test for equal variances (not shown) shows a p-value of $p = .42$ indicating that variances may be assumed equal, as is desirable for an ANOVA test.

FIGURE 11.27 **MegaStat Two-Factor ANOVA Results**

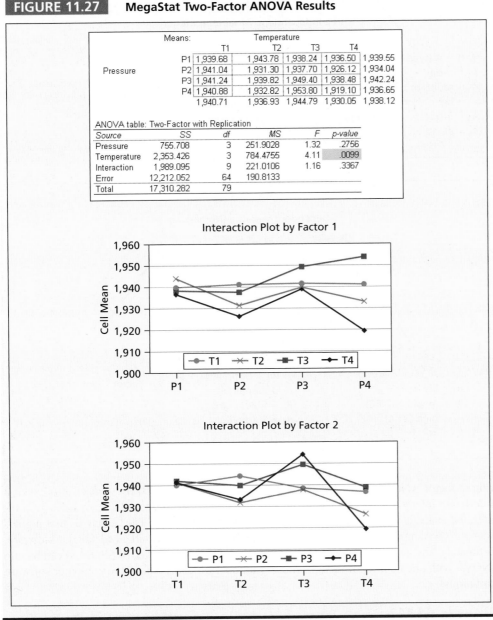

Means:		T1	Temperature T2	T3	T4	
Pressure	P1	1,939.68	1,943.78	1,938.24	1,936.50	1,939.55
	P2	1,941.04	1,931.30	1,937.70	1,926.12	1,934.04
	P3	1,941.24	1,939.82	1,949.40	1,938.48	1,942.24
	P4	1,940.88	1,932.82	1,953.80	1,919.10	1,936.65
		1,940.71	1,936.93	1,944.79	1,930.05	1,938.12

ANOVA table: Two-Factor with Replication

Source	SS	df	MS	F	p-value
Pressure	755.708	3	251.9028	1.32	.2756
Temperature	2,353.426	3	784.4755	4.11	.0099
Interaction	1,989.095	9	221.0106	1.16	.3367
Error	12,212.052	64	190.8133		
Total	17,310.282	79			

Higher-Order ANOVA Models

Why limit ourselves to two factors? Although a three-factor data set cannot be shown in a two-dimensional table, the idea of a three-factor ANOVA is not difficult to grasp. Consider the hospital LOS and paint viscosity problems introduced at the beginning of this chapter. Figure 11.28 adds a third factor (gender) to the hospital model and Figure 11.29 adds a third factor (solvent ratio) to the paint viscosity model.

FIGURE 11.28

Three-Factor ANOVA Model for Hospital Length of Stay

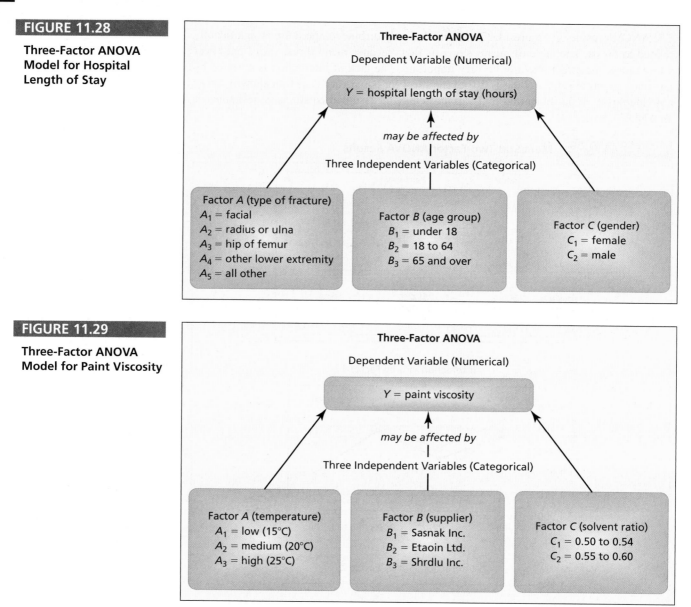

Three-Factor ANOVA

Dependent Variable (Numerical)

Y = hospital length of stay (hours)

may be affected by

Three Independent Variables (Categorical)

Factor A (type of fracture)
A_1 = facial
A_2 = radius or ulna
A_3 = hip of femur
A_4 = other lower extremity
A_5 = all other

Factor B (age group)
B_1 = under 18
B_2 = 18 to 64
B_3 = 65 and over

Factor C (gender)
C_1 = female
C_2 = male

FIGURE 11.29

Three-Factor ANOVA Model for Paint Viscosity

Three-Factor ANOVA

Dependent Variable (Numerical)

Y = paint viscosity

may be affected by

Three Independent Variables (Categorical)

Factor A (temperature)
A_1 = low (15°C)
A_2 = medium (20°C)
A_3 = high (25°C)

Factor B (supplier)
B_1 = Sasnak Inc.
B_2 = Etaoin Ltd.
B_3 = Shrdlu Inc.

Factor C (solvent ratio)
C_1 = 0.50 to 0.54
C_2 = 0.55 to 0.60

A three-factor ANOVA allows more two-factor interactions ($A \times B$, $A \times C$, $B \times C$) and even a three-factor interaction ($A \times B \times C$). However, since the computations are already done by computer, the analysis would be no harder than a two-factor ANOVA. The "catch" is that higher-order ANOVA models are beyond Excel's capabilities, so you will need fancier software. Fortunately, any general-purpose statistical package (e.g., MINITAB, SPSS, SAS) can handle ANOVA with *any* number of factors with *any* number of levels (subject to computer software limitations).

LO11

Recognize the need for experimental design and GLM (optional).

What Is GLM?

The **general linear model** (GLM) is a versatile tool for estimating large and complex ANOVA models. Besides allowing more than two factors, GLM permits unbalanced data (unequal sample size within treatments) and any desired subset of interactions among factors (including three-way interactions or higher) as long as you have enough observations (i.e., enough degrees of freedom) to compute the effects. GLM can also provide predictions and identify unusual observations. GLM does not require equal variances, although care must be taken to avoid sparse or empty cells in the data matrix. Data are expected to be in stacked format (one column for Y and one column for each factor A, B, C, etc.). The output of GLM is easily understood by anyone who is familiar with ANOVA, as you can see in Mini Case 11.4.

Mini Case 11.4

Hospital Maternity Stay 🖅 **MaternityLOS**

The data set consists of 4,409 maternity hospital visits whose DRG (diagnostic-related group) code is 373 (simple delivery without complicating diagnoses). The dependent variable of interest is the length of stay (LOS) in the hospital. The model contains one discrete numerical factor and two categorical factors: the number of surgical stops (*NumStops*), the CCS diagnostic code (*CCSDiag*), and the CCS procedure code (*CCSProc*). CCS codes are a medical classification scheme developed by the American Hospital Research Council to help hospitals and researchers organize medical information. The proposed model has three factors and one interaction:

$$LOS = f(NumStops, CCSDiag, CCSProc, CCSDiag \times CCSProc)$$

Before starting the GLM analysis, a frequency tabulation was prepared for each factor. The tabulation (not shown) revealed that some factor levels were observed too rarely to be useful. Cross-tabulations (not shown) also revealed that some treatments would be empty or very sparse. Based on this preliminary data screening, the factors were recoded to avoid GLM estimation problems. *NumStops* was recoded as a binary variable (2 if there were 1 or 2 stops, 3 if there were 3 or more stops). *CCSDiag* codes with a frequency less than 100 were recoded as 999. Patients whose *CCSProc* code occurred less than 10 times (19 patients) were deleted from the sample, leaving a sample of 4,390 patients.

MINITAB's menu and GLM results are shown in Figure 11.30. The first thing shown is the number of levels for each factor and the discrete values of each factor. Frequencies of the factor values are not shown, but can be obtained from MINITAB's Tables command.

FIGURE 11.30   **MINITAB GLM Menu and Results**

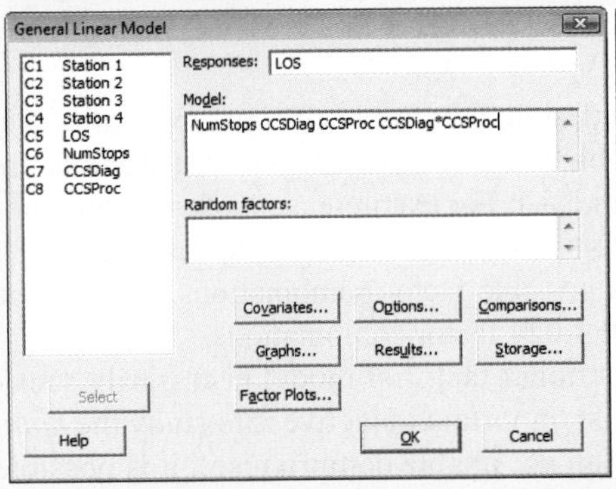

General Linear Model: LOS versus NumStops, CCSDiag, CCSProc

Factor	Type	Levels	Values
NumStops	fixed	2	2, 3
CCSDiag	fixed	9	181, 184, 185, 190, 191, 193, 195, 196, 999
CCSProc	fixed	6	133, 135, 136, 137, 139, 140

Analysis of Variance for LOS, using Adjusted SS for Tests

Source	DF	Seq SS	Adj SS	Adj MS	F	P
NumStops	1	1340	7385	7385	3.25	0.072
CCSDiag	8	446299	94498	11812	5.19	0.000
CCSProc	5	37139	45061	9012	3.96	0.001
CCSDiag*CCSProc	40	194618	194618	4865	2.14	0.000
Error	4335	9865440	9865440	2276		
Total	4389	10544837				

S = 47.7050   R-Sq = 6.44%   R-Sq(adj) = 5.28%

The p-values from the ANOVA table suggest that *NumStops* is significant at $\alpha = .10$ ($p = .072$) while the other two main effects *CCSDiag* and *CCSProc* ($p = .000$ and $p = .001$) are highly significant (such small p-values would arise less than once in 1,000 samples if there were no relationship). The interaction $CCSDiag \times CCSProc$ is also highly significant ($p = .000$). Because the sample size is large, even slight effects could be *significant*, so further analysis may be needed to see if the effects are also *important*.

What Is Experimental Design?

Experimental design refers to the number of factors under investigation, the number of levels assigned to each factor, the way factor levels are defined, and the way observations are obtained. *Fully crossed* or *full factorial* designs include all possible combinations of factor

LO11

Recognize the need for experimental design and GLM (optional).

levels. **Fractional factorial designs**, for reasons of economy, limit data collection to a subset of possible factor combinations. If all levels of one factor are fully contained in another, the design is **nested** or **hierarchical**. **Balanced designs** are characterized by an equal number of observations for each factor combination. In a *fixed-effects model* the levels of each factor are predetermined, which implies that our inferences are valid only for the specified factor levels. For example, if a firm has only three paint suppliers (S_1, S_2, S_3), these would be our factor levels. In a *random effects model* the factor levels would be chosen randomly from a population of potential factor levels. For example, if a firm has 20 paint suppliers (S_1 through S_{20}) but we only want to study three of them, we might choose three at random (say S_7, S_{11}, and S_{18}) from the 6,840 possible ways to choose 3 items from 20. Fixed effects are by far the most common models used in business analysis, where randomization and controlled experiments are not practical.

Experimental design is a specialized topic that goes far beyond this textbook. However, you may need to interact professionally with engineers or quality improvement teams that are working on product design, reliability, and product performance. It is therefore helpful to have a general idea of what experimental design is all about and to learn some of the basic terminology. If you become more deeply involved, you can ask your employer to send you to a 3-day training class in experimental design to boost your skills.

2^k Models

When there are k factors, each with two levels, we have a *2^k factorial design*. Reducing a factor to two levels is a useful simplification that reduces the data requirements in a replicated experiment, because the data matrix will have fewer cells. Even a continuous factor (e.g., *Pressure*) can be "binarized" into roughly equal groups (*Low, High*) by cutting the data array at the median. The 2^k design is especially useful when the number of factors is very large. In automotive engineering, for example, it is not uncommon to study more than a dozen factors that are predictive of exhaust emissions. Even when each factor is limited to only two levels, full factorial 2^k experiments with replication can require substantial data-collection effort.

Fractional Factorial Designs

Unlike a full factorial design, a *fractional factorial* design, for reasons of economy, limits data collection to a subset of the possible factor combinations. Fractional factorial designs are important in real-life situations where many factors exist. For example, suppose that automobile combustion engineers are investigating 10 factors, each with two levels, to determine their effect on emissions. This would yield $2^{10} = 1,024$ possible factor combinations. It would be impractical and uneconomical to gather data for all 1,024 factor combinations.

By excluding some factor combinations, a fractional factorial model necessarily sacrifices some of the interaction effects. But if the most important objective is to study the *main effects* (which is frequently the case, or is at least an acceptable compromise), it is possible to get by with a much smaller number of observations. It often is possible to estimate some, though not all, interaction effects in a fractional factorial experiment. Templates are published to guide experimenters in choosing the correct design and sample size for the desired number of factors (see Related Reading) to make efficient use of available data.

Nested or Hierarchical Design

If all levels of one factor are fully contained within another, the design is *nested* or *hierarchical*. Using most computer packages, nested designs can be represented using simple notation like

$$Defects = f(Experience, Method (Machine))$$

In this model, *Machine* is nested within *Method* so the effect of *Machine* cannot appear as a main effect. Presumably the nature of the manufacturing process dictates that *Machine* depends on *Method*. Although the model is easy to state, this example is not intended to suggest that estimates of nested models are easy to interpret.

Random Effects Models

In a *fixed-effects model* the levels of each factor are predetermined, which implies that our inferences are valid only for the specified factor levels. In a *random effects model* the factor levels are chosen randomly from a population of potential factor levels. Computation and interpretation of random effects are more complicated, and not all tests may be feasible. Novices are advised that estimation of random effects models should be preceded by further study (see Related Reading).

CHAPTER SUMMARY

ANOVA tests whether a numerical dependent variable (**response variable**) is associated with one or more categorical independent variables (**factors**) with several **levels.** Each level or combination of levels is a treatment. A **one-factor ANOVA** compares means in c columns of data. It is a generalization of a two-tailed t test for two independent sample means. Fisher's **F statistic** is a ratio of two variances (treatment versus error). It is compared with a right-tailed critical value from an F table or from Excel for appropriate numerator and denominator degrees of freedom. Alternatively, we can compare the p-value for the F test statistic with the desired level of significance (any p-value less than α is significant). An **unreplicated two-factor ANOVA** can be viewed as a **randomized block model** if only one factor is of research interest. A **replicated two-factor ANOVA** (or full factorial model) has more than one observation per treatment, permitting inclusion of an interaction test in addition to tests for the **main effects. Interaction effects** can be seen as crossing lines on plots of factor means. The **Tukey test** compares individual treatment means. We test for homogeneous variances (an assumption of ANOVA) using **Hartley's test** or **Levene's test.** The **general linear model** (GLM) can be used when there are more than two factors. **Experimental design** helps make efficient use of limited data. Other general advice:

- ANOVA may be helpful even if those who collected the data did not utilize a formal experimental design (often the case in real-world business situations).

- ANOVA calculations are tedious because of the sums required, so computers are generally used.

- One-factor ANOVA is the most common and suffices for many business situations.

- ANOVA is an overall test. To tell which specific pairs of treatment means differ, use the Tukey test.

- Although real-life data may not perfectly meet the normality and equal-variance assumptions, ANOVA is reasonably robust (and alternative tests do exist).

KEY TERMS

analysis of variance (ANOVA), *439*
balanced designs, *476*
experimental design, *475*
explained variance, *439*
factors, *439*
fixed-effects model, *443*
fractional factorial designs, *476*
full factorial, *464*
general linear model, *474*
Hartley's test, *452*

hierarchical design, *476*
homogeneous variances, *452*
interaction, *441*
interaction effect, *464*
interaction plots, *473*
Levene's test, *454*
main effects, *464*
mean squares, *444*
multiple comparison, *450*
nested design, *476*
one-factor ANOVA, *442*

partitioned sum of squares, *444*
randomized block model, *457*
replication, *464*
response variable, *439*
treatment, *439*
Tukey's studentized range test, *450*
two-factor ANOVA without replication, *456*
unexplained variance, *439*

CHAPTER REVIEW

Note: Questions labeled * are based on optional material from this chapter.

1. Explain each term: (a) explained variation; (b) unexplained variation; (c) factor; (d) treatment.

2. (a) Explain the difference between one-factor and two-factor ANOVA. (b) Write the linear model form of one-factor ANOVA. (c) State the hypotheses for a one-factor ANOVA in two different ways. (d) Why is one-factor ANOVA used a lot?

3. (a) State three assumptions of ANOVA. (b) What do we mean when we say that ANOVA is fairly robust to violations of these assumptions?

4. (a) Sketch the format of a one-factor ANOVA data set (completely randomized model). (b) Must group sizes be the same for one-factor ANOVA? Is it better if they are? (c) Explain the concepts of variation *between treatments* and variation *within treatments*. (d) What is the F statistic? (e) State the degrees of freedom for the F test in one-factor ANOVA.

5. (a) Sketch the format of a two-factor ANOVA data set without replication. (b) State the hypotheses for a two-factor ANOVA without replication. (c) What is the difference between a randomized block model and a two-factor ANOVA without replication? (d) What do the two F statistics represent in a two-factor ANOVA without replication? (e) What are their degrees of freedom?

6. (a) Sketch the format of a two-factor ANOVA data set with replication. (b) What is gained by replication? (c) State the hypotheses for a two-factor ANOVA with replication. (d) What do the three F statistics represent in a two-factor ANOVA with replication? (e) What are their degrees of freedom?

7. (a) What is the purpose of the Tukey test? (b) Why can't we just compare all possible pairs of group means using the two-sample t test?

8. (a) What does a test for homogeneity of variances tell us? (b) Why should we test for homogeneity of variances? (c) Explain what Hartley's test measures. (d) Why might we use Levene's test instead of the Hartley's test?

*9. What is the general linear model and why is it useful?

*10. (a) What is a 2^k design, and what are its advantages? (b) What is a fractional factorial design, and what are its advantages? (c) What is a nested or hierarchical design? (d) How is a random effects model different than a fixed-effects model?

CHAPTER EXERCISES

connect

Instructions: You may use Excel, MegaStat, MINITAB, or another computer package of your choice. Attach appropriate copies of the output or capture the screens, tables, and relevant graphs and include them in a written report. Try to state your conclusions succinctly in language that would be clear to a decision maker who is a nonstatistician. Exercises marked * are based on optional material. Answer the following questions, or those your instructor assigns.

a. Choose an appropriate ANOVA model. State the hypotheses to be tested.

b. Display the data visually (e.g., dot plots or MegaStat's line plots). What do the displays show?

c. Do the ANOVA calculations using the computer.

d. State the decision rule for $\alpha = .05$ and make the decision. Interpret the p-value.

e. In your judgment, are the observed differences in treatment means (if any) large enough to be of practical importance?

f. Given the nature of the data, would more data collection be practical?

g. Perform Tukey multiple comparison tests and discuss the results.

h. Perform a test for homogeneity of variances. Explain fully.

11.21 Below are grade point averages for 25 randomly chosen university business students during a recent semester. *Research question:* Are the mean grade point averages the same for students in these four class levels? GPA2

Grade Point Averages of 25 Business Students

Freshman (5 students)	Sophomore (7 students)	Junior (7 students)	Senior (6 students)
1.91	3.89	3.01	3.32
2.14	2.02	2.89	2.45
3.47	2.96	3.45	3.81
2.19	3.32	3.67	3.02
2.71	2.29	3.33	3.01
	2.82	2.98	3.17
	3.11	3.26	

11.22 The XYZ Corporation is interested in possible differences in days worked by salaried employees in three departments in the financial area. A survey of 23 randomly chosen employees reveals the data shown below. Because of the casual sampling methodology in this survey, the sample sizes are unequal. *Research question:* Are the mean annual attendance rates the same for employees in these three departments? DaysWorked

Days Worked Last Year by 23 Employees

Department	Days Worked									
Budgets (5 workers)	278	260	265	245	258					
Payables (10 workers)	205	270	220	240	255	217	266	239	240	228
Pricing (8 workers)	240	258	233	256	233	242	244	249		

11.23 Mean output of solar cells of three types are measured six times under random light intensity over a period of 5 minutes, yielding the results shown. *Research question:* Is the mean solar cell output the same for all cell types? 🖾 **SolarWatts**

Solar Cell Output (watts)

Cell Type	Output (watts)					
A	123	121	123	124	125	127
B	125	122	122	121	122	126
C	126	128	125	129	131	128

11.24 In a bumper test, three types of autos were deliberately crashed into a barrier at 5 mph, and the resulting damage (in dollars) was estimated. Five test vehicles of each type were crashed, with the results shown below. *Research question:* Are the mean crash damages the same for these three vehicles? 🖾 **Crash1**

Crash Damage ($)

Goliath	Varmint	Weasel
1,600	1,290	1,090
760	1,400	2,100
880	1,390	1,830
1,950	1,850	1,250
1,220	950	1,920

11.25 The waiting time (in minutes) for emergency room patients with non-life-threatening injuries was measured at four hospitals for all patients who arrived between 6:00 and 6:30 PM on a certain Wednesday. The results are shown below. *Research question:* Are the mean waiting times the same for emergency patients in these four hospitals? 🖾 **ERWait**

Emergency Room Waiting Time (minutes)

Hospital A (5 patients)	Hospital B (4 patients)	Hospital C (7 patients)	Hospital D (6 patients)
10	8	5	0
19	25	11	20
5	17	24	9
26	36	16	5
11		18	10
		29	12
		15	

11.26 The results shown below are mean productivity measurements (average number of assemblies completed per hour) for a random sample of workers at each of three plants. *Research question:* Are the mean hourly productivity levels the same for workers in these three plants? 🖾 **Productivity**

Hourly Productivity of Assemblers in Plants

Plant	Finished Units Produced Per Hour									
A (9 workers)	3.6	5.1	2.8	4.6	4.7	4.1	3.4	2.9	4.5	
B (6 workers)	2.7	3.1	5.0	1.9	2.2	3.2				
C (10 workers)	6.8	2.5	5.4	6.7	4.6	3.9	5.4	4.9	7.1	8.4

11.27 Below are results of braking tests of the Ford Explorer on glare ice, packed snow, and split traction (one set of wheels on ice, the other on dry pavement), using three braking methods. *Research questions:* Is the mean stopping distance affected by braking method and/or by surface type? **Braking**

Stopping Distance from 40 mph to 0 mph

Method	Ice	Split Traction	Packed Snow
Pumping	441	223	149
Locked	455	148	146
ABS	460	183	167

Source: *Popular Science* 252, no. 6 (June 1998), p. 78.

11.28 An MBA director examined GMAT scores for the first ten MBA applicants (assumed to be a random sample of early applicants) for four academic quarters. *Research question:* Do the mean GMAT scores for early applicants differ by quarter? **GMAT**

GMAT Scores of First Ten Applicants

Fall	490	580	440	580	430	420	640	470	530	640
Winter	310	590	730	710	540	450	670	390	500	470
Spring	500	450	510	570	610	490	450	590	640	650
Summer	450	590	710	240	510	670	610	550	540	540

11.29 An ANOVA study was conducted to compare dental offices in five small towns. The response variable was the number of days each dental office was open last year. *Research question:* Is there a difference in the means among these five towns? **DaysOpen**

Dental Clinic Days Open During the Last Year in Five Towns

Chalmers	Greenburg	Villa Nueve	Ulysses	Hazeltown
230	194	206	198	214
215	193	200	186	196
221	208	208	206	194
205	198	206	189	190
232		232	181	203
210		208		

11.30 The Environmental Protection Agency (EPA) advocates a maximum arsenic level in water of 10 micrograms per liter. Below are results of EPA tests on randomly chosen wells in a suburban Michigan county. *Research question:* Is the mean arsenic level affected by well depth and/or age of well? **Arsenic**

Arsenic Level in Wells (micrograms per liter)

Well Depth	Age of Well (years)		
	Under 10	10 to 19	20 and Over
Shallow	5.4	6.1	6.8
	4.3	4.1	5.4
	6.1	5.8	5.7
Medium	3.4	5.1	4.5
	3.7	3.7	5.5
	4.3	4.4	4.6
Deep	2.4	3.8	3.9
	2.9	2.7	2.9
	2.7	3.4	4.0

11.31 Is a state's income related to its high school dropout rate? *Research question:* Do the high school dropout rates differ among the five income quintiles? 📷 **Dropout**

State High School Dropout Rates by Income Groups

Lowest Income Quintile		2nd Income Quintile		3rd Income Quintile		4th Income Quintile		Highest Income Quintile	
State	Dropout %	State	Dropout %	State	Dropout %	State	Dropout %	State	Dropout %
Mississippi	40.0	Kentucky	34.3	N. Carolina	39.5	Oregon	26.0	Minnesota	15.3
W. Virginia	24.2	S. Carolina	44.5	Wyoming	23.3	Ohio	30.5	Illinois	24.6
New Mexico	39.8	N. Dakota	15.5	Missouri	27.6	Pennsylvania	25.1	California	31.7
Arkansas	27.3	Arizona	39.2	Kansas	25.5	Michigan	27.2	Colorado	28.0
Montana	21.5	Maine	24.4	Nebraska	12.1	Rhode Island	31.3	N. Hampshire	27.0
Louisiana	43.0	S. Dakota	28.1	Texas	39.4	Alaska	33.2	Maryland	27.4
Alabama	39.0	Tennessee	40.1	Georgia	44.2	Nevada	26.3	New York	39.0
Oklahoma	26.9	Iowa	16.8	Florida	42.2	Virginia	25.7	New Jersey	20.4
Utah	16.3	Vermont	19.5	Hawaii	36.0	Delaware	35.9	Massachusetts	25.0
Idaho	22.0	Indiana	28.8	Wisconsin	21.9	Washington	25.9	Connecticut	28.2

Source: *Statistical Abstract of the United States, 2002.*

11.32 In a bumper test, three test vehicles of each of three types of autos were crashed into a barrier at 5 mph, and the resulting damage was estimated. Crashes were from three angles: head-on, slanted, and rear-end. The results are shown below. *Research questions:* Is the mean repair cost affected by crash type and/or vehicle type? Are the observed effects (if any) large enough to be of practical importance (as opposed to statistical significance)? 📷 **Crash2**

5 mph Collision Damage ($)

Crash Type	Goliath	Varmint	Weasel
Head-On	700	1,700	2,280
	1,400	1,650	1,670
	850	1,630	1,740
Slant	1,430	1,850	2,000
	1,740	1,700	1,510
	1,240	1,650	2,480
Rear-end	700	860	1,650
	1,250	1,550	1,650
	970	1,250	1,240

11.33 As a volunteer for a consumer research group, LaShonda was assigned to analyze the freshness of three brands of tortilla chips. She examined four randomly chosen bags of chips for four brands of chips from three different stores. She recorded the number of days from the current date until the "fresh until" expiration date printed on the package. *Research Question:* Do mean days until the expiration date differ by brand or store? *Note:* Some data values are negative. 📂 **Freshness**

Days Until Expiration Date on Package

	Store 1	*Store 2*	*Store 3*
Brand A	−1	25	17
	−1	24	18
	20	10	21
	22	27	6
Brand B	−7	15	29
	30	−8	40
	24	6	24
	23	31	50
Brand C	16	11	41
	7	16	17
	16	30	27
	19	21	18
Brand D	21	42	31
	11	32	30
	10	38	39
	19	28	45

11.34 Three samples of each of three types of PVC pipe of equal wall thickness are tested to failure under three temperature conditions, yielding the results shown below. *Research questions:* Is mean burst strength affected by temperature and/or by pipe type? Is there a "best" brand of PVC pipe? Explain. 📂 **PVCPipe**

Burst Strength of PVC Pipes (psi)

Temperature	*PVC 1*	*PVC 2*	*PVC 3*
Hot (70° C)	250	301	235
	273	285	260
	281	275	279
Warm (40° C)	321	342	302
	322	322	315
	299	339	301
Cool (10° C)	358	375	328
	363	355	336
	341	354	342

11.35 Below are data on truck production (number of vehicles completed) during the second shift at five truck plants for each day in a randomly-chosen week. *Research Question:* Are the mean production rates the same by plant and by day? 📂 **Trucks**

Trucks Produced During Second Shift

	Mon	*Tue*	*Wed*	*Thu*	*Fri*
Plant A	130	157	208	227	216
Plant B	204	230	252	250	196
Plant C	147	208	234	213	179
Plant D	141	200	288	260	188

11.36 To check pain-relieving medications for potential side effects on blood pressure, it is decided to give equal doses of each of four medications to test subjects. To control for the potential effect of weight, subjects are classified by weight groups. Subjects are approximately the same age and are in general good health. Two subjects in each category are chosen at random from a large group of male prison volunteers. Subjects' blood pressures 15 minutes after the dose are shown below. *Research question:* Is mean blood pressure affected by body weight and/or by medication type? 📁 **Systolic**

Systolic Blood Pressure of Subjects (mmHg)

Ratio of Subject's Weight to Normal Weight	Medication M1	Medication M2	Medication M3	Medication M4
Under 1.1	131	146	140	130
	135	136	132	125
1.1 to 1.3	136	138	134	131
	145	145	147	133
1.3 to 1.5	145	149	146	139
	152	157	151	141

11.37 To assess the effects of instructor and student gender on student course scores, an experiment was conducted in 11 sections of managerial accounting classes ranging in size from 25 to 66 students. The factors were instructor gender (M, F) and student gender (M, F). There were 11 instructors (7 male, 4 female). Steps were taken to eliminate subjectivity in grading, such as common exams and sharing exam grading responsibility among all instructors so no one instructor could influence exam grades unduly. (a) What type of ANOVA is this? (b) What conclusions can you draw? (c) Discuss sample size and raise any questions you think may be important.

Analysis of Variance for Students' Course Scores

Source of Variation	Sum of Squares	Degrees of Freedom	Mean Square	F Ratio	p-Value
Instructor gender (I)	97.84	1	97.84	0.61	0.43
Student gender (S)	218.23	1	218.23	1.37	0.24
Interaction ($I \times S$)	743.84	1	743.84	4.66	0.03
Error	63,358.90	397	159.59		
Total	64,418.81	400			

Source: Marlys Gascho Lipe, "Further Evidence on the Performance of Female Versus Male Accounting Students," *Issues in Accounting Education* 4, no. 1 (Spring 1989), pp. 144–50.

11.38 In a market research study, members of a consumer test panel are asked to rate the visual appeal (on a 1 to 10 scale) of the texture of dashboard plastic trim in a mockup of a new fuel cell car. The manufacturer is testing four finish textures. Panelists are assigned randomly to evaluate each texture. The test results are shown below. Each cell shows the average rating by panelists who evaluated each texture. *Research question:* Is mean rating affected by age group and/or by surface type? 📁 **Texture**

Mean Ratings of Dashboard Surface Texture

Age Group	Shiny	Satin	Pebbled	Pattern
Youth (under 21)	6.7	6.6	5.5	4.3
Adult (21 to 39)	5.5	5.3	6.2	5.9
Middle-Age (40 to 61)	4.5	5.1	6.7	5.5
Senior (62 and over)	3.9	4.5	6.1	4.1

11.39 This table shows partial results for a one-factor ANOVA, (a) Calculate the F test statistic. (b) Calculate the p-value using Excel's function =FDIST(F,DF1,DF2). (c) Find the critical value $F_{.05}$ from Appendix F or using Excel's function =FINV(.05,DF1,DF2). (d) Interpret the results.

ANOVA						
Source of Variation	SS	df	MS	F	p-value	$F_{.05}$
Between groups	3207.5	3	1069.17			
Within groups	441730	36	12270.28			
Total	444937.5	39				

11.40 (a) What kind of ANOVA is this (one-factor, two-factor, or two-factor with replication)? (b) Calculate each F test statistic. (b) Calculate the p-value for each F test using Excel's function =FDIST(F,DF1,DF2). (c) Interpret the results.

ANOVA					
Source of Variation	SS	df	MS	F	p-value
Factor A	36,598.56	3	12,199.52		
Factor B	22,710.29	2	11,355.15		
Interaction	177,015.38	6	29,502.56		
Error	107,561.25	36	2,987.81		
Total	343,885.48	47			

11.41 Here is an Excel ANOVA table for an experiment to assess the effects of ambient noise level and plant location on worker productivity. (a) What kind of ANOVA is this (one-factor, two-factor, two-factor replicated)? (b) Describe the original data format (i.e., how many rows, columns, and observations per cell). (c) At $\alpha = 0.05$ what are your conclusions?

ANOVA						
Source of Variation	SS	df	MS	F	p-value	$F_{.05}$
Plant location	3.0075	3	1.0025	2.561	0.1200	3.863
Noise level	8.4075	3	2.8025	7.16	0.0093	3.863
Error	3.5225	9	0.3914			
Total	14.9375					

11.42 Several friends go bowling several times per month. They keep track of their scores over several months. An ANOVA was performed. (a) What kind of ANOVA is this (one-factor, two-factor, etc.)? (b) How many friends were there? How many months were observed? How many observations per bowler per month? Explain how you know. (c) What are your conclusions about bowling scores? Explain, referring either to the F tests or p-values.

ANOVA						
Source of Variation	SS	df	MS	F	p-value	F crit
Month	1702.389	2	851.194	11.9793	0.0002	3.4028
Bowler	4674.000	3	1558.000	21.9265	0.0000	3.0088
Interaction	937.167	6	156.194	2.1982	0.0786	2.5082
Within	1705.333	24	71.056			
Total	9018.889	35				

11.43 Air pollution (micrograms of particulate per ml of air) was measured along four freeways at each of five different times of day, with the results shown below. (a) What kind of ANOVA is this (one-factor, two-factor, etc.)? (b) What is your conclusion about air pollution? Explain, referring either to the F tests or p-values. (c) Do you think the variances can be assumed equal? Explain your reasoning. Why does it matter? (d) Perform Hartley's test to test for unequal variances.

SUMMARY	Count	Sum	Average	Variance
Chrysler	5	1584	316.8	14333.7
Davidson	5	1047	209.4	3908.8
Reuther	5	714	142.8	2926.7
Lodge	5	1514	302.8	11947.2
12:00A-6:00A	4	505	126.25	872.9
6:00A-10:00A	4	1065	266.25	11060.3
10:00A-3:00P	4	959	239.75	5080.3
3:00P-7:00P	4	1451	362.75	14333.6
7:00P-12:00A	4	879	219.75	7710.9

ANOVA

Source of Variation	SS	df	MS	F	p-value	F crit
Freeway	100957.4	3	33652.45	24.903	0.000	3.490
Time of Day	116249.2	4	29062.3	21.506	0.000	3.259
Error	16216.4	12	1351.367			
Total	233423	19				

11.44 A company has several suppliers of office supplies. It receives several shipments each quarter from each supplier. The time (days) between order and delivery was recorded for several randomly chosen shipments from each supplier in each quarter, and an ANOVA was performed. (a) What kind of ANOVA is this (one-factor, two-factor, etc.)? (b) How many suppliers were there? How many quarters? How many observations per supplier per quarter? Explain how you know. (c) What are your conclusions about shipment time? Explain, referring either to the F tests or p-values.

ANOVA

Source of Variation	SS	df	MS	F	p-value	F crit
Quarter	148.04	3	49.34667	6.0326	0.0009	2.7188
Supplier	410.14	4	102.535	12.5348	0.0000	2.4859
Interaction	247.06	12	20.5883	2.5169	0.0073	1.8753
Within	654.40	80	8.180			
Total	1459.64	99				

11.45 Several friends go bowling several times per month. They keep track of their scores over several months. An ANOVA was performed. (a) What kind of ANOVA is this (one-factor, two-factor, etc.)? (b) How could you tell how many friends there were in the sample just from the ANOVA table? Explain. (c) What are your conclusions about bowling scores? Explain, referring either to the F test or p-value. (d) Do you think the variances can be assumed equal? Explain your reasoning.

SUMMARY				
Bowler	*Count*	*Sum*	*Average*	*Variance*
Mary	15	1856	123.733	77.067
Bill	14	1599	114.214	200.797
Sally	12	1763	146.917	160.083
Robert	15	2211	147.400	83.686
Tom	11	1267	115.182	90.164

ANOVA						
Source of Variation	*SS*	*df*	*MS*	*F*	*p-value*	*F crit*
Between Groups	14465.63	4	3616.408	29.8025	0.0000	2.5201
Within Groups	7523.444	62	121.3459			
Total	21989.07	66				

11.46 Are large companies more profitable *per dollar of assets?* The largest 500 companies in the world in 2000 were ranked according to their number of employees, with groups defined as follows: Small = Under 25,000 employees, Medium = 25,000 to 49,999 employees, Large = 50,000 to 99,000 employees, Huge = 100,000 employees or more. An ANOVA was performed using the company's profit-to-assets ratio (percent) as the dependent variable. (a) What kind of ANOVA is this (one-factor, two-factor, etc.)? (b) What is your conclusion about the research question? Explain, referring either to the *F* test or *p*-value. (c) What can you learn from the plots that compare the groups? (d) Do you think the variances can be assumed equal? Explain your reasoning. (e) Perform Hartley's test to test for unequal variances. (f) Which groups of companies have significantly different means? Explain.

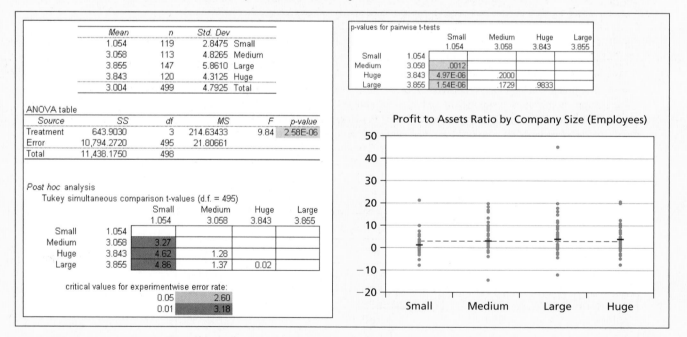

RELATED READING   Box, George E.; J. Stuart Hunter; and William G. Hunter. *Statistics for Experimenters.* 2nd ed. John Wiley & Sons, 2005.

Hilbe, Joseph M. "Generalized Linear Models." *The American Statistician* 48, no. 3 (August 1994), pp. 255–65.

Kutner, Michael H.; Christopher Nachtsheim; John Neter; and William Li. *Applied Linear Statistical Models.* 5th ed. McGraw-Hill, 2005.

Montgomery, Douglas C. *Design and Analysis of Experiments.* 5th ed. John Wiley & Sons, 2000.

Chapter 11   Online Learning Resources

The Online Learning Center (OLC) at www.mhhe.com/doane3e has several *LearningStats* demonstrations to help you understand analysis of variance. Your instructor may assign one or more of them, or you may decide to download the ones that sound interesting.

Topic	LearningStats Demonstrations
Excel examples	▣ Examples: ANOVA Tests
	▣ ANOVA Simulation
Tables	▣ Appendix F—Critical Values of *F*

Key: ▣ = Excel

CHAPTER 12

Simple Regression

Chapter Contents

Chapter Learning Objectives

When you finish this chapter you should be able to

LO1   Calculate and test a correlation coefficient for significance.

LO2   Fit a simple regression on an Excel scatter plot.

LO3   Explain the OLS method and use its terminology correctly.

LO4   Apply the formulas for the slope and intercept.

LO5   Make and interpret confidence intervals for regression coefficients.

LO6   Test hypotheses about the slope and intercept by using t tests.

LO7   Perform regression with Excel or other software.

LO8   Interpret the standard error, R^2, ANOVA table, and F test.

LO9   Distinguish between confidence and prediction intervals.

LO10 Test residuals for violations of regression assumptions.

LO11 Identify unusual residuals and high-leverage observations.

LO12 Explain the role of data conditioning and data transformations.

Up to this point, our study of the discipline of statistical analysis has primarily focused on learning how to describe and make inferences about single variables. It is now time to learn how to describe and summarize relationships *between* variables. Businesses of all types can be quite complex. Understanding how different variables in our business processes are related to each other helps us predict and, hopefully, improve our business performance.

Examples of quantitative variables that might be related to each other include: spending on advertising and sales revenue, produce delivery time and percentage of spoiled produce, premium and regular gas prices, preventive maintenance spending and manufacturing productivity rates. It may be that with some of these pairs there is one variable that we would like to be able to *predict* such as sales revenue, percentage of spoiled produce, and productivity rates. But first we must learn how to *visualize, describe,* and *quantify* the relationships between variables such as these.

Visual Displays

Analysis of **bivariate data** (i.e., two variables) typically begins with a **scatter plot** that displays each observed data pair (x_i, y_i) as a dot on an *X-Y* grid. This diagram provides a visual indication of the strength of the relationship or association between the two random variables. This simple display requires no assumptions or computation. A scatter plot is typically the precursor to more complex analytical techniques. Figure 12.1 shows a scatter plot comparing the price per gallon of regular unleaded gasoline to the price per gallon of premium gasoline.

We look at scatter plots to get an initial idea of the relationship between two random variables. Is there an evident pattern to the data? Is the pattern linear or nonlinear? Are there data points that are not part of the overall pattern? We would characterize the fuel price relationship as linear (although not perfectly linear) and positive (as diesel prices increase, so do regular unleaded prices). We see one pair of values set slightly apart from the rest, above and to the right. This happens to be the state of Hawaii.

Correlation Coefficient

A visual display is a good first step in analysis but we would also like to quantify the strength of the association between two variables. Therefore, accompanying the scatter plot is the

FIGURE 12.1

Fuel Prices (*n* = 50)
📁 **FuelPrices**

Source: AAA Fuel Gauge Report,
May 27, 2007, www.fuelgaugereport.com

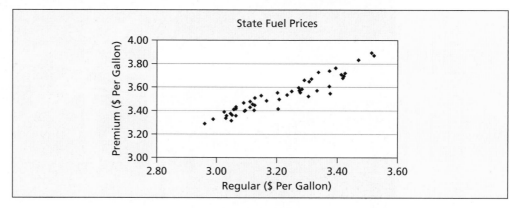

LO1

Calculate and test a
correlation coefficient
for significance.

sample correlation coefficient (also called the Pearson correlation coefficient.) This statistic measures the degree of linearity in the relationship between two random variables X and Y and is denoted r. Its value will fall in the interval $[-1, 1]$.

Strong Negative Correlation	*No Correlation*	*Strong Positive Correlation*
-1.00	0.00	$+1.00$

When r is near 0 there is little or no linear relationship between X and Y. An r-value near $+1$ indicates a strong positive relationship, while an r-value near -1 indicates a strong negative relationship.

$$(12.1) \qquad r = \frac{\sum_{i=1}^{n}(x_i - \bar{x})(y_i - \bar{y})}{\sqrt{\sum_{i=1}^{n}(x_i - \bar{x})^2}\sqrt{\sum_{i=1}^{n}(y_i - \bar{y})^2}} \qquad \text{(sample correlation coefficient)}$$

To simplify the notation here and elsewhere in this chapter, we define three terms called **sums of squares**:

$$(12.2) \quad SS_{xx} = \sum_{i=1}^{n}(x_i - \bar{x})^2 \qquad SS_{yy} = \sum_{i=1}^{n}(y_i - \bar{y})^2 \qquad SS_{xy} = \sum_{i=1}^{n}(x_i - \bar{x})(y_i - \bar{y})$$

Using this notation, the formula for the sample correlation coefficient can be written

$$(12.3) \qquad r = \frac{SS_{xy}}{\sqrt{SS_{xx}}\sqrt{SS_{yy}}} \qquad \text{(sample correlation coefficient)}$$

Excel Tip

To calculate a sample correlation coefficient, use Excel's function =CORREL(array1,array2) where array1 is the range for X and array2 is the range for Y. Data may be in rows or columns. Arrays must be the same length.

The correlation coefficient for the variables shown in Figure 12.1 is $r = .947$, which is not surprising. We would expect to see a strong linear positive relationship between state regular unleaded gasoline prices and premium gasoline prices. Figure 12.2 shows prototype scatter plots. We see that a correlation of .500 implies a great deal of random variation, and even a correlation of .900 is far from "perfect" linearity. The last scatter plot shows $r = .00$ despite an obvious *curvilinear* relationship between X and Y. This illustrates the fact that a correlation coefficient only measures the degree of *linear* relationship between X and Y.

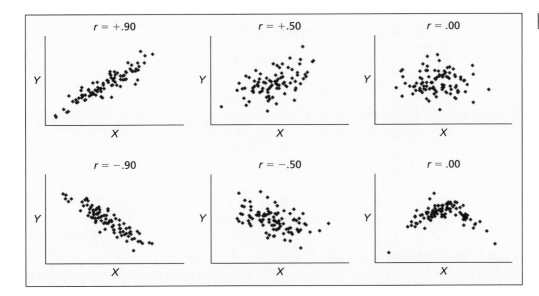

FIGURE 12.2

Scatter Plots Showing Various Correlation Coefficient Values (*n* = 100)

Correlation analysis has many business applications. For example:

- Financial planners study correlations between asset classes over time, in order to help their clients diversify their portfolios.
- Marketing analysts study correlations between customer online purchases in order to develop new Web advertising strategies.
- Human resources experts study correlations between measures of employee performance in order to devise new job-training programs.

Tests for Significance Using Student's *t*

The sample correlation coefficient *r* is an estimate of the **population correlation coefficient** **ρ** (the Greek letter *rho*). There is no flat rule for a "high" correlation because sample size must be taken into consideration. To test the hypothesis H_0: $\rho = 0$, the test statistic is

$$t_{\text{calc}} = r\sqrt{\frac{n-2}{1-r^2}} \qquad \text{(test for zero correlation)} \qquad \textbf{(12.4)}$$

We compare this *t* test statistic with a critical value of *t* for a one-tailed or two-tailed test from Appendix D using $d.f. = n - 2$ degrees of freedom and any desired α. Recall that we lose a degree of freedom for each parameter that we estimate when we calculate a statistic. Because both $\bar{x}$ and $\bar{y}$ are used to calculate *r*, we lose 2 degrees of freedom and so $d.f. = n - 2$. After calculating the *t* **statistic**, we can find its *p*-value by using Excel's function =TDIST(t,deg_freedom,tails). MINITAB directly calculates the *p*-value for a two-tailed test without displaying the *t* statistic.

In its admission decision process, a university's MBA program examines an applicant's score on the GMAT (Graduate Management Aptitude Test), which has both verbal and quantitative components. Figure 12.3 shows the scatter plot with the sample correlation coefficient for 30 MBA applicants randomly chosen from 1,961 MBA applicant records at a public university in the Midwest. Is the correlation (*r* = .4356) between verbal and quantitative GMAT scores statistically significant? It is not clear from the scatter plot that there is a statistically significant linear relationship.

Step 1: State the Hypotheses
We will use a two-tailed test for significance at $\alpha = .05$. The hypotheses are

H_0: $\rho = 0$
H_1: $\rho \neq 0$

EXAMPLE

MBA Applicants

📁 **MBA**

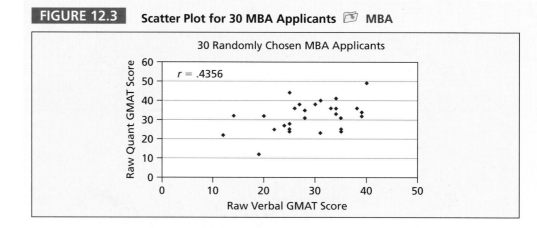

FIGURE 12.3 Scatter Plot for 30 MBA Applicants 📁 MBA

Step 2: Specify the Decision Rule

For a two-tailed test using $d.f. = n - 2 = 30 - 2 = 28$ degrees of freedom, Appendix D gives $t_{.025} = 2.048$. The decision rule is

Reject H_0 if $t_{calc} > 2.048$ or if $t_{calc} < -2.048$.

Step 3: Calculate the Test Statistic

To calculate the test statistic we first need to calculate the value for r. Using Excel's function =CORREL(array1,array2) we find $r = .4356$ for the variables *Quant GMAT* and *Verbal GMAT*. We must then calculate t_{calc}.

$$t_{calc} = r\sqrt{\frac{n-2}{1-r^2}} = .4356\sqrt{\frac{30-2}{1-(.4356)^2}} = 2.561$$

Step 4: Make a Decision

The test statistic value ($t_{calc} = 2.561$) exceeds the critical value $t_{.025} = 2.048$, so we reject the hypothesis of zero correlation at $\alpha = .05$. We can also find the *p*-value using the Excel function =TDIST(t,deg_freedom,tails). The two-tailed *p*-value for GMAT score is =TDIST(2.561,28,2) = .0161. We would reject $\rho = 0$ since $p < .05$.

Critical Value for Correlation Coefficient

An equivalent approach is to calculate a critical value for the correlation coefficient. First, look up the critical value of t from Appendix D with $d.f. = n - 2$ degrees of freedom for either a one-tailed or two-tailed test, with the α you choose. Then, the critical value of the correlation coefficient, $r_{critical}$, is

(12.5) $$r_{critical} = \frac{t}{\sqrt{t^2 + n - 2}}$$ (critical value for a correlation coefficient)

An advantage of this method is that you get a benchmark for the correlation coefficient. Its disadvantage is that there is no *p*-value and it is inflexible if you change your mind about α. MegaStat uses this method, giving two-tail critical values for $\alpha = .05$ and $\alpha = .01$.

Table 12.1 shows that, as sample size increases, the critical value of r becomes smaller. Thus, in very large samples, even very small correlations could be "significant." In a larger

TABLE 12.1

Values for $r_{critical}$ for Different Sample Sizes

Sample Size	$r_{critical}$
$n = 25$	.396
$n = 50$	.279
$n = 100$	.197
$n = 200$	.139

sample, smaller values of the sample correlation coefficient can be considered "significant." While a larger sample does give a better estimate of the true value of ρ, a larger sample does *not* mean that the correlation is stronger nor does its increased *significance* imply increased *importance*.

Tip

In large samples, small correlations may be significant, even if the scatter plot shows little evidence of linearity. Thus, a *significant* correlation may lack practical *importance*.

12.1 For each sample, do a test for zero correlation. (a) Use Appendix D to find the critical value of t_α. (b) State the hypotheses about ρ. (c) Perform the *t* test and report your decision.

   a. $r = +.45, n = 20, \alpha = .05$, two-tailed test
   b. $r = -.35, n = 30, \alpha = .10$, two-tailed test
   c. $r = +.60, n = 7, \alpha = .05$, right-tailed test
   d. $r = -.30, n = 61, \alpha = .01$, left-tailed test

SECTION EXERCISES

connect

Instructions for Exercises 12.2 and 12.3: (a) Make an Excel scatter plot. What does it suggest about the population correlation between X and Y? (b) Make an Excel worksheet to calculate SS_{xx}, SS_{yy}, and SS_{xy}. Use these sums to calculate the sample correlation coefficient. Check your work by using Excel's function =CORREL(array1,array2). (c) Use Appendix D to find $t_{.025}$ for a two-tailed test for zero correlation at $\alpha = .05$. (d) Calculate the *t* test statistic. Can you reject $\rho = 0$? (e) Use Excel's function =TDIST(t,deg_freedom,tails) to calculate the two-tail *p*-value.

12.2 College Student Weekly Earnings in Dollars (*n* = 5) 📊 WeekPay

Hours Worked (X)	Weekly Pay (Y)
10	93
15	171
20	204
20	156
35	261

12.3 Phone Hold Time for Concert Tickets in Seconds (*n* = 5) 📊 CallWait

Operators (X)	Wait Time (Y)
4	385
5	335
6	383
7	344
8	288

Instructions for Exercises 12.4–12.6: (a) Make a scatter plot of the data. What does it suggest about the correlation between X and Y? (b) Use Excel, MegaStat, or MINITAB to calculate the correlation coefficient. (c) Use Excel or Appendix D to find $t_{.025}$ for a two-tailed test at $\alpha = .05$. (d) Calculate the *t* test statistic. (e) Can you reject $\rho = 0$?

12.4 Moviegoer Snack Spending (*n* = 10) 📊 Movies

Age (X)	Spent (Y)	Age (X)	Spent (Y)
30	2.85	33	6.75
50	6.50	36	3.60
34	1.50	26	6.10
12	6.35	18	8.35
37	6.20	46	4.35

12.5 Annual Percent Return on Mutual Funds ($n = 17$) 🗂 Portfolio	
Last Year (X)	This Year (Y)
11.9	15.4
19.5	26.7
11.2	18.2
14.1	16.7
14.2	13.2
5.2	16.4
20.7	21.1
11.3	12.0
−1.1	12.1
3.9	7.4
12.9	11.5
12.4	23.0
12.5	12.7
2.7	15.1
8.8	18.7
7.2	9.9
5.9	18.9

12.6 Order Size and Shipping Cost ($n = 12$) 🗂 ShipCost	
Orders (X)	Ship Cost (Y)
1,068	4,489
1,026	5,611
767	3,290
885	4,113
1,156	4,883
1,146	5,425
892	4,414
938	5,506
769	3,346
677	3,673
1,174	6,542
1,009	5,088

Mini Case   12.1

Do Loyalty Cards Promote Sales Growth?

A business can achieve sales growth by increasing the number of new customers. Another way is by increasing business from existing customers. Loyal customers visit more often, thus contributing to sales growth. Loyalty cards are used by many companies to foster positive relationships with their customers. Customers carry a card that records the number of purchases or visits they make. They are rewarded with a free item or discount after so many visits. But do these loyalty cards provide incentive to repeat customers to visit more often? Surprisingly, Noodles & Company found out that this wasn't happening in some markets. After several years of running a loyalty card program without truly measuring their impact on the business, in 2005, Noodles performed a correlation analysis on the variables "Sales Growth Percentage" and "Loyalty Card Sales Percentage." The results showed that in some markets there was no significant correlation, meaning the loyalty cards weren't associated with increased sales revenue. However, in other markets there was actually *a statistically significant negative correlation.* In other words, loyalty cards were associated with a decrease in sales growth. Why? Ultimately, the free visits that customers had earned were replacing visits that they would have otherwise paid full price for. Moreover, the resources the company was devoting to the program were taking away from more proven sales building techniques, such as holding non-profit fundraisers or tastings for local businesses. Based on this analysis, Noodles & Company made the decision to discontinue their loyalty card program and focused on other approaches to building loyal customers. See Chapter Exercise 12.56.

12.2
SIMPLE REGRESSION

What Is Simple Regression?

Correlation coefficients and scatter plots provide clues about relationships among variables and may suffice for some purposes. But often, the analyst would like to mathematically model the relationship for prediction purposes. For example, a business might hypothesize that

- Advertising expenditures predict quarterly sales revenue.
- Number of dependents predicts employee prescription drug expenses.

- Apartment size predicts monthly rent.
- Number of diners predicts business lunch expense.
- Assembly line speed predicts number of product defects.

The hypothesized relationship may be linear, quadratic, or some other form. For now we will focus on the simple linear model. This straight-line model is often referred to as a **simple regression**. The slope and intercept of the simple regression equation are used to describe the relationship between the two variables.

In a simple regression, we define one variable as the **response variable** (the *dependent variable*) and one variable as the **predictor variable** (the *independent variable*). If the relationship can be estimated, a business can explore policy questions such as:

- How much extra sales will be generated, on average, by a $1 million increase in advertising expenditures? What would expected sales be with no advertising?
- How much do prescription drug costs per employee rise, on average, with each extra dependent? What would be the expected cost if the employee had no dependents?
- How much extra rent, on average, is paid per extra square foot?
- How much extra luncheon cost, on average, is generated by each additional member of the group? How much could be saved by restricting luncheon groups to three persons?
- If the assembly line speed is increased by 20 units per hour, what would happen to the mean number of product defects?

Terms You Should Know

The *response* variable is the *dependent* variable. This is the Y variable. The *predictor* variable is the *independent* variable. This is the X variable. Only the dependent variable (not the independent variable) is treated as a random variable.

Interpreting an Estimated Regression Equation

The intercept and slope of an estimated regression can provide useful information. For example:

$Sales = 268 + 7.37\, Ads$	Each extra $1 million of advertising will generate $7.37 million of sales on average. The firm would average $268 million of sales with zero advertising. However, the intercept may not be meaningful because $Ads = 0$ may be outside the range of observed data.
$DrugCost = 410 + 550\, Dependents$	Each extra dependent raises the mean annual prescription drug cost by $550. An employee with zero dependents averages $410 in prescription drugs.
$Rent = 150 + 1.05\, SqFt$	Each extra square foot adds $1.05 to monthly apartment rent. The intercept is not meaningful because no apartment can have $SqFt = 0$.
$Cost = 15.22 + 19.96\, Persons$	Each additional diner increases the mean dinner cost by $19.96. The intercept is not meaningful because $Persons = 0$ would not be observable.
$Defects = 3.2 + 0.045\, Speed$	Each unit increase in assembly line speed adds an average of 0.045 defects per million. The intercept is not meaningful since zero assembly line speed implies no production at all.

Cause and Effect?

When we propose a regression model, we might have a causal mechanism in mind, but cause and effect is not proven by a simple regression. We cannot assume that the explanatory variable is "causing" the variation we see in the response variable.

Prediction Using Regression

One of the main uses of regression is to make predictions. Once we have a fitted regression equation that shows the estimated relationship between X (the independent variable) and Y (the dependent variable), we can plug in any value of X to obtain the prediction for Y. For example:

$Sales = 268 + 7.37\ Ads$	If the firm spends \$10 million on advertising, its predicted sales would be \$341.7 million, that is, $Sales = 268 + 7.37(10) = 341.7$.
$DrugCost = 410 + 550\ Dependents$	If an employee has four dependents, the predicted annual drug cost would be \$2,610, that is, $DrugCost = 410 + 550(4) = 2,610$.
$Rent = 150 + 1.05\ SqFt$	The predicted rent on an 800 square foot apartment is \$990, that is, $Rent = 150 + 1.05(800) = 990$.
$Cost = 15.22 + 19.96\ Persons$	The predicted cost of dinner for two couples would be \$95.06, that is, $Cost = 15.22 + 19.96(4) = 95.06$.
$Defects = 3.2 + 0.045\ Speed$	If 100 units per hour are produced, the predicted defect rate is 7.7 defects per million, that is, $Defects = 3.2 + 0.045(100) = 7.7$.

Range of X

Predictions from our fitted regression model are stronger within the range of our observed x values. The relationship seen in the scatter plot may not be true for values far outside our observation window. *Extrapolation* outside the observed range of x is always tempting but should be approached with caution.

SECTION EXERCISES

12.7 (a) Interpret the slope of the fitted regression $HomePrice = 125,000 + 150\ SquareFeet$. (b) What is the prediction for $HomePrice$ if $SquareFeet = 2,000$? (c) Would the intercept be meaningful if this regression applies to home sales in a certain subdivision?

12.8 (a) Interpret the slope of the fitted regression $Sales = 842 - 37.5\ Price$. (b) If $Price = 20$, what is the prediction for $Sales$? (c) Would the intercept be meaningful if this regression represents DVD sales at Blockbuster?

12.9 (a) Interpret the slope of the fitted regression $CarTheft = 1,667 - 35.3 MedianAge$. Note: $CarTheft$ is the number of car thefts per 100,000 people by state, and $MedianAge$ is the median age of the population. (b) What is the prediction for $CarTheft$ if $MedianAge$ is 40? (c) Would the intercept be meaningful if this regression applies to car thefts per 100,000 people by state?

12.3
REGRESSION TERMINOLOGY

Models and Parameters

The model's *unknown population parameters* are denoted by Greek letters β_0 (the **intercept**) and β_1 (the **slope**). The *assumed model* for a linear relationship is

(12.6) $y = \beta_0 + \beta_1 x + \varepsilon$ (assumed regression equation)

This relationship is assumed to hold for all pairs of (x_i, y_i) observations $(i = 1, 2, \ldots, n)$. Inclusion of a random error ε is necessary because other unspecified variables may also affect Y and also because there may be measurement error in Y. The error is not observable. We assume that the error term ε is a normally distributed random variable with mean 0 and standard deviation σ. Thus, the regression model actually has three unknown parameters: β_0, β_1, and σ. From the sample, we estimate the **regression equation** and use it to predict the *expected* value of Y for a given value of X:

$$\hat{y} = b_0 + b_1 x \qquad \text{(estimated regression equation)} \tag{12.7}$$

Roman letters denote the *coefficients* b_0 (the estimated intercept) and b_1 (the estimated slope). For a given value x_i, the estimated value of the dependent variable is $\hat{y}_i$. (You can read this as "y-hat".) The difference between the observed value y_i and its estimated value $\hat{y}_i$ is called a **residual** and is denoted e_i. The residual is the vertical distance between each y_i and the regression line on a scatter plot of (x_i, y_i) values.

What Is a Residual?

A residual is calculated as the observed value of y minus the estimated value of y:

$$e_i = y_i - \hat{y}_i \qquad \text{(residual)} \tag{12.8}$$

The residuals may be used to estimate σ, the standard deviation of the errors.

Fitting a Regression on a Scatter Plot

LO2

Fit a simple regression on an Excel scatter plot.

From a scatter plot, we could visually estimate the slope and intercept. Although this method is inexact, experiments suggest that people are pretty good at "eyeball" line fitting. We instinctively try to adjust the line to ensure that the line passes through the "center" of the scatter of data points, to match the data as closely as possible. In other words, we try to minimize the vertical distances between the line and the observed y values.

A more precise method is to let Excel do the estimates. We enter observations on the independent variable $x_1, x_2, \ldots, x_n$ and the dependent variable $y_1, y_2, \ldots, y_n$ into separate columns, and let Excel fit the regression equation, as illustrated in Figure 12.4.* Excel will choose the regression coefficients so as to produce a good fit.

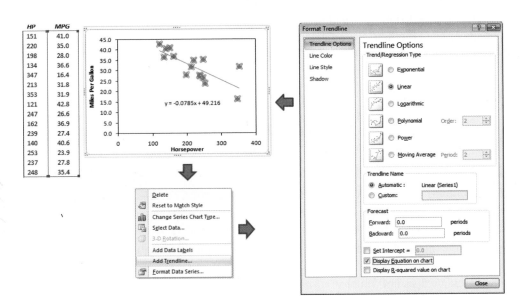

FIGURE 12.4

Excel's Trendline Menus

---

*Excel calls its regression equation a "trendline," although actually that would refer to a time-series trend.

TABLE 12.2

Piper Cheyenne Fuel Usage 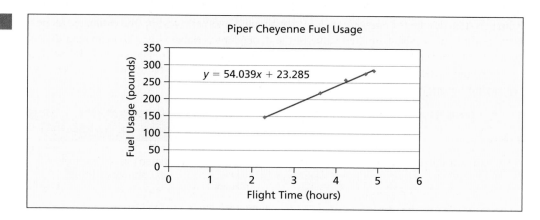 **Cheyenne**

Source: *Flying* 130, no. 4 (April 2003), p. 99.

Flight Hours	Fuel Used (lbs.)
2.3	145
4.2	258
3.6	219
4.7	276
4.9	283

FIGURE 12.5

Fitted Regression

To use Excel to fit a regression line to the scatter plot, follow these steps:

- Step 1: Highlight the data columns.
- Step 2: Click on Insert and choose Scatter to create a graph.
- Step 3: Click on the scatter plot points to select the data.
- Step 4: Right-click and choose Add Trendline.
- Step 5: Choose Options and check Display equation on chart.

Illustration: Piper Cheyenne Fuel Consumption Cheyenne

Table 12.2 shows a sample of fuel consumption and flight hours for five legs of a cross-country test flight in a Piper Cheyenne, a twin-engine piston business aircraft. Figure 12.5 displays the Excel graph and its fitted regression equation.

Slope Interpretation   The fitted regression is $\hat{y} = 23.285 + 54.039x$. The slope ($b_1 = 54.039$) says that for each additional hour of flight, the Piper Cheyenne consumed about 54 pounds of fuel (1 gallon $\approx$ 6 pounds). This estimated slope is a *statistic,* since a different sample might yield a different estimate of the slope. Bear in mind also that the sample size is very small.

Intercept Interpretation   The intercept ($b_0 = 23.285$) suggests that even if the plane is not flying ($x = 0$) some fuel would be consumed. However, the intercept has little meaning in this case, not only because zero flight hour makes no logical sense, but also because extrapolating to $x = 0$ is beyond the range of the observed data.

Regression Caveats

- The "fit" of the regression does *not* depend on the sign of its slope. The sign of the fitted slope merely tells whether X has a positive or negative association with Y.
- View the intercept with skepticism unless $x = 0$ is logically possible and was actually observed in the data set.
- Regression does not demonstrate cause-and-effect between X and Y. A good fit only shows that X and Y vary together. Both could be affected by another variable or by the way the data are defined.

12.10 The regression equation *NetIncome* = 2,277 + .0307 *Revenue* was estimated from a sample of 100 leading world companies (variables are in millions of dollars). (a) Interpret the slope. (b) Is the intercept meaningful? Explain. (c) Make a prediction of *NetIncome* when *Revenue* = 20,000. (Data are from www.forbes.com and *Forbes* 172, no. 2 [July 21, 2003], pp. 108–110.) 📁 **Global100**

12.11 The regression equation *HomePrice* = 51.3 + 2.61 *Income* was estimated from a sample of 34 cities in the eastern United States. Both variables are in thousands of dollars. *HomePrice* is the median selling price of homes in the city, and *Income* is median family income for the city. (a) Interpret the slope. (b) Is the intercept meaningful? Explain. (c) Make a prediction of *HomePrice* when *Income* = 50 and also when *Income* = 100. (Data are from *Money Magazine* 32, no. 1 [January 2004], pp. 102–103.) 📁 **HomePrice1**

12.12 The regression equation *Credits* = 15.4 − .07 *Work* was estimated from a sample of 21 statistics students. *Credits* is the number of college credits taken and *Work* is the number of hours worked per week at an outside job. (a) Interpret the slope. (b) Is the intercept meaningful? Explain. (c) Make a prediction of *Credits* when *Work* = 0 and when *Work* = 40. What do these predictions tell you? 📁 **Credits**

12.13 Below are fitted regressions for *Y* = asking price of a used vehicle and *X* = the age of the vehicle. The observed range of *X* was 1 to 8 years. The sample consisted of all vehicles listed for sale in a particular week in 2005. (a) Interpret the slope of each fitted regression. (b) Interpret the intercept of each fitted regression. Does the intercept have meaning? (c) Predict the price of a 5-year-old Chevy Blazer. (d) Predict the price of a 5-year-old Chevy Silverado. (Data are from *AutoFocus* 4, Issue 38 (Sept. 17–23, 2004) and are for educational purposes only.) 📁 **CarPrices**

Chevy Blazer: *Price* = 16,189 − 1,050 *Age* (*n* = 21 vehicles, observed *X* range was 1 to 8 years).

Chevy Silverado: *Price* = 22,591 − 1,339 *Age* (*n* = 24 vehicles, observed *X* range was 1 to 10 years).

12.14 Refer back to the regression equation in exercise 12.10: *NetIncome* = 2,277 + .0307*Revenue*. Recall that the variables are both in millions of dollars. (a) Calculate the residual for the *x, y* pair (*$41,078, $8,301*). Did the regression equation underestimate or overestimate the net income? (b) Calculate the residual for the *x, y* pair (*$61,768, $893*). Did the regression equation underestimate or overestimate the net income?

12.15 Refer back to the regression equation in exercise 12.12: *Credits* = 15.4 − .07*Work*. (a) Calculate the residual for the *x, y* pair (*14, 18*). Did the regression equation underestimate or overestimate the credits? (b) Calculate the residual for the *x, y* pair (*30, 6*). Did the regression equation underestimate or overestimate the credits?

Slope and Intercept

The **ordinary least squares** method (or **OLS** method for short) is used to estimate a regression so as to ensure the best fit. "Best" fit in this case means that we have selected the slope and intercept so that our residuals are as small as possible. Recall that a residual, $e_i, = y_i - \hat{y}_i$, is the difference between the observed *y* and the estimated *y*. Residuals can be either positive or negative. It is a characteristic of the OLS estimation method that the residuals around the regression line always sum to zero. That is, the positive residuals exactly cancel the negative ones:

$$\sum_{i=1}^{n}(y_i - \hat{y}_i) = 0 \qquad \text{(OLS residuals always sum to zero)} \qquad (12.9)$$

LO3

Explain the OLS method and use its terminology correctly.

Therefore to work with an equation that has a nonzero sum we square the residuals, just as we squared the deviations from the mean when we developed the equation for variance back in Chapter 4. The fitted coefficients b_0 and b_1 are chosen so that the fitted linear model $\hat{y} = b_0 + b_1 x$ has the smallest possible sum of squared residuals (*SSE*):

$$SSE = \sum_{i=1}^{n}(y_i - \hat{y}_i)^2 = \sum_{i=1}^{n}(y_i - b_0 - b_1 x_i)^2 \qquad \text{(sum to be minimized)} \qquad (12.10)$$

This is an optimization problem that can be solved for b_0 and b_1 by using Excel's Solver Add-In. However, we can also use calculus to solve for b_0 and b_1.

$$b_1 = \frac{\sum\limits_{i=1}^{n}(x_i - \bar{x})(y_i - \bar{y})}{\sum\limits_{i=1}^{n}(x_i - \bar{x})^2} \qquad \text{(OLS estimator for slope)} \qquad \textbf{(12.11)}$$

$$b_0 = \bar{y} - b_1\bar{x} \qquad \text{(OLS estimator for intercept)} \qquad \textbf{(12.12)}$$

If we use the notation for sums of squares (see formula 12.2), then the OLS formula for the slope can be written

$$b_1 = \frac{SS_{xy}}{SS_{xx}} \qquad \text{(OLS estimator for slope)} \qquad \textbf{(12.13)}$$

These formulas require only a few spreadsheet operations to find the means, deviations around the means, and their products and sums. They are built into Excel and many calculators. The OLS formulas give unbiased and consistent estimates* of β_0 and β_1. *The OLS regression line always passes through the point $(\bar{x}, \bar{y})$ for any data, as illustrated in Figure 12.6.*

FIGURE 12.6

OLS Regression Line Always Passes Through $(\bar{x}, \bar{y})$.

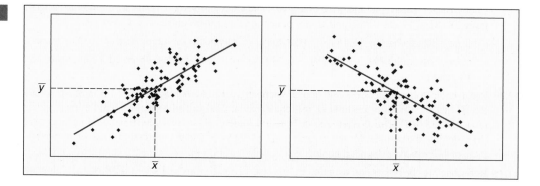

LO4

Apply the formulas for the slope and intercept.

Illustration: Exam Scores and Study Time

Table 12.3 shows study time and exam scores for 10 students. The worksheet in Table 12.4 shows the calculations of the sums needed for the slope and intercept. Figure 12.7 shows a fitted regression line. The vertical line segments in the scatter plot show the differences

TABLE 12.3

Study Time and Exam Scores 📄 **ExamScores**

Student	Study Hours	Exam Score
Tom	1	53
Mary	5	74
Sarah	7	59
Oscar	8	43
Cullyn	10	56
Jaime	11	84
Theresa	14	96
Knut	15	69
Jin-Mae	15	84
Courtney	19	83
Sum	105	701
Mean	$\bar{x} = 10.5$	$\bar{y} = 70.1$

*Recall from Chapter 9 that an unbiased estimator's expected value is the true parameter and that a consistent estimator approaches ever closer to the true parameter as the sample size increases.

TABLE 12.4

**Worksheet for Slope
and Intercept
Calculations**
ExamScores

Student	x_i	y_i	$x_i - \bar{x}$	$y_i - \bar{y}$	$(x_i - \bar{x})(y_i - \bar{y})$	$(x_i - \bar{x})^2$
Tom	1	53	−9.5	−17.1	162.45	90.25
Mary	5	74	−5.5	3.9	−21.45	30.25
Sarah	7	59	−3.5	−11.1	38.85	12.25
Oscar	8	43	−2.5	−27.1	67.75	6.25
Cullyn	10	56	−0.5	−14.1	7.05	0.25
Jaime	11	84	0.5	13.9	6.95	0.25
Theresa	14	96	3.5	25.9	90.65	12.25
Knut	15	69	4.5	−1.1	−4.95	20.25
Jin-Mae	15	84	4.5	13.9	62.55	20.25
Courtney	19	83	8.5	12.9	109.65	72.25
Sum	105	701	0	0	$SS_{xy} = 519.50$	$SS_{xx} = 264.50$
Mean	$\bar{x} = 10.5$	$\bar{y} = 70.1$				

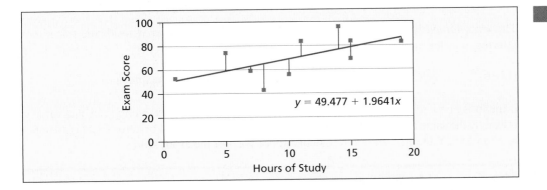

FIGURE 12.7

**Scatter Plot with Fitted
Line and Residuals
Shown as Vertical
Line Segments**

between the actual and fitted exam scores (i.e., residuals). The OLS residuals always sum to zero. We have:

$$b_1 = \frac{SS_{xy}}{SS_{xx}} = \frac{519.50}{264.50} = 1.9641 \qquad \text{(fitted slope)}$$

$$b_0 = \bar{y} - b_1\bar{x} = 70.1 - (1.9641)(10.5) = 49.477 \qquad \text{(fitted intercept)}$$

Interpretation The fitted regression *Score* $= 49.477 + 1.9641$ *Study* says that, on average, each additional hour of study yields a little less than 2 additional exam points (the slope). A student who did not study (*Study* $= 0$) would expect a score of about 49 (the intercept). In this example, the intercept is meaningful because zero study time not only is possible (though hopefully uncommon) but also was almost within the range of observed data. The scatter plot shows an imperfect fit, since not all of the variation in exam scores can be explained by study time. The remaining *unexplained* variation in exam scores reflects other factors (e.g., previous night's sleep, class attendance, test anxiety). We can use the fitted regression equation $\hat{y} = 1.9641x + 49.477$ to find each student's *expected* exam score. Each prediction is a *conditional mean,* given the student's study hours. For example:

Student and Study Time	Expected Exam Score
Oscar, $x = 8$ hours	$\hat{y} = 49.48 + 1.964\,(8) = 65.19$ (65 to nearest integer)
Theresa, $x = 14$ hours	$\hat{y} = 49.48 + 1.964\,(14) = 76.98$ (77 to nearest integer)
Courtney, $x = 19$ hours	$\hat{y} = 49.48 + 1.964\,(19) = 86.79$ (87 to nearest integer)

Oscar's actual exam score was only 43, so he did worse than his predicted score of 65. Theresa scored 96, far above her predicted score of 77. Courtney, who studied the longest (19 hours), scored 83, fairly close to her predicted score of 87. These examples show that study time is not a perfect predictor of exam scores.

Sources of Variation in Y

In a regression, we seek to explain the variation in the dependent variable around its mean. We express the *total variation* as a sum of squares (denoted *SST*):

(12.14)
$$SST = \sum_{i=1}^{n} (y_i - \bar{y})^2 \qquad \text{(total sum of squares)}$$

We can split the total variation into two parts:

SST	=	SSR	+	SSE
(*total* variation around the mean)		(variation explained by the *regression*)		(unexplained or *error* variation)

The *explained variation* in Y (denoted *SSR*) is the sum of the squared differences between the conditional mean $\hat{y}_i$ (conditioned on a given value x_i) and the unconditional mean $\bar{y}$ (same for all x_i):

(12.15)
$$SSR = \sum_{i=1}^{n} (\hat{y}_i - \bar{y})^2 \qquad \text{(regression sum of squares, explained)}$$

The *unexplained variation* in Y (denoted *SSE*) is the sum of *squared* residuals, sometimes referred to as the **error sum of squares**.*

(12.16)
$$SSE = \sum_{i=1}^{n} (y_i - \hat{y}_i)^2 \qquad \text{(error sum of squares, unexplained)}$$

If the fit is good, *SSE* will be relatively small compared to *SST*. If each observed data value y_i is exactly the same as its estimate $\hat{y}_i$ (i.e., a perfect fit), then *SSE* will be zero. There is no upper limit on *SSE*. Table 12.5 shows the calculation of *SSE* for the exam scores.

TABLE 12.5			Calculations of Sums of Squares ExamScores				
Student	**Hours** x_i	**Score** y_i	**Estimated Score** $\hat{y}_i = 1.9641x_i + 49.477$	**Residual** $y_i - \hat{y}_i$	$(y_i - \hat{y}_i)^2$	$(\hat{y}_i - \bar{y})^2$	$(y_i - \bar{y})^2$
Tom	1	53	51.441	1.559	2.43	348.15	292.41
Mary	5	74	59.298	14.702	216.15	116.68	15.21
Sarah	7	59	63.226	−4.226	17.86	47.25	123.21
Oscar	8	43	65.190	−22.190	492.40	24.11	734.41
Cullyn	10	56	69.118	−13.118	172.08	0.96	198.81
Jaime	11	84	71.082	12.918	166.87	0.96	193.21
Theresa	14	96	76.974	19.026	361.99	47.25	670.81
Knut	15	69	78.939	−9.939	98.78	78.13	1.21
Jin-Mae	15	84	78.939	5.061	25.61	78.13	193.21
Courtney	19	83	86.795	−3.795	14.40	278.72	166.41
					SSE = 1,568.57	*SSR* = 1,020.34	*SST* = 2,588.90

Assessing Fit: Coefficient of Determination

Because the magnitude of *SSE* is dependent on sample size and on the units of measurement (e.g. dollars, kilograms, ounces) we want a *unit-free* benchmark to assess the fit of the regression equation. We can obtain a measure of *relative fit* by comparing *SST* to *SSR*. Recall that total variation in Y can be expressed as

$$SST = SSR + SSE$$

By dividing both sides by *SST* we now have the sum of two proportions on the right hand side.

$$\frac{SST}{SST} = \frac{SSR}{SST} + \frac{SSE}{SST} \quad \text{or} \quad 1 = \frac{SSR}{SST} + \frac{SSE}{SST}$$

---

*But bear in mind that the residual e_i (observable) is not the same as the true error ε_i (unobservable).

The first proportion SSR/SST has a special name: **coefficient of determination** or R^2. You can calculate this statistic in two ways.

$$R^2 = \frac{SSR}{SST} \quad \text{or} \quad R^2 = 1 - \frac{SSE}{SST} \qquad (12.17)$$

The range of the coefficient of determination is $0 \le R^2 \le 1$. The highest possible R^2 is 1 because, if the regression gives a perfect fit, then $SSE = 0$:

$$R^2 = 1 - \frac{SSE}{SST} = 1 - \frac{0}{SST} = 1 - 0 = 1 \quad \text{if } SSE = 0 \text{ (perfect fit)}$$

The lowest possible R^2 is 0 because, if knowing the value of X does not help predict the value of Y, then $SSE = SST$:

$$R^2 = 1 - \frac{SSE}{SST} = 1 - \frac{SST}{SST} = 1 - 1 = 0 \quad \text{if } SSE = SST \text{ (worst fit)}$$

For the exam scores, the coefficient of determination is

$$R^2 = 1 - \frac{SSE}{SST} = 1 - \frac{1{,}568.57}{2{,}588.90} = 1 - .6059 = .3941$$

Because a coefficient of determination always lies in the range $0 \le R^2 \le 1$, it is often expressed as a *percent of variation explained*. Since the exam score regression yields $R^2 = .3941$, we could say that X (hours of study) "explains" 39.41 percent of the variation in Y (exam scores). On the other hand, 60.59 percent of the variation in exam scores is *not* explained by study time. The *unexplained variation* reflects factors not included in our model (e.g., reading skills, hours of sleep, hours of work at a job, physical health, etc.) or just plain random variation. Although the word "explained" does not necessarily imply causation, in this case we have *a priori* reason to believe that causation exists, that is, that increased study time improves exam scores.

Tip

In a bivariate regression, R^2 is the square of the correlation coefficient r. Thus, if $r = .50$ then $R^2 = .25$. For this reason, MegaStat (and some textbooks) denotes the coefficient of determination as r^2 instead of R^2. In this textbook, the uppercase notation R^2 is used to indicate the difference in their definitions. It is tempting to think that a low R^2 indicates that the model is not useful. Yet in some applications (e.g., predicting crude oil future prices) even a slight improvement in predictive power can translate into millions of dollars.

SECTION EXERCISES

connect

Instructions for Exercises 12.16 and 12.17: (a) Make an Excel worksheet to calculate SS_{xx}, SS_{yy}, and SS_{xy} (the same worksheet you used in Exercises 12.2 and 12.3). (b) Use the formulas to calculate the slope and intercept. (c) Use your estimated slope and intercept to make a worksheet to calculate SSE, SSR, and SST. (d) Use these sums to calculate the R^2. (e) To check your answers, make an Excel scatter plot of X and Y, select the data points, right-click, select Add Trendline, select the Options tab, and choose Display equation on chart and Display R-squared value on chart.

12.16 College Student Weekly Earnings in Dollars ($n = 5$) WeekPay

Hours Worked (X)	Weekly Pay (Y)
10	93
15	171
20	204
20	156
35	261

12.17 Phone Hold Time for Concert Tickets in Seconds ($n = 5$) CallWait

Operators (X)	Wait Time (Y)
4	385
5	335
6	383
7	344
8	288

Instructions for Exercises 12.18–12.20: (a) Use Excel to make a scatter plot of the data. (b) Select the data points, right-click, select Add Trendline, select the Options tab, and choose Display equation on chart and Display R-squared value on chart. (c) Interpret the fitted slope. (d) Is the intercept meaningful? Explain. (e) Interpret the R^2.

12.18 Moviegoer Snack Spending ($n = 10$) Movies		12.19 Annual Percent Return on Mutual Funds ($n = 17$) Portfolio		12.20 Order Size and Shipping Cos ($n = 12$) ShipCost	
Age (X)	Spent (Y)	Last Year (X)	This Year (Y)	Orders (X)	Ship Cost (Y)
30	2.85	11.9	15.4	1,068	4,489
50	6.50	19.5	26.7	1,026	5,611
34	1.50	11.2	18.2	767	3,290
12	6.35	14.1	16.7	885	4,113
37	6.20	14.2	13.2	1,156	4,883
33	6.75	5.2	16.4	1,146	5,425
36	3.60	20.7	21.1	892	4,414
26	6.10	11.3	12.0	938	5,506
18	8.35	−1.1	12.1	769	3,346
46	4.35	3.9	7.4	677	3,673
		12.9	11.5	1,174	6,542
		12.4	23.0	1,009	5,088
		12.5	12.7		
		2.7	15.1		
		8.8	18.7		
		7.2	9.9		
		5.9	18.9		

12.5 TESTS FOR SIGNIFICANCE

LO5

Make and interpret confidence intervals for regression coefficients.

Standard Error of Regression

A measure of overall fit is the **standard error** of the estimate, denoted s:

$$(12.18) \qquad s = \sqrt{\frac{SSE}{n-2}} \qquad \text{(standard error)}$$

If the fitted model's predictions are perfect ($SSE = 0$), the standard error s will be zero. In general, a smaller value of s indicates a better fit. For the exam scores, we can use SSE from Table 12.5 to find s:

$$s = \sqrt{\frac{SSE}{n-2}} = \sqrt{\frac{1,568.57}{10-2}} = \sqrt{\frac{1,568.57}{8}} = 14.002$$

The standard error s is an estimate of σ (the standard deviation of the unobservable errors). Because it measures overall fit, the standard error s serves somewhat the same function as the coefficient of determination. However, unlike R^2, the magnitude of s depends on the units of measurement of the dependent variable (e.g., dollars, kilograms, ounces) and on the data magnitude. For this reason, R^2 is often the preferred measure of overall fit because its scale is always 0 to 1. The main use of the standard error s is to construct confidence intervals.

Confidence Intervals for Slope and Intercept

Once we have the standard error s, we construct confidence intervals for the coefficients from the formulas shown below. Excel, MegaStat, and MINITAB find them automatically.

$$(12.19) \qquad s_{b_1} = \frac{s}{\sqrt{\sum_{i=1}^{n}(x_i - \bar{x})^2}} \qquad \text{(standard error of slope)}$$

$$(12.20) \qquad s_{b_0} = s\sqrt{\frac{1}{n} + \frac{\bar{x}^2}{\sum_{i=1}^{n}(x_i - \bar{x})^2}} \qquad \text{(standard error of intercept)}$$

For the exam score data, plugging in the sums from Table 12.4, we get

$$s_{b_1} = \frac{s}{\sqrt{\sum_{i=1}^{n}(x_i - \bar{x})^2}} = \frac{14.002}{\sqrt{264.50}} = 0.86095$$

$$s_{b_0} = s\sqrt{\frac{1}{n} + \frac{\bar{x}^2}{\sum_{i=1}^{n}(x_i - \bar{x})^2}} = 14.002\sqrt{\frac{1}{10} + \frac{(10.5)^2}{264.50}} = 10.066$$

These standard errors are used to construct confidence intervals for the true slope and intercept, using Student's t with $d.f. = n - 2$ degrees of freedom and any desired confidence level. Some software packages (e.g., Excel and MegaStat) provide confidence intervals automatically, while others do not (e.g., MINITAB).

$$b_1 - t_{\alpha/2}s_{b_1} \leq \beta_1 \leq b_1 + t_{\alpha/2}s_{b_1} \qquad \text{(CI for true slope)} \qquad \textbf{(12.21)}$$

$$b_0 - t_{\alpha/2}s_{b_0} \leq \beta_0 \leq b_0 + t_{\alpha/2}s_{b_0} \qquad \text{(CI for true intercept)} \qquad \textbf{(12.22)}$$

For the exam scores, degrees of freedom are $n - 2 = 10 - 2 = 8$, so from Appendix D we get $t_{.025} = 2.306$ for 95 percent confidence. The 95 percent confidence intervals for the coefficients are

Slope

$$b_1 - t_{.025}s_{b_1} \leq \beta_1 \leq b_1 + t_{.025}s_{b_1}$$

$$1.9641 - (2.306)(0.86101) \leq \beta_1 \leq 1.9641 + (2.306)(0.86101)$$

$$-0.0213 \leq \beta_1 \leq 3.9495$$

Intercept

$$b_0 - t_{\alpha/2}s_{b_0} \leq \beta_0 \leq b_0 + t_{\alpha/2}s_{b_0}$$

$$49.477 - (2.306)(10.066) \leq \beta_0 \leq 49.477 + (2.306)(10.066)$$

$$26.26 \leq \beta_0 \leq 72.69$$

These confidence intervals are fairly wide. The width of any confidence interval can be reduced by obtaining a larger sample, partly because the t-value would shrink (toward the normal z-value) but mainly because the standard errors shrink as n increases. For the exam scores, the confidence interval for the slope includes zero, suggesting that the true slope could be zero.

Hypothesis Tests

Is the true slope different from zero? This is an important question because if $\beta_1 = 0$, then X does not influence Y and the regression model collapses to a constant β_0 plus a random error term:

Initial Model	*If $\beta_1 = 0$*	*Then*
$y = \beta_0 + \beta_1 x + \varepsilon$	$y = \beta_0 + (0)x + \varepsilon$	$y = \beta_0 + \varepsilon$

We could also test for a zero intercept. For either coefficient, we use a t test with $d.f. = n - 2$ degrees of freedom. The hypotheses and their test statistics are:

Coefficient	*Hypotheses*	*Test Statistic*	
Slope	H_0: $\beta_1 = 0$ H_1: $\beta_1 \neq 0$	$t_{calc} = \dfrac{b_1 - 0}{s_{b_1}}$	**(12.23)**
Intercept	H_0: $\beta_0 = 0$ H_1: $\beta_0 \neq 0$	$t_{calc} = \dfrac{b_0 - 0}{s_{b_0}}$	**(12.24)**

LO6

Test hypotheses about the slope and intercept by using t tests.

Usually we are interested in testing whether the parameter is equal to zero as shown here, but you may substitute another value in place of 0 if you wish. The critical value of t is obtained from Appendix D or from Excel's function =TINV(probability, *d.f.*). Often, the researcher uses a two-tailed test as the starting point, because rejection in a two-tailed test always implies rejection in a one-tailed test (but not vice versa).

Useful Fact

The test for zero slope is the same as the test for zero correlation. That is, the t test for zero slope (formula 12.23) will always yield *exactly* the same t_{calc} as the t test for zero correlation (formula 12.4).

Test for Zero Slope: Exam Scores 📂 ExamScores

For the exam scores, we would anticipate a positive slope (i.e., more study hours should improve exam scores) so we will use a right-tailed test:

Hypotheses	Test Statistic	Critical Value	Decision
$H_0: \beta_1 \leq 0$ $H_1: \beta_1 > 0$	$t_{calc} = \dfrac{b_1 - 0}{s_{b_1}} = \dfrac{1.9641 - 0}{0.86095} = 2.281$	$t_{.05} = 1.860$	Reject H_0 (i.e., slope is positive)

We can reject the hypothesis of a zero slope in a right-tailed test. (We would be unable to do so in a two-tailed test because the critical value of our t statistic would be 2.306.) Once we have the test statistic for the slope or intercept, we can find the p-value by using Excel's function =TDIST(t, deg_freedom, tails). The p-value method is preferred by researchers, because it obviates the need for prior specification of α.

Parameter	Excel Function	p-Value
Slope	=TDIST(2.281,8,1)	.025995 (right-tailed test)

Using Excel: Exam Scores 📂 ExamScores

These calculations are normally done by computer (we have demonstrated the calculations only to illustrate the formulas). The Excel menu to accomplish these tasks is shown in Figure 12.8. The resulting output, also shown in Figure 12.8, can be used to verify our calculations. Excel always does two-tailed tests, so you must halve the p-value if you need a one-tailed test. You may specify the confidence level, but Excel's default is 95 percent confidence.

FIGURE 12.8

Excel's Regression Menus

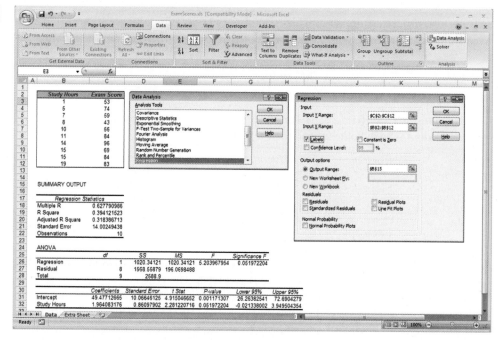

Tip

Avoid checking the Constant is Zero box in Excel's menu. This would force the intercept through the origin, changing the model drastically. Leave this option to the experts.

Using MegaStat: Exam Scores ExamScores

Figure 12.9 shows MegaStat's menu, and Figure 12.10 shows MegaStat's regression output for this data. The output format is similar to Excel's, except that MegaStat highlights coefficients that differ significantly from zero at $\alpha = .05$ in a two-tailed test.

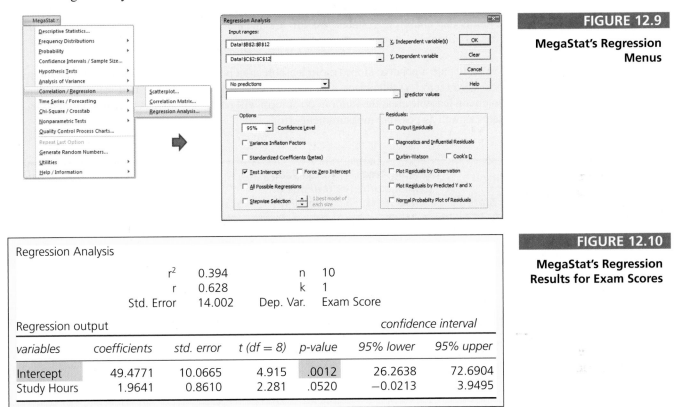

FIGURE 12.9

MegaStat's Regression Menus

FIGURE 12.10

MegaStat's Regression Results for Exam Scores

Regression Analysis

r^2	0.394	n	10
r	0.628	k	1
Std. Error	14.002	Dep. Var.	Exam Score

Regression output

variables	coefficients	std. error	t (df = 8)	p-value	95% lower	95% upper
Intercept	49.4771	10.0665	4.915	.0012	26.2638	72.6904
Study Hours	1.9641	0.8610	2.281	.0520	−0.0213	3.9495

Using MINITAB: Exam Scores ExamScores

Figure 12.11 shows MINITAB's regression menus, and Figure 12.12 shows MINITAB's regression output for this data. MINITAB gives you the same general output as Excel, but with strongly rounded results.*

FIGURE 12.11

MINITAB's Regression Menus

*You may have noticed that both Excel and MINITAB calculated something called "adjusted R-Square." For a bivariate regression, this statistic is of little interest, but in the next chapter it becomes important.

FIGURE 12.12

MINITAB's Regression Results for Exam Scores

The regression equation is
Score = 49.5 + 1.96 Hours

Predictor	Coef	SE Coef	T	P
Constant	49.48	10.07	4.92	0.001
Hours	1.9641	0.8610	2.28	0.052

S = 14.00   R-Sq = 39.4%   R-Sq(adj) = 31.8%

Application: Retail Sales 🖺 RetailSales

Table 12.6 shows data for gross leasable area (X) and retail sales (Y) in shopping malls in $n = 24$ randomly chosen U.S. states. We will assume a linear relationship between X and Y:

$$Sales = \beta_0 + \beta_1\ Area + \varepsilon$$

We anticipate a positive slope (more leasable area permits more retail sales) and an intercept near zero (zero leasable space would imply no retail sales). Since retail sales do not depend solely on leasable area, the random error term will reflect all other factors that influence retail sales as well as possible measurement error.

TABLE 12.6

Leasable Area and Retail Sales 🖺 RetailSales

State	Leasable Area (millions of square feet)	Retail Sales (billions of dollars)	State	Leasable Area (millions of square feet)	Retail Sales (billions of dollars)
AK	8	3.3	MT	10	3.0
AR	41	10.2	ND	10	3.2
AZ	150	36.8	NM	32	9.1
CA	755	182.8	NY	266	65.2
CO	125	35.3	OH	270	59.9
FL	488	144.5	OK	63	17.8
IL	282	63.4	RI	24	5.6
KS	62	16.7	SD	8	1.9
MA	123	35.7	TX	410	127.0
MI	155	37.0	VA	187	47.9
MN	76	20.7	VT	9	2.8
MO	129	33.0	WI	82	21.7

Based on the scatter plot and Excel's fitted linear regression, displayed in Figure 12.13, the linear model seems justified. The very high R^2 says that *Area* "explains" about 98 percent of the variation in *Sales*. Although it is reasonable to assume causation between *Area* and *Sales* in this model, the high R^2 alone does not prove cause-and-effect.

FIGURE 12.13

Leasable Area and Retail Sales 🖺 RetailSales

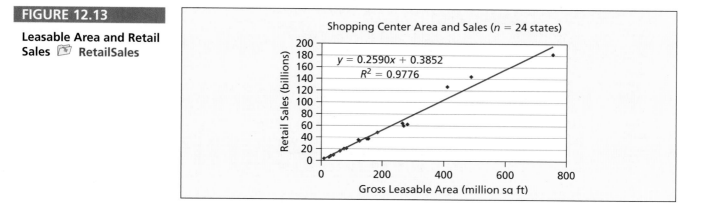

Shopping Center Area and Sales ($n = 24$ states)

$y = 0.2590x + 0.3852$
$R^2 = 0.9776$

Using MegaStat For a more detailed look, we examine MegaStat's regression output for this data, shown in Figure 12.14. On average, each extra million square feet of leasable space yields an extra $259.4 billion in retail sales ($b_1 = .2590$). The slope is nonzero in MegaStat's two-tail test ($t = 30.972$) as indicated by its tiny p-value (1.22×10^{-19}). MegaStat's yellow highlight indicates that the slope differs significantly from zero at $\alpha = .01$, and the narrow confidence interval for the slope [0.2417 to 0.2764] does not enclose zero. We conclude that this sample result (non-zero slope) did not arise by chance—rarely will you see such small p-values (except perhaps in time series data). But the intercept ($b_0 = 0.3852$) does not differ significantly from zero (p-value $= .8479$, $t = 0.194$) and the confidence interval for the intercept [−3.7320, 4.5023] includes zero. These conclusions are in line with our prior expectations.

Regression output					Confidence Interval	
Variables	Coefficients	Std. Error	t (df = 26)	p-value	95% lower	95% upper
Intercept	0.3852	1.9853	0.194	.8479	−3.7320	4.5023
Area	0.2590	0.0084	30.972	1.22E-19	0.2417	0.2764

FIGURE 12.14

MegaStat Regression Results for Retail Sales
RetailSales

Tip

The test for zero slope always yields a t statistic that is identical to the test for zero correlation coefficient. Therefore, it is not necessary to do both tests. Since regression output always includes a t-test for the slope, that is the test we usually use.

Mini Case   12.2

Does Per Person Spending Predict Weekly Sales? 📷 **NoodlesRevenue**

Can Noodles & Company predict their average weekly sales at a restaurant from the average amount a person spends when visiting their restaurant? A random sample of data from 74 restaurants was used to answer this question. The scatter plot in Figure 12.15 below shows the relationship between *average spending per person and average weekly sales.*

FIGURE 12.15 **Noodles Weekly Sales**

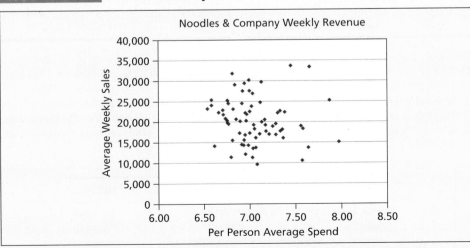

TABLE 12.7		MegaStat Regression Results for Weekly Sales				
Regression Output					**Confidence Interval**	
Variables	**Coefficients**	**Std. Error**	**t (d.f. = 72)**	**p-value**	**95% lower**	**95% upper**
Intercept	32,710.5607	14,987.2764	2.183	.0323	2,833.9717	62,587.1497
Per Person Spend	−1,751.4472	2,125.6830	−0.824	.4127	−5,988.9187	2,486.0243

The scatter plot shows almost no relationship between the two variables. This observation is also supported by the regression results shown in Table 12.7.

The regression results show that b_1, the estimate for β_1, is −$1,751.45. It would appear that on average for each additional dollar an individual spends in a restaurant weekly sales would decrease by $1,751.45 – seemingly a large number. But notice that the confidence interval [−$5,988.92, $2,486.02] contains zero and the standard error ($2,125.68) is larger than the estimated coefficient. When we perform a two-tailed test for zero slope with H_0: $\beta_1 = 0$ and H_1: $\beta_1 \neq 0$ the p-value for this test is .4127. Because this p-value is much greater than any value of α we might choose, we *fail to reject* the null hypothesis of zero slope. Both the hypothesis for zero slope and the confidence interval show that the slope is not significantly different from zero. Our conclusion is that average weekly sales *should not be* predicted by per person average spending. Based on the information we have here, our best prediction of average weekly sales at a Noodles & Company restaurant is simply the mean ($\bar{y} = \$20,373$).

SECTION EXERCISES

connect

Instructions for Exercises 12.21 and 12.22: (a) Perform a regression using MegaStat or Excel. (b) State the null and alternative hypotheses for a two-tailed test for a zero slope. (c) Report the p-value and the 95 percent confidence interval for the slope shown in the regression results. (d) Is the slope significantly different from zero? Explain your conclusion.

12.21 College Student Weekly Earnings in Dollars ($n = 5$) WeekPay

Hours Worked (X)	Weekly Pay (Y)
10	93
15	171
20	204
20	156
35	261

12.22 Phone Hold Time for Concert Tickets in Seconds ($n = 5$) CallWait

Operators (X)	Wait Time (Y)
4	385
5	335
6	383
7	344
8	288

12.23 A regression was performed using data on 32 NFL teams in 2003. The variables were Y = current value of team (millions of dollars) and X = total debt held by the team owners (millions of dollars). (a) Write the fitted regression equation. (b) Construct a 95 percent confidence interval for the slope. (c) Perform a right-tailed t test for zero slope at $\alpha = .05$. State the hypotheses clearly. (d) Use Excel to find the p-value for the t statistic for the slope. (Data are from *Forbes* 172, no. 5, pp. 82–83.) NFL

variables	coefficients	std. error
Intercept	557.4511	25.3385
Debt	3.0047	0.8820

12.24 A regression was performed using data on 16 randomly selected charities in 2003. The variables were $Y =$ expenses (millions of dollars) and $X =$ revenue (millions of dollars). (a) Write the fitted regression equation. (b) Construct a 95 percent confidence interval for the slope. (c) Perform a right-tailed t test for zero slope at $\alpha = .05$. State the hypotheses clearly. (d) Use Excel to find the p-value for the t statistic for the slope. (Data are from *Forbes* 172, no. 12, p. 248, and www.forbes.com.) 📁 **Charities**

variables	coefficients	std. error
Intercept	7.6425	10.0403
Revenue	0.9467	0.0936

Decomposition of Variance

A regression seeks to explain variation in the dependent variable around its mean. A simple way to see this is to express the deviation of y_i from its mean $\bar{y}$ as the sum of the deviation of y_i from the regression estimate $\hat{y}_i$ plus the deviation of the regression estimate $\hat{y}_i$ from the mean $\bar{y}$:

$$y_i - \bar{y} = (y_i - \hat{y}_i) + (\hat{y}_i - \bar{y}) \quad \text{(adding and subtracting } \hat{y}_i) \quad \textbf{(12.25)}$$

It can be shown that this same decomposition also holds for the *sums of squares:*

$$\sum_{i=1}^{n}(y_i - \bar{y})^2 = \sum_{i=1}^{n}(y_i - \hat{y}_i)^2 + \sum_{i=1}^{n}(\hat{y}_i - \bar{y})^2 \quad \text{(sums of squares)} \quad \textbf{(12.26)}$$

As we have already seen, this *decomposition of variance* may be written as

SST	=	SSE	+	SSR
(*total* variation around the mean)		(unexplained or *error* variation)		(variation explained by the *regression*)

12.6 ANALYSIS OF VARIANCE: OVERALL FIT

LO8

Interpret the standard error, R^2, ANOVA table, and F test.

F Statistic for Overall Fit

To test a regression for overall significance, we use an F test to compare the explained (SSR) and unexplained (SSE) sums of squares. We divide each sum by its respective degrees of freedom to obtain *mean squares* (MSR and MSE). The F statistic is the ratio of these two mean squares. Calculations of the F statistic are arranged in a table called the *analysis of variance* or ANOVA table (see Table 12.8). The ANOVA table also contains the sums required to

TABLE 12.8

ANOVA Table for a Simple Regression

Source of Variation	Sum of Squares	df	Mean Square	F	Excel p-value
Regression (explained)	$SSR = \sum_{i=1}^{n}(\hat{y}_i - \bar{y})^2$	1	$MSR = \dfrac{SSR}{1}$	$F_{calc} = \dfrac{MSR}{MSE}$	=FDIST(F_{calc},1, n−2)
Residual (unexplained)	$SSE = \sum_{i=1}^{n}(y_i - \hat{y}_i)^2$	n − 2	$MSE = \dfrac{SSE}{n-2}$		
Total	$SST = \sum_{i=1}^{n}(y_i - \bar{y})^2$	n − 1			

calculate $R^2 = SSR/SSE$. An ANOVA table is provided automatically by any regression software (e.g., Excel, MegaStat).

The formula for the F test statistic is:

(12.27) $\quad F_{calc} = \dfrac{MSR}{MSE} = \dfrac{SSR/1}{SSE/(n-2)} = (n-2)\dfrac{SSR}{SSE}$ $\qquad$ (*F* statistic for simple regression)

The F statistic reflects both the sample size and the ratio of SSR to SSE. For a given sample size, a larger F statistic indicates a better fit (larger SSR relative to SSE), while F close to zero indicates a poor fit (small SSR relative to SSE). The F statistic must be compared with a critical value $F_{1,n-2}$ from Appendix F for whatever level of significance is desired, and we can find the p-value by using Excel's function =FDIST(F_{calc},1,n−2). Software packages provide the p-value automatically.

EXAMPLE

Exam Scores:
F Statistic

📁 **ExamScores**

Figure 12.16 shows MegaStat's ANOVA table for the exam scores. The F statistic is

$$F_{calc} = \frac{MSR}{MSE} = \frac{1020.3412}{196.0698} = 5.20$$

From Appendix F the critical value of $F_{1,8}$ at the 5 percent level of significance would be 5.32, so the exam score regression is not quite significant at $\alpha = .05$. The p-value of .052 says a sample such as ours would be expected about 52 times in 1,000 samples if X and Y were unrelated. In other words, if we reject the hypothesis of no relationship between X and Y, we face a Type I error risk of 5.2 percent. This p-value might be called *marginally significant*.

FIGURE 12.16   **MegaStat's ANOVA Table for Exam Data**

ANOVA table

Source	SS	df	MS	F	p-value
Regression	1,020.3412	1	1,020.3412	5.20	.0520
Residual	1,568.5588	8	196.0698		
Total	2,588.9000	9			

From the ANOVA table, we can calculate the standard error from the mean square for the residuals:

$$s = \sqrt{MSE} = \sqrt{196.0698} = 14.002 \qquad \text{(standard error for exam scores)}$$

Tip

In a simple regression, the F test always yields the same p-value as a two-tailed t test for zero slope, which in turn always gives the same p-value as a two-tailed test for zero correlation. The relationship between the test statistics is $F_{calc} = t_{calc}^2$.

SECTION EXERCISES

connect

12.25 Below is a regression using $X =$ home price (000), $Y =$ annual taxes (000), $n = 20$ homes. (a) Write the fitted regression equation. (b) Write the formula for each t statistic and verify the t statistics shown below. (c) State the degrees of freedom for the t tests and find the two-tail critical value for t by using Appendix D. (d) Use Excel's function =TDIST(t, deg_freedom, tails) to verify the p-value shown for each t statistic (slope, intercept). (e) Verify that $F = t^2$ for the slope. (f) In your own words, describe the fit of this regression.

R²	0.452
Std. Error	0.454
n	12

ANOVA table

Source	SS	df	MS	F	p-value
Regression	1.6941	1	1.6941	8.23	.0167
Residual	2.0578	10	0.2058		
Total	3.7519	11			

Regression output | | | | | confidence interval | |

variables	coefficients	std. error	t (df =10)	p-value	95% lower	95% upper
Intercept	1.8064	0.6116	2.954	.0144	0.4438	3.1691
Slope	0.0039	0.0014	2.869	.0167	0.0009	0.0070

12.26 Below is a regression using X average price, $Y =$ units sold, $n = 20$ stores. (a) Write the fitted regression equation. (b) Write the formula for each t statistic and verify the t statistics shown below. (c) State the degrees of freedom for the t tests and find the two-tail critical value for t by using Appendix D. (d) Use Excel's function =TDIST(t, deg_freedom, tails) to verify the p-value shown for each t statistic (slope, intercept). (e) Verify that $F = t^2$ for the slope. (f) In your own words, describe the fit of this regression.

R²	0.200
Std. Error	26.128
n	20

ANOVA table

Source	SS	df	MS	F	p-value
Regression	3,080.89	1	3,080.89	4.51	.0478
Residual	12,288.31	18	682.68		
Total	15,369.20	19			

Regression output | | | | | confidence interval | |

variables	coefficients	std. error	t (df =18)	p-value	95% lower	95% upper
Intercept	614.9300	51.2343	12.002	.0000	507.2908	722.5692
Slope	−109.1120	51.3623	−2.124	.0478	−217.0202	−1.2038

Instructions for Exercises 12.27–12.29: (a) Use Excel's **Data Analysis > Regression** (or MegaStat or MINITAB) to obtain regression estimates. (b) Interpret the 95 percent confidence interval for the slope. Does it contain zero? (c) Interpret the t test for the slope and its p-value. (d) Interpret the F statistic. (e) Verify that the p-value for F is the same as for the slope's t statistic, and show that $t^2 = F$. (f) Describe the fit of the regression.

12.27 Moviegoer Snack Spending ($n = 10$) 🎬 **Movies**

Age (X)	Spent (Y)	Age (X)	Spent (Y)
30	2.85	33	6.75
50	6.50	36	3.60
34	1.50	26	6.10
12	6.35	18	8.35
37	6.20	46	4.35

12.28 Annual Percent Return on Mutual Funds (n = 17) 📁 Portfolio	
Last Year (X)	**This Year (Y)**
11.9	15.4
19.5	26.7
11.2	18.2
14.1	16.7
14.2	13.2
5.2	16.4
20.7	21.1
11.3	12.0
−1.1	12.1
3.9	7.4
12.9	11.5
12.4	23.0
12.5	12.7
2.7	15.1
8.8	18.7
7.2	9.9
5.9	18.9

12.29 Order Size and Shipping Cost (n = 12) 📁 ShipCost	
Orders (X)	**Ship Cost (Y)**
1,068	4,489
1,026	5,611
767	3,290
885	4,113
1,156	4,883
1,146	5,425
892	4,414
938	5,506
769	3,346
677	3,673
1,174	6,542
1,009	5,088

Mini Case   12.3

Airplane Cockpit Noise 📁 Cockpit

Career airline pilots face the risk of progressive hearing loss, due to the noisy cockpits of most jet aircraft. Much of the noise comes not from engines but from air roar, which increases at high speeds. To assess this workplace hazard, a pilot measured cockpit noise at randomly selected points during the flight by using a handheld meter. Noise level (in decibels) was measured in seven different aircraft at the first officer's left ear position using a handheld meter. For reference, 60 dB is a normal conversation, 75 is a typical vacuum cleaner, 85 is city traffic, 90 is a typical hair dryer, and 110 is a chain saw. Table 12.9 shows 61 observations on cockpit noise (decibels) and airspeed (knots indicated air speed, KIAS) for a Boeing 727, an older type of aircraft lacking design improvements in newer planes.

The scatter plot in Figure 12.17 suggests that a linear model provides a reasonable description of the data. The fitted regression shows that each additional knot of airspeed increases the noise level by 0.0765 dB. Thus, a 100-knot increase in airspeed would add

TABLE 12.9   Cockpit Noise Level and Airspeed for B-727 (n = 61) 📁 Cockpit

Speed	Noise	Speed	Noise	Speed	Noise	Speed	Noise	Speed	Noise	Speed	Noise
250	83	380	93	340	90	330	91	350	90	272	84.5
340	89	380	91	340	91	360	94	380	92	310	88
320	88	390	94	380	96	370	94.5	310	88	350	90
330	89	400	95	385	96	380	95	295	87	370	91
346	92	400	96	420	97	395	96	280	86	405	93
260	85	405	97	230	82	365	91	320	88	250	82
280	84	320	89	340	91	320	88	330	90		
395	92	310	88.5	250	86	250	85	320	88		
380	92	250	82	320	89	250	82	340	89		
400	93	280	87	340	90	320	88	350	90		
335	91	320	89	320	90	305	88	270	84		

FIGURE 12.17   **Scatter Plot of Cockpit Noise Data Courtesy of Capt. R. E. Hartl (ret) of Delta Airlines.**

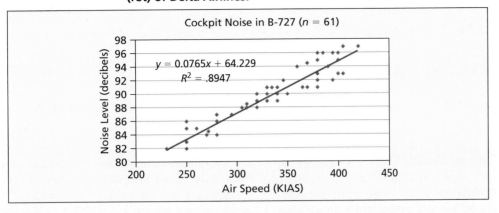

about 7.65 dB of noise. The intercept of 64.229 suggests that if the plane were not flying ($KIAS = 0$) the noise level would be only slightly greater than a normal conversation.

The regression results in Figure 12.18 show that the fit is very good ($R^2 = .895$) and that the regression is highly significant ($F = 501.16$, p-value $< .001$). Both the slope and intercept have p-values below .001, indicating that the true parameters are nonzero. Thus, the regression is significant, as well as having practical value.

FIGURE 12.18   **Regression Results of Cockpit Noise**

Regression Analysis

r^2	0.895	n	61	
r	0.946	k	1	
Std. Error	1.292	Dep. Var.	**Noise**	

ANOVA table

Source	SS	df	MS	F	p-value
Regression	836.9817	1	836.9817	501.16	1.60E-30
Residual	98.5347	59	1.6701		
Total	935.5164	60			

Regression output   confidence interval

variables	coefficients	std. error	t (df = 59)	p-value	95% lower	95% upper
Intercept	64.2294	1.1489	55.907	8.29E-53	61.9306	66.5283
Speed	0.0765	0.0034	22.387	1.60E-30	0.0697	0.0834

How to Construct an Interval Estimate for Y

The regression line is an estimate of the *conditional mean* of Y (i.e., the expected value of Y for a given value of X). But the estimate may be too high or too low. To make this *point estimate* more useful, we need an *interval estimate* to show a range of likely values. To do this, we insert the x_i value into the fitted regression equation, calculate the estimated $\hat{y}_i$, and use the formulas shown below. The first formula gives a **confidence interval** for the conditional mean of Y, while the second is a **prediction interval** for individual values of Y. The formulas

12.7

CONFIDENCE AND PREDICTION INTERVALS FOR Y

are similar, except that prediction intervals are wider because *individual Y* values vary more than the *mean of Y*.

(12.28)
$$\hat{y}_i \pm t_{\alpha/2}s \sqrt{\frac{1}{n} + \frac{(x_i - \bar{x})^2}{\sum_{i=1}^{n}(x_i - \bar{x})^2}} \qquad \text{(confidence interval for mean of } Y)$$

(12.29)
$$\hat{y}_i \pm t_{\alpha/2}s \sqrt{1 + \frac{1}{n} + \frac{(x_i - \bar{x})^2}{\sum_{i=1}^{n}(x_i - \bar{x})^2}} \qquad \text{(prediction interval for individual } Y)$$

Let's use formula 12.29 to predict the exam score for a student who studies 4 hours, using the regression model developed in Section 12.4. What is the 95 percent prediction interval? The student's predicted exam score (see Table 12.5) would be $\hat{y} = 1.9641 (4) + 49.477 = 57.333$. For 95 percent confidence with $d.f. = n - 2 = 10 - 2 = 8$ we use $t_{.025} = 2.306$. Using the sums from Table 12.4, the 95 percent prediction interval is:

$$57.333 \pm (2.306)(14.002)\sqrt{1 + \frac{1}{10} + \frac{(4 - 10.5)^2}{264.5}} \quad \text{or } 57.33 \pm 36.24$$

This very wide interval says that we cannot make precise predictions of the exam score for a student who studies 4 hours. This is not surprising since the fit for the exam score data ($R^2 = .3941$) was not very high. Prediction intervals are more precise when R^2 is high.

Interval width varies with the value of x_i, being narrowest when x_i is near its mean (note that when $x_i = \bar{x}$ the last term under the square root disappears completely). For some data sets, the degree of narrowing near $\bar{x}$ is almost indiscernible, while for other data sets it is quite pronounced. These calculations are usually done by computer (see Figure 12.19). Both MegaStat and MINITAB, for example, will let you type in the x_i values and will give both confidence and prediction intervals *only* for that x_i value, but you must make your own graphs.

FIGURE 12.19

MegaStat's Confidence and Prediction Intervals

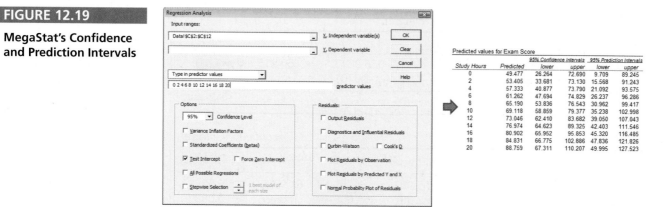

Two Illustrations: Exam Scores and Retail Sales

📄 **ExamScores** 📄 **RetailSales**

Since there will be a different interval for every X value, it is helpful to see confidence and prediction intervals over the entire range of X. Figure 12.20 shows confidence and prediction intervals for exam scores and retail sales. The contrast between the two graphs is striking. Confidence and prediction intervals for exam scores are wide and clearly narrower for X values near the mean. The prediction bands for exam scores for large X values (e.g., $x = 20$ hours of study) even extend above 100 points (presumably the upper limit for an exam score). In contrast, the intervals for retail sales appear narrow and only slightly wider for X values below or above the mean. While the prediction bands for retail sales seem narrow,

FIGURE 12.20

Confidence and Prediction Intervals Illustrated

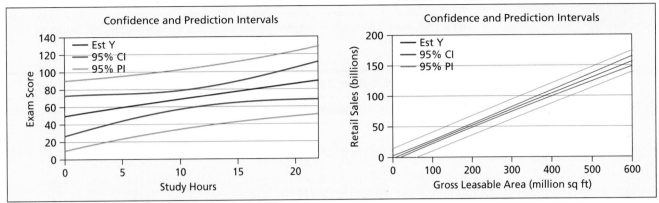

they still represent billions of dollars (e.g., for $x = 500$ the retail sales prediction interval has a width of about \$33 billion). This shows that a high R^2 does not guarantee precise predictions.

Quick Rules for Confidence and Prediction Intervals

Because the confidence interval formulas are complex enough to discourage their use, we are motivated to consider approximations. When x_i is not too far from $\bar{x}$, the last term under the square root is small and might be ignored. As a further simplification, we might ignore $1/n$ in the individual Y formula (if n is large, then $1/n$ will be small). These simplifications yield the quick confidence and prediction intervals shown below. If you want a *really* quick 95 percent interval, you can plug in $t = 2$ (since most 95 percent t-values are not far from 2).

$$\hat{y}_i \pm t_{\alpha/2}\frac{s}{\sqrt{n}} \qquad \text{(quick confidence interval for mean of } Y\text{)} \qquad \textbf{(12.30)}$$

$$\hat{y}_i \pm t_{\alpha/2}s \qquad \text{(quick prediction interval for individual } Y\text{)} \qquad \textbf{(12.31)}$$

These quick rules lead to constant width intervals and are *not* conservative (i.e., the resulting intervals will be somewhat too narrow). They work best for large samples and when X is near its mean. They are questionable when X is near either extreme of its range. Yet they often are close enough to convey a general idea of the accuracy of your predictions. Their purpose is to give a quick answer without getting lost in unwieldy formulas.

12.30 Refer to the Weekly Earnings data set below. (a) Use MegaStat or MINITAB to find confidence and prediction intervals for Y using the following set of x values: 12, 17, 21, 25, and 30. (b) Report the 95 percent confidence interval and prediction interval for $x = 17$. (c) Calculate the 95 percent confidence interval for μ_y using the appropriate method from Chapter 8. (d) Compare the result from part (c) to the confidence interval you reported in part (b). How are they different?

SECTION EXERCISES

College Student Weekly Earnings ($n = 5$) WeekPay	
Hours Worked (X)	*Weekly Pay (Y)*
10	93
15	171
20	204
20	156
35	261

12.31 Refer to the Revenue and Profit data set below. Data are in billions of dollars. (a) Use MegaStat or MINITAB to find confidence and prediction intervals for Y using the following set of x values: 1.8, 15, and 30. (b) Report the 95 percent confidence interval and prediction interval for $x = 15$. (c) Calculate the 95 percent confidence interval for μ_y using the appropriate method from Chapter 8. (d) Compare the result from part (c) to the confidence interval you reported in part (b). How are they different?

Revenue and Profit of Entertainment Companies ($n = 9$) 🗂 Entertainment	
Revenue (X)	**Profit (Y)**
1.792	−0.020
8.931	1.146
2.446	−0.978
1.883	−0.162
2.490	0.185
43.877	2.639
1.311	0.155
26.585	1.417
27.061	1.267

12.8
RESIDUAL TESTS

LO10

Test residuals for violations of regression assumptions.

Three Important Assumptions

Recall that the dependent variable ia a random variable that has an error component, ε. The OLS method makes several assumptions about the random error term ε. Although ε is unobservable, clues may be found in the residuals e_i. Three important assumptions can be tested:

- Assumption 1: The errors are normally distributed.
- Assumption 2: The errors have constant variance (i.e., they are *homoscedastic*).
- Assumption 3: The errors are independent (i.e., they are *nonautocorrelated*).

Since we cannot observe the error ε we must rely on the residuals e_i from the fitted regression for clues about possible violations of these assumptions. Regression residuals often violate one or more of these assumptions. Fortunately, regression is fairly robust in the face of moderate violations of these assumptions. We will examine each violation, explain its consequences, show how to check it, and discuss possible remedies.

Non-Normal Errors

Non-normality of errors is usually considered a mild violation, since the regression parameter estimates b_0 and b_1 and their variances remain unbiased and consistent. The main ill consequence is that confidence intervals for the parameters may be untrustworthy, because the normality assumption is used to justify using Student's t to construct confidence intervals. However, if the sample size is large (say, $n > 30$), the confidence intervals should be OK. An exception would be if outliers exist, posing a serious problem that cannot be cured by large sample size.

Histogram of Residuals   A simple way to check for non-normality is to make a histogram of the residuals. You can use either plain residuals or **standardized residuals**. A *standardized residual* is obtained by dividing each residual by its standard error. Histogram shapes will be the same, but standardized residuals offer the advantage of a predictable scale (between −3 and +3 unless there are outliers). A simple "eyeball test" can usually reveal outliers or serious asymmetry. Figure 12.21 shows a standardized residual histogram for Mini Case 12.2. There are no outliers and the histogram is roughly symmetric, albeit possibly platykurtic (i.e., flatter than normal).

Normal Probability Plot   Another visual test for normality is the probability plot. It is produced as an option by MINITAB and MegaStat. The hypotheses are

H_0: Errors are normally distributed

H_1: Errors are not normally distributed

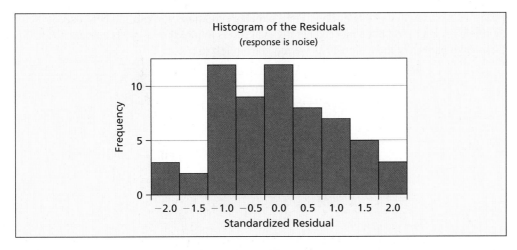

FIGURE 12.21

Cockpit Noise Residuals (Histogram) Cockpit

If the null hypothesis is true, the residual probability plot should be linear. For example in Figure 12.22 we see slight deviations from linearity at the lower and upper ends of the residual probability plot for Mini Case 12.3 (cockpit noise). But overall, the residuals seem to be consistent with the hypothesis of normality. There are more tests for normality, but the histogram and probability plot suffice for most purposes.

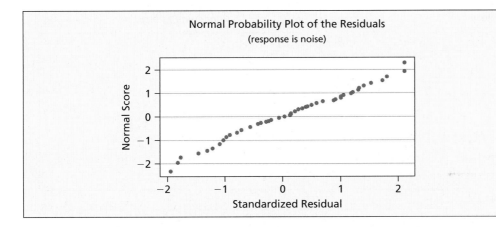

FIGURE 12.22

Cockpit Noise Residuals (Normal Probability Plot)

What to Do About Non-Normality?   First, consider trimming outliers—but only if they clearly are mistakes. Second, can you increase the sample size? If so, it will help assure asymptotic normality of the estimates. Third, you could try a logarithmic transformation of both X and Y. However, this is a new model specification which may require advice from a professional statistician. We will discuss data transformations later in this chapter. Fourth, you could do nothing—just be aware of the problem.

Tip

Non-normality is not considered a major violation, so don't worry too much about it *unless* you have major outliers.

Heteroscedastic Errors (Nonconstant Variance)

The regression should fit equally well for all values of X. If the error magnitude is constant for all X, the errors are **homoscedastic** (the ideal condition). If the errors increase or decrease with X, they are **heteroscedastic**. Although the OLS regression parameter estimates b_0 and b_1 are still unbiased and consistent, their estimated variances are biased and are neither efficient nor asymptotically efficient. In the most common form of heteroscedasticity, the variances of the estimators are likely to be understated, resulting in overstated t statistics and artificially narrow confidence intervals. Your regression estimates may thus seem more significant than is warranted.

Tests for Heteroscedasticity   For a simple regression, you can see heteroscedasticity on the XY scatter plot, but a more general visual test is to plot the residuals against X. Ideally, there is no pattern in the residuals as we move from left to right:

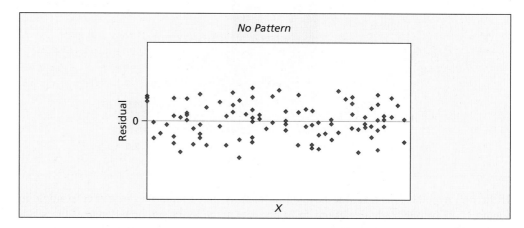

Notice that the residuals *always* have a mean of zero. Although many patterns of nonconstant variance might exist, the "fan-out" pattern (increasing residual variance) is most common:

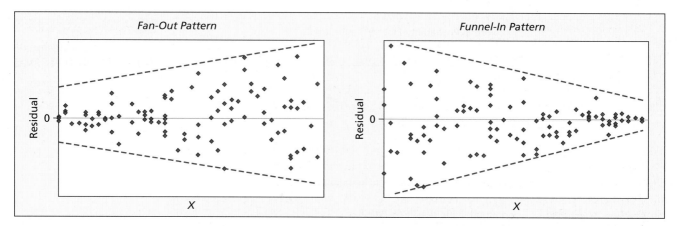

Residual plots provide a fairly sensitive "eyeball test" for heteroscedasticity. The residual plot is therefore considered an important tool in the statistician's diagnostic kit. The hypotheses are

H_0: Errors have constant variance (homoscedastic)

H_1: Errors have nonconstant variance (heteroscedastic)

Figure 12.23 shows a residual plot for Mini Case 12.3 (cockpit noise). In the residual plot, we see residuals of the same magnitude as we look from left to right. A random pattern like this

FIGURE 12.23

Cockpit Noise Residual Plot

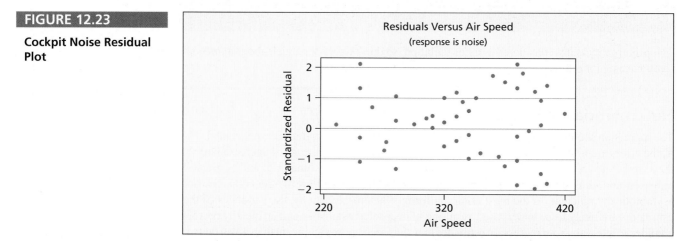

is consistent with the hypothesis of homoscedasticity (constant variance), although some observers might see a hint of a "fan-out" pattern.

What to Do About Heteroscedasticity?   Heteroscedasticity may arise in economic time-series data if X and Y increase in magnitude over time, causing the errors also to increase. In financial data (e.g., GDP) heteroscedasticity can sometimes be reduced by expressing the data in constant dollars (dividing by a price index). In cross-sectional data (e.g., total crimes in a state) heteroscedasticity may be mitigated by expressing the data in relative terms (e.g., per capita crime). A more general approach to reducing heteroscedasticity is to transform both X and Y (e.g., by taking logs). However, this is a new model specification, which requires a reverse transformation when making predictions of Y. This approach will be considered later in this chapter.

Tip

Although it can widen the confidence intervals for the coefficients, heteroscedasticity does not bias the estimates. At this stage of your training, it is sufficient just to recognize its existence.

Autocorrelated Errors

In a regression, each residual e_t should be independent of its predecessors $e_{t-1}, e_{t-2}, \ldots, e_{t-n}$. **Autocorrelation** is a pattern of nonindependent errors, mainly found in time-series data.* Violations of this assumption can show up in different ways. In the simple model of *first-order autocorrelation* we would find that e_t is correlated with the prior residual e_{t-1}. The OLS estimators b_0 and b_1 are still unbiased and consistent, but their estimated variances are biased in a way that typically leads to confidence intervals that are too narrow and t statistics that are too large. Thus, the model's fit may be overstated.

Runs Test for Autocorrelation   *Positive* autocorrelation is indicated by runs of residuals with the *same* sign, while *negative autocorrelation* is indicated by runs of residuals with *alternating* signs. Such patterns can sometimes be seen in a plot of the residuals against the order of data entry. In the *runs test,* we count the number of sign reversals (i.e., how often does the residual plot cross the zero centerline?). If the pattern is random, the number of sign changes should be approximately $n/2$. Fewer than $n/2$ centerline crossings would suggest positive autocorrelation, while more than $n/2$ centerline crossings would suggest negative autocorrelation. For example, if $n = 50$, we would expect about 25 centerline crossings. In the first illustration, there are only 11 crossings (positive autocorrelation) while in the second illustration there are 36 crossings (negative autocorrelation). Positive autocorrelation is common in economic time-series regressions, due to the cyclical nature of the economy. It is harder to envision logical reasons for negative autocorrelation, and in fact it is rarely observed.

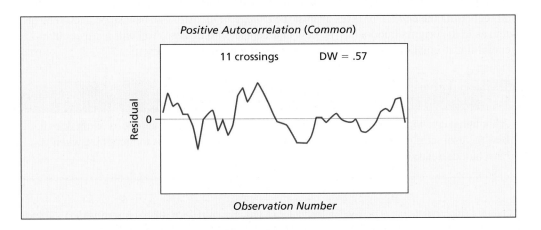

---

*Cross-sectional data may exhibit autocorrelation, but typically it is an artifact of the order of data entry.

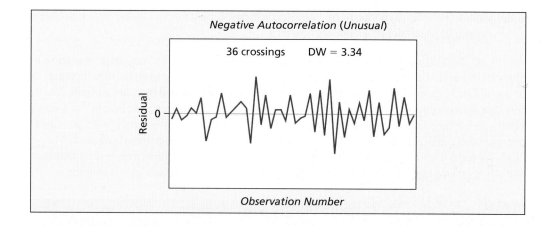

Durbin-Watson Test   The most widely used test for autocorrelation is the **Durbin-Watson test**. The hypotheses are

H_0: Errors are nonautocorrelated

H_1: Errors are autocorrelated

The Durbin-Watson test statistic for autocorrelation is

(12.32) $$DW = \frac{\sum_{t=2}^{n}(e_t - e_{t-1})^2}{\sum_{t=1}^{n} e_t^2}$$ (Durbin-Watson test statistic)

When there is no autocorrelation, the *DW* statistic will be near 2, though its range is from 0 to 4. For a formal hypothesis test, a special table is required. For now, we simply note that in general

$DW < 2$ suggests positive autocorrelation (common).

$DW \approx 2$ suggests no autocorrelation (ideal).

$DW > 2$ suggests negative autocorrelation (rare).

What to Do About Autocorrelation?   First-order time-series autocorrelation can be reduced by transforming both variables. A very simple transformation is the *method of first differences* in which both variables are redefined as *changes:*

$\Delta x_t = x_t - x_{t-1}$ (change in X from period $t - 1$ to period t)

$\Delta y_t = y_t - y_{t-1}$ (change in Y from period $t - 1$ to period t)

Then we regress ΔY against ΔX. This transformation can easily be done in a spreadsheet by subtracting each cell from its predecessor and then re-running the regression. One observation is lost, since the first observation has no predecessor. The method of first differences has logical appeal, since there is little conceptual difference between regressing taxes against income and regressing the *change in taxes* against the *change in income*. The new slope should be the same as in the original model but the new intercept should be zero. You will learn about more general transformations, favored by researchers, if you study econometrics.*

Tip

Although it can widen the confidence intervals for the coefficients, autocorrelation does not bias the estimates. At this stage of your training, it is sufficient just to recognize when you have autocorrelation.

---

*Chapter 14 discusses the use of time-series data for forecasting. Autocorrelation will be revisited and you will learn that some forecasting models actually try to take advantage of the dependency among error terms.

Mini Case   12.4

Exports and Imports   Exports

We often see headlines about the persistent imbalance in U.S. foreign trade (e.g., "U.S. Trade Deficit Sets Record," *International Herald Tribune,* March 14, 2007). But when U.S. imports increase, other nations acquire dollar balances which economists predict will lead to increased purchases of U.S. goods and services, thereby increasing U.S. exports (i.e., trade imbalances are supposed to be self-correcting). Figure 12.24 shows a regression based on U.S. exports and imports for 1959–2005. To reduce autocorrelation (these are time-series data) the model regresses the *change* in exports against the *change* in imports for each period ($n = 46$ years). The fitted model is $\triangle Exports = 5.2849 + 0.5193\ \triangle Imports$. As expected, the slope is positive and significant ($t = 10.277$, *p*-value $< .0001$) and the fit is fairly good ($R^2 = .7059$) despite the first-differences data transformation. But the slope ($b_1 = 0.5193$) indicates that the change in exports is only about half the change in imports, so the trade imbalance remains a puzzle. An economist would perhaps want to examine the role of exchange rate inflexibility vis-à-vis China or other factors, in constructing a more complex model.

FIGURE 12.24   **Excel Scatter Plot and Regression**

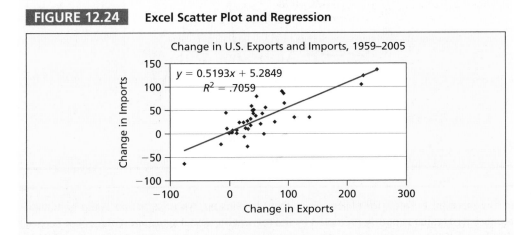

The residuals appear normal (the probability plot in Figure 12.25 is roughly linear with no obvious outliers) and homoscedastic (Figure 12.26 shows no pattern in the plot of residuals against predicted *Y*). But autocorrelation still appears to be a problem (Figure 12.27 shows 9 centerline crossings in the residual plot over time, and has a Durbin-Watson statistic $DW = 0.78$, which suggests positive autocorrelation).

FIGURE 12.25   **Residual Test for Non-Normality**

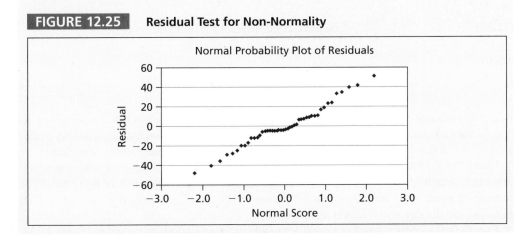

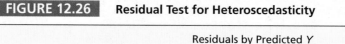

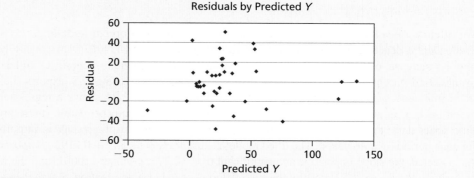

Residual Test for Heteroscedasticity

Residual Test for Autocorrelation

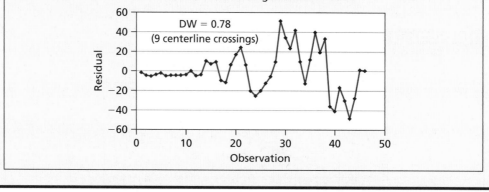

12.9
UNUSUAL
OBSERVATIONS

In a regression, we look for observations that are unusual. An observation could be unusual because its Y-value is poorly predicted by the regression model (*unusual residual*) or because its unusual X-value greatly affects the regression line (*high leverage*). Tests for unusual residuals and high leverage are important diagnostic tools in evaluating the fitted regression.

LO11

Identify unusual residuals and high-leverage observations.

Unusual Residuals

Because every regression may have different Y units (e.g., stock price in dollars, shipping time in days) it is helpful to *standardize* the residuals by dividing each residual, e_i, by its individual standard error, s_{e_i}.

(12.33) $\qquad e_i^* = \dfrac{e_i}{s_{e_i}} \qquad$ (standardized residual for observation i)

where

$$s_{e_i} = s\sqrt{1 - h_i} \quad \text{and} \quad h_i = \frac{1}{n} + \frac{(x_i - \bar{x})^2}{\sum(x_i - \bar{x})^2}$$

Notice that this calculation requires a unique adjustment for each residual based on the observation's distance from the mean. We will refer to this value e_i^* as a *standardized residual*. An equivalent name for this value is **studentized residual** which is used by many software packages.

Using the Empirical Rule as a rule of thumb, any standardized residual whose absolute value is 2 or more is unusual, and any residual whose absolute value is 3 or more would be considered an outlier. There are subtle differences in the way Excel, MegaStat, and MINITAB calculate and display standardized residuals.

Excel's Data Analysis > Regression provides residuals as an option, as shown in Figure 12.28. Excel calculates its "standardized residuals" by dividing each residual by the standard deviation of the column of residuals. This procedure is not quite correct, but generally suffices to identify unusual residuals. Using the Empirical Rule, there are no unusual residuals in Figure 12.28.

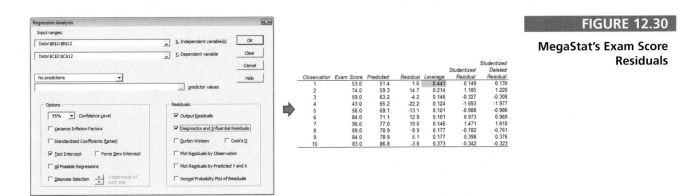

FIGURE 12.28

Excel's Exam Score Residuals

MINITAB gives the same general output as Excel, but with rounded results and more detailed residual information. Its menus are shown in Figure 12.29. MINITAB reports standardized residuals, which usually are close in value to Excel's "standardized" residuals.

MINITAB's results confirm that there are no unusual residuals in the exam score regression. An attractive feature of MINITAB is that the actual and fitted Y-values are displayed (Excel shows only the fitted Y-values). MINITAB also gives the standard error for the mean of Y (the column labeled SE Fit), which you can multiply by $t_{\alpha/2}$ to get the confidence interval width.

FIGURE 12.29

MINITAB's Exam Score Residuals

MegaStat gives the same general output as Excel and MINITAB. Its regression menu is shown in Figure 12.30. Like MINITAB, it offers studentized residuals but MegaStat also shows *studentized deleted residuals*. This is yet another way to identify unusual residuals. The calculation is equivalent to rerunning the regression n times, with each observation omitted in turn, and recalculating the studentized residuals. Further calculation details are reserved for an advanced statistics class, but interpretation is simple. A studentized deleted residual whose absolute value is 2 or more is unusual and one whose absolute value is 3 or more is typically considered an outlier. To make the output more readable, MegaStat rounds off the values (like MINITAB) and highlights unusual and outlier standardized residuals.

FIGURE 12.30

MegaStat's Exam Score Residuals

High Leverage

A high **leverage** statistic indicates that the observation is far from the mean of X. Such observations have great influence on the regression estimates, because they are at the "end of the lever." Figure 12.31 illustrates this concept. One individual worked 65 hours, while the others worked between 12 and 42 hours. This individual will have a big effect on the slope estimate, because he is so far above the mean of X. Yet this highly leveraged data point is *not* an outlier (i.e., the fitted regression line comes very close to the data point, so its residual will be small).

FIGURE 12.31

Illustration of High Leverage **Leverage**

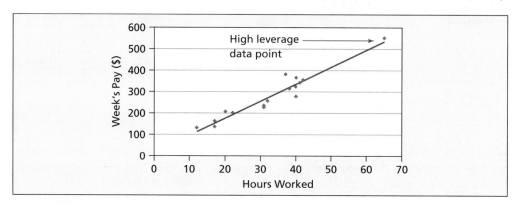

The leverage for observation i is denoted h_i and is calculated as

$$h_i = \frac{1}{n} + \frac{(x_i - \bar{x})^2}{\sum\limits_{i=1}^{n}(x_i - \bar{x})^2} \qquad \textbf{(12.34)}$$

High Leverage

As a rule of thumb for a simple regression, a leverage statistic that exceeds $4/n$ is unusual (if $x_i = \bar{x}$ the leverage statistic h_i is $1/n$ so the rule of thumb is just four times this value).

EXAMPLE

Exam Scores: Leverage and Influence

 ExamScores

We see from Figure 12.32 that two data points (Tom and Courtney) are likely to have high leverage because Tom studied for only 1 hour (far below the mean) while Courtney studied for 19 hours (far above the mean). Using the sums from Table 12.4 (p. 501) we can calculate their leverages:

$$h_{\text{Tom}} = \frac{1}{10} + \frac{(1 - 10.5)^2}{264.50} = .441 \qquad \text{(Tom's leverage)}$$

$$h_{\text{Courtney}} = \frac{1}{10} + \frac{(19 - 10.5)^2}{264.50} = .373 \qquad \text{(Courtney's leverage)}$$

FIGURE 12.32   **Scatter Plot for Exam Data** **ExamScores**

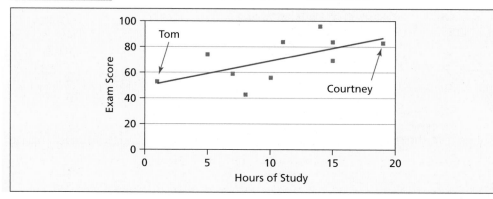

By the quick rule, Tom's leverage exceeds $4/n = 4/10 = .400$, so it appears that his observation is *influential*. Yet, despite his high leverage, the regression fits Tom's actual exam score well, so his residual is not unusual. This illustrates that *high leverage* and *unusual residuals* are two different concepts.

Mini Case   12.5

Body Fat   BodyFat

Is waistline a good predictor of body fat? Table 12.10 shows a random sample of 50 men's body fat (percent) and girths (centimeters). Figure 12.33 suggests that a linear regression is appropriate, and the MegaStat output in Figure 12.34 shows that the regression is highly significant ($F = 97.68$, $t = 9.883$, p-value $= .0000$).

TABLE 12.10	Abdomen Measurement and Body Fat ($n = 50$ men)						
Girth	**Fat%**	**Girth**	**Fat%**	**Girth**	**Fat%**	**Girth**	**Fat%**
99.1	19.0	78.0	7.3	93.0	18.1	95.0	21.6
76.0	8.4	83.2	13.4	76.0	13.7	86.0	8.8
83.1	9.2	85.6	22.3	106.1	28.1	90.6	19.5
88.5	21.8	90.3	20.2	109.3	23.0	105.5	31.0
118.0	33.6	104.5	16.8	104.3	30.8	79.4	10.4
104.3	31.7	95.6	18.4	100.5	16.5	*126.2*	33.1
79.5	6.4	103.1	27.7	77.9	7.4	98.0	20.2
108.8	24.6	89.9	17.4	101.6	18.2	95.5	21.9
81.9	4.1	104.0	26.4	99.7	25.1	73.7	11.2
76.6	12.8	95.3	11.3	96.7	16.1	86.4	10.9
88.7	12.3	105.0	27.1	95.8	30.2	*122.1*	45.1
90.9	8.5	83.5	17.2	104.8	25.4		
89.0	26.0	86.7	10.7	92.4	25.9		

Data are from a larger sample of 252 men in Roger W. Johnson, *Journal of Statistics Education* 4, No. 1 (1996).

FIGURE 12.33	**Body Fat Regression**

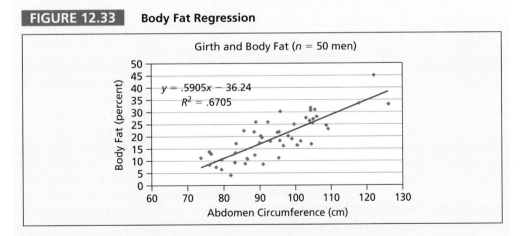

MegaStat's table of residuals, shown in Figure 12.35, highlights four unusual observations. Observations 5, 45, and 50 have high leverage values (exceeding $4/n = 4/50 = .08$) because their abdomen measurements (italicized and boldfaced in Table 12.10) are far from the mean. Observation 37 has a large studentized deleted residual (actual body fat of 30.20 percent is much greater than the predicted 20.33 percent). "Well-behaved" observations are omitted because they are not unusual according to any of the diagnostic criteria (leverage, studentized residual, or studentized deleted residual).

FIGURE 12.34 **Body Fat Scatter Plot**

Regression Analysis

r^2	0.671	n	50
r	0.819	k	1
Std. Error	5.086	Dep. Var.	Fat%1

ANOVA table

Source	SS	df	MS	F	p-value
Regression	2,527.1190	1	2,527.1190	97.68	3.71E-13
Residual	1,241.8162	48	25.8712		
Total	3,768.9352	49			

Regression output   confidence interval

variables	coefficients	std. error	t (df = 48)	p-value	95% lower	95% upper
Intercept	−36.2397	5.6690	−6.393	6.28E-08	−47.6379	−24.8415
Abdomen	0.5905	0.0597	9.883	3.71E-13	0.4704	0.7107

FIGURE 12.35 **Unusual Body Fat Residuals**

Observation	Fat%	Predicted	Residual	Leverage	Studentized Residual	Studentized Deleted Residual
5	33.60	33.44	0.16	0.099	0.033	0.032
37	30.20	20.33	9.87	0.020	1.960	2.022
45	33.10	38.28	−5.18	0.162	−1.114	−1.116
50	45.10	35.86	9.24	0.128	1.945	2.005

12.10 OTHER REGRESSION PROBLEMS

LO12

Explain the role of data conditioning and data transformations.

Outliers

We have mentioned outliers under the discussion of non-normal residuals. However, outliers are the source of many other woes, including loss of fit. What causes outliers? An outlier may be an error in recording the data. If so, the observation should be deleted. But how can you tell? Impossible or bizarre data values are *prima facie* reasons to discard a data value. For example, in a sample of body fat data, one adult man's weight was reported as 205 pounds and his height as 29.5 inches (probably a typographical error that should have been 69.5 inches). It is reasonable to discard the observation on grounds that it represents a population different from the other men. An outlier may be an observation that has been influenced by an unspecified "lurking" variable that should have been controlled but wasn't. If so, we should try to identify the lurking variable and formulate a *multiple* regression model that includes the lurking variable(s) as predictors.

Model Misspecification

If a relevant predictor has been omitted, then the model is *misspecified*. Instead of simple regression, you should use *multiple regression*. Such a situation is so common that it is almost a warning against relying on bivariate regression, since we usually can think of more than one explanatory variable. As you will see in the next chapter, multiple regression is computationally easy because the computer does all the work. In fact, most computer packages just call it "regression" regardless of the number of predictors.

Ill-Conditioned Data

Variables in the regression should be of the same general order of magnitude, and most people take steps intuitively to make sure this is the case (**well-conditioned data**). Unusually large or small data (called **ill-conditioned**) can cause loss of regression accuracy or can create awkward estimates with exponential notation. Consider the data in Table 12.11 for 30 randomly selected large companies (only a few of the 30 selected are shown in this table). The table shows two ways of displaying the same data, but with the decimal point changed. Figures 12.36 and 12.37 show Excel scatter plots with regression lines. Their appearance is the same, but the first graph has disastrously crowded axis labels. The graphs have the same slope and R^2, but the first regression has an unintelligible intercept (4E+07).

Company	Net Income in Thousands	Revenue in Thousands	Net Income in Millions	Revenue in Millions
Allstate	1,714,000	30,142,000	1,714	30,142
American Int'l Group	5,493,000	70,272,000	5,493	70,272
Barclays	3,348,000	26,565,000	3,348	26,565
⋮	⋮	⋮	⋮	⋮
Volkswagen Group	2,432,000	84,707,000	2,432	84,707
Wachovia	3,693,000	23,455,000	3,693	23,455
Walt Disney	1,024,000	26,255,000	1,024	26,255

TABLE 12.11

Net Income and Revenue for Selected Global 100 Companies
Global30

Source: www.forbes.com and *Forbes* 172, no. 2 (July 21, 2003), pp. 108–110.

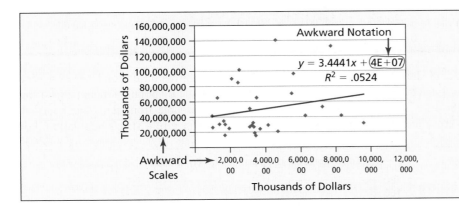

FIGURE 12.36

Ill-Conditioned Data

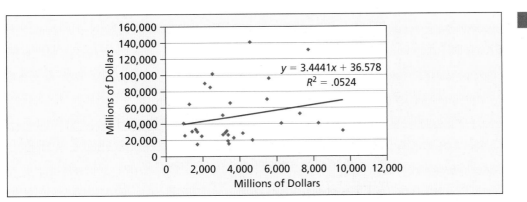

FIGURE 12.37

Well-Conditioned Data

Awkwardly small numbers may also require adjustment. For example, the number of automobile thefts per capita in the United States in 1990 was 0.004207. However, this statistic is easier to work with if it is reported "per 100,000 population" as 420.7. Worst of all would be to mix very large data with very small data. For example, in 1999 the per capita income in New York was $27,546 and the number of active physicians per capita was 0.00395. To avoid mixing magnitudes, we can redefine the variables as per capita income in thousands of dollars (27.546) and the number of active physicians per 10,000 population (39.5).

Tip

Adjust the magnitude of your data *before* running the regression.

Spurious Correlation   Prisoners

In a **spurious correlation**, two variables appear related because of the way they are defined. For example, consider the hypothesis that a state's spending on education is a linear function of its prison population. Such a hypothesis seems absurd, and we would expect the regression to be insignificant. But if the variables are defined as *totals* without adjusting for population, we will observe significant correlation. This phenomenon is called the *size effect* or the *problem of totals*. Table 12.12 shows selected data, first with the variables as *totals* and then as adjusted for population.

TABLE 12.12

State Spending on Education and State and Federal Prisoners   Prisoners

Source: *Statistical Abstract of the United States, 2001.*

State	Total Population (millions)	Using Totals		Using Per Capita Data	
		K–12 Spending ($ billions)	No. of Prisoners (thousands)	K–12 Spending per Capita ($)	Prisoners per 1,000 Pop.
Alabama	4.447	4.52	24.66	1,016	5.54
Alaska	0.627	1.33	3.95	2,129	6.30
⋮	⋮	⋮	⋮	⋮	⋮
Wisconsin	5.364	8.48	20.42	1,580	3.81
Wyoming	0.494	0.76	1.71	1,543	3.47

Figure 12.38 shows that, contrary to expectation, the regression on totals gives a very strong fit to the data. Yet Figure 12.39 shows that if we divide by population and adjust the decimals, the fit is nonexistent and the slope is indistinguishable from zero. The spurious correlation arose merely because both variables reflect the size of a state's population. For

FIGURE 12.38

Spurious Model Using Totals

FIGURE 12.39

Better Model: Per Capita Data

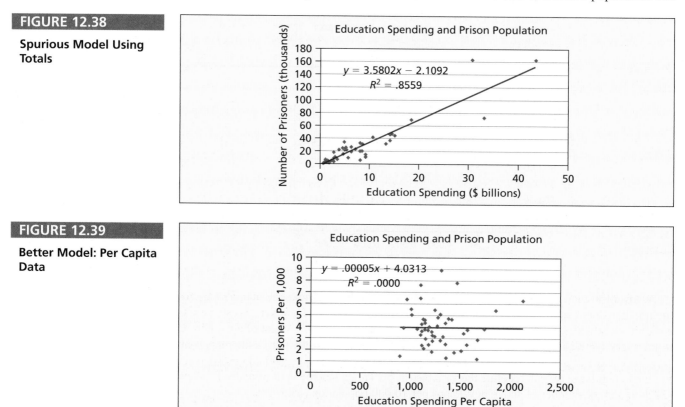

Education Spending and Prison Population

$y = 3.5802x - 2.1092$
$R^2 = .8559$

Education Spending and Prison Population

$y = .00005x + 4.0313$
$R^2 = .0000$

example, New York and California lie far to the upper right on the first scatter plot because they are populous states, while less populous states like South Dakota and Delaware are near the origin.

Model Form and Variable Transforms 📂 MPG1

Sometimes a relationship cannot be modeled using a linear regression. For example, Figure 12.40 shows fuel efficiency (city MPG) and engine size (horsepower) for a sample of 93 vehicles with a nonlinear model form fitted by Excel. This is one of several nonlinear forms offered by Excel (there are also logarithmic and exponential functions). Figure 12.41 shows an alternative, which is a linear regression after taking *logarithms* of each variable. These logarithms are in base 10, but any base will do (scientists prefer base *e*). This is an example of a **variable transform**. An advantage of the **log transformation** is that it reduces heteroscedasticity and improves the normality of the residuals, especially when dealing with totals (the *size problem* mentioned earlier). But log transforms will not work if any data values are zero or negative.

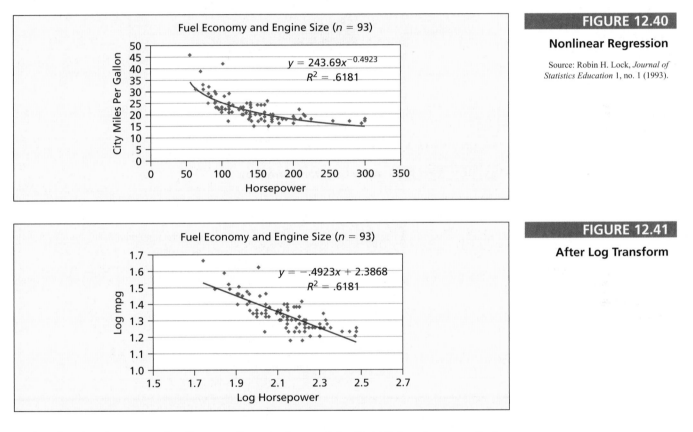

FIGURE 12.40

Nonlinear Regression

Source: Robin H. Lock, *Journal of Statistics Education* 1, no. 1 (1993).

FIGURE 12.41

After Log Transform

Excel makes it easy to fit all sorts of regression models. But fit is only one criterion for evaluating a regression model. Since nonlinear or transformed models might be hard to justify or explain to others, the principle of *Occam's Razor* (choosing the simplest explanation that fits the facts) favors linear regression, unless there are other compelling factors.

Mini Case   12.6

CEO Compensation 📂 CEO

Do highly compensated executives lead their corporations to outperform other firms? Statistics student Greg Burks examined 1-year total shareholder returns in 2001 less the S&P 500 average (i.e., percentage points above or below the S&P average) as a function of total CEO compensation in 2001 for the top 200 U.S. corporations. A scatter plot is shown in Figure 12.42. There appears to be little relationship, but a dozen or so hugely compensated CEOs (e.g., those earning over 50 million) stretch the X-axis scale while many others are clustered near the origin. A log transformation of X (using base 10) is shown in Figure 12.43. Neither fitted regression is significant. That is, there is little relationship between CEO compensation and stockholder returns (if anything, the slope is negative). However, the transformed data give a clearer picture. An advantage of the log transformation is that it improves the scatter of the residuals, producing a more homoscedastic distribution. In short, a log transformation with skewed data is an excellent option to consider.

FIGURE 12.42   **CEO Compensation and Stock Returns**

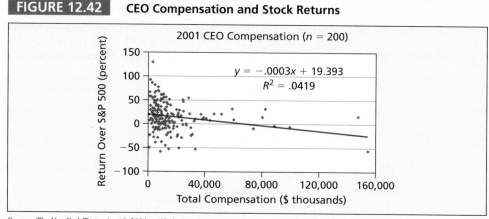

Source: *The New York Times*, Apr. 4, 2004, pp. 8–9.

FIGURE 12.43   **After Log Transformation**

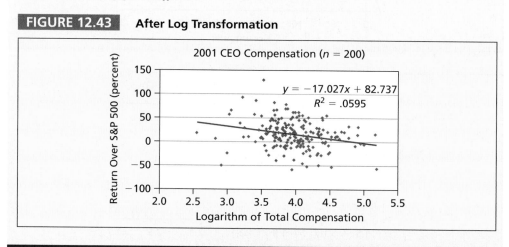

CHAPTER SUMMARY

The **sample correlation coefficient** r measures linear association between X and Y, with values near 0 indicating a lack of linearity while values near -1 (negative correlation) or $+1$ (positive correlation) suggest linearity. The t **test** is used to test hypotheses about the **population correlation** ρ. In **simple regression** there is an assumed linear relationship between the independent variable X (the **predictor**) and the dependent variable Y (the **response**). The slope (β_1) and intercept (β_0) are unknown **parameters** that are estimated from a sample. **Residuals** are the differences between **observed** and **fitted** Y-values. The **ordinary least squares** (OLS) method yields **regression coefficients** for the slope (b_1) and intercept (b_0) that minimize the sum of squared residuals. The **coefficient of determination** (R^2) measures the overall fit of the regression, with R^2 near 1 signifying a good fit and R^2 near 0 indicating a poor fit. The F **statistic** in the **ANOVA table** is used to test for significant overall regression, while the t **statistics** (and their p-values) are used to test hypotheses about the slope and intercept. The **standard error** of the regression is used to create **confidence intervals** or **prediction intervals** for Y. Regression assumes that the errors are normally distributed, independent random variables with constant variance σ^2. **Residual tests** identify possible **violations** of assumptions (**non-normality, autocorrelation, heteroscedasticity**). Data values with high **leverage** (unusual X-values) have strong influence on the regression. Unusual **standardized residuals** indicate cases where the regression gives a poor fit. **Ill-conditioned** data may lead to **spurious** correlation or other problems. **Data transforms** may help, but they also change the **model specification.**

autocorrelation, *521*
bivariate data, *489*
coefficient of
    determination, *503*
confidence interval, *515*
Durbin-Watson test, *522*
error sum of squares, *502*
heteroscedastic, *519*
homoscedastic, *519*
ill-conditioned data, *529*
intercept, *496*
leverage, *526*
log transformation, *531*

non-normality, *518*
ordinary least squares
    (OLS), *499*
population correlation
    coefficient, ρ, *491*
prediction interval, *515*
predictor variable, *495*
regression equation, *497*
R^2, *503*
residual, *497*
response variable, *495*
sample correlation
    coefficient, r, *490*

scatter plot, *489*
simple regression, *495*
slope, *496*
spurious correlation, *530*
standard error, *504*
standardized residuals, *518*
studentized residuals, *524*
sums of squares, *490*
t statistic, *491*
variable transform, *531*
well-conditioned data, *529*

Commonly Used Formulas in Simple Regression

Sample correlation coefficient: $r = \dfrac{\sum\limits_{i=1}^{n}(x_i - \bar{x})(y_i - \bar{y})}{\sqrt{\sum\limits_{i=1}^{n}(x_i - \bar{x})^2}\sqrt{\sum\limits_{i=1}^{n}(y_i - \bar{y})^2}}$

Test statistic for zero correlation: $t_{\text{calc}} = r\sqrt{\dfrac{n-2}{1-r^2}}$ with $d.f. = n - 2$

True regression line: $y = \beta_0 + \beta_1 x + \varepsilon$

Fitted regression line: $\hat{y} = b_0 + b_1 x$

Slope of fitted regression: $b_1 = \dfrac{\sum\limits_{i=1}^{n}(x_i - \bar{x})(y_i - \bar{y})}{\sum\limits_{i=1}^{n}(x_i - \bar{x})^2}$

Intercept of fitted regression: $b_0 = \bar{y} - b_1\bar{x}$

Sum of squared residuals: $SSE = \sum\limits_{i=1}^{n}(y_i - \hat{y}_i)^2 = \sum\limits_{i=1}^{n}(y_i - b_0 - b_1 x_i)^2$

Coefficient of determination: $R^2 = 1 - \dfrac{\sum\limits_{i=1}^{n}(y_i - \hat{y}_i)^2}{\sum\limits_{i=1}^{n}(y_i - \bar{y})^2} = 1 - \dfrac{SSE}{SST}$

Standard error of the estimate: $s = \sqrt{\dfrac{\sum\limits_{i=1}^{n}(y_i - \hat{y}_i)^2}{n-2}} = \sqrt{\dfrac{SSE}{n-2}}$

Standard error of the slope: $s_{b_1} = \dfrac{s}{\sqrt{\sum\limits_{i=1}^{n}(x_i - \bar{x})^2}}$ with $d.f. = n - 2$

t test for zero slope: $t_{\text{calc}} = \dfrac{b_1 - 0}{s_{b_1}}$

Confidence interval for true slope: $b_1 - t_{\alpha/2}s_{b_1} \leq \beta_1 \leq b_1 + t_{\alpha/2}s_{b_1}$

Confidence interval for conditional mean of Y: $\hat{y}_i \pm t_{\alpha/2}s \sqrt{\dfrac{1}{n} + \dfrac{(x_i - \bar{x})^2}{\sum\limits_{i=1}^{n}(x_i - \bar{x})^2}}$

Prediction interval for Y: $\hat{y}_i \pm t_{\alpha/2}s \sqrt{1 + \dfrac{1}{n} + \dfrac{(x_i - \bar{x})^2}{\sum\limits_{i=1}^{n}(x_i - \bar{x})^2}}$

CHAPTER REVIEW

1. (a) How does correlation analysis differ from regression analysis? (b) What does a correlation coefficient reveal? (c) State the quick rule for a significant correlation and explain its limitations. (d) What sums are needed to calculate a correlation coefficient? (e) What are the two ways of testing a correlation coefficient for significance?

2. (a) What is a simple regression model? (b) State three caveats about regression. (c) What does the random error component in a regression model represent? (d) What is the difference between a regression residual and the true random error?

3. (a) Explain how you fit a regression to an Excel scatter plot. (b) What are the limitations of Excel's scatter plot fitted regression?

4. (a) Explain the logic of the ordinary least squares (OLS) method. (b) How are the least squares formulas for the slope and intercept derived? (c) What sums are needed to calculate the least squares estimates?

5. (a) Why can't we use the sum of the residuals to assess fit? (b) What sums are needed to calculate R^2? (c) Name an advantage of using the R^2 statistic instead of the standard error s_{yx} to measure fit. (d) Why do we need the standard error s_{yx}?

6. (a) Explain why a confidence interval for the slope or intercept would be equivalent to a two-tailed hypothesis test. (b) Why is it especially important to test for a zero slope?

7. (a) What does the F statistic show? (b) What is its range? (c) What is the relationship between the F test and the t tests for the slope and correlation coefficient?

8. (a) For a given X, explain the distinction between a confidence interval for the conditional mean of Y and a prediction interval for an individual Y-value. (b) Why is the individual prediction interval wider? (c) Why are these intervals narrowest when X is near its mean? (d) When can quick rules for these intervals give acceptable results, and when not?

9. (a) What is a residual? (b) What is a standardized residual and why is it useful? (c) Name two alternative ways to identify unusual residuals.

10. (a) When does a data point have high leverage (refer to the scatter plot)? (b) Name one test for unusual leverage.

11. (a) Name three assumptions about the random error term in the regression model. (b) Why are the residuals important in testing these assumptions?

12. (a) What are the consequences of non-normal errors? (b) Explain two tests for non-normality. (c) What can we do about non-normal residuals?

13. (a) What is heteroscedasticity? Identify its two common forms. (b) What are its consequences? (c) How do we test for it? (d) What can we do about it?

14. (a) What is autocorrelation? Identify two main forms of it. (b) What are its consequences? (c) Name two ways to test for it. (d) What can we do about it?

15. (a) Why might there be outliers in the residuals? (b) What actions could be taken?

16. (a) What is ill-conditioned data? How can it be avoided? (b) What is spurious correlation? How can it be avoided?

17. (a) What is a log transform? (b) What are its advantages and disadvantages?

Instructions: Choose one or more of the data sets *A–J* below, or as assigned by your instructor. The first column is the *X*, or independent, variable and the second column is the *Y*, or dependent, variable. Use a spreadsheet or a statistical package (e.g., MegaStat or MINITAB) to obtain the simple regression and required graphs. Write your answers to exercises 12.32 through 12.47 (or those assigned by your instructor) in a concise report, labeling your answers to each question. Insert tables and graphs in your report as appropriate. You may work with a partner if your instructor allows it.

12.32 Are the variables cross-sectional data or time-series data?

12.33 How do you imagine the data were collected?

12.34 Is the sample size sufficient to yield a good estimate? If not, do you think more data could easily be obtained, given the nature of the problem?

12.35 State your *a priori* hypothesis about the sign of the slope. Is it reasonable to suppose a cause and effect relationship?

12.36 Make a scatter plot of *Y* against *X*. Discuss what it tells you.

12.37 Use Excel's Add Trendline feature to fit a linear regression to the scatter plot. Is a linear model credible?

12.38 Interpret the slope. Does the intercept have meaning, given the range of the data?

12.39 Use Excel, MegaStat, or MINITAB to fit the regression model, including residuals and standardized residuals.

12.40 (a) Does the 95 percent confidence interval for the slope include zero? If so, what does this tell you? If not, what does it mean? (b) Do a two-tailed *t* test for zero slope at $\alpha = .05$. State the hypotheses, degrees of freedom, and critical value for your test. (c) Interpret the *p*-value for the slope. (d) Did the sample support your hypothesis about the sign of the slope?

12.41 (a) Based on the R^2 and ANOVA table for your model, how would you assess the fit? (b) Interpret the *p*-value for the *F* statistic. (c) Would you say that your model's fit is good enough to be of practical value?

12.42 Study the table of residuals. Identify as *outliers* any standardized residuals that exceed 3 and as *unusual* any that exceed 2. Can you suggest any reasons for these unusual residuals?

12.43 (a) Make a histogram (or normal probability plot) of the residuals and discuss its appearance. (b) Do you see evidence that your regression may violate the assumption of normal errors?

12.44 Inspect the residual plot to check for heteroscedasticity and report your conclusions.

12.45 Is an autocorrelation test appropriate for your data? If so, perform one or more tests of the residuals (eyeball inspection of residual plot against observation order, runs test, and/or Durbin-Watson test).

12.46 Use MegaStat or MINITAB to generate 95 percent confidence and prediction intervals for various *X*-values.

12.47 Use MegaStat or MINITAB to identify observations with high leverage.

DATA SET A	Median Income and Median Home Prices in Selected Eastern Cities ($n = 34$ cities) 🖥 HomePrice1	
City	*Income*	*Home*
Alexandria, VA	59.976	290.000
Bernards Twp., NJ	112.435	279.900
Brentwood, TN	107.866	338.250
⋮	⋮	⋮
Sugarland Run, VA	103.350	278.250
Sully, VA	92.942	290.000
Wellington, FL	76.076	230.000

Source: *Money Magazine* 32, no. 1 (January, 2004), pp. 102–103.

Note: Values are in thousands of dollars. Data are for educational purposes only.

DATA SET B	Employees and Revenue in Large Automotive Companies in 1999 ($n = 24$ companies) 🖥 CarFirms	
Company	*Employees*	*Revenue*
BMW	119.9	35.9
DaimlerChrysler	441.5	154.6
Dana	86.4	12.8
⋮	⋮	⋮
TRW	78.0	11.9
Volkswagen	297.9	76.3
Volvo	70.3	26.8

Source: Project by statistics students Paul Ruskin, Kristy Bielewski, and Linda Stengel.

Note: Employees are in thousands and *Revenue* is in billions.

DATA SET C — Estimated and Actual Length of Stay in Months (*n* = 16 patients) ☞ Hospital

Patient	ELOS	ALOS
1	10.5	10
2	4.5	2
3	7.5	4
⋮	⋮	⋮
14	6	10
15	7.5	7
16	3	5.5

Source: Records of a hospital outpatient cognitive retraining clinic.

Note: ELOS used a 42-item assessment instrument combined with expert team judgment. Patients had suffered head trauma, stroke, or other medical conditions affecting cognitive function.

DATA SET D — Single-Engine Aircraft Performance (*n* = 52 airplanes) ☞ Airplanes

Mfgr/Model	TotalHP	Cruise
AMD CH 2000	116	100
Beech Baron 58	600	200
Beech Baron 58P	650	241
⋮	⋮	⋮
Sky Arrow 650 TC	81	98
Socata TB20 Trinidad	250	163
Tiger AG-5B	180	143

Source: New and used airplane reports in *Flying* (various issues).

Note: Cruise is in knots (nautical miles per hour). Data are for educational purposes only and should not be used as a guide to aircraft performance. *TotalHP* is total horse power.

DATA SET E — Ages and Weights of 31 Randomly Chosen U.S. Nickels (*n* = 31 nickels) ☞ Nickels

Obs	Age (yrs)	Weight (gm)
1	2	5.043
2	15	4.893
3	22	4.883
⋮	⋮	⋮
29	21	4.927
30	1	5.035
31	16	4.983

Source: As an independent project, a statistics student weighed randomly-chosen circulated nickels on a scale whose accuracy is 0.001 gram.

Note: Coin age is the difference between the measurement year and the mint year.

DATA SET F — U.S. Annual Percent Inflation in Prices of Commodities and Services (*n* = 47 years) ☞ Inflation

Year	Commodities %	Services %
1960	0.9	3.4
1961	0.6	1.7
1962	0.9	2.0
⋮	⋮	⋮
2004	2.3	2.9
2005	3.6	3.3
2006	2.4	3.8

Source: *Economic Report of the President, 2007.*

Note: Data are year-to-year percent changes in the Consumer Price Index (CPI) in these two categories.

DATA SET G — Mileage and Vehicle Weight (*n* = 43 vehicles) ☞ MPG2

Vehicle	Weight	City MPG
Acura CL	3450	20
Accura TSX	3320	23
BMW 3-Series	3390	19
⋮	⋮	⋮
Toyota Sienna	4120	19
Volkswagen Jetta	3045	34
Volvo C70	3690	20

Source: *Consumer Reports New Car Buying Guide 2003–2004* (Consumers Union, 2003).

Note: Sample is the first vehicle on every 5th page starting at page 40. Data are for statistical education only and should not be viewed as a guide to vehicle performance.

DATA SET H — Pasta Sauce Per Gram Total Calories and Fat Calories (*n* = 20 products) ☞ Pasta

Product	Fat Cal/gm	Cal/gm
Barilla Roasted Garlic & Onion	0.20	0.64
Barilla Tomato & Basil	0.12	0.56
Classico Tomato & Basil	0.08	0.40
⋮	⋮	⋮
Ragu Roasted Garlic	0.19	0.70
Ragu Traditional	0.20	0.56
Sutter Home Tomato & Garlic	0.16	0.64

Source: Independent project by statistics students Donna Bennett, Nicole Cook, Latrice Haywood, and Robert Malcolm.

Note: Data are intended for educational purposes only and should not be viewed as a nutrition guide.

DATA SET I	**Temperature and Energy Usage for a Residence (*n* = 24 months)** 📷 **Electric**	
Month	*Avg Temp (F°)*	*Usage (kWh)*
1	62	436
2	71	464
3	76	446
⋮	⋮	⋮
22	25	840
23	38	867
24	48	606

Source: Electric bills for a residence and NOAA weather data.

DATA SET J	**Life Expectancy and Birth Rates (*n* = 153 nations)** 📷 **BirthRates**	
Nation	*Life Expectancy*	*Birth rate*
Afghanistan	46.6	41.03
Albania	72.1	18.59
Algeria	70.2	22.34
⋮	⋮	⋮
Yemen	60.6	43.30
Zambia	37.4	41.01
Zimbabwe	36.5	24.59

Source: Central Intelligence Agency, *The World Factbook, 2003.*

12.48 Researchers found a correlation coefficient of $r = .50$ on personality measures for identical twins. A reporter interpreted this to mean that "the environment orchestrated one-half of their personality differences." Do you agree with this interpretation? Discuss. (See *Science News* 140 [December 7, 1991], p. 377.)

12.49 A study of the role of spreadsheets in planning in 55 small firms defined Y = "satisfaction with sales growth" and X = "executive commitment to planning." Analysis yielded an overall correlation of $r = .3043$. Do a two-tailed test for zero correlation at $\alpha = .025$.

12.50 In a study of stock prices from 1970 to 1994, the correlation between Nasdaq closing prices on successive days (i.e., with a 1-day lag) was $r = .13$ with a t statistic of 5.47. Interpret this result. (See David Nawrocki, "The Problems with Monte Carlo Simulation," *Journal of Financial Planning* 14, no. 11 [November 2001], p. 96.)

12.51 Regression analysis of free throws by 29 NBA teams during the 2002–2003 season revealed the fitted regression $Y = 55.2 + .73X$ ($R^2 = .874$, $s_{yx} = 53.2$) where Y = total free throws made and X = total free throws attempted. The observed range of X was from 1,620 (New York Knicks) to 2,382 (Golden State Warriors). (a) Find the expected number of free throws made for a team that shoots 2,000 free throws. (b) Do you think that the intercept is meaningful? *Hint:* Make a scatter plot and let Excel fit the line. (c) Use the quick rule to make a 95 percent prediction interval for Y when $X = 2,000$. 📷 **FreeThrows**

12.52 In the following regression, X = weekly pay, Y = income tax withheld, and $n = 35$ McDonald's employees. (a) Write the fitted regression equation. (b) State the degrees of freedom for a two-tailed test for zero slope, and use Appendix D to find the critical value at $\alpha = .05$. (c) What is your conclusion about the slope? (d) Interpret the 95 percent confidence limits for the slope. (e) Verify that $F = t^2$ for the slope. (f) In your own words, describe the fit of this regression.

R^2	0.202
Std. Error	6.816
n	35

ANOVA table

Source	*SS*	*df*	*MS*	*F*	*p-value*
Regression	387.6959	1	387.6959	8.35	.0068
Residual	1,533.0614	33	46.4564		
Total	1,920.7573	34			

Regression output					*confidence interval*	
variables	*coefficients*	*std. error*	*t (df = 33)*	*p-value*	*95% lower*	*95% upper*
Intercept	30.7963	6.4078	4.806	.0000	17.7595	43.8331
Slope	0.0343	0.0119	2.889	.0068	0.0101	0.0584

12.53 In the following regression, $X =$ monthly maintenance spending (dollars), $Y =$ monthly machine downtime (hours), and $n = 15$ copy machines. (a) Write the fitted regression equation. (b) State the degrees of freedom for a two-tailed test for zero slope, and use Appendix D to find the critical value at $\alpha = .05$. (c) What is your conclusion about the slope? (d) Interpret the 95 percent confidence limits for the slope. (e) Verify that $F = t^2$ for the slope. (f) In your own words, describe the fit of this regression.

R²	0.370
Std. Error	286.793
n	15

ANOVA table

Source	SS	df	MS	F	p-value
Regression	628,298.2	1	628,298.2	7.64	.0161
Residual	1,069,251.8	13	82,250.1		
Total	1,697,550.0	14			

Regression output   confidence interval

variables	coefficients	std. error	t (df = 13)	p-value	95% lower	95% upper
Intercept	1,743.57	288.82	6.037	.0000	1,119.61	2,367.53
Slope	−1.2163	0.4401	−2.764	.0161	−2.1671	−0.2656

12.54 In the following regression, $X =$ total assets (\$ billions), $Y =$ total revenue (\$ billions), and $n = 64$ large banks. (a) Write the fitted regression equation. (b) State the degrees of freedom for a two-tailed test for zero slope, and use Appendix D to find the critical value at $\alpha = .05$. (c) What is your conclusion about the slope? (d) Interpret the 95 percent confidence limits for the slope. (e) Verify that $F = t^2$ for the slope. (f) In your own words, describe the fit of this regression.

R²	0.519
Std. Error	6.977
n	64

ANOVA table

Source	SS	df	MS	F	p-value
Regression	3,260.0981	1	3,260.0981	66.97	1.90E-11
Residual	3,018.3339	62	48.6828		
Total	6,278.4320	63			

Regression output   confidence interval

variables	coefficients	std. error	t (df = 62)	p-value	95% lower	95% upper
Intercept	6.5763	1.9254	3.416	.0011	2.7275	10.4252
X1	0.0452	0.0055	8.183	1.90E-11	0.0342	0.0563

12.55 Do stock prices of competing companies move together? Below are daily closing prices of two computer services firms (IBM = International Business Machines Corporation, EDS = Electronic Data Systems Corporation). (a) Calculate the sample correlation coefficient (e.g., using Excel or MegaStat). (b) At $\alpha = .01$ can you conclude that the true correlation coefficient is greater than zero? (c) Make a scatter plot of the data. What does it say? (Data are from Center for Research and Security Prices, University of Chicago.) 📄 **StockPrices**

Daily Closing Price ($) of Two Stocks in October and November 2004 (*n* = 42 days)

Date	IBM	EDS
9/1/04	84.22	19.31
9/2/04	84.57	19.63
9/3/04	84.39	19.19
⋮	⋮	⋮
10/27/04	90.00	21.26
10/28/04	89.50	21.41
10/29/04	89.75	21.27

12.56 Below are percentages for *annual sales growth* and *net sales attributed to loyalty card usage* at 74 Noodles & Company restaurants. (a) Make a scatter plot. (b) Find the correlation coefficient and interpret it. (c) Test the correlation coefficient for significance, clearly stating the degrees of freedom. (d) Does it appear that loyalty card usage is associated with increased sales growth? 📄 **LoyaltyCard**

Annual Sales Growth (%) and Loyalty Card Usage (% of Net Sales) (*n* = 74 restaurants)

Store	Growth%	Loyalty%
1	−8.3	2.1
2	−4.0	2.5
3	−3.9	1.7
⋮	⋮	⋮
72	20.8	1.1
73	25.5	0.6
74	28.8	1.8

Source: Noodles & Company

12.57 Below are fertility rates (average children born per woman) in 15 EU nations for 2 years. (a) Make a scatter plot. (b) Find the correlation coefficient and interpret it. (c) Test the correlation coefficient for significance, clearly stating the degrees of freedom. (Data are from the World Health Organization.) 📄 **Fertility**

Fertility Rates for EU Nations (*n* = 15)

Nation	1990	2000
Austria	1.5	1.3
Belgium	1.6	1.5
Denmark	1.6	1.7
⋮	⋮	⋮
Spain	1.4	1.1
Sweden	2.0	1.4
U.K.	1.8	1.7

12.58 Consider the following prices and accuracy ratings for 27 stereo speakers. (a) Make a scatter plot of accuracy rating as a function of price. (b) Calculate the correlation coefficient. At $\alpha = .05$, does the correlation differ from zero? (c) In your own words, describe the scatter plot. (Data are from *Consumer Reports* 68, no. 11 [November 2003], p. 31. Data are intended for statistical education and not as a guide to speaker performance.) 📄 **Speakers**

Price and Accuracy of Selected Stereo Speakers (*n* = 27)

Brand and Model	Type	Price ($)	Accuracy
BIC America Venturi DV62si	Shelf	200	91
Bose 141	Shelf	100	86
Bose 201 Series V	Shelf	220	89
⋮	⋮	⋮	⋮
Sony SS-MB350H	Shelf	100	92
Sony SS-MF750H	Floor	280	91
Sony SS-X30ED	Shelf	500	83

12.59 Choose *one* of these three data sets. (a) Make a scatter plot. (b) Let Excel estimate the regression line, with fitted equation and R^2. (c) Describe the fit of the regression. (d) Write the fitted regression equation and interpret the slope. (e) Do you think that the estimated intercept is meaningful? Explain.

Commercial Real Estate (*X* = assessed value, $000; *Y* = floor space, sq. ft.) (*n* = 15)
 Assessed

Assessed	Size
1,796	4,790
1,544	4,720
2,094	5,940
⋮	⋮
1,678	4,880
710	1,620
678	1,820

Sasnak Co. Salaries (*X* = employee age; *Y* = employee salary, $000) (*n* = 23)
 Salaries

Employee	Age	Salary
Mary	23	28.6
Frieda	31	53.3
Alicia	44	73.8
⋮	⋮	⋮
Marcia	54	75.8
Ellen	44	79.8
Iggy	36	70.2

Poway Big Homes, Ltd. (*X* = home size, sq. ft.; *Y* = selling price, $000) (*n* = 20)
 HomePrice2

SqFt	Price
3,570	861
3,410	740
2,690	563
⋮	⋮
3,020	720
2,320	575
3,130	785

12.60 Simple regression was employed to establish the effects of childhood exposure to lead. The effective sample size was about 122 subjects. The independent variable was the level of dentin lead (parts per million). Below are regressions using various dependent variables. (a) Calculate the *t* statistic for each slope. (b) From the *p*-values, which slopes differ from zero at $\alpha = .01$? (c) Do you feel that cause and effect can be assumed? *Hint:* Do a Web search for information about effects of childhood lead exposure. (Data are from H. L. Needleman et al., *The New England Journal of Medicine* 322, no. 2 [January 1990], p. 86.)

Dependent Variable	R^2	Estimated Slope	Std Error	p-value
Highest grade achieved	.061	−0.027	0.009	.008
Reading grade equivalent	.121	−0.070	0.018	.000
Class standing	.039	−0.006	0.003	.048
Absence from school	.071	4.8	1.7	.006
Grammatical reasoning	.051	0.159	0.062	.012
Vocabulary	.108	−0.124	0.032	.000
Hand-eye coordination	.043	0.041	0.018	.020
Reaction time	.025	11.8	6.66	.080
Minor antisocial behavior	.025	−0.639	0.36	.082

12.61 Below are recent financial ratios for a random sample of 20 integrated health care systems. *Operating Margin* is total revenue minus total expenses divided by total revenue plus net operating profits. *Equity Financing* is fund balance divided by total assets. (a) Make a scatter plot of $Y =$ operating margin and $X =$ equity financing (both variables are in percent). (b) Use Excel to fit the regression, with fitted equation and R^2. (c) In your own words, describe the fit. (Data are from *Hospitals & Health Networks* 71, no. 6 [March 20, 1997], pp. 48–49. Copyright © 1997 by Health Forum, Inc. Used with permission. Data are intended for statistical education and not as a guide to financial performance.) 📁 **HealthCare**

Financial Ratios for Selected Health Care Systems ($n = 20$)

Name of Health Care System	Operating Margin	Equity Financing
Albert Einstein Healthcare Network	3.89	35.58
Alliant Health Systems	8.23	59.68
Baptist Memorial Health Care System	2.56	40.48
⋮	⋮	⋮
OSF Healthcare Network	4.75	54.21
Samaritan Health System	0.00	59.73
Scottsdale Memorial Health System	10.79	46.21

12.62 Consider the following data on 20 chemical reactions, with $Y =$ chromatographic retention time (seconds) and $X =$ molecular weight (gm/mole). (a) Make a scatter plot. (b) Use Excel to fit the regression, with fitted equation and R^2. (c) In your own words, describe the fit. (Data provided by John Seeley of Oakland University.) 📁 **Chemicals**

Retention Time and Molecular Weight ($n = 20$)

Name	Retention Time	Molecular Weight
alpha-pinene	234.50	136.24
cyclopentene	95.27	68.12
p-diethylbenzene	284.00	134.22
⋮	⋮	⋮
pentane	78.00	72.15
isooctane	136.90	114.23
hexane	106.00	86.18

12.63 A common belief among faculty is that teaching ratings are lower in large classes. Below are MINITAB results from a regression using $Y =$ mean student evaluation of the professor and $X =$ class size for 364 business school classes taught during the 2002–2003 academic year. Ratings are on a scale of 1 (lowest) to 5 (highest). (a) What do these regression results tell you about the relationship between class size and faculty ratings? (b) Is a bivariate model adequate? If not, suggest additional predictors to be considered.

Predictor	Coef	SE Coef	T	P
Constant	4.18378	0.07226	57.90	0.000
Enroll	0.000578	0.002014	0.29	0.774

$S = 0.5688$ R-Sq = 0.0%   R-Sq(adj) = 0.0%

12.64 Below are revenue and profit (both in $ billions) for nine large entertainment companies. (a) Make a scatter plot of profit as a function of revenue. (b) Use Excel to fit the regression, with fitted equation and R^2. (c) In your own words, describe the fit. (Data are from *Fortune* 149, no. 7 [April 5, 2005], p. F-50.) 📂 **Entertainment**

Revenue and Profit of Entertainment Companies ($n = 9$)

Company	Revenue	Profit
AMC Entertainment	1.792	−0.020
Clear Channel Communication	8.931	1.146
Liberty Media	2.446	−0.978
⋮	⋮	⋮
Univision Communications	1.311	0.155
Viacom	26.585	1.417
Walt Disney	27.061	1.267

12.65 Below are fitted regressions based on used vehicle ads. Observed ranges of X are shown. The assumed regression model is *AskingPrice* = f(*VehicleAge*). (a) Interpret the slopes. (b) Are the intercepts meaningful? Explain. (c) Assess the fit of each model. (d) Is a bivariate model adequate to explain vehicle prices? If not, what other predictors might be considered? (Data are from *Detroit's AutoFocus* 4, Issue 38 [September 17–23, 2004]. Data are for educational purposes only and should not be viewed as a guide to vehicle prices.)

Vehicle	n	Intercept	Slope	R^2	Min Age	Max Age
Ford Explorer	31	22,252	−2,452	.643	2	6
Ford F-150 Pickup	43	26,164	−2,239	.713	1	37
Ford Mustang	33	21,308	−1,691	.328	1	10
Ford Taurus	32	13,160	−906	.679	1	14

12.66 Below are results of a regression of Y = average stock returns (in percent) as a function of X = average price/earnings ratios for the period 1949–1997 (49 years). Separate regressions were done for various holding periods (sample sizes are therefore variable). (a) Summarize what the regression results tell you. (b) Would you anticipate autocorrelation in this type of data? Explain. (Data are from Ruben Trevino and Fiona Robertson, "P/E Ratios and Stock Market Returns," *Journal of Financial Planning* 15, no. 2 [February 2002], p. 78.)

Holding Period	Intercept	Slope	t	R^2	p
1-Year	28.10	−0.92	1.86	.0688	.0686
2-Year	26.11	−0.86	2.57	.1252	.0136
5-Year	20.67	−0.57	2.99	.1720	.0046
8-Year	24.73	−0.94	6.93	.5459	.0000
10-Year	24.51	−0.95	8.43	.6516	.0000

12.67 Adult height is somewhat predictable from average height of both parents. For females, a commonly used equation is *YourHeight* = *ParentHeight* − 2.5 while for males the equation is *YourHeight* = *ParentHeight* + 2.5. (a) Test these equations on yourself (or on somebody else). (b) How well did the equations predict your height? (c) How do you suppose these equations were derived?

CHAPTER 12 Online Learning Resources

The Online Learning Center (OLC) at www.mhhe.com/doane3e has several *LearningStats* demonstrations to help you understand simple regression. Your instructor may assign one or more of them, or you may decide to download the ones that sound interesting.

Topic	LearningStats Demonstrations
Correlation	Overview of Correlation Scatter Plot Simulation
Regression	Overview of Simple Regression Using Excel for Regression
Ordinary least squares estimators	Least Squares Method Demonstration Derivation of OLS Estimators Effect of Model Form Effect of X Range
Confidence and prediction intervals	Confidence and Prediction Intervals Superimposing Many Fitted Regressions
Violations of assumptions	Non-Normal Errors Heteroscedastic Errors Autocorrelated Errors

Key: = PowerPoint   = Word   = Excel

CHAPTER

Multiple Regression

Chapter Contents

Chapter Learning Objectives

When you finish this chapter you should be able to

LO1 Use a fitted multiple regression equation to make predictions.

LO2 Interpret the R^2 and perform an F test for overall significance.

LO3 Test individual predictors for significance.

LO4 Interpret confidence intervals for regression coefficients.

LO5 Incorporate a categorical variable into a multiple regression model.

LO6 Detect multicollinearity and assess its effects.

LO7 Analyze residuals to check for violations of residual assumptions.

LO8 Identify unusual residuals and high leverage observations.

LO9 Explain the role of data conditioning and data transformations.

Simple or Multiple?

Multiple regression extends *simple regression* to include several independent variables (or *predictors*). Everything you learned about simple regression is a special case of multiple regression. The interpretation of multiple regression is similar, except that two-dimensional *X-Y* scatter plots are of limited value in higher-dimensional models. Since all calculations are done by computer, there is no extra computational burden. In fact, statisticians make no distinction between simple and multiple regression—they just call it *regression*.

Multiple regression is required when a single-predictor model is inadequate to describe the true relationship between the dependent variable Y (the response variable) and its potential predictors ($X_1, X_2, X_3, \ldots$). Adding predictors is more than a matter of "improving the fit." Rather, it is a question of specifying a correct model. Omission of relevant predictors (*model misspecification*) can cause biased estimates and misleading results. A low R^2 in a simple regression model does not necessarily mean that X and Y are unrelated, but may simply indicate that the model is incorrectly specified.

LO1

Use a fitted multiple regression equation to make predictions.

Limitations of Simple Regression

- Multiple relationships usually exist.
- Biased estimates if relevant predictors are omitted.
- Lack of fit does not show that X is unrelated to Y if the true model is multivariate.

Because multiple predictors usually are relevant, simple regression is only used when there is a compelling need for a simple model, or when other predictors have only modest effects and a single logical predictor "stands out" as doing a very good job all by itself.

Regression Terminology

The **response variable** (Y) is assumed to be related to the k **predictors** ($X_1, X_2, \ldots, X_k$) by a linear equation called the *population regression model:*

$$y = \beta_0 + \beta_1 x_1 + \beta_2 x_2 + \cdots + \beta_k x_k + \varepsilon \qquad \textbf{(13.1)}$$

A *random error* ε represents everything that is not part of the model. The unknown regression coefficients $\beta_0, \beta_1, \beta_2, \ldots, \beta_k$ are *parameters* and are denoted by Greek letters. Each coefficient β_j shows the change in the expected value of Y for a unit change in X_j while holding everything else constant (*ceteris paribus*). The errors are assumed to be unobservable, independent random disturbances that are normally distributed with zero mean and constant variance, that is, $\varepsilon \sim N(0, \sigma^2)$. Under these assumptions, the ordinary least squares (OLS) estimation method yields unbiased, consistent, efficient estimates of the unknown parameters. The *sample estimates* of the regression coefficients are denoted by Roman letters $b_0, b_1, b_2, \ldots, b_k$. The *predicted* value of the response variable is denoted $\hat{y}$ and is calculated by inserting the values of the predictors into the *estimated regression equation:*

(13.2) $\qquad \hat{y} = b_0 + b_1 x_1 + b_2 x_2 + \cdots + b_k x_k \qquad$ (predicted value of Y)

In this chapter, we will not show formulas for the estimated coefficients $b_0, b_1, b_2, \ldots, b_k$ because they entail matrix algebra. All regression equations are estimated by computer software (Excel, MegaStat, MINITAB, etc.) utilizing the appropriate formulas.

Figure 13.1 illustrates the idea of a multiple regression model. Some of the proposed predictors may be useful, while others may not. We won't know until the regression is actually fitted. If an estimated coefficient has a positive ($+$) sign, then higher X values are associated with higher Y values, and conversely if an estimated coefficient has a negative sign.

In a simple regression (one predictor) the fitted regression is a *line,* while in multiple regression (more than one predictor) the fitted regression is a *surface* or *plane* as illustrated in Figure 13.2. If there are more than two predictors, no diagram can be drawn, and the fitted regression is represented by a hyperplane.

FIGURE 13.1

Visualizing a Multiple Regression

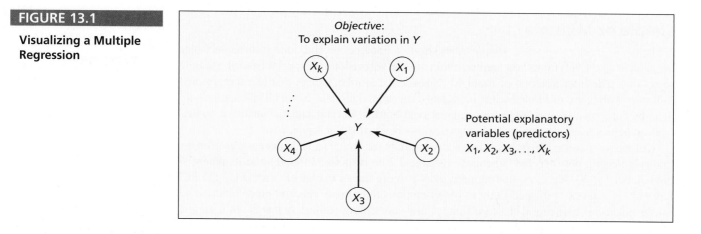

FIGURE 13.2

Fitted Regression: Bivariate versus Multivariate

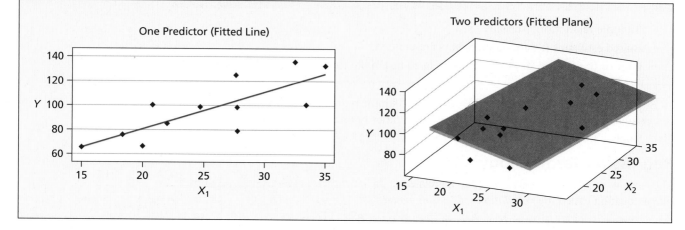

Data Format

To obtain a fitted regression we need n observed values of the response variable Y and its proposed predictors $X_1, X_2, \ldots, X_k$. A multivariate data set is a single column of Y-values and k columns of X-values. The form of this $n \times k$ matrix of observations is shown in Figure 13.3.

Response	Predictors			
Y	X_1	X_2	...	X_k
y_1	x_{11}	x_{12}	...	x_{1k}
y_2	x_{21}	x_{22}	...	x_{2k}
⋮	⋮	⋮	⋮	⋮
y_n	x_{n1}	x_{n2}	...	x_{nk}

FIGURE 13.3

Data for a Multiple Regression

In Excel's Data Analysis > Regression you are required to have the X data in contiguous columns. However, MegaStat and MINITAB permit nonadjacent columns of X data. Flexibility in choosing data columns is useful if you decide to omit one or more X data columns and re-run the regression (e.g., to seek parsimony).

Illustration: Home Prices

Table 13.1 shows sales of 30 new homes in an upscale development. Although the selling price of a home (the *response variable*) may depend on many factors, we will examine three potential *explanatory variables*.

Definition of Variable	*Short Name*
Y = selling price of a home (thousands of dollars)	*Price*
X_1 = home size (square feet)	*SqFt*
X_2 = lot size (thousand square feet)	*LotSize*
X_3 = number of bathrooms	*Baths*

Using short variable names instead of Y and X we may write the regression model in an intuitive form:

$$Price = \beta_0 + \beta_1\, SqFt + \beta_2\, LotSize + \beta_3\, Baths + \varepsilon$$

		Characteristics of 30 New Homes NewHomes							**TABLE 13.1**
Home	**Price**	**SqFt**	**LotSize**	**Baths**	**Home**	**Price**	**SqFt**	**LotSize**	**Baths**
1	505.5	2,192	16.4	2.5	16	675.1	3,076	19.8	3.0
2	784.1	3,429	24.7	3.5	17	710.4	3,259	20.8	3.5
3	649.0	2,842	17.7	3.5	18	674.7	3,162	19.4	4.0
4	689.8	2,987	20.3	3.5	19	663.6	2,885	23.2	3.0
5	709.8	3,029	22.2	3.0	20	606.6	2,550	20.2	3.0
6	590.2	2,616	20.8	2.5	21	758.9	3,380	19.6	4.5
7	643.3	2,978	17.3	3.0	22	723.7	3,131	22.5	3.5
8	789.7	3,595	22.4	3.5	23	621.8	2,754	19.2	2.5
9	683.0	2,838	27.4	3.0	24	622.4	2,710	21.6	3.0
10	544.3	2,591	19.2	2.0	25	631.3	2,616	20.8	2.5
11	822.8	3,633	26.9	4.0	26	574.0	2,608	17.3	3.5
12	637.7	2,822	23.1	3.0	27	863.8	3,572	29.0	4.0
13	618.7	2,994	20.4	3.0	28	652.7	2,924	21.8	2.5
14	619.3	2,696	22.7	3.5	29	844.2	3,614	25.5	3.5
15	490.5	2,134	13.4	2.5	30	629.9	2,600	24.1	3.5

Logic of Variable Selection

Before doing the estimation, it is desirable to state our hypotheses about the sign of the coefficients in the model. In so doing, we force ourselves to think about our motives for including each predictor, instead of just throwing predictors into the model willy-nilly. In the home price example, each predictor is expected to contribute positively to the selling price.

Predictor	Anticipated Sign	Reasoning
SqFt	>0	Larger homes cost more to build and give greater utility to the buyer.
LotSize	>0	Larger lots are desirable for privacy, gardening, and play.
Baths	>0	Additional baths give more utility to the purchaser with a family.

Explicit *a priori* reasoning about cause-and-effect permits us to compare the regression estimates with our expectation and to recognize any surprising results that may occur.

Estimated Regression

A regression equation can be estimated by using Excel, MegaStat, MINITAB, or any other statistical package. Using the sample of $n = 30$ home sales, we obtain the fitted regression and its statistics of fit (R^2 is the coefficient of determination, SE is the standard error):

$$Price = -28.85 + 0.171\ SqFt + 6.78\ LotSize + 15.53\ Baths\ (R^2 = .956,\ SE = 20.31)$$

The intercept is not meaningful, since there can be no home with $SqFt = 0$, $LotSize = 0$, and $Baths = 0$. Each additional square foot seems to add about 0.171 (i.e., $171, since *Price* is measured in thousands of dollars) to the average selling price, *ceteris paribus*. The coefficient of *LotSize* implies that, on average, each additional thousand square feet of lot size adds 6.78 (i.e., $6,780) to the selling price. The coefficient of *Baths* says that, on average, each additional bathroom adds 15.53 (i.e., $15,530) to the selling price. Although the three-predictor model's fit ($R^2 = .956$) is good, its standard error (20.31 or $20,310) suggests that prediction intervals will be rather wide.

Predictions from a Fitted Regression

We can use the fitted regression model to make predictions for various assumed predictor values. For example, what would be the expected selling price of a 2,800 square foot home with 2-1/2 baths on a lot with 18,500 square feet? In the fitted regression equation, we simply plug in $SqFt = 2800$, $LotSize = 18.5$, and $Baths = 2.5$ to get the predicted selling price:

$$SqFt = 2800 \qquad LotSize = 18.5 \qquad Baths = 2.5$$
$$Price = -28.85 + 0.171\,(2800) + 6.78\,(18.5) + 15.53\,(2.5) = 614.23\ or\ \$614,230$$

Although we could plug in any desired values of the predictors (*SqFt, LotSize, Baths*) it is risky to use predictor values outside the predictor value ranges in the data set used to estimate the fitted regression. For example, it would be risky to choose $SqFt = 4000$ since no home this large was seen in the original data set. Although the prediction might turn out to be reasonable, we would be extrapolating beyond the range of observed data.

Common Misconceptions about Fit

A common mistake is to assume that the model with the best fit is preferred. Sometimes a model with a low R^2 may give useful predictions, while a model with a high R^2 may conceal problems. Fit is only one criterion for assessing a regression. For example, a bivariate model using only *SqFt* as a predictor does a pretty good job of predicting *Price* and has an attractive simplicity:

$$Price = 15.47 + 0.222 \, SqFt \, (R^2 = .914, s = 27.28)$$

Should we perhaps prefer the simpler model? The principle of **Occam's Razor** says that a complex model that is only slightly better may not be preferred if a simpler model will do the job. However, in this case the three-predictor model is not very complex and is based on solid *a priori* logic.

Principle of Occam's Razor

When two explanations are otherwise equivalent, we prefer the simpler, more parsimonious one.

Also, a high R^2 only indicates a good fit for the observed data set ($i = 1, 2, \ldots, n$). If we wanted to use the fitted regression equation to predict Y from a different set of X's, the fit might not be the same. For this reason, if the sample is large enough, a statistician likes to use half the data to *estimate* the model and the other half to *test* the model's predictions.

Regression Modeling

The choice of predictors and model form (e.g., linear or nonlinear) are tasks of *regression modeling*. To begin with, we restrict our attention to predictors that meet the test of *a priori* logic, to avoid endless "data shopping." Naturally, we want predictors that are significant in "explaining" the variation in Y (i.e., predictors that improve the "fit"). But we also prefer predictors that add new information, rather than mirroring one another.

For example, we would expect that *LotSize* and *SqFt* are related (a bigger house may require a bigger lot) and likewise *SqFt* and *Baths* (a bigger house is likely to require more baths). If so, there may be overlap in their contributions to explaining *Price*. Closely related predictors can introduce instability in the regression estimates. If we include too many predictors, we violate the principle of Occam's Razor, which favors simple models, *ceteris paribus*. In this chapter, you will see how these criteria can be used to develop and assess regression models.

Four Criteria for Regression Assessment

- **Logic**   Is there an *a priori* reason to expect a causal relationship between the predictors and the response variable?
- **Fit**   Does the *overall* regression show a significant relationship between the predictors and the response variable?
- **Parsimony** Does *each predictor* contribute significantly to the explanation? Are some predictors not worth the trouble?
- **Stability** Are the predictors related to one another so strongly that regression estimates become erratic?

SECTION EXERCISES

connect

13.1 Observations are taken on net revenue from sales of a certain plasma TV at 50 retail outlets. The regression model was Y = net revenue (thousands of dollars), X_1 = shipping cost (dollars per unit), X_2 = expenditures on print advertising (thousands of dollars), X_3 = expenditure on electronic media ads (thousands), X_4 = rebate rate (percent of retail price). (a) Write the fitted regression equation. (b) Interpret each coefficient. (c) Would the intercept be likely to have meaning in this regression? (d) Use the fitted equation to make a prediction for *NetRevenue* when *ShipCost* = 10, *PrintAds* = 50, *WebAds* = 40, and *Rebate%* = 15. 📖 **PlasmaTV**

Predictor	Coefficient
Intercept	4.306
ShipCost	−0.082
PrintAds	2.265
WebAds	2.498
Rebate%	16.697

13.2 Observations are taken on sales of a certain mountain bike in 30 sporting goods stores. The regression model was Y = total sales (thousands of dollars), X_1 = display floor space (square meters), X_2 = competitors' advertising expenditures (thousands of dollars), X_3 = advertised price (dollars per unit). (a) Write the fitted regression equation. (b) Interpret each coefficient. (c) Would the intercept seem to have meaning in this regression? (d) Make a prediction for *Sales* when *FloorSpace* = 80, *CompetingAds* = 100, and *Price* = 1,200. 📖 **Bikes**

Predictor	Coefficient
Intercept	1225.44
FloorSpace	11.52
CompetingAds	−6.935
Price	−0.1496

VAILRESORTS **13.3** Vail Resorts asked a random sample of guests to rate their satisfaction on various attributes of their visit on a scale of 1–5 with 1 = very unsatisfied and 5 = very satisfied. The estimated regression model was Y = overall satisfaction score, X_1 = lift line wait, X_2 = amount of ski trail grooming, X_3 = safety patrol visibility, and X_4 = friendliness of guest services. (a) Write the fitted regression equation. (b) Interpret each coefficient. (c) Would the intercept seem to have meaning in this regression? (d) Make a prediction for *Overall Satisfaction* when a guest's satisfaction in all four areas is rated a 5. 📖 **VailGuestSat2**

Predictor	Coefficient
Intercept	2.8931
LiftWait	0.1542
AmountGroomed	0.2495
SkiPatrolVisibility	0.0539
FriendlinessHosts	−0.1196

13.4 A regression model to predict Y, the state-by-state 2005 burglary crime rate per 100,000 people, used the following four state predictors: X_1 = median age in 2005, X_2 = number of 2005 bankruptcies per 1,000 people, X_3 = 2004 federal expenditures per capita, and X_4 = 2005 high school graduation percentage. (a) Write the fitted regression equation. (b) Interpret each coefficient. (c) Would the intercept seem to have meaning in this regression? (d) Make a prediction for *Burglary* when X_1 = 35 years, X_2 = 7.0 bankruptcies per 1,000, X_3 = \$6,000, and X_4 = 80 percent. 📖 **Burglary**

Predictor	Coefficient
Intercept	4,198.5808
AgeMed	−27.3540
Bankrupt	17.4893
FedSpend	−0.0124
HSGrad%	−29.0314

As in simple regression, there is one residual for every observation in a multiple regression:

$$e_i = y_i - \hat{y}_i \qquad \text{for } i = 1, 2, \ldots, n$$

Figure 13.4 illustrates the residual for one data value in a two-predictor regression. Each expected value of Y is a point on the fitted regression plane for a given pair of X values (x_1, x_2). The residual is the vertical distance from the actual y_i value for those particular X values (x_1, x_2) to $\hat{y}_i$. Just as in simple regression, we use the sum of squared residuals (SSE) as a measure of "fit" of the model.

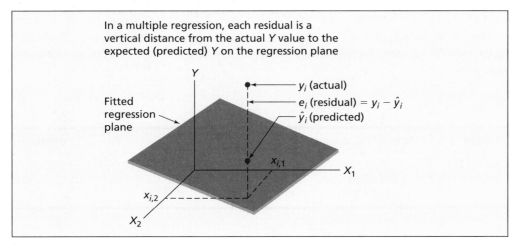

FIGURE 13.4

Residual in Two-Predictor Model

LO2

Interpret the R^2 and perform an F test for overall significance.

F Test for Significance

Overall fit of a regression is assessed using the *F* **test**. For a regression with k predictors, the hypotheses to be tested are

H_0: All the true coefficients are zero ($\beta_1 = \beta_2 = \cdots = \beta_k = 0$)

H_1: At least one of the coefficients is nonzero

The basis for the F test is the **ANOVA table**, which decomposes variation of the response variable around its mean into two parts:

$$
\begin{array}{ccccc}
SST & = & SSR & + & SSE \\
\text{Total} & & \text{Explained by} & & \text{Unexplained} \\
\text{variation} & & \text{regression} & & \text{error}
\end{array}
$$

$$\sum_{i=1}^{n}(y_i - \bar{y})^2 = \sum_{i=1}^{n}(\hat{y}_i - \bar{y})^2 + \sum_{i=1}^{n}(y_i - \hat{y}_i)^2 \qquad \textbf{(13.3)}$$

The OLS method of estimation will minimize the sum of the squared residuals represented by the SSE term, in formula 13.3 above, where SSE is the *unexplained* variation in Y. Each predicted value $\hat{y}_i$ is based on a fitted regression equation with k predictors. The ANOVA calculations for a k-predictor model can be summarized in a table like Table 13.2.

TABLE 13.2   **ANOVA Table Format**

Source of Variation	Sum of Squares	df	Mean Square	F	Excel p-Value
Regression (explained)	$SSR = \sum_{i=1}^{n}(\hat{y}_i - \bar{y})^2$	k	$MSR = \dfrac{SSR}{k}$	$F_{calc} = \dfrac{MSR}{MSE}$	=FDIST(F_{calc}, k, n − k−1)
Residual (unexplained)	$SSE = \sum_{i=1}^{n}(y_i - \hat{y}_i)^2$	$n - k - 1$	$MSE = \dfrac{SSE}{n - k - 1}$		
Total	$SST = \sum_{i=1}^{n}(y_i - \bar{y})^2$	$n - 1$			

When F_{calc} is close to 1, the values of MSR and MSE are close in magnitude. This suggests that *none* of the predictors provide a good predictive model for Y (i.e., all β_j are equal to 0). When the value of MSR is much greater than MSE, this suggests that at least one of the predictors in the regression model is significant (i.e., at least one β_j is not equal to 0).

After simplifying the ratios in Table 13.2, the formula for the F test statistic is:

$$F_{calc} = \frac{MSR}{MSE} = \frac{\sum_{i=1}^{n}(\hat{y}_i - \bar{y})^2}{\sum_{i=1}^{n}(y_i - \hat{y}_i)^2}\left(\frac{n-k-1}{k}\right)$$

(13.4)

MINITAB and MegaStat will do all the calculations and print the ANOVA table. Table 13.3 shows the ANOVA table for the home price regression with $n = 30$ observations and $k = 3$ predictors.

	Source	**Sum of Squares**	**d.f.**	**Mean Square**	**F**	**p-value**
TABLE 13.3	Regression	232,450	3	77,483	187.92	.0000
ANOVA Results for Three-Predictor Home Price Regression	Error	10,720	26	412.32		
	Total	243,170	29			

The hypotheses to be tested are

H_0: All the coefficients are zero ($\beta_1 = \beta_2 = \beta_3 = 0$)

H_1: At least one coefficient is nonzero

Calculation of the sums SSR, SSE, and SST would be tedious without the computer. The F test statistic is $F_{calc} = MSR/MSE = 77{,}483/412.32 = 187.92$. Degrees of freedom are $k = 3$ for the numerator and $n - k - 1 = 30 - 3 - 1 = 26$ for the denominator. For $\alpha = .05$, Appendix F gives a critical value of $F_{3,26} = 2.98$, so the regression clearly is significant overall. MINITAB and MegaStat calculate the p-value (.000) for the F statistic. Alternatively, we can also use Excel's function =FDIST(187.92,3,26) to verify the p-value (.000).

Coefficient of Determination (R^2)

The most common measure of overall fit is the **coefficient of determination** or R^2, which is based on the ANOVA table's sums of squares. It can be calculated in two ways by using the error sum of squares (SSE), regression sum of squares (SSR), and total sum of squares (SST). The formulas are illustrated using the three-predictor regression of home prices.

(13.5) $$R^2 = 1 - \frac{SSE}{SST} = 1 - \frac{\sum_{i=1}^{n}(y_i - \hat{y}_i)^2}{\sum_{i=1}^{n}(y_i - \bar{y}_i)^2} = 1 - \frac{10{,}720}{243{,}170} = 1 - .044 = .956$$

or equivalently

(13.6) $$R^2 = \frac{SSR}{SST} = \frac{\sum_{i=1}^{n}(\hat{y}_i - \bar{y}_i)^2}{\sum_{i=1}^{n}(y_i - \bar{y}_i)^2} = \frac{232{,}450}{243{,}170} = .956$$

For the home price data, the R^2 statistic indicates that 95.6 percent of the variation in selling price is "explained" by our three predictors. While this indicates a very good fit, there is still some unexplained variation. Adding more predictors can *never* decrease the R^2. However, when R^2 already is high, there is not a lot of room for improvement.

Adjusted R^2

In multiple regression, it is possible to raise the coefficient of determination R^2 by including additional predictors. This may tempt you to imagine that we should always include many predictors to get a "better fit." To discourage this tactic (called *overfitting* the model) an adjustment can be made to the R^2 statistic to penalize the inclusion of useless predictors. The **adjusted coefficient of determination** using n observations and k predictors is

$$R^2_{adj} = 1 - \frac{\left(\dfrac{SSE}{n-k-1}\right)}{\left(\dfrac{SST}{n-1}\right)} \qquad \text{(adjusted } R^2\text{)} \tag{13.7}$$

R^2_{adj} is always less than or equal to R^2. As you add predictors, R^2 will not decrease. But R^2_{adj} may rise, remain the same, or fall, depending on whether the added predictors increase R^2 sufficiently to offset the penalty. If R^2_{adj} is substantially smaller than R^2, it suggests that the model contains useless predictors. For the home price data with three predictors, both statistics are similar ($R^2 = .956$ and $R^2_{adj} = .951$), which suggests that the model does not contain useless predictors.

$$R^2_{adj} = 1 - \frac{\left(\dfrac{10,720}{26}\right)}{\left(\dfrac{243,170}{29}\right)} = .951$$

There is no fixed rule of thumb for comparing R^2 and R^2_{adj}. A smaller gap between R^2 and R^2_{adj} indicates a more parsimonious model. A large gap would suggest that if some weak predictors were deleted, a leaner model would be obtained without losing very much predictive power.

How Many Predictors?

One way to prevent overfitting the model is to limit the number of predictors based on the sample size. A conservative rule (**Evans' Rule**) suggests that n/k should be at least 10 (i.e., at least 10 observations per predictor). A more relaxed rule (**Doane's Rule**) suggests that n/k be only at least 5 (i.e., at least 5 observations per predictor). For the home price regression with $n = 30$ and $k = 3$ example, $n/k = 30/3 = 10$ so either guideline is met.

> *Evans' Rule (conservative)*: $n/k \geq 10$ (at least 10 observations per predictor)
>
> *Doane's Rule (relaxed)*: $n/k \geq 5$ (at least 5 observations per predictor)

These rules are merely suggestions. Technically, a regression is possible as long as the sample size exceeds the number of predictors. But when n/k is small, the R^2 no longer gives a reliable indication of fit. Sometimes, researchers must work with small samples that cannot be enlarged. For example, a start-up business selling health food might have only 12 observations on quarterly sales. Should they attempt a regression model to predict sales using four predictors (advertising, product price, competitor prices, and population density)? Although $n = 12$ and $k = 3$ would violate even the lax guideline ($n/k = 12/4 = 3$), the firm might feel that an imperfect analysis is better than none at all.

13.5 Refer to the ANOVA table below. (a) State the degrees of freedom for the F test for overall significance. (b) Use Appendix F to look up the critical value of F for $\alpha = .05$. (c) Calculate the F statistic. Is the regression significant overall? (d) Calculate R^2 and R^2_{adj}, showing your formulas clearly. ☞ **PlasmaTV**

SECTION EXERCISES

connect™

Source	d.f.	SS	MS
Regression	4	259,412	64,853
Error	45	224,539	4,990
Total	49	483,951	

13.6 Refer to the ANOVA table below. (a) State the degrees of freedom for the F test for overall significance. (b) Use Appendix F to look up the critical value of F for $\alpha = .05$. (c) Calculate the F statistic. Is the regression significant overall? (d) Calculate R^2 and R^2_{adj}, showing your formulas clearly. 📁 **Bikes**

Source	d.f.	SS	MS
Regression	3	1,196,410	398,803
Error	26	379,332	14,590
Total	29	1,575,742	

VAILRESORTS **13.7** Refer to the ANOVA table below. (a) State the degrees of freedom for the F test for overall significance. (b) Use Appendix F to look up the critical value of F for $\alpha = .05$. (c) Calculate the F statistic. Is the regression significant overall? (d) Calculate R^2 and R^2_{adj}, showing your formulas clearly. 📁 **VailResortsSat2**

Source	SS	df	MS
Regression	33.0730	4	8.2682
Residual	317.9868	497	0.6398
Total	351.0598	501	

13.8 Refer to the ANOVA table below. (a) State the degrees of freedom for the F test for overall significance. (b) Use Appendix F to look up the critical value of F for $\alpha = .05$. (c) Calculate the F statistic. Is the regression significant overall? (d) Calculate R^2 and R^2_{adj}, showing your formulas clearly. 📁 **Burglary**

Source	SS	df	MS
Regression	1,182,733	4	295,683
Residual	1,584,952	45	35,221
Total	2,767,685	49	

13.3
PREDICTOR SIGNIFICANCE

Hypothesis Tests

Each estimated coefficient shows the change in the conditional mean of Y associated with a one-unit change in an explanatory variable, holding the other explanatory variables constant. If a predictor coefficient β_j, is equal to zero it means that the explanatory variable X_j, does not help explain variation in the response variable Y. We are usually interested in testing each fitted coefficient to see whether it is significantly different from zero. If there is an *a priori* reason to anticipate a particular direction of association, we could choose a right-tailed or left-tailed test. For example, we would expect *SqFt* to have a positive effect on *Price,* so a right-tailed test might be used. However, the default choice is a two-tailed test because, if the null hypothesis can be rejected in a two-tailed test, it can also be rejected in a one-tailed test at the same level of significance.

LO3

Test individual predictors for significance.

Hypothesis Tests for Coefficient of Predictor X_j

Left-Tailed Test	*Two-Tailed Test*	*Right-Tailed Test*
$H_0: \beta_j = 0$	$H_0: \beta_j = 0$	$H_0: \beta_j = 0$
$H_1: \beta_j < 0$	$H_1: \beta_j \neq 0$	$H_1: \beta_j > 0$

Tip

Software packages like Excel, MegaStat, or MINITAB report only two-tail p-values because, if you can reject H_0 in a two-tailed test, you can also reject H_0 in a one-tailed test at the same α.

If we cannot reject the hypothesis that a coefficient is zero, then the corresponding predictor does not contribute to the prediction of Y. For example, consider a three-predictor model:

$$y = \beta_0 + \beta_1 x_1 + \beta_2 x_2 + \beta_3 x_3 + \varepsilon$$

Does X_2 help us to predict Y? To find out, we might choose a two-tailed test:

H_0: $\beta_2 = 0$ (X_2 is *not* related to Y)

H_1: $\beta_2 \neq 0$ (X_2 *is* related to Y)

If we are unable to reject H_0, the term involving x_2 will drop out:

$$y = \beta_0 + \beta_1 x_1 + \boxed{0 x_2} + \beta_3 x_3 + \varepsilon \qquad (x_2 \text{ term drops out if } \beta_2 = 0)$$

and the regression will collapse to a *two-variable* model:

$$y = \beta_0 + \beta_1 x_1 + \beta_3 x_3 + \varepsilon$$

Test Statistic

Rarely would a fitted coefficient be *exactly* zero, so we use a t test to test whether the difference from zero* is *significant*. For predictor X_j the test statistic for k predictors is Student's t with $n - k - 1$ degrees of freedom. To test for a zero coefficient, we take the ratio of the fitted coefficient b_j to its standard error s_j:

$$t_{\text{calc}} = \frac{b_j - 0}{s_j} \qquad \text{(test statistic for coefficient of predictor } X_j\text{)} \qquad \textbf{(13.8)}$$

We can use Appendix D to find a critical value of t for a chosen level of significance α, or we could find the p-value for the t statistic using Excel's function =TDIST(t, deg_freedom, tails). All computer packages report the t statistic and the p-value for each predictor, so we actually do not need tables. To test for a zero coefficient, we could alternatively construct a confidence interval for the true coefficient β_j, and see whether the interval includes zero. Excel and MegaStat show a confidence interval for each coefficient, using this form:

$$b_j - t_{\alpha/2} s_j \leq \beta_j \leq b_j + t_{\alpha/2} s_j \qquad \text{(95\% confidence interval for coefficient } \beta_j\text{)} \qquad \textbf{(13.9)}$$

MegaStat allows 99, 95, or 90 percent confidence intervals, while in Excel you can enter any confidence level you wish. All calculations are provided by Excel, so you only have to know how to interpret the results.

Tip

Checking to see whether the confidence interval includes zero is equivalent to a two-tailed test of H_0: $\beta_j = 0$.

Regression output contains many statistics, but some of them are especially important in getting the "big picture." Figure 13.5 shows a typical regression printout ($Y =$ car theft rate in the 50 states) with certain key features circled and comments that a statistician might make.

---

*You needn't use 0 in the t test. For example, if you want to know whether an extra square foot adds at least \$200 to a home's selling price, you would use 200 instead of 0 in the formula for the test statistic. However, $\beta = 0$ is the default hypothesis in Excel and other statistical packages.

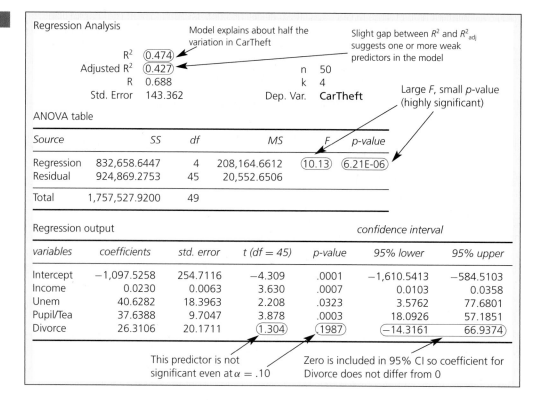

ANOVA table

Source	SS	df	MS	F	p-value
Regression	832,658.6447	4	208,164.6612	10.13	6.21E-06
Residual	924,869.2753	45	20,552.6506		
Total	1,757,527.9200	49			

Regression output

variables	coefficients	std. error	t (df = 45)	p-value	95% lower	95% upper
Intercept	−1,097.5258	254.7116	−4.309	.0001	−1,610.5413	−584.5103
Income	0.0230	0.0063	3.630	.0007	0.0103	0.0358
Unem	40.6282	18.3963	2.208	.0323	3.5762	77.6801
Pupil/Tea	37.6388	9.7047	3.878	.0003	18.0926	57.1851
Divorce	26.3106	20.1711	1.304	1987	−14.3161	66.9374

EXAMPLE

Home Prices

Figure 13.6 shows MegaStat's fitted regression for the three-predictor model of home prices, including a table of estimated coefficients, standard errors, *t* statistics, and *p*-values. MegaStat computes two-tail *p*-values, as do most statistical packages. Notice that 0 is within the 95 percent confidence interval for *Baths,* while the confidence intervals for *SqFt* and *LotSize* do not include 0. This suggests that the hypothesis of a zero coefficient can be rejected for *SqFt* and *LotSize* but not for *Baths.*

FIGURE 13.6   **MegaStat's Regression for Home Prices (three predictors)**

variables	coefficients	std. error	t(df = 26)	p-value	95% lower	95% upper
Intercept	−28.8477	29.7115	−0.971	0.3405	−89.9206	32.2251
SqFt	0.1709	0.0154	11.064	0.0000	0.1392	0.2027
LotSize	6.7777	1.4213	4.769	0.0001	3.8562	9.6992
Baths	15.5347	9.2083	1.687	0.1036	−3.3932	34.4626

Regression output — confidence interval

There are four estimated coefficients (counting the intercept). For reasons stated previously, the intercept is of no interest. For the three predictors, each *t* test uses $n - k - 1$ degrees of freedom. Since we have $n = 30$ observations and $k = 3$ predictors, we have $n - k - 1 = 30 - 3 - 1 = 26$ degrees of freedom. From Appendix D we can obtain two-tailed critical values of *t* for α equal to .10, .05, or .01 ($t_{.05} = 1.706$, $t_{.025} = 2.056$, and $t_{.005} = 2.779$). However, since *p*-values are provided, we do not really need these critical values.

SqFt: $t_{calc} = 0.1709/0.01545 = 11.06$ (*p*-value $= .0000$)

LotSize: $t_{calc} = 6.778/1.421 = 4.77$ (*p*-value $= .0001$)

Baths: $t_{calc} = 15.535/9.208 = 1.69$ (*p*-value $= .1036$)

The coefficients of *SqFt* and *LotSize* differ significantly from zero at any common α because their *p*-values are practically zero. The coefficient of *Baths* is not quite significant at $\alpha = .10$. Based on the *t*-values, we conclude that *SqFt* is a very strong predictor of *Price*, followed closely by *LotSize*, while *Baths* is of marginal significance.

SECTION EXERCISES

connect

13.9 Observations are taken on net revenue from sales of a certain plasma TV at 50 retail outlets. The regression model was Y = net revenue (thousands of dollars), X_1 = shipping cost (dollars per unit), X_2 = expenditures on print advertising (thousands of dollars), X_3 = expenditure on electronic media ads (thousands), X_4 = rebate rate (percent of retail price). (a) Calculate the *t* statistic for each coefficient to test for $\beta = 0$. (b) Look up the critical value of Student's *t* in Appendix D for a two-tailed test at $\alpha = .01$. Which coefficients differ significantly from zero? (c) Use Excel to find the *p*-value for each coefficient. 📂 **PlasmaTV**

Predictor	Coefficient	SE
Intercept	4.310	70.82
ShipCost	−0.0820	4.678
PrintAds	2.265	1.050
WebAds	2.498	0.8457
Rebate%	16.697	3.570

13.10 Observations are taken on sales of a certain mountain bike in 30 sporting goods stores. The regression model was Y = total sales (thousands of dollars), X_1 = display floor space (square meters), X_2 = competitors' advertising expenditures (thousands of dollars), X_3 = advertised price (dollars per unit). (a) Calculate the *t* statistic for each coefficient to test for $\beta = 0$. (b) Look up the critical value of Student's *t* in Appendix D for a two-tailed test at $\alpha = .01$. Which coefficients differ significantly from zero? (c) Use Excel to find the *p*-value for each coefficient. 📂 **Bikes**

Predictor	Coefficient	SE
Intercept	1225.4	397.3
FloorSpace	11.522	1.330
CompetingAds	−6.935	3.905
Price	−0.14955	0.08927

13.11 A random sample of 502 Vail Resorts' guests were asked to rate their satisfaction on various attributes of their visit on a scale of 1–5 with 1 = very unsatisfied and 5 = very satisfied. The regression model was Y = overall satisfaction score, X_1 = lift line wait, X_2 = amount of ski trail grooming, X_3 = ski patrol visibility, and X_4 = friendliness of guest services. (a) Calculate the *t* statistic for each coefficient to test for $\beta_j = 0$. (b) Look up the critical value of Student's *t* in Appendix D for a two-tailed test at $\alpha = .01$. Which coefficients differ significantly from zero? (c) Use Excel to find a *p*-value for each coefficient. 📂 **VailGuestSat2**

VAILRESORTS

Predictor	Coefficient	SE
Intercept	2.8931	0.3680
LiftWait	0.1542	0.0440
AmountGroomed	0.2495	0.0529
SkiPatrolVisibility	0.0539	0.0443
FriendlinessHosts	−0.1196	0.0623

13.12 A regression model to predict Y, the state burglary rate per 100,000 people for 2005, used the following four state predictors: $X_1 =$ median age in 2005, $X_2 =$ number of 2005 bankruptcies, $X_3 =$ 2004 federal expenditures per capita (a *leading* predictor), and $X_4 =$ 2005 high school graduation percentage. (a) Calculate the t statistic for each coefficient to test for $\beta_j = 0$. (b) Look up the critical value of Student's t in Appendix D for a two-tailed test at $\alpha = .01$. Which coefficients differ significantly from zero? (c) Use Excel to find a p-value for each coefficient. 📷 **Burglary**

Predictor	Coefficient	SE
Intercept	4,198.5808	799.3395
AgeMed	−27.3540	12.5687
Bankrupt	17.4893	12.4033
FedSpend	−0.0124	0.0176
HSGrad%	−29.0314	7.1268

13.4
CONFIDENCE INTERVALS FOR Y

LO4

Interpret confidence intervals for regression coefficients.

Standard Error

Another important measure of fit is the **standard error (s) of the regression**, derived from the sum of squared residuals (SSE) for n observations and k predictors:

$$(13.10) \quad s = \sqrt{\frac{\sum_{i=1}^{n}(y_i - \hat{y}_i)^2}{n - k - 1}} = \sqrt{\frac{SSE}{n - k - 1}} \quad \text{(standard error of the regression)}$$

The standard error is measured in the same units as the response variable Y (dollars, square feet, etc). A smaller s indicates a better fit. If all predictions were perfect (i.e., if $y_i = \hat{y}_i$ for all observations), then s would be zero. However, perfect predictions are unlikely.

EXAMPLE

Home Prices II

From the ANOVA table for the three-predictor home price model we obtain $SSE = 10,720$, so

$$s = \sqrt{\frac{SSE}{n - k - 1}} = \sqrt{\frac{10,720}{30 - 3 - 1}} = 20.31$$

$s = 20.31$ (i.e., $\$20,310$ since Y is measured in thousands of dollars) suggests that the model has room for improvement, despite its good fit ($R^2 = .956$). Forecasters find the standard error more useful than R^2 because s tells more about the *practical utility* of the forecasts, especially when it is used to make confidence or prediction intervals.

Approximate Confidence and Prediction Intervals for Y

We can use the standard error to create approximate confidence or prediction intervals for values of $X_1, X_2, \ldots, X_k$ that are not far from their respective means.* Although these approximate intervals somewhat understate the interval widths, they are helpful when you only need a general idea of the accuracy of your model's predictions.

$$(13.11) \quad \hat{y}_i \pm t_{\alpha/2}\frac{s}{\sqrt{n}} \quad \text{(approximate confidence interval for conditional mean of } Y)$$

$$(13.12) \quad \hat{y}_i \pm t_{\alpha/2}s \quad \text{(approximate prediction interval for individual } Y\text{-value)}$$

---

*The exact formulas for a confidence or prediction interval for $\mu_{Y|X}$ or Y require matrix algebra. If you need exact intervals, you should use MINITAB or a similar computer package. You must specify the value of *each predictor* for which the confidence interval or prediction is desired.

For home prices using the three-predictor model ($s = 20.31$) the 95 percent confidence interval would require $n - k - 1 = 30 - 3 - 1 = 26$ degrees of freedom. From Appendix D we obtain $t_{.025} = 2.056$ so the *approximate* intervals are

$$\hat{y}_i \pm (2.056)\frac{20.31}{\sqrt{30}} \text{ or } \hat{y}_i \pm 7.62 \quad \text{(95\% confidence interval for conditional mean)}$$

$$\hat{y}_i \pm (2.056)(20.31) \text{ or } \hat{y}_i \pm 41.76 \quad \text{(95\% prediction interval for individual home price)}$$

Exact 95 percent confidence and prediction intervals for a home with $SqFt = 2,950$, $LotSize = 21$, and $Baths = 3$ (these values are very near the predictor means for our sample) are $\hat{y}_i \pm 8.55$ and $\hat{y}_i \pm 42.61$, respectively. Thus, our *approximate* intervals are not conservative (i.e., slightly too narrow). Nonetheless, the approximate intervals provide a ballpark idea of the accuracy of the model's predictions. Despite its good fit ($R^2 = .956$) we see that the three-predictor model's predictions are far from perfect. For example, the 95 percent prediction interval for an individual home price is $\hat{y}_i \pm \$41,760$.

Quick 95 Percent Confidence and Prediction Interval for *Y*

The *t*-values for a 95 percent confidence level are typically near 2 (as long as *n* is not too small). This suggests quick interval, without using a *t* table:

$$\hat{y}_i \pm 2\frac{s}{\sqrt{n}} \quad \text{(quick 95\% confidence interval for conditional mean of } Y) \qquad \textbf{(13.13)}$$

$$\hat{y}_i \pm 2s \quad \text{(quick 95\% prediction interval for individual } Y\text{-value)} \qquad \textbf{(13.14)}$$

These quick formulas are suitable only for rough calculations when you lack access to regression software or *t* tables (e.g., when taking a statistics exam).

13.13 A regression of accountants' starting salaries in a large firm was estimated using 40 new hires and five predictors (college GPA, gender, score on CPA exam, years' prior experience, size of graduating class). The standard error was $3,620. Find the approximate width of a 95 percent prediction interval for an employee's salary, assuming that the predictor values for the individual are near the means of the sample predictors. Would the quick rule give similar results?

13.14 An agribusiness performed a regression of wheat yield (bushels per acre) using observations on 25 test plots with four predictors (rainfall, fertilizer, soil acidity, hours of sun). The standard error was 1.17 bushels. Find the approximate width of a 95 percent prediction interval for wheat yield, assuming that the predictor values for a test plot are near the means of the sample predictors. Would the quick rule give similar results?

Mini Case   13.1

Birth Rates and Life Expectancy 📄 BirthRates1

Table 13.4 shows the birth rate (Y = births per 1,000 population), life expectancy (X_1 = life expectancy at birth), and literacy (X_2 = percent of population that can read and write) for a random sample of 49 world nations.

TABLE 13.4   Birth Rates, Life Expectancy, and Literacy in Selected World Nations

Nation	BirthRate	LifeExp	Literate
Albania	18.59	72.1	93
Algeria	22.34	70.2	62
Australia	12.71	80.0	100
⋮	⋮	⋮	⋮
Yemen	43.30	60.6	38
Zambia	41.01	37.4	79
Zimbabwe	24.59	36.5	85

FIGURE 13.7 MegaStat's Output for Birth Rate Data

Regression Analysis: Birth Rates

R^2	0.743	n	49
Adjusted R^2	0.732	k	2
Std. Error	5.190	Dep. Var.	**BirthRate**

ANOVA table

Source	SS	df	MS	F	p-value
Regression	3,578.2364	2	1,789.1182	66.42	0.0000
Residual	1,239.1479	46	26.9380		
Total	4,817.3843	48			

Regression output — confidence interval

variables	coefficients	std. error	t(df = 46)	p-value	95% lower	95% upper
Intercept	65.8790	3.8513	17.106	0.0000	58.1268	73.6312
LifeExp	−0.3618	0.0666	−5.431	0.0000	−0.4960	−0.2277
Literate	−0.2330	0.0415	−5.610	0.0000	−0.3166	−0.1494

From Figure 13.7, the fitted regression equation is $BirthRate = 65.9 - 0.362\,LifeExp - 0.233\,Literate$, which says, *ceteris paribus,* that one year's increase in *LifeExp* is associated with 0.362 fewer babies per 1,000 persons, while one extra percent of *Literate* is associated with 0.233 fewer babies per 1,000 persons. The coefficient of determination is fairly high ($R^2 = .743$) and the overall regression is significant ($F_{calc} = 66.42$, p-value = .000). Since both predictors are significant ($t_{calc} = -5.431$ and $t_{calc} = -5.610$, p-values near .000) the evidence favors the hypothesis that birth rates tend to fall as nations achieve higher life expectancy and greater literacy. Although cause-and-effect is unproven, the conclusions are consistent with what we know about nutrition, health, and education.

Source: Central Intelligence Agency, *The World Factbook, 2003.*

13.5 BINARY PREDICTORS

LO5

Incorporate a categorical variable into a multiple regression model.

What Is a Binary Predictor?

We cannot directly include a *categorical* variable (qualitative data) as a predictor in a regression, because regression requires *numerical* data (quantitative data). But through simple data coding, we can convert categorical data into useful predictors. A **binary predictor** has two values, denoting the presence or absence of a condition (usually coded 0 and 1). Statisticians like to use intuitive names for the binary variable. For example:

For *n* Graduates from an MBA Program

Employed = 1 (if the individual is currently employed)
Employed = 0 (otherwise)

For *n* Quarters of Sales Data

Recession = 1 (if the sales data is for a recession year)
Recession = 0 (otherwise)

For *n* Business Schools

AACSB = 1 (if the school is accredited by the AACSB)
AACSB = 0 (otherwise)

For *n* States

$West = 1$ (if the state is west of the Mississippi)

$West = 0$ (otherwise)

Binary predictors are easy to create and are extremely important, because they allow us to capture the effects of nonquantitative (categorical) variables such as gender (female, male) or stock fund type (load, no-load). Such variables are also called **dummy** or **indicator variables**.

Tip

Name the binary variable for the characteristic that is present when the variable is 1 (e.g., *Male*) so that others can immediately see what the "1" stands for.

Effects of a Binary Predictor

A binary predictor is sometimes called a **shift variable** because it shifts the regression plane up or down. Suppose that we have a two-predictor fitted regression $y = b_0 + b_1 x_1 + b_2 x_2$ where x_1 is a binary predictor. Since the only values that x_1 can take on are either 0 or 1, its contribution to the regression is either b_1 or nothing, as seen in this example:

If $x_1 = 0$, then $y = b_0 + b_1(0) + b_2 x_2$, so $y = b_0 + b_2 x_2$.

If $x_1 = 1$, then $y = b_0 + b_1(1) + b_2 x_2$, so $y = (b_0 + b_1) + b_2 x_2$.

The coefficient b_2 is the same, regardless of the value of x_1, but the intercept either is b_0 (when $x_1 = 0$) or $b_0 + b_1$ (when $x_1 = 1$).

For example, suppose we have a fitted regression of fuel economy based on a sample of 43 cars:

$$MPG = 39.5 - 0.00463 \ Weight + 1.51 \ Manual$$

where

Weight = vehicle curb weight as tested (pounds)

Manual = 1 if manual transmission, 0 if automatic

If *Manual* = 0, then

$$MPG = 39.5 - 0.00463 \ Weight + 1.51(0)$$

$$= 39.5 - 0.00463 \ Weight$$

If *Manual* = 1, then

$$MPG = 39.5 - 0.00463 \ Weight + 1.51(1)$$

$$= 41.01 - 0.00463 \ Weight$$

Thus, the binary variable shifts the intercept, leaving the slope unchanged. The situation is illustrated in Figure 13.8. In this case, we see that, although a manual transmission raises *MPG* slightly (by 1.51 miles per gallon, on average) the change in the intercept is rather small (i.e., manual transmission did not have a very large effect). A different sample could, of course, yield a different result. Many experts feel that the choice of automatic versus manual transmission makes very little difference in fuel economy today.

Testing a Binary for Significance

We test the degree of significance of the binary predictor just as we would test any other predictor, using a *t* test. In multiple regression, binary predictors require no special treatment.

FIGURE 13.8

Binary Shift Variable Illustrated

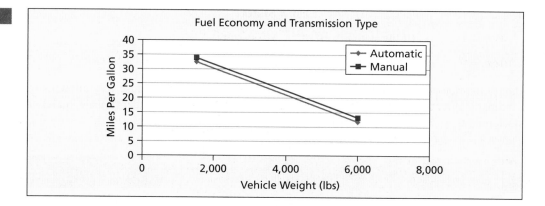

EXAMPLE

Subdivision Home Prices
📁 OakKnoll

We know that location is an important determinant of home price. But how can we include "location" in a regression? The answer is to code it as a binary predictor. Table 13.5 shows 20 home sales in two different subdivisions, Oak Knoll and Hidden Hills. We create a binary predictor, arbitrarily designating *OakKnoll* = 1 if the home is in the Oak Knoll subdivision, and *OakKnoll* = 0 otherwise. We then do an ordinary regression, shown in Figure 13.9.

TABLE 13.5   Home Prices with Binary Predictor 📁 OakKnoll

Obs	Price ($000)	SqFt	OakKnoll	Subdivision
1	615.6	3,055	0	Hidden Hills
2	557.4	2,731	0	Hidden Hills
3	472.6	2,515	0	Hidden Hills
4	595.3	3,011	0	Hidden Hills
5	696.9	3,267	1	Oak Knoll
6	409.2	2,061	1	Oak Knoll
7	814.2	3,842	1	Oak Knoll
8	592.4	2,777	1	Oak Knoll
9	695.5	3,514	0	Hidden Hills
10	495.3	2,145	1	Oak Knoll
11	488.4	2,277	1	Oak Knoll
12	605.4	3,200	0	Hidden Hills
13	635.7	3,065	0	Hidden Hills
14	654.8	2,998	0	Hidden Hills
15	565.6	2,875	0	Hidden Hills
16	642.2	3,000	0	Hidden Hills
17	568.9	2,374	1	Oak Knoll
18	686.5	3,393	1	Oak Knoll
19	724.5	3,457	0	Hidden Hills
20	749.7	3,754	0	Hidden Hills

The model has a rather good fit ($R^2 = .922$) and is significant overall ($F_{calc} = 100.94$, p-value $= .0000$). Both predictors have a significant effect on *Price* at $\alpha = .05$, although *SqFt* ($t_{calc} = 14.008$, p-value $= .0000$) is a much stronger predictor than *OakKnoll* ($t_{calc} = 2.340$, p-value $= .0317$). The fitted coefficient of *OakKnoll* tells us that, on average, a home in the Oak Knoll subdivision sells for 33.538 more than a home in Hidden Hills (i.e., \$33,538 since *Price* is in thousands of dollars). Rounded off a bit, the fitted regression equation is *Price* $= 10.6 + 0.199$ *SqFt* $+ 33.5$ *OakKnoll*. The intercept ($t_{calc} = 0.237$, p-value $= .8154$) does not differ significantly from zero, as can also be seen from the 95 percent confidence interval for the intercept (which includes zero).

FIGURE 13.9 **Oak Knoll Regression for 20 Home Sales**

Regression Analysis: Subdivision Binary (n = 20)

R^2	0.922			
Adjusted R^2	0.913		n	20
R	0.960		k	2
Std. Error	29.670		Dep. Var.	**Price (000)**

ANOVA table

Source	SS	df	MS	F	p-value
Regression	177,706.7957	2	88,853.3979	100.94	.0000
Residual	14,964.9538	17	880.2914		
Total	192,671.7495	19			

Regression output   confidence interval

variables	coefficients	std. error	t(df = 17)	p-value	95% lower	95% upper
Intercept	10.6185	44.7725	0.237	.8154	−83.8433	105.0803
SqFt	0.1987	0.0142	14.008	0.0000	0.1688	0.2286
OakKnoll	33.5383	14.3328	2.340	.0317	3.2986	63.7780

More Than One Binary

A variable like gender (male, female) requires only one binary predictor (e.g., *Male*) because *Male* = 0 would indicate a female. But what if we need several binary predictors to code the data? This occurs when the number of categories to be coded exceeds two. For example, we might have home sales in five subdivisions, or quarterly Walmart profits, or student GPA by class level:

Home sales by subdivision: *OakKnoll, HiddenHills, RockDale, Lochmoor, KingsRidge*

Walmart profit by quarter: *Qtr1, Qtr2, Qtr3, Qtr4*

GPA by class level: *Freshman, Sophomore, Junior, Senior, Master's, Doctoral*

Each category is a binary variable denoting the presence (1) or absence (0) of the characteristic of interest. For example:

Freshman = 1 if the student is a freshman, 0 otherwise

Sophomore = 1 if the student is a sophomore, 0 otherwise

Junior = 1 if the student is a junior, 0 otherwise

Senior = 1 if the student is a senior, 0 otherwise

Master's = 1 if the student is a master's candidate, 0 otherwise

Doctoral = 1 if the student is a PhD candidate, 0 otherwise

But if there are *c* categories (assuming they are mutually exclusive and collectively exhaustive), we need only *c* − 1 binaries to code each observation. This is equivalent to omitting any *one* of the categories. This is possible because the *c* − 1 remaining binary values uniquely determine the remaining binary. For example, Table 13.6 shows that we could omit the last binary column without losing any information. Since only one column can be 1 and the other columns must be 0, the following relation holds:

$$Freshman + Sophomore + Junior + Senior + Master's + Doctoral = 1$$

that is,

$$Doctoral = 1 - Freshman - Sophomore - Junior - Senior - Master's$$

TABLE 13.6

Why We Need Only $c - 1$ Binaries to Code c Categories

Name	Freshman	Sophomore	Junior	Senior	Master's	Doctoral
Jaime	0	0	1	0	0	0
Fritz	0	1	0	0	0	0
Mary	0	0	0	0	0	1
Jean	0	0	0	1	0	0
Otto	0	0	0	0	1	0
Gail	1	0	0	0	0	0
etc.	...	...	...	...	...	...

That Mary is a doctoral student can be inferred from the fact that 0 appears in all the other columns. Since Mary is *not* in any of the other five categories, she must be in the sixth category:

$$Doctoral = 1 - 0 - 0 - 0 - 0 - 0 = 1$$

There is nothing special about the last column; we could have omitted any other column instead. Similarly, we might omit the *KingsRidge* data column from home sales data, since a home that is not in one of the first four subdivisions must be *KingsRidge*. We could omit the *Qtr4* column from the Walmart time series, since if an observation is not from the first, second, or third quarter, it must be from *Qtr4*:

Home sales: *OakKnoll, HiddenHills, RockDale, Lochmoor, ~~KingsRidge~~*

Walmart profit: *Qtr1, Qtr2, Qtr3, ~~Qtr4~~*

Again, there is nothing special about omitting the last category. We can omit any single binary instead. The omitted binary becomes the base reference point for the regression; that is, it is part of the intercept. No information is lost.

What If I Forget to Exclude One Binary?

If you include all c binaries for c categories, you will introduce a serious problem for the regression estimation, because one column in the X data matrix will then be a perfect linear combination of the other column(s). The least squares estimation would then fail because the data matrix would be singular (i.e., would have no inverse). MINITAB automatically checks for such a situation and omits one of the offending predictors, while Excel merely gives an error. It is safer to decide for yourself which binary to exclude.

Mini Case   13.2

Age or Gender Bias?   Oxnard

We can't use simple t tests to compare employee groups based on gender or age or job classification because they fail to take into account relevant factors such as education and experience. A simplistic salary equity study that fails to account for such control variables would be subject to criticism. Instead, we can use binary variables to study the effects of age, experience, gender, and education on salaries within a corporation. Gender and education can be coded as binary variables, and age can be forced into a binary variable that defines older employees explicitly, rather than assuming that age has a linear effect on salary.

Table 13.7 shows salaries for 25 employees in the advertising department at Oxnard Petro, Ltd. As an initial step in a salary equity study, the human resources consultant performed a linear regression using the proposed model $Salary = \beta_0 + \beta_1 \, Male + \beta_2 \, Exper + \beta_3 \, Ovr50 + \beta_4 \, MBA$. *Exper* is the employee's experience in years; *Salary* is in thousands of dollars. Binaries are used for gender ($Male = 0, 1$), age ($Ovr50 = 0, 1$), and MBA degree ($MBA = 0, 1$). Can we reject the hypothesis that the coefficients of *Male* and *Ovr50* are zero? If so, it would suggest salary inequity based on gender and/or age.

TABLE 13.7	Salaries of Advertising Staff of Oxnard Petro, Ltd.					

Obs	Employee	Salary	Male	Exper	Ovr50	MBA
1	Mary	28.6	0	0	0	1
2	Frieda	53.3	0	4	0	1
3	Alicia	73.8	0	12	0	0
4	Tom	26.0	1	0	0	0
5	Nicole	77.5	0	19	0	0
6	Xihong	95.1	1	17	0	0
7	Ellen	34.3	0	1	0	1
8	Bob	63.5	1	9	0	0
9	Vivian	96.4	0	19	0	0
10	Cecil	122.9	1	31	0	0
11	Barry	63.8	1	12	0	0
12	Jaime	111.1	1	29	1	0
13	Wanda	82.5	0	12	0	1
14	Sam	80.4	1	19	1	0
15	Saundra	69.3	0	10	0	0
16	Pete	52.8	1	8	0	0
17	Steve	54.0	1	2	0	1
18	Juan	58.7	1	11	0	0
19	Dick	72.3	1	14	0	0
20	Lee	88.6	1	21	0	0
21	Judd	60.2	1	10	0	0
22	Sunil	61.0	1	7	0	0
23	Marcia	75.8	0	18	0	0
24	Vivian	79.8	0	19	0	0
25	Igor	70.2	1	12	0	0

The coefficients in Figure 13.10 suggest that, *ceteris paribus,* a male (*Male* = 1) makes $3,013 more on average than a female. However, the coefficient of *Male* does not differ significantly from zero even at $\alpha = .10$ ($t_{calc} = 0.86$, p-value = .399). The evidence for age discrimination is a little stronger. Although an older employee (*Ovr50* = 1) makes $8,598 less than others, on average, the p-value for *Ovr50* ($t_{calc} = -1.36$, p-value = .189) is not convincing at $\alpha = .10$. The coefficient of MBA indicates that, *ceteris paribus,* MBA degree holders earn $9,587 more than others, and the coefficient differs from zero at $\alpha = .10$ ($t_{calc} = 1.92$, p-value = .070). Salaries at Oxnard Petro are dominated by *Exper* ($t_{calc} = 12.08$, p-value = .000). Each additional year of experience adds $3,019, on average, to an employee's salary. The regression is significant overall ($F_{calc} = 52.62, p = .000$) and has a good fit ($R^2 = .913$). Although the sample fails Evans' 10:1 ratio test for n/k, it passes Doane's 5:1 ratio test. A more complete salary equity study might consider additional predictors.

FIGURE 13.10	MINITAB Results for Oxnard Salary Equity Study

```
The regression equation is
Salary = 28.9 + 3.01 Male − 8.60 Ovr50 + 3.02 Exper + 9.59 MBA

Predictor      Coef     SE Coef        T        P
Constant     28.878       4.925     5.86    0.000
Male          3.013       3.496     0.86    0.399
Ovr50        −8.598       6.324    −1.36    0.189
Exper        3.0190      0.2499    12.08    0.000
MBA           9.587       5.003     1.92    0.070

S = 7.44388    R-Sq = 91.3%    R-Sq(adj) = 89.6%
```

Regional Binaries

One very common use of binaries is to code regions. Figure 13.11 shows how the 50 states of the United States could be divided into four regions by using these binaries:

Midwest = 1 if state is in the Midwest, 0 otherwise

Neast = 1 if state is in the Northeast, 0 otherwise

Seast = 1 if state is in the Southeast, 0 otherwise

West = 1 if state is in the West, 0 otherwise

For example, we can use regression to analyze the U.S. voting patterns in the 2000 U.S. presidential election. Binary predictors could permit us to analyze the effects of region (a qualitative variable) on voting patterns.

FIGURE 13.11

Four Regional Binaries

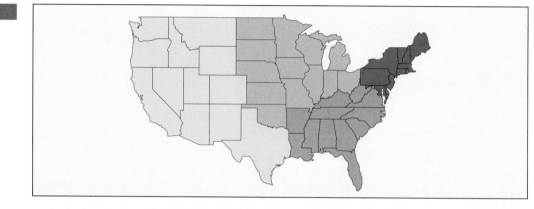

Mini Case   13.3

Regional Voting Patterns 📁 Election2000

Table 13.8 shows an abbreviated data set for the 50 U.S. states. There are four regional binaries. Arbitrarily, we omit the *Seast* column, which becomes the baseline for the regression to examine a hypothesis about the effects of population age, urbanization, college graduation rates, unionization, and region on voting patterns in the 2000 U.S. presidential election. The dependent variable (*Bush%*) is the percentage vote for George W. Bush, and the proffered hypothesis to be investigated is

$$Bush\% = \beta_0 + \beta_1\,Age65\% + \beta_2\,Urban\% + \beta_3\,ColGrad\% + \beta_4\,Union\%$$

$$+ \beta_5\,Midwest + \beta_6\,Neast + \beta_7\,West$$

TABLE 13.8   **Characteristics of U.S. States in 2000 Election**

State	Bush%	Age65%	Urban%	ColGrad%	Union%	Midwest	Neast	Omitted Seast	West
AL	56.5	13.0	69.9	20.4	9.6	0	0	1	0
AK	58.6	5.7	41.5	28.1	21.9	0	0	0	1
AZ	51.0	13.0	88.2	24.6	6.4	0	0	0	1
AR	51.3	14.0	49.9	18.4	5.8	0	0	1	0
CA	41.7	10.6	96.7	27.5	16.0	0	0	0	1
CO	50.8	9.7	83.9	34.6	9.0	0	0	0	1
CT	38.4	13.8	95.6	31.6	16.3	0	1	0	0
⋮	⋮	⋮	⋮	⋮	⋮	⋮	⋮	⋮	⋮
etc.	etc.	etc.	etc.	etc.	etc.	etc.	etc.	etc.	etc.

FIGURE 13.12   **MINITAB Output for Voting Patterns**

The regression equation is
Bush% = 94.6 − 1.29 Age65% − 0.0983 Urban% − 0.582 ColGrad% − 0.728 Union%
     + 5.67 Midwest − 1.61 Neast + 3.75 West

Predictor	Coef	SE Coef	T	P	VIF
Constant	94.550	7.525	12.56	0.000	
Age65%	−1.2869	0.4010	−3.21	0.003	1.6
Urban%	−0.09827	0.03476	−2.83	0.007	1.4
ColGrad%	−0.5815	0.1933	−3.01	0.004	1.9
Union%	−0.7281	0.1327	−5.49	0.000	1.5
Midwest	5.671	2.034	2.79	0.008	2.2
Neast	−1.606	2.490	−0.65	0.522	2.9
West	3.748	2.007	1.87	0.069	2.2

S = 4.28656   R-Sq = 79.3%   R-Sq(adj) = 75.8%

Analysis of Variance

Source	DF	SS	MS	F	P
Regression	7	2948.11	421.16	22.92	0.000
Residual Error	42	771.73	18.37		
Total	49	3719.84			

The fitted regression shown in Figure 13.12 has four quantitative predictors and three binaries. The regression is significant overall (F_{calc} = 22.92, *p*-value = .000). It suggests that, *ceteris paribus,* the percent of voters choosing Bush was lower in states with older citizens, greater urbanization, higher percentage of college graduates, and more unionization. The Bush vote was, *ceteris paribus,* significantly higher in the Midwest (t_{calc} = 2.79, *p*-value = .008) and, to a lesser extent, in the West (t_{calc} = 1.87, *p*-value = .069). The coefficient of *Neast* suggests less Bush support in the Northeast (t_{calc} = −0.65, *p*-value = .522) but the coefficient of *Neast* is not statistically significant (perhaps masked by quantitative variables such as *Urban%* and *Union%,* which tend to distinguish the northeastern states). Using regional binaries allows us to analyze the effects of these *qualitative* factors. Those who say statistics can only deal with numbers must think again.

SECTION EXERCISES

connect

13.15 A regression model to predict the price of a condominium for a weekend getaway in a resort community included the following predictor variables: number of nights needed, number of bedrooms, whether the condominium complex had a swimming pool or not, and whether or not a parking garage was available. (a) Identify the quantitative predictor variable(s). (b) How many binary variables would be included in the model? (c) Write the proposed model form for predicting condominium price.

13.16 A regression model to predict the price of diamonds included the following predictor variables: the weight of the stone (in carats where 1 carat = 0.2 grams), the color rating (D, E, F, G, H, or I), and the clarity rating (IF, VVS1, VVS2, VS1, or VS2). (a) Identify the quantitative predictor variable(s). (b) How many indicator variables would be included in the model in order to prevent the least squares estimation from failing? (c) Write the proposed model form for predicting a diamond price.

13.17 Refrigerator prices are affected by characteristics such as whether or not the refrigerator is on sale, whether or not it is listed as a Sub-Zero brand, the number of doors (one door or two doors), and the placement of the freezer compartment (top, side, or bottom). The table below shows the regression output from a regression model using the natural log of price as the dependent variable. The model was developed by the Bureau of Labor Statistics. (a) Write the regression model, being careful to exclude the base indicator variable. (b) Find the p-value for each coefficient, using 319 degrees of freedom. Using an $\alpha = .01$, which predictor variable(s) are *not* significant predictors? (c) By how much does the natural log of refrigerator price decrease from a *two door, side freezer model* to a *two door, top freezer model*? (d) Which model demands a higher price: the side freezer or the one door with freezer model?

Variable	Coefficient	Standard Error	t Statistic
Intercept	5.484092	0.13081309	41.923
Sale price	−0.0733	0.02338826	−3.134
Sub-Zero brand	1.11962	0.14615699	7.660
Total capacity (in cubic ft)	0.06956	0.00535103	12.999
Two door, freezer on bottom	0.046569	0.0808569	0.576
Two door, side freezer	Base		
Two door, freezer on top	−0.343246	0.03595873	−9.546
One door with freezer	−0.709558	0.13097047	−5.418
One door, no freezer	−0.881981	0.14913992	−5.914

Source: www.bls.gov/cpi/cpirfr.htm

13.18 A model was developed to predict the length of a sentence (the response variable) for a male convicted of assault using the following predictor variables: age (in years), number of prior felony convictions, whether the criminal was married or not (1 = married), and whether the criminal was employed or not (1 = employed). The table below shows the regression output. (a) Write the regression model. (b) Using 45 *d.f.*, find the p-value for each coefficient. Using an $\alpha = .01$, which predictor variable(s) are *not* significant predictors of length of sentence? (c) Interpret the coefficient of Married. (d) How much shorter is the sentence if the criminal is employed? (e) Predict the length of sentence for an unmarried, unemployed 25-year old male with one prior conviction. Show your calculations. 🗂 **Sentencing**

Variable	Coefficient	Standard Error	t Statistic
Intercept	3.2563	4.3376	0.751
Age	0.5219	0.1046	4.989
Convictions	7.7412	1.0358	7.474
Married?	−6.0852	2.5809	−2.358
Employed?	−14.3402	2.5356	−5.656

13.6
TESTS FOR NONLINEARITY AND INTERACTION

Tests for Nonlinearity

Sometimes the effect of a predictor is nonlinear. A simple example would be estimating the volume of lumber to be obtained from a tree. This is a practical problem facing a timber farm, since the manager can inventory the trees and measure their heights and diameters without cutting any trees. In addition to improving the accuracy of asset valuation on the balance sheet, the manager can decide the best time to cut the trees, based on their expected growth rates.

The volume of lumber that can be milled from a tree depends on the height of the tree and its radius, that is, *Volume* = f(*Height, Radius*). But what is the appropriate model form? Figure 13.13 shows the MINITAB regression output for two regressions of *Volume* on *Height* and *Radius:*

Model 1: Volume = $-58.0 + 0.3393$ *Height* $+ 9.4163$ *Radius* ($R^2 = .948$, $s = 3.88$)

Model 2: Volume = $-27.5 + 0.3488$ *Height* $+ 0.6738$ *Radius*^{2} ($R^2 = .973$, $s = 2.78$)

FIGURE 13.13

Regression Results for Tree Data

```
Model 1: The regression equation is
Volume = -58.0 + 0.339 Height + 9.42 Radius

Predictor      Coef     SE Coef       T        P
Constant    -57.988       8.638    -6.71    0.000
Height       0.3393      0.1302     2.61    0.014
Radius       9.4163      0.5285    17.82    0.000

S = 3.88183     R-Sq = 94.8%     R-Sq(adj) = 94.4%
```

```
Model 2: The regression equation is
Volume = -27.5 + 0.349 Height + 0.674 Radius2

Predictor      Coef     SE Coef       T        P
Constant    -27.512       6.558    -4.20    0.000
Height      0.34881     0.09315     3.74    0.001
Radius2     0.67383     0.02672    25.22    0.000

S = 2.79946     R-Sq = 97.3%     R-Sq(adj) = 97.1%
```

If we regard a log as a cylinder, we would prefer the second regression because the usable volume of a cylinder is proportional to the square of its radius.* The t statistics for both *Height* and *Radius* are improved in model 2, and the higher R^2 and reduced standard errors indicate a better fit. Although we introduced a squared term for the radius predictor variable, the model still is said to be linear because none of the parameters (i.e., β_0, β_1, or β_2) show up as exponents nor do we divide any parameter by another.

To test for suspected nonlinearity of any *predictor*, we can include its square in the regression. For example, instead of

$$y = \beta_0 + \beta_1 x_1 + \beta_2 x_2 + \varepsilon \tag{13.15}$$

we would use

$$y = \beta_0 + \beta_1 x_1 + \beta_2 x_1^2 + \beta_3 x_2 + \beta_4 x_2^2 + \varepsilon \tag{13.16}$$

If the coefficients of the squared predictors (β_2 and β_4) do not differ significantly from zero then the model collapses to the form in formula 13.15. On the other hand, rejection of the hypothesis H_0: $\beta_2 = 0$ would suggest a quadratic relationship between Y and X_1 and rejection of the hypothesis H_0: $\beta_4 = 0$ would suggest a quadratic relationship between Y and X_2. Some researchers include squared predictors as a matter of course in large studies. Squared predictors add model complexity and impose a cost of reduced degrees of freedom for significance tests (we lose 1 degree of freedom for each squared predictor), but the potential reward is a more appropriate model specification.

For example, rising total U.S. petroleum consumption from 1980 through 2004 can be fairly well described by a linear time trend model ($R^2 = .8691$). Yet, adding a squared predictor (making it a quadratic model) gives an even better fit ($R^2 = .9183$) and the x_t^2 term is significant ($t_{\text{calc}} = 3.640$). This suggests a nonlinear trend, using $x_t = 1, 2, \ldots, 25$ to represent the year.

Linear: $\hat{y}_t = 0.2012\,x_t + 15.029$ ($R^2 = 0.8691$)

Quadratic: $\hat{y}_t = 0.0074\,x_t^2 + 0.0078\,x_t + 15.899$ ($R^2 = 0.9183$)

---

*$V = \pi h r^2$ would describe the relationship between the tree's radius (r), height (h), and volume (V). A logarithmic model $ln(Volume) = \beta_0 + \beta_1\,ln(Height) + \beta_2\,ln(Radius)$ might be even more appropriate, although the resulting R^2 and SE would not be comparable to the models shown above because the dependent variable would be in different units.

Tests for Interaction

We can test for **interaction** between two predictors by including their product in the regression. For example, we might hypothesize that Y depends on X_1 and X_2, and $X_1 X_2$. To test for interaction, we estimate the model:

$$y = \beta_0 + \beta_1 x_1 + \beta_2 x_2 + \beta_3 x_1 x_2 + \varepsilon \qquad (13.17)$$

If the t test for β_3 allows us to reject the hypothesis $H_0: \beta_3 = 0$, then we conclude that there is a significant interaction effect that transcends the roles of X_1 and X_2 separately (similar to the two-factor ANOVA tests for interaction in Chapter 11). Interaction effects require careful interpretation and cost 1 degree of freedom per interaction. However, if the interaction term improves the model specification, it is well worth the cost. For example, a bank's lost revenue (*Loss*) due to loan defaults depends on the loan size (*Size*) and the degree of risk (*Risk*). Small loans may be risky but may not contribute much to the total losses. Large loans may be less risky but potentially represent a large loss. An interaction term (*Size* × *Risk*) would be large if either predictor is large, thereby capturing the effect of both predictors. Thus, the interaction term might be a significant predictor in the model:

$$Loss = b_0 + b_1 \; Size + b_2 \; Risk + b_3 \; Size \times Risk$$

Mini Case 13.4

Cockpit Noise 🖾 CockpitNoise

Cockpit sound level was measured 61 times at various flight phases for seven different B-727 aircraft (an older model) at the first officer's left ear position using a handheld meter. Sound level was measured in decibels. For reference, 60 dB is a normal conversation, 75 is a typical vacuum cleaner, 85 is city traffic, 90 is a typical hair dryer, and 110 is a chain saw. The proposed regression model is $Noise = \beta_0 + \beta_1 \; Climb + \beta_2 \; Descent + \beta_3 \; Speed + \beta_4 \; Speed^2 + \beta_5 \; Alt + \beta_6 \; Alt^2$. The airspeed (*Speed*) is in KIAS (knots indicated air speed) or nautical miles per hour. Altitude (*Alt*) is in thousands of feet above MSL (mean sea level). Squared predictors (*SpeedSqr* and *AltSqr*) are included for tests of nonlinearity (*SpeedSqr* is divided by 1,000 to improve data conditioning). There are three flight phases, represented by binaries (*Climb*, *Cruise*, *Descent*) but *Cruise* is omitted from the regression since it is implied by the other two binaries (i.e., if *Climb* = 0 and *Descent* = 0 then necessarily *Cruise* = 1). Table 13.9 shows a partial data list.

TABLE 13.9		Cockpit Noise in B-727 Aircraft 🖾 CockpitNoise						
Obs	*Noise*	*Climb*	*Cruise*	*Descent*	*Speed*	*Alt*	*SpeedSqr*	*AltSqr*
1	83	1	0	0	250	10	62.50	100
2	89	1	0	0	340	15	115.60	225
3	88	1	0	0	320	18	102.40	324
4	89	0	1	0	330	24	108.90	576
5	92	0	1	0	346	27	119.72	729
⋮	⋮	⋮	⋮	⋮	⋮	⋮	⋮	⋮
61	82	0	0	1	250	4.5	62.50	20.25

Regression results are shown in Figure 13.14. The coefficient of *Climb* indicates a slight average reduction in *Noise* of 0.814 decibels during the climb flight phase (relative to the baseline of *Cruise*). The coefficient of *Descent* indicates a significant reduction of 1.66 decibels during the descent flight phase. *Speed* and *Alt* have nonlinear effects, as indicated by the significance of *SpeedSqr* ($t_{calc} = 2.336$, p-value $= .0232$) and *AltSqr* ($t_{calc} = -2.348$, p-value $= .0226$).

FIGURE 13.14	MegaStat's Regression Results for Cockpit Noise

Regression Analysis: Cockpit Noise ($n = 61$ flights)

R^2	0.920		
Adjusted R^2	0.911	n	61
R	0.959	k	6
Std. Error	1.179	Dep. Var.	**Noise**

ANOVA table

Source	SS	df	MS	F	p-value
Regression	860.4680	6	143.4113	103.19	0.0000
Residual	75.0484	54	1.3898		
Total	935.5164	60			

Regression output   confidence interval

variables	coefficients	std. error	t(df = 54)	p-value	95% lower	95% upper
Intercept	83.0833	8.0747	10.289	0.0000	66.8946	99.2721
Climb	−0.8140	0.5649	−1.441	0.1553	−1.9465	0.3185
Descent	−1.6612	0.5557	−2.989	0.0042	−2.7754	−0.5471
Speed	−0.0492	0.0525	−0.936	0.3533	−0.1545	0.0561
Alt	0.3134	0.1328	2.361	0.0219	0.0472	0.5796
SpeedSqr	0.1867	0.0799	2.336	0.0232	0.0265	0.3470
AltSqr	−0.0074	0.0031	−2.348	0.0226	−0.0137	−0.0011

Source: Capt. R. E. Hartl (ret).

13.7 MULTI-COLLINEARITY

What Is Multicollinearity?

When the independent variables $X_1, X_2, \ldots, X_m$ are intercorrelated instead of being independent, we have a condition known as **multicollinearity**. If only two predictors are correlated, we have **collinearity**. Almost any data set will have some degree of correlation among the predictors. The depth of our concern would depend on the *degree* of multicollinearity.

LO6

Detect multicollinearity and assess its effects.

Variance Inflation

Multicollinearity does not bias the least squares estimates or the predictions for Y, but it does induce *variance inflation*. When predictors are strongly intercorrelated, the variances of their estimated coefficients tend to become inflated, widening the confidence intervals for the true coefficients $\beta_1, \beta_2, \ldots, \beta_k$ and making the t statistics less reliable. It can thus be difficult to identify the separate contribution of each predictor to "explaining" the response variable, due to the entanglement of their roles. Consequences of variance inflation can range from trivial to severe. In the most extreme case, when one X data column is an exact linear function of one or more other X data columns, the least squares estimation will fail.* That could happen, for example, if you inadvertently included the same predictor twice, or if you forgot to omit one of the c binaries used to code c attribute categories. Some software packages (e.g., MINITAB) will check for perfect multicollinearity and will remove one of the offending predictors, but don't count on it.

Variance inflation generally does not cause major problems, and some researchers suggest that it is best ignored except in extreme cases. However, it is a good idea to investigate the degree of multicollinearity in the regression model. There are several ways to do this.

---

*If the X data matrix has no inverse, we cannot solve for the OLS estimates.

Correlation Matrix

To check whether two predictors are correlated (*collinearity*) we can inspect the **correlation matrix** for the predictors using Excel's function =CORREL(Data) or MegaStat's Correlation Matrix or MINITAB's Stat > Basic Statistics > Correlation. The correlation matrix for Mini Case 13.4 (cockpit noise) is shown in Table 13.10. The response variable (*Noise*) is not included, since collinearity *among the predictors* is the condition we are investigating. Cells above the diagonal are redundant and hence are not shown. Correlations that differ from zero at $\alpha = .05$ in a two-tailed test are highlighted in blue in Table 13.10. In this example, a majority of the predictors are significantly correlated, which is not an unusual situation in regression modeling. The very high correlations between *Speed* and *SpeedSqr* and between *Alt* and *AltSqr* are highlighted in yellow. These are an artifact of the model specification (i.e., using squared predictors as tests for nonlinearity) and are not necessarily a cause for removal of either predictor.

TABLE 13.10

Correlation Matrix for Cockpit Noise Data
  CockpitNoise

	Climb	Cruise	Descent	Speed	Alt	SpeedSqr
Cruise	−0.391					
Descent	−0.694	−0.391				
Speed	−0.319	−0.044	0.353			
Alt	−0.175	0.584	−0.282	0.063		
SpeedSqr	−0.351	−0.055	0.393	0.997	0.040	
AltSqr	−0.214	0.624	−0.274	−0.087	0.972	−0.103

Significant predictor correlations do not *per se* indicate a serious problem. **Klein's Rule** (see Related Reading) suggests that we should worry about the stability of the regression coefficient estimates only when a pairwise predictor correlation exceeds the multiple correlation coefficient R (i.e., the square root of R^2). In Mini Case 13.4 (cockpit noise) the correlations between *Speed* and *SpeedSqr* ($r = .997$) and between *Alt* and *AltSqr* ($r = .972$) do exceed the multiple correlation coefficient ($R = .959$), which suggests that the confidence intervals and t tests may be affected.

Variance Inflation Factor (VIF)

Although the matrix scatter plots and correlation matrix are easy to understand, they only show correlations between *pairs* of predictors (e.g., X_1 and X_2). A general test for multicollinearity should reveal more complex relationships *among* predictors. For example, X_2 might be a linear function of $X_1, X_3,$ and X_4 even though its pairwise correlation with each is not very large.

The **variance inflation factor (VIF)** for each predictor provides a more comprehensive test. For a given predictor X_j the VIF is defined as

(13.18)
$$VIF_j = \frac{1}{1 - R_j^2}$$

where R_j^2 is the coefficient of determination when predictor j is regressed against *all* the other predictors (excluding Y).

Response Variable	Explanatory Variables	R^2
X_1	$X_2, X_3, \ldots, X_k$	R_1^2
X_2	$X_1, X_3, \ldots, X_k$	R_2^2
$\vdots$	$\vdots$	$\vdots$
X_k	$X_1, X_2, \ldots, X_{k-1}$	R_k^2

If predictor j is unrelated to the other predictors, its R_j^2 will be 0 and its VIF will be 1 (an ideal situation that will rarely be seen with actual data). Some possible situations are:

R_j^2	VIF_j	Interpretation
0.00	$\dfrac{1}{1 - R_j^2} = \dfrac{1}{1 - 0.00} = 1.0$	No variance inflation
0.50	$\dfrac{1}{1 - R_j^2} = \dfrac{1}{1 - 0.50} = 2.0$	Mild variance inflation
0.90	$\dfrac{1}{1 - R_j^2} = \dfrac{1}{1 - 0.90} = 10.0$	Strong variance inflation
0.99	$\dfrac{1}{1 - R_j^2} = \dfrac{1}{1 - 0.99} = 100.0$	Severe variance inflation

There is no limit on the magnitude of a VIF. Some researchers suggest that when a VIF exceeds 10, there is cause for concern, or even removal of predictor j from the model. But that rule of thumb is perhaps too conservative. A VIF of 10 says that the other predictors "explain" 90 percent of the variation in predictor j. While a VIF of 10 shows that predictor j is strongly related to the other predictors, it is not necessarily indicative of instability in the least squares estimates. Removing a relevant predictor is a step that should not be taken lightly, for it could result in misspecification of the model. A better way to think of it is that a large VIF is a warning to consider whether predictor j really belongs in the model.

Are Coefficients Stable?

Evidence of instability would be when X_1 and X_2 have a high pairwise correlation with Y, yet one or both predictors have insignificant t statistics in the fitted multiple regression. Another symptom would be if X_1 and X_2 are positively correlated with Y, yet one of them has a negative slope in the multiple regression. As a general test, you can try dropping a collinear predictor from the regression and watch what happens to the fitted coefficients in the re-estimated model. If they do not change very much, multicollinearity was probably not a concern. If dropping one collinear predictor causes sharp changes in one or more of the remaining coefficients in the model, then your multicollinearity may be causing instability. Keep in mind that a predictor must be significantly different from zero in order to say that it "changed" in the re-estimation.

Both MegaStat and MINITAB will calculate variance inflation factors, but you must request it as an option. Their VIF menu options are shown in Figure 13.15.

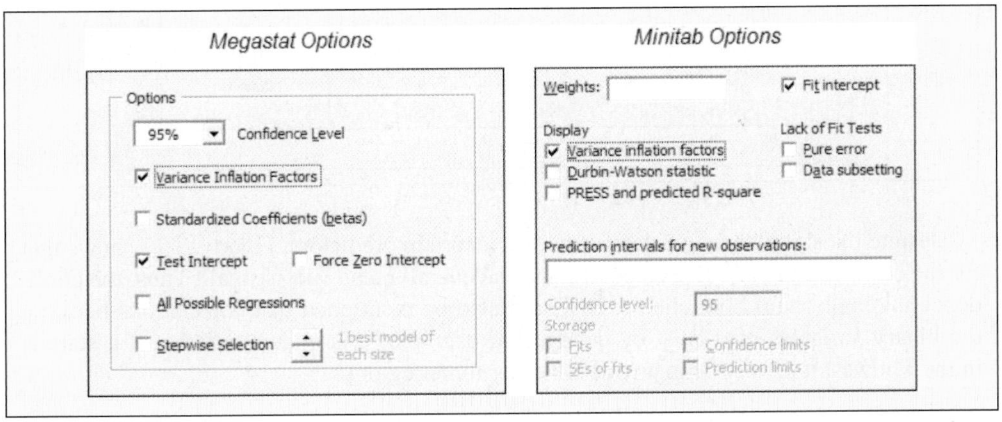

FIGURE 13.15

MegaStat and Minitab VIF Menu Options

Mini Case   13.5

Regional Voting Patterns 📁 Election2000

Mini Case 13.3 investigated a hypothesis about predictors for the percentage vote for George W. Bush in each of the 50 states. The proffered model was $Bush\% = \beta_0 + \beta_1\ Age65\% + \beta_2\ Urban\% + \beta_3\ ColGrad\% + \beta_4\ Union\% + \beta_5\ Midwest + \beta_6\ Neast + \beta_7\ West$. Table 13.11 and Figure 13.16 show the correlation matrix and matrix plot for the predictors (binary predictors omitted from the scatter plots). A quick rule says that a correlation is significant if it exceeds $2/\sqrt{n} = 2/\sqrt{50} = 0.28$. By this rule, a majority of the predictor correlations are significant at $\alpha = .05$ (shaded cells in table). However, none is close to the multiple correlation coefficient ($R = .890$) so by Klein's Rule we should not worry.

| **TABLE 13.11** | **Correlation Matrix for 2000 Election Predictors 📁 Election2000** |

	Age65%	**Urban%**	**ColGrad%**	**Union%**	**Midwest**	**Neast**	**Seast**
Urban%	−0.030						
ColGrad%	−0.204	0.406					
Union%	0.006	0.342	0.308				
Midwest	0.237	−0.140	−0.031	0.088			
Neast	0.230	0.266	0.439	0.335	−0.315		
Seast	0.073	−0.109	−0.454	−0.482	−0.333	−0.298	
West	−0.513	−0.006	0.057	0.063	−0.370	−0.331	−0.350

| **FIGURE 13.16** | **MINITAB's Matrix Scatter Plot for 2000 Election Predictors** |

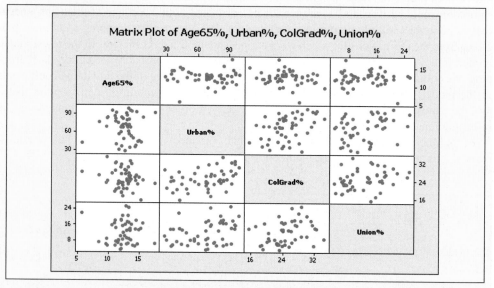

Despite the significant correlations between certain predictors, Figure 13.17 shows that for the election data no VIF exceeds 10 and the overall mean VIF is small. Thus, the confidence intervals should be reliable. It should also be mentioned that correlations between the binary variables may exist by design. For example, it is understood that if a state is in the Midwest it *cannot* be in any of the other three regions.

FIGURE 13.17   MegaStat's VIFs for Election Study   Election2000

Regression output						confidence interval		
variables	coefficients	std. error	t(df = 42)	p-value	95% lower	95% upper	VIF
Intercept	94.5502	7.5254	12.564	0.0000	79.3633	109.7370	
Age65%	−1.2869	0.4010	−3.210	0.0025	−2.0961	−0.4777	1.555
Urban%	−0.0983	0.0348	−2.827	0.0072	−0.1684	−0.0281	1.361
ColGrad%	−0.5815	0.1933	−3.008	0.0044	−0.9716	−0.1914	1.853
Union%	−0.7281	0.1327	−5.485	0.0000	−0.9960	−0.4602	1.517
Midwest	5.6715	2.0340	2.788	0.0079	1.5666	9.7763	2.166
Neast	−1.6063	2.4902	−0.645	0.5224	−6.6318	3.4191	2.896
West	3.7483	2.0071	1.868	0.0688	−0.3022	7.7988	2.210

13.19 Using the "Vail Guest Satisfaction Survey" data, construct a correlation matrix of the 11 independent variables. The response variable is *ovalue*. (a) Identify the four pairs of independent variables that have the highest pairwise correlation values. Do they show significant correlation? (b) Using MegaStat or MINITAB, run the regression with all 11 predictor variables, calculating the VIF for each predictor. (c) Did you see any cause for concern based on the VIF values? Why or why not?   VailGuestSat2

VAILRESORTS

13.20 Using the "Metals" data, construct a correlation matrix of the six independent variables. The response variable is *Price/lb*. (a) Identify any pairs of independent variables that have a significant pairwise correlation. (b) Using MegaStat or MINITAB, run the regression with all six predictor variables, calculating the VIF for each predictor. (c) Did you see any cause for concern based on the VIF values? Why or why not?   Metals

---

Recall that the least squares method makes several assumptions about the random error ε. Although ε is unobservable, clues may be found in the residuals e_i. We routinely test three important assumptions:

- *Assumption* 1: The errors are normally distributed.
- *Assumption* 2: The errors have constant variance (i.e., they are homoscedastic).
- *Assumption* 3: The errors are independent (i.e., they are nonautocorrelated).

Regression residuals often violate one or more of these assumptions. The consequences may be mild, moderate, or severe, depending on various factors. **Residual tests** for violations of regression assumptions are routinely provided by regression software. These tests were discussed in detail in Sections 12.8 and 12.9. We briefly review each assumption.

13.8
VIOLATIONS OF ASSUMPTIONS

LO7

Analyze residuals to check for violations of residual assumptions.

Non-Normal Errors

Except when there are major outliers, non-normal residuals are usually considered a mild violation. The regression coefficients and their variances remain unbiased and consistent. The main ill consequence is that confidence intervals for the parameters may be unreliable because the normality assumption is used to construct them. However, if the sample size is large (say, $n > 30$) the confidence intervals generally are OK unless serious outliers exist. The hypotheses are:

H_0: Errors are normally distributed

H_1: Errors are not normally distributed

A simple "eyeball test" of the *histogram of residuals* can usually reveal outliers or serious asymmetry. You can use either plain residuals or standardized (i.e., studentized) residuals. Standardized residuals offer the advantage of a predictable scale (between −3 and +3 unless there are outliers). Another visual test for normality is the *probability plot*, which is produced as an option by MINITAB and MegaStat. If the null hypothesis is true, the probability plot should be approximately linear.

Nonconstant Variance (Heteroscedasticity)

The regression should fit equally well for all values of *X*. If the error variance is constant, the errors are *homoscedastic*. If the error variance is nonconstant, the errors are *heteroscedastic*. This violation is potentially serious. Although the least squares regression parameter estimates are still unbiased and consistent, their estimated variances are biased and are neither efficient nor asymptotically efficient. In the most common form of heteroscedasticity, the variances of the estimators are likely to be understated, resulting in overstated *t* statistics and artificially narrow confidence intervals. In a multiple regression, a visual test for constant variance can be performed by examining scatter plots of the residuals against each predictor or against the fitted *Y*-values. Ideally, there will be no pattern and the vertical spread (residual variance) will be similar regardless of the *X*-values. The hypotheses are:

H_0: Errors have constant variance (homoscedastic)

H_1: Errors have nonconstant variance (heteroscedastic)

In a multiple regression, to avoid looking at all *k* residual plots (one for each predictor) we usually just examine the plot of residuals against the predicted *Y*-values. Although many patterns of nonconstant variance might exist, the "fan-out" pattern of increasing variance is most common (see Figure 13.18). The zero line appears more or less in the center of the residual plot, since the residuals always sum to zero.

FIGURE 13.18

Heteroscedastic Residual Plots

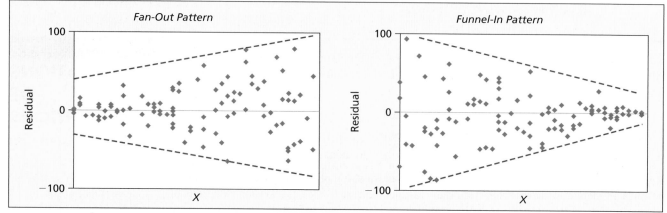

EXAMPLE   The foreclosure rate by state for 2007 was regressed against that state's share of all new mortgages issued in 2005 that were subprime (i.e., loans that fall into risky categories based on the borrower's credit rating or the high amount of the loan). The explanatory variable explained approximately 25 percent ($R^2 = .251$) of the variation in state foreclosure rates; however, the plot of residuals against predicted foreclosure rate shows a clear heteroscedastic pattern, shown in Figure 13.19.

The presence of nonconstant error variance can cause the confidence interval for the regression coefficient to be narrower than it should be because the standard error of the slope estimate is possibly underestimated. In this example the 95 percent confidence interval for the slope of the estimated regression equation is [43.8599, 131.9923]. It is possible that the true confidence interval should be wider than this. Techniques for reducing the effect of heteroscedasticity include transforming either the *X* or *Y* variable and or expressing the variables in relative terms. It is also important to consider other explanatory variables that might better explain variation in *Y* than our chosen *X* variable. You will have a chance to examine this data is more detail in the end of chapter exercises.   **Foreclosures**

FIGURE 13.19   **Heteroscedastic Residual Plot**

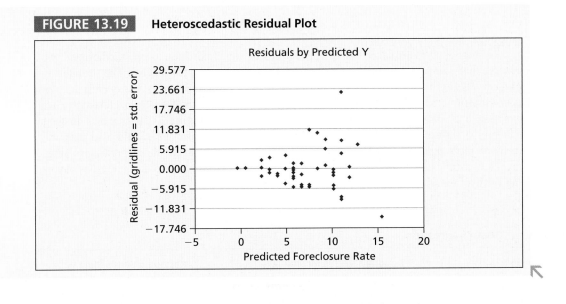

FIGURE 13.19   Heteroscedastic Residual Plot (*Residuals by Predicted Y*)

Mini Case   13.6

Non-Normality and Heteroscedasticity   📁 **HeartDeaths**

Figure 13.20 shows MINITAB regression diagnostics for a regression model of heart deaths in all 50 U.S. states for the year 2000. The dependent variable is *Heart* = heart deaths per 100,000 population and the three predictors are *Age65%* = percent of population age 65 and

FIGURE 13.20

MINITAB Diagnostics for Heart Death Regression

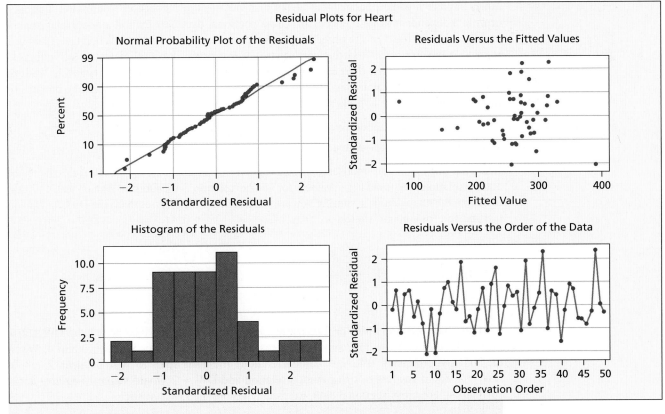

Residual Plots for Heart

over, *Income* = per capita income in thousands of dollars, and *Black%* = percent of population that is African American.

The histogram is arguably bell-shaped. Since the residuals have been standardized, we can see that there are no outliers (more than 3 standard errors from zero). The probability plot reveals slight deviations from linearity at the lower and upper ends, but overall the plot is consistent with the hypothesis of normality. For an overall test for heteroscedasticity, we can look at the plot of residuals against the fitted *Y*-values in Figure 13.20. It shows no clear pattern, so we are disinclined to suspect heteroscedasticity. But we should also examine residual plots against each predictor. The residual plots for the three predictors (Figure 13.21) show no pronounced consistent "fan-out" or "funnel-in" pattern, thereby favoring the hypothesis of homoscedasticity (constant variance).

FIGURE 13.21

MINITAB Residual Plots for Heart Death Regression

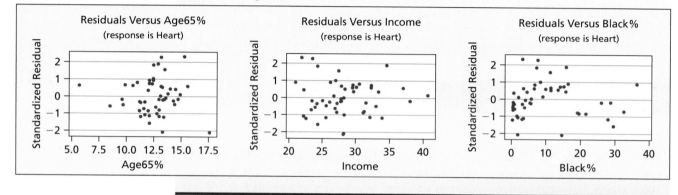

Autocorrelation

If you are working with time-series data, you need to be aware of the possibility of *autocorrelation,* a pattern of nonindependent errors that violates the regression assumption that each error is independent of its predecessor. Cross-sectional data may exhibit autocorrelation, but usually it is an artifact of the order of data entry and so may be ignored. When the errors in a regression are autocorrelated, the least squares estimators of the coefficients are still unbiased and consistent. However, their estimated variances are biased in a way that typically leads to confidence intervals that are too narrow and *t* statistics that are too large. Thus, the model's fit may be overstated. The hypotheses are:

H_0: Errors are nonautocorrelated

H_1: Errors are autocorrelated

Since the true errors are unobservable, we rely on the residuals $e_1, e_2, \ldots, e_n$ for evidence of autocorrelation. The most common test for autocorrelation is the Durbin-Watson test. Using e_t to denote the *t*th residual (assuming you are working with time-series data) the Durbin-Watson test statistic for autocorrelation is

(13.19) $$DW = \frac{\sum\limits_{t=2}^{n}(e_t - e_{t-1})^2}{\sum\limits_{t=1}^{n}e_t^2} \qquad \text{(Durbin-Watson test statistic)}$$

If you study econometrics or forecasting, you will use a special table to test the DW statistic for significance. For now, simply note that the DW statistic lies between 0 and 4. When the null hypothesis is true (no autocorrelation) the DW statistic will be near 2, while $DW < 2$ would suggest *positive* autocorrelation and $DW > 2$ would suggest *negative* autocorrelation. For cross-sectional data, we usually ignore the DW statistic.

Unusual Observations

LO8

Identify unusual residuals and high leverage observations.

Several tests for unusual observations are routinely provided by regression software. An observation may be unusual for two reasons: (1) because the fitted model's prediction is poor (*unusual residuals*), or (2) because one or more observations may be having a large influence on the regression estimates (*unusual leverage*). Unusual observations may be highlighted (MegaStat), displayed separately and marked (MINITAB), or not indicated at all (Excel).

To check for unusual residuals, we can simply inspect the residuals to find instances where the model does not predict well. For example, the model might fit well in Alabama but not in Alaska. We apply the Empirical Rule (standardized residuals more than $2s$ from zero are *unusual,* while residuals more than $3s$ from zero are outliers).

Unusual Residuals MegaStat highlights unusual residuals in blue, while MINITAB marks them with an "R." As explained in Chapter 12, different software packages may use different definitions for "standardized" or "studentized" residuals, but usually they give similar indications of "unusual" residuals. For example, in Figure 13.22 the last two columns of the printout can be interpreted the same even though there are slight differences in the values.

FIGURE 13.22

MegaStat Output for Heart Death Regression

Regression Analysis: Heart Deaths per 100,000

R^2	0.779		
Adjusted R^2	0.764	n	50
R	0.883	k	3
Std. Error	27.422	Dep. Var.	**Heart**

ANOVA table

Source	*SS*	*df*	*MS*	*F*	*p-value*
Regression	121,809.5684	3	40,603.1895	54.00	0.0000
Residual	34,590.3558	46	751.9643		
Total	156,399.9242	49			

Regression output

					confidence interval		
variables	*coefficients*	*std. error*	*t(df = 46)*	*p-value*	*95% lower*	*95% upper*	*VIF*
Intercept	−37.0813	39.2007	−0.946	0.3491	−115.9882	41.8256	
Age65%	24.2509	2.0753	11.686	0.0000	20.0736	28.4282	1.018
Income	−1.0800	0.9151	−1.180	0.2440	−2.9220	0.7620	1.012
Black%	2.2682	0.4116	5.511	0.0000	1.4398	3.0967	1.013

Unusual Observations

Observation	*Heart*	*Predicted*	*Residual*	*Leverage*	*Studentized Residual*	*Studentized Deleted Residual*
AK	90.90	76.62	14.28	0.304	0.624	0.620
CT	278.10	274.33	3.77	0.208	0.154	0.153
FL	340.40	392.45	−52.05	0.177	−2.092	−2.176
HI	203.30	259.06	−55.76	0.037	−2.072	−2.152
MS	337.20	316.02	21.18	0.223	0.876	0.874
OK	335.40	274.87	60.53	0.047	2.261	2.372
UT	130.80	145.05	−14.25	0.172	−0.571	−0.567
WV	377.50	317.55	59.95	0.108	2.315	2.436

Unusual Leverage   To check for unusual leverage, we look at the *leverage statistic* for each observation. It shows how far the predictors are from their means. As you saw in Chapter 12 (Section 12.8) such observations potentially have great influence on the regression estimates, because they are at the "end of the lever."

High Leverage

For n observations and k predictors, an observation is considered to be a high leverage observation if the leverage statistic exceeds

$$\frac{2(k+1)}{n}.$$

MegaStat will highlight high leverage values in green and MINITAB will mark those values with an "X."

Mini Case   13.7

Unusual Observations 📁 HeartDeaths

Figure 13.22 shows MegaStat's regression results for a regression model of heart deaths in the 50 U.S. states for the year 2000 (variables are drawn from the *LearningStats* state database). The response variable is *Heart* = heart deaths per 100,000 population, with predictors *Age65%* = percent of population age 65 and over, *Income* = per capita income in thousands of dollars, and *Black%* = percent of population classified as African American. The fitted regression is

$$Heart = -37.1 + 24.3 \, Age65\% - 1.08 \, Income + 2.27 \, Black\%$$

Age65% has the anticipated positive sign and is highly significant, and similarly for *Black%*. Income has a negative sign but is not significant even at $\alpha = .10$. The regression overall is significant ($F = 54.00$, p-value = .0000). The R^2 shows that the predictors explain 77.9 percent of the variation in *Heart* among the states. The adjusted R^2 is 76.4 percent, indicating that no unhelpful predictors are present. Since this is cross-sectional data, the DW statistic was not requested.

   Figure 13.22, lists eight unusual observations (the other 42 states are not unusual). Five states (AK, CT, FL, MS, UT), are highlighted because they have unusual *leverage*—a leverage statistic that exceeds $2(k+1)/n = (2)(3+1)/50 = 0.16$, One or more predictors for these states must differ greatly from the mean of that predictor, but only by inspecting the *X* data columns (*Age65%, Income,* or *Black%*) could we identify their unusual *X* values. Four states are highlighted because they have unusual *residuals*—a gap of at least two standard deviations (studentized residuals) between actual and predicted *Heart* values. FL and HI are more than 2 standard deviations lower than predicted, while OK and WV are more than 2 standard deviations higher than predicted. One state, FL, is unusual with respect to both residual and leverage.

13.9

OTHER REGRESSION TOPICS

Outliers

An outlier may be due to an error in recording the data. If so, the observation should be deleted. But how can you tell? Impossible or truly bizarre data values are apparent reasons to discard an observation. For example, a realtor's database of recent home sales in a million-dollar neighborhood contained this observation:

Price	BR	Bath	Basement	Built	SqFeet	Garage
95,000	4	3	Y	2001	4,335	Y

The 95,000 price is probably a typographical error. Even if the price were correct, it would be reasonable to discard the observation on grounds that it represents a different population than the other homes (e.g., a "gift" sale by a wealthy parent to a newlywed couple).

Missing Predictors

An outlier may also be an observation that has been influenced by an unspecified "lurking" variable that should have been controlled but wasn't. In this case, we should try to identify the lurking variable and formulate a multiple regression model that includes both predictors. For example, a reasonable model such as $Y =$ home price, $X_1 =$ square feet, and $X_2 =$ lot size might give poor predictions unless we add a neighborhood binary predictor (you can probably think of areas where a large house on a large lot might still command a poor price). If there are unspecified "lurking" variables, our fitted regression model will not give accurate predictions.

Ill-Conditioned Data

All variables in the regression should be of the same general order of magnitude (not too small, not too large). If your coefficients come out in exponential notation (e.g., 7.3154 E+06), you probably should adjust the decimal point in one or more variables to a convenient magnitude, as long as you treat all the values in the same data column consistently. Decimal adjustments for each data column need not be the same.

Significance in Large Samples

Statistical significance may not imply *practical importance*. In a large sample, we can obtain very large t statistics with low p-values for our predictors when, in fact, their effect on Y is very slight. There is an old saying in statistics that you can make anything significant if you get a large enough sample. In medical research, where thousands of patients are enrolled in clinical trials, this is a familiar problem. It can become difficult in such models to figure out which *significant* variables are really *important*.

Model Specification Errors

If you estimate a linear model when actually a nonlinear model is required, or when you omit a relevant predictor, then you have a *misspecified model*. How can you detect misspecification? You can:

- Plot the residuals against estimated Y (should be no discernable pattern).
- Plot the residuals against actual Y (should be no discernable pattern).
- Plot the fitted Y against the actual Y (should be a 45-degree line).

What are the cures for misspecification? Start by looking for a missing relevant predictor, seek a model with a better theoretical basis, or redefine your variables (e.g., assume a multiplicative model of the form $y = \beta_0 x_1^{\beta_1} x_2^{\beta_2} \cdots x_m^{\beta_m}$ for a production function, which becomes linear if you take logarithms). Model specification is a topic that will be covered in considerable depth if you study econometrics. For now, just remember that *residual patterns* are clues that the model may be incorrectly specified.

Missing Data

If many values in a data column are missing, we might want to discard that variable. If a Y data value is missing, we must discard the entire observation. If any X data values are missing, the conservative action is to discard the entire observation. However, since discarding an entire observation would mean losing other good information, statisticians have developed procedures for imputing missing values, such as using the mean of the X data column or by a regression procedure to "fit" the missing X-value from the complete observations. Imputing missing values requires specialized software and expert statistical advice.

Binary Dependent Variable

We have seen that binary predictors pose no special problem. However, when the response variable Y is binary (0, 1) the least squares estimation method no longer is appropriate. Specialized regression methods such as logit and probit are called for. MINITAB and other software packages handle this situation easily, but a different interpretation is required.

Stepwise and Best Subsets Regression

It may have occurred to you that there ought to be a way to automate the task of fitting the "best" regression using k predictors. The *stepwise regression* procedure uses the power of the computer to fit the best model using 1, 2, 3, . . . , k predictors. For example, aerospace engineers had a large data set of 469 observations on *Thrust* (takeoff thrust of a jet turbine) along with seven potential predictors (*TurbTemp, AirFlow, TurbSpeed, OilTemp, OilPres, RunTime, ThermCyc*). In the absence of a theoretical model, a stepwise regression was run, with the results shown in Figure 13.23. Only p-values are shown for each predictor, along with R^2, R^2_{adj}, and standard error. You can easily assess the effect of adding more predictors. In this example, most p-values are tiny due to the large n. While stepwise regression is an efficient way to identify the "best" model for each number of predictors (1, 2, . . . , k), it is appropriate only when there is no theoretical model that specifies which predictors *should* be used. A further degree of automation of the regression task is to perform *best subsets* regression using all possible combinations of predictors. This option is offered by many computer packages, but is not recommended because it yields too much output and too little additional insight.

FIGURE 13.23

MegaStat's Stepwise Regression of Turbine Data 📂 **Turbines**

Regression Analysis—Stepwise Selection displaying the best model of each size

469 observations
Thrust is the dependent variable

p-values for the coefficients

Nvar	TurbTemp	Airflow	TurbSpeed	OilTemp	OilPres	RunTime	ThermCyc	s	Adj R²	R²
1		.0000						12.370	.252	.254
2		.0000			.0004			12.219	.270	.273
3	.0003	.0000					.0005	12.113	.283	.287
4		.0000		.0081	.0000		.0039	12.041	.291	.297
5	.0010	.0000		.0009	.0003		.0006	11.914	.306	.314
6	.0010	.0000	.1440	.0037	.0005		.0010	11.899	.308	.317
7	.0008	.0000	.1624	.0031	.0007	.2049	.0006	11.891	.309	.319

CHAPTER SUMMARY

Multivariate regression extends simple regression to include multiple **predictors** of the **response variable.** Criteria to judge a fitted regression model include **logic, fit, parsimony,** and **stability.** Using too many predictors violates the principle of **Occam's Razor,** which favors a simpler model if it is adequate. If the R^2 differs greatly from R^2_{adj}, the model may contain unhelpful predictors. The ANOVA table and *F* **test** measure overall significance, while the *t* **test** is used to test hypotheses about individual predictors. A **confidence interval** for each unknown **parameter** is equivalent to a two-tailed hypothesis test for $\beta = 0$. The **standard error** of the regression is used to create **confidence intervals** or **prediction intervals** for Y. A **binary predictor** (also called a **dummy variable** or an **indicator**) has value 1 if the condition of interest is present, 0 otherwise. For c categories, we only include $c - 1$ binaries or the regression will fail. Including a squared predictor provides a test for **nonlinearity** of the predictors. Including the product of two predictors is a test for **interaction.** Collinearity (correlation between *two* predictors) is detected in the **correlation matrix,** while **multicollinearity** (when a predictor depends on *several* other predictors) is identified from the **variance inflation factor** (VIF) for each predictor. Regression assumes that the errors are normally distributed, independent random variables with constant variance. **Residual tests** identify possible **non-normality, autocorrelation,** or **heteroscedasticity.**

KEY TERMS

Commonly Used Formulas

Population regression model for k predictors: $y = \beta_0 + \beta_1 x_1 + \beta_2 x_2 + \cdots + \beta_k x_k + \varepsilon$

Fitted regression equation for k predictors: $\hat{y} = b_0 + b_1 x_1 + b_2 x_2 + \cdots + b_k x_k$

Residual for ith observation: $e_i = y_i - \hat{y}_i$ (for $i = 1, 2, \ldots, n$)

ANOVA sums: $SST = SSR + SSE$

SST (total sum of squares): $\sum_{i=1}^{n}(y_i - \bar{y})^2$

SSR (regression sum of squares): $\sum_{i=1}^{n}(\hat{y}_i - \bar{y})^2$

SSE (error sum of squares): $\sum_{i=1}^{n}(y_i - \hat{y}_i)^2$

MSR (regression mean square): $MSR = SSR/k$

MSE (error mean square): $MSE = SSE/(n - k - 1)$

F test statistic for overall significance: $F_{calc} = MSR/MSE$

Coefficient of determination: $R^2 = 1 - \dfrac{SSE}{SST}$ or $R^2 = \dfrac{SSR}{SST}$

Adjusted R^2: $R_{adj}^2 = 1 - \dfrac{\left(\dfrac{SSE}{n - k - 1}\right)}{\left(\dfrac{SST}{n - 1}\right)}$

Test statistic for coefficient of predictor X_j: $t_{calc} = \dfrac{b_j - 0}{s_j}$ where s_j is the standard error of b_j

Confidence interval for coefficient β_j: $b_j - t_{\alpha/2}s_j \le \beta_j \le b_j + t_{\alpha/2}s_j$

Estimated standard error of the regression: $s = \sqrt{\dfrac{\sum_{i=1}^{n}(y_i - \hat{y}_i)^2}{n - k - 1}} = \sqrt{\dfrac{SSE}{n - k - 1}}$

Approximate confidence interval for $E(Y/X)$: $\hat{y}_i \pm t_{\alpha/2}\dfrac{s}{\sqrt{n}}$

Approximate prediction interval for Y: $\hat{y}_i \pm t_{n-k-1}s$

Variance inflation factor for predictor j: $VIF_j = \dfrac{1}{1 - R_j^2}$

Evans' Rule (conservative): $n/k \ge 10$ (10 observations per predictor)

Doane's Rule (relaxed): $n/k \ge 5$ (5 observations per predictor)

1. (a) List two limitations of simple regression. (b) Why is estimating a multiple regression model just as easy as simple regression?

2. (a) What does ε represent in the regression model? (b) What assumptions do we make about ε? What is the distinction between Greek letters (β) and Roman letters (b) in representing a regression equation?

3. (a) Describe the format of a multiple regression data set. (b) Why is it a good idea to write down our *a priori* reasoning about a proposed regression?

4. (a) Why does a higher R^2 not always indicate a good model? (b) State the principle of Occam's Razor. (c) List four criteria for assessing a regression model.

CHAPTER REVIEW

5. (a) What is the role of the F test in multiple regression? (b) How is the F statistic calculated from the ANOVA table? (c) Why are tables rarely needed for the F test?

6. (a) Why is testing $H_0: \beta = 0$ a very common test for a predictor? (b) How many degrees of freedom do we use in a t test for an individual predictor's significance?

7. (a) Explain why a confidence interval for a predictor coefficient is equivalent to a two-tailed test of significance. (b) Why are t tables rarely needed in performing significance tests?

8. (a) What does a coefficient of determination (R^2) measure? (b) When R^2 and R^2_{adj} differ considerably, what does it indicate?

9. State some guidelines to prevent inclusion of too many predictors in a regression.

10. (a) State the formula for the standard error of the regression. (b) Why is it sometimes preferred to R^2 as a measure of "fit"? (c) What is the formula for a quick prediction interval for individual Y-values? (d) When you need an exact prediction, what must you do?

11. (a) What is a binary predictor? (b) Why is a binary predictor sometimes called a "shift variable"? (c) How do we test a binary predictor for significance?

12. If we have c categories for an attribute, why do we only use $c - 1$ binaries to represent them in a fitted regression?

13. (a) Explain why it might be useful to include a quadratic term in a regression. (b) Explain why it might be useful to include an interaction term between two predictors in a regression. (c) Name a drawback to including quadratic or interaction terms in a regression.

14. (a) What is multicollinearity? (b) What are its potential consequences? (c) Why is it a matter of degree? (d) Why might it be ignored?

15. (a) How does multicollinearity differ from collinearity? (b) Explain how we can use the correlation matrix to test for collinearity. (c) State a quick rule to test for significant collinearity in a correlation matrix. (d) What is Klein's Rule?

16. (a) State the formula for a variance inflation factor (VIF) for a predictor. (b) Why does the VIF provide a more general test for multicollinearity than a correlation matrix or a matrix plot? (c) State a rule of thumb for detecting strong variance inflation.

17. If multicollinearity is severe, what might its symptoms be?

18. (a) How can we detect an unusual residual? An outlier? (b) How can we identify an influential observation?

19. (a) Name two ways to detect non-normality of the residuals. (b) What are the potential consequences of this violation? (c) What remedies might be appropriate?

20. (a) Name two ways to detect heteroscedastic residuals. (b) What are the potential consequences of this violation? (c) What remedies might be appropriate?

21. (a) Name two ways to detect autocorrelated residuals. (b) What are the potential consequences of this violation? (c) What remedies might be appropriate?

22. (a) What is a lurking variable? How might it be inferred? (b) What are ill-conditioned data?

CHAPTER EXERCISES

connect

Instructions for Data Sets: Choose one of the data sets $A - J$ below or as assigned by your instructor. Only the first three and last three observations are shown for each data set (files are on the CD). In each data set, the dependent variable (*response*) is the first variable. Choose the independent variables (*predictors*) as you judge appropriate. Use a spreadsheet or a statistical package (e.g., MegaStat or MINITAB) to perform the necessary regression calculations and to obtain the required graphs. Write a concise report answering questions 13.21 through 13.37 (or a subset of these questions assigned by your instructor). Label sections of your report to correspond to the questions. Insert tables and graphs in your report as appropriate. You may work with a partner if your instructor allows it.

13.21 Is this cross-sectional data or time-series data? What is the unit of observation (e.g., firm, individual, year)?

13.22 Are the X and Y data well-conditioned? If not, make any transformations that may be necessary and explain.

13.23 State your *a priori* hypotheses about the sign ($+$ or $-$) of each predictor and your reasoning about cause and effect. Would the intercept have meaning in this problem? Explain.

13.24 Does your sample size fulfill Evans' Rule ($n/k \geq 10$) or at least Doane's Rule ($n/k \geq 5$)?

13.25 Perform the regression and write the estimated regression equation (round off to 3 or 4 significant digits for clarity). Do the coefficient signs agree with your *a priori* expectations?

13.26 Does the 95 percent confidence interval for each predictor coefficient include zero? What conclusion can you draw? *Note:* Skip this question if you are using MINITAB, since predictor confidence intervals are not shown.

13.27 Do a two-tailed t test for zero slope for each predictor coefficient at $\alpha = .05$. State the degrees of freedom and look up the critical value in Appendix D (or from Excel).

13.28 (a) Which p-values indicate predictor significance at $\alpha = .05$? (b) Do the p-values support the conclusions you reached from the t tests? (c) Do you prefer the t test or the p-value approach? Why?

13.29 Based on the R^2 and ANOVA table for your model, how would you describe the fit?

13.30 Use the standard error to construct an *approximate* prediction interval for Y. Based on the width of this prediction interval, would you say the predictions are good enough to have practical value?

13.31 (a) Generate a correlation matrix for your predictors. Round the results to three decimal places. (b) Based on the correlation matrix, is collinearity a problem? What rules of thumb (if any) are you using?

13.32 (a) If you did not already do so, re-run the regression requesting variance inflation factors (VIFs) for your predictors. (b) Do the VIFs suggest that multicollinearity is a problem? Explain.

13.33 (a) If you did not already do so, request a table of standardized residuals. (b) Are any residuals *outliers* (three standard errors) or *unusual* (two standard errors)?

13.34 If you did not already do so, request leverage statistics. Are any observations influential? Explain.

13.35 If you did not already do so, request a histogram of standardized residuals and/or a normal probability plot. Do the residuals suggest non-normal errors? Explain.

13.36 If you did not already do so, request a plot of residuals versus the fitted Y. Is heteroscedasticity a concern?

13.37 If you are using time-series data, perform one or more tests for autocorrelation (visual inspection of residuals plotted against observation order, runs test, Durbin-Watson test). Is autocorrelation a concern?

DATA SET A   **Mileage and Other Characteristics of Randomly Selected Vehicles ($n = 43$, $k = 4$)** ⌧ Mileage

Obs	Vehicle	City	Length	Width	Weight	Japan
1	Acura CL	20	192	69	3,450	1
2	Accura TSX	23	183	59	3,320	1
3	BMW 3-Series	19	176	69	3,390	0
⋮	⋮	⋮	⋮	⋮	⋮	⋮
41	Toyota Sienna	19	200	77	4,120	1
42	Volkswagen Jetta	34	172	68	3,045	0
43	Volvo C70	20	186	72	3,690	0

City = EPA miles per gallon in city driving, *Length* = vehicle length (inches), *Width* = vehicle width (inches), *Weight* = weight (pounds), *Japan* = 1 if carmaker is Japanese, 0 otherwise.

Source: *Consumer Reports New Car Buying Guide 2003–2004* (Consumers Union, 2003). Sampling methodology was to select the vehicle on every fifth page starting at page 40. Data are intended for purposes of statistical education and should not be viewed as a guide to vehicle performance.

DATA SET B   **Noodles & Company Sales, Seating, and Demographic Data ($n = 74$, $k = 5$)** ⌧ Noodles2

Obs	Sales/SqFt	Seats-Inside	Seats-Patio	MedIncome	MedAge	BachDeg%
1	702	66	18	45.2	34.4	31
2	210	69	16	51.9	41.2	20
3	365	67	10	51.4	40.3	24
⋮	⋮	⋮	⋮	⋮	⋮	⋮
72	340	63	28	60.9	43.5	21
73	401	72	15	73.8	41.6	29
74	327	76	24	64.2	31.4	15

Sales/SqFt = sales per square foot of floor space, *Seats-Inside* = number of interior seats, *Seats-Patio* = number of outside seats. The three demographic variables refer to a three-mile radius of the restaurant: *MedIncome* = median family income, *MedAge* = median age, and *BachDeg%* = percentage of population with at least a bachelor's degree.

Source: Noodles & Company.

DATA SET C   Assessed Value of Small Medical Office Buildings ($n = 32$, $k = 5$)
📁 Assessed

Obs	Assessed	Floor	Offices	Entrances	Age	Freeway
1	1796	4790	4	2	8	0
2	1544	4720	3	2	12	0
3	2094	5940	4	2	2	0
⋮	⋮	⋮	⋮	⋮	⋮	⋮
30	1264	3580	3	2	27	0
31	1162	3610	2	1	8	1
32	1447	3960	3	2	17	0

Assessed = assessed value (thousands of dollars), *Floor* = square feet of floor space, *Offices* = number of offices in the building, *Entrances* = number of customer entrances (excluding service doors), *Age* = age of the building (years), *Freeway* = 1 if within one mile of freeway, 0 otherwise.

DATA SET D   Changes in Consumer Price Index, Capacity Utilization, Changes in Money Supply Components, and Unemployment ($n = 41$, $k = 4$)
📁 Money

Year	ChgCPI	CapUtil	ChgM1	ChgM2	Unem
1966	2.9	91.1	2.5	4.6	3.8
1967	3.1	87.2	6.6	9.3	3.8
1968	4.2	87.1	7.7	8.0	3.6
⋮	⋮	⋮	⋮	⋮	⋮
2004	2.7	76.6	5.3	5.8	5.5
2005	3.4	78.8	−0.2	4.0	5.1
2006	3.2	80.4	−0.5	5.3	4.6

ChCPI = percent change in the Consumer Price Index (CPI) over previous year, *CapUtil* = percent utilization of manufacturing capacity in current year, *ChgM1* = percent change in currency and demand deposits (M1) over previous year, *ChgM2* = percent change in small time deposits and other near-money (M2) over previous year, *Unem* = civilian unemployment rate in percent.

Source: *Economic Report of the President, 2007.*

DATA SET E   College Graduation Rate and Selected Characteristics of U.S. States ($n = 50$, $k = 8$) 📁 ColGrads

State	ColGrad%	Dropout	EdSpend	Urban	Age	Femlab	Neast	Seast	West
AL	15.6	35.3	3,627	60.4	33.0	51.8	0	1	0
AK	23.0	31.6	8,330	67.5	29.4	64.9	0	0	1
AZ	20.3	27.5	4,309	87.5	32.2	55.6	0	0	1
⋮	⋮	⋮	⋮	⋮	⋮	⋮	⋮	⋮	⋮
WV	12.3	22.7	4,911	36.1	35.4	44.2	0	1	0
WI	17.7	15.8	5,871	65.7	32.9	63.1	0	0	0
WY	18.8	21.4	5,723	65.0	32.0	61.8	0	0	1

ColGrad% = percent of state population with a college degree, *Dropout* = percent of high school students who do not graduate, *EdSpend* = per capita spending on K–12 education, *Urban* = percent of state population living in urban areas, *Age* = median age of state's population, *FemLab* = percent of adult females who are in the labor force, *Neast* = 1 if state is in the Northeast, 0 otherwise, *Seast* = 1 if state is in the Southeast, 0 otherwise, *West* = 1 if state is in the West, 0 otherwise. *Midwest* is the omitted fourth binary.

Source: *Statistical Abstract of the United States, 1990.*

DATA SET F   Characteristics of Selected Piston Aircraft (*n* = 55 m, *k* = 4)   CruiseSpeed

Obs	Mfgr/Model	Cruise	Year	TotalHP	NumBlades	Turbo
1	Cessna Turbo Stationair TU206	148	1981	310	3	1
2	Cessna 310 R	194	1975	570	3	0
3	Piper 125 Tri Pacer	107	1951	125	2	0
⋮	⋮	⋮	⋮	⋮	⋮	⋮
53	OMF Aircraft Symphony	128	2002	160	2	0
54	Liberty XL-2	132	2003	125	2	0
55	Piper 6X	148	2004	300	3	0

Cruise = best cruise speed (knots indicated air speed) at 65–75 percent power, *Year* = year of manufacture, *TotalHP* = total horsepower (both engines if twin), *NumBlades* = number of propeller blades, *Turbo* = 1 if turbocharged, 0 otherwise.

Source: *Flying Magazine* (various issues). Data are for educational purposes only and not as a guide to performance.

DATA SET G   Characteristics of Randomly Chosen Hydrocarbons (*n* = 35, *k* = 7)   Retention

Obs	Name	Ret	MW	BP	RI	H1	H2	H3	H4
1	2,4,4-trimethyl-2-pentene	153.57	112.215	105.06	1.4135	0	1	0	0
2	1,5-cyclooctadiene	237.56	108.183	150.27	1.4905	0	0	0	1
3	methylcyclohexane	153.57	98.188	101.08	1.4206	0	0	1	0
⋮	⋮	⋮	⋮	⋮	⋮	⋮	⋮	⋮	⋮
33	ethylbenzene	209.700	106.170	136.000	1.4950	0	0	0	0
34	m-ethyl toluene	247.800	120.194	161.480	1.4941	0	0	0	0
35	3-methylhexane	132.320	100.204	92.000	1.3861	1	0	0	0

Ret = Chromatographic retention time (seconds), *MW* = molecular weight (gm/mole), *BP* = boiling point in °C, *RI* = refractive index (dimensionless), *Class* = hydrocarbon class (*H1* = acyclic saturated, *H2* = acyclic unsaturated, *H3* = cyclic saturated, *H4* = cyclic unsaturated, *H5* = aromatic is the omitted fifth binary.)

Source: Data are courtesy of John Seeley of Oakland University.

DATA SET H   2007 Foreclosure Rates (*n* = 50, *k* = 7)   Foreclosures2

State	Foreclosure	MassLayoff	SubprimeShare	PriceIncomeRatio	Ownership	5YrApp	UnempChange	%HousMoved
Alabama	2.70	5.96	28%	4.04	76.6	32.51	0.00%	0.448
Alaska	4.90	2.78	18%	5.54	66.0	53.91	−4.62%	0.426
Arizona	15.20	1.56	26%	6.79	71.1	96.55	−7.32%	0.383
⋮	⋮	⋮	⋮	⋮	⋮	⋮	⋮	⋮
West Virginia	0.50	1.05	21%	4.34	81.3	35.82	−2.13%	0.502
Wisconsin	4.90	12.50	21%	4.83	71.1	36.37	4.26%	0.428
Wyoming	1.50	0.96	23%	5.06	72.8	62.56	−9.09%	0.498

Each observation shows the 2007 state foreclosure rate, *MassLayoff* = Mass Layoff events per 100,000 people, *SubprimeShare* = Share of new mortgages that were subprime in 2005, *PriceIncomeRatio* = average home prices to median household income ratio, *Ownership* = Home Ownership rates (%) in 2005, *5YrApp* = Period Ended Dec 06 Average 5Yr home price appreciation, *UnempChange* = 2007 Unemployment rate percent change, *%HousMoved* = % of housing that was moved into in 2000–2005.

Source: MBA Project by Steve Rohlwing and Rediate Eshetu.

DATA SET I   Body Fat and Personal Measurements for Males ($n = 50, k = 8$) 🗇 BodyFat2

Obs	Fat%	Age	Weight	Height	Neck	Chest	Abdomen	Hip	Thigh
1	12.6	23	154.25	67.75	36.2	93.1	85.2	94.5	59.0
2	6.9	22	173.25	72.25	38.5	93.6	83.0	98.7	58.7
3	24.6	22	154.00	66.25	34.0	95.8	87.9	99.2	59.6
⋮	⋮	⋮	⋮	⋮	⋮	⋮	⋮	⋮	⋮
48	6.4	39	148.50	71.25	34.6	89.8	79.5	92.7	52.7
49	13.4	45	135.75	68.50	32.8	92.3	83.4	90.4	52.0
50	5.0	47	127.50	66.75	34.0	83.4	70.4	87.2	50.6

Fat% = percent body fat, *Age* = age (yrs.), *Weight* = weight (lbs.), *Height* = height (in.), *Neck* = neck circumference (cm), *Chest* = chest circumference (cm), *Abdomen* = abdomen circumference (cm), *Hip* = hip circumference (cm), *Thigh* = thigh circumference (cm).

Data are a subsample of 252 males analyzed in Roger W. Johnson (1996), "Fitting Percentage of Body Fat to Simple Body Measurements," *Journal of Statistics Education* 4, no. 1.

DATA SET J   Used Vehicle Prices ($n = 637, k = 4$) 🗇 Vehicles

Obs	Model	Price	Age	Car	Truck	SUV
1	Astro GulfStream Conversion	12,988	3	0	0	0
2	Astro LS 4.3L V6	5,950	9	0	0	0
3	Astro LS V6	19,995	4	0	0	0
⋮	⋮	⋮	⋮	⋮	⋮	⋮
635	DC 300M Autostick	10,995	6	1	0	0
636	DC 300M Special Edition	22,995	1	1	0	0
637	GM 3500 4×4 w/8ft bed and plow	17,995	5	0	1	0

Price = asking price ($), *Age* = vehicle age (yrs), *Car* = 1 if passenger car, 0 otherwise, *Truck* = 1 if truck, 0 otherwise, *SUV* = 1 if sport utility vehicle, 0 otherwise. (*Van* is the omitted fourth binary).

Source: *Detroit AutoFocus* 4, Issue 38 (Sept. 17–23, 2004). Data are for educational purposes only and should not be used as a guide to depreciation.

GENERAL EXERCISES

13.38 In a model of Ford's quarterly revenue $TotalRevenue = \beta_0 + \beta_1\ CarSales + \beta_2\ TruckSales + \beta_3\ SUVSales + \varepsilon$, the three predictors are measured in number of units sold (not dollars). (a) Interpret each slope. (b) Would the intercept be meaningful? (c) What factors might be reflected in the error term? Explain.

13.39 In a study of paint peel problems, a regression was suggested to predict defects per million (the response variable). The intended predictors were supplier (four suppliers, coded as binaries) and substrate (four materials, coded as binaries). There were 11 observations. Explain why regression is impractical in this case, and suggest a remedy.

13.40 A hospital emergency room analyzed $n = 17,664$ hourly observations on its average occupancy rates using six binary predictors representing days of the week and two binary predictors representing the 8-hour work shift (12 A.M.–8 A.M., 8 A.M.–4 P.M., 4 P.M.–12 A.M.) when the ER census was taken. The fitted regression equation was $AvgOccupancy = 11.2 + 1.19\ Mon - 0.187\ Tue - 0.785\ Wed - 0.580\ Thu - 0.451\ Fri - 0.267\ Sat - 4.58\ Shift1 - 1.65\ Shift2$ ($SE = 6.18$, $R^2 = .094$, $R^2_{adj} = .093$). (a) Why did the analyst use only six binaries for days when there are 7 days in a week? (b) Why did the analyst use only two work shift binaries when there are three work shifts? (c) Which is the busiest day? (d) Which is the busiest shift? (e) Interpret the intercept. (f) Assess the regression's fit.

13.41 Using test data on 20 types of laundry detergent, an analyst fitted a regression to predict *CostPerLoad* (average cost per load in cents per load) using binary predictors *TopLoad* (1 if washer is a top-loading model, 0 otherwise) and *Powder* (if detergent was in powder form, 0 otherwise). Interpret the results. (Data are from *Consumer Reports* 68, no. 8 [November 2003], p. 42.) 🗇 **Laundry**

R^2	0.117				
Adjusted R^2	0.006		n	19	
R	0.341		k	2	
Std. Error	5.915		Dep. Var.	**Cost Per Load**	

ANOVA table

Source	SS	df	MS	F	p-value
Regression	73.8699	2	36.9350	1.06	.3710
Residual	559.8143	16	34.9884		
Total	633.6842	18			

Regression output   confidence interval

variables	coefficients	std. error	t(df = 16)	p-value	95% lower	95% upper
Intercept	26.0000	4.1826	6.216	1.23E-05	17.1333	34.8667
Top-Load	−6.3000	4.5818	−1.375	.1881	−16.0130	3.4130
Powder	−0.2714	2.9150	−0.093	.9270	−6.4509	5.9081

13.42 A researcher used stepwise regression to create regression models to predict *BirthRate* (births per 1,000) using five predictors: *LifeExp* (life expectancy in years), *InfMort* (infant mortality rate), *Density* (population density per square kilometer), *GDPCap* (Gross Domestic Product per capita), and *Literate* (literacy percent). Interpret these results.   📄 **BirthRates2**

Regression Analysis—Stepwise Selection (best model of each size)

153   observations
BirthRate is the dependent variable

p-values for the coefficients

Nvar	LifeExp	InfMort	Density	GDPCap	Literate	s	Adj R^2	R^2
1		.0000				6.318	.722	.724
2		.0000			.0000	5.334	.802	.805
3		.0000		.0242	.0000	5.261	.807	.811
4	.5764	.0000		.0311	.0000	5.273	.806	.812
5	.5937	.0000	.6289	.0440	.0000	5.287	.805	.812

13.43 A sports enthusiast created an equation to predict *Victories* (the team's number of victories in the National Basketball Association regular season play) using predictors *FGP* (team field goal percentage), *FTP* (team free throw percentage), *Points* = (team average points per game), *Fouls* (team average number of fouls per game), *TrnOvr* (team average number of turnovers per game), and *Rbnds* (team average number of rebounds per game). The fitted regression was *Victories* = −281 + 523 *FGP* + 3.12 *FTP* + 0.781 *Points* − 2.90 *Fouls* + 1.60 *TrnOvr* + 0.649 *Rbnds* (R^2 = .802, F = 10.80, SE = 6.87). The strongest predictors were *FGP* (t = 4.35) and *Fouls* (t = −2.146). The other predictors were only marginally significant and *FTP* and *Rbnds* were not significant. The matrix of correlations is shown below. At the time of this analysis, there were 23 NBA teams. (a) Do the regression coefficients make sense? (b) Is the intercept meaningful? Explain. (c) Is the sample size a problem (using Evans' Rule or Doane's Rule)? (d) Why might collinearity account for the lack of significance of some predictors? (Data are from a research project by MBA student Michael S. Malloy.)

	FGP	FTP	Points	Fouls	TrnOvr	Rbnds
FGP	1.000					
FTP	−0.039	1.000				
Points	0.475	0.242	1.000			
Fouls	−0.014	0.211	0.054	1.000		
TrnOvr	0.276	0.028	0.033	0.340	1.000	
Rbnds	0.436	0.137	0.767	−0.032	0.202	1.000

13.44 An expert witness in a case of alleged racial discrimination in a state university school of nursing introduced a regression of the determinants of *Salary* of each professor for each year during an 8-year period ($n = 423$) with the following results, with dependent variable *Salary* and predictors *Year* (year in which the salary was observed), *YearHire* (year when the individual was hired), *Race* (1 if individual is black, 0 otherwise), and *Rank* (1 if individual is an assistant professor, 0 otherwise). Interpret these results.

Variable	Coefficient	t	p
Intercept	−3,816,521	−29.4	.000
Year	1,948	29.8	.000
YearHire	−826	−5.5	.000
Race	−2,093	−4.3	.000
Rank	−6,438	−22.3	.000
$R^2 = 0.811$		$R^2_{adj} = 0.809$	$s = 3,318$

13.45 Analysis of a Detroit Marathon ($n = 1,015$ men, $n = 150$ women) produced the regression results shown below, with dependent variable *Time* (the marathon time in minutes) and predictors *Age* (runner's age), *Weight* (runner's weight in pounds), *Height* (runner's height in inches), and *Exp* (1 if runner had prior marathon experience, 0 otherwise). (a) Interpret the coefficient of *Exp*. (b) Does the intercept have any meaning? (c) Why do you suppose squared predictors were included? (d) Plug in your own *Age, Height, Weight,* and *Exp* to predict your own running time. Do you believe it? (Data courtesy of Detroit Striders.)

Variable	Men ($n = 1,015$)		Women ($n = 150$)	
	Coefficient	t	Coefficient	t
Intercept	−366		−2,820	
Age	−4.827	−6.1	−3.593	−2.5
Age^2	0.07671	7.1	0.05240	2.6
Weight	−1.598	−1.9	3.000	0.7
Weight^2	0.008961	3.4	−0.004041	−2.0
Height	24.65	1.5	96.13	1.6
Height^2	−0.2074	−1.7	−0.8040	−1.8
Exp	−41.74	−17.0	−28.65	−4.3
	$R^2 = 0.423$		$R^2 = 0.334$	

13.46 Using test data on 43 vehicles, an analyst fitted a regression to predict *CityMPG* (miles per gallon in city driving) using as predictors *Length* (length of car in inches), *Width* (width of car in inches), and *Weight* (weight of car in pounds). Interpret the results. Do you see evidence that some predictors were unhelpful? ☞ **CityMPG**

R^2	0.682			
Adjusted R^2	0.658	n	43	
R	0.826	k	3	
Std. Error	2.558	Dep. Var.	**CityMPG**	

ANOVA table

Source	SS	df	MS	F	p-value
Regression	547.3722	3	182.4574	27.90	8.35E-10
Residual	255.0929	39	6.5408		
Total	802.4651	42			

Regression output   confidence interval

variables	coefficients	std. error	t(df = 39)	p-value	95% lower	95% upper	VIF
Intercept	39.4492	8.1678	4.830	.0000	22.9283	55.9701	
Length (in)	−0.0016	0.0454	−0.035	.9725	−0.0934	0.0902	2.669
Width (in)	−0.0463	0.1373	−0.337	.7379	−0.3239	0.2314	2.552
Weight (lbs)	−0.0043	0.0008	−5.166	.0000	−0.0060	−0.0026	2.836

13.47 A researcher used stepwise regression to create regression models to predict *CarTheft* (thefts per 1000) using four predictors: *Income* (per capita income), *Unem* (unemployment percent), *Pupil/Tea* (pupil-to-teacher ratio), and *Divorce* (divorces per 1,000 population) for the 50 U.S. states. Interpret these results. ☞ **CarTheft**

Regression Analysis—Stepwise Selection (best model of each size)

  50   observations
  CarTheft is the dependent variable

p-values for the coefficients

Nvar	Income	Unem	Pupil/Tea	Divorce	Std. Err	Adj R^2	R^2
1			.0004		167.482	.218	.234
2	.0018		.0000		152.362	.353	.379
3	.0013	.0157	.0001		144.451	.418	.454
4	.0007	.0323	.0003	.1987	143.362	.427	.474

RELATED READING

Evans, Martin G. "The Problem of Analyzing Multiplicative Composites." *American Psychologist*, January 1991, p. 675 (Evans' Rule).

Kennedy, Peter. *A Guide to Econometrics*. 5th ed. MIT Press, 2003, p. 132 (Klein's Rule).

Kutner, Michael H.; Christopher J. Nachtsheim; and John Neter. *Applied Linear Regression Models*. 4th ed. McGraw-Hill/Irwin, 2004.

Ryan, Thomas P. *Modern Regression Methods*. Wiley, 1996.

CHAPTER 13   Online Learning Resources

The Online Learning Center (OLC) at www.mhhe.com/doane3e has several *LearningStats* demonstrations to help you understand multiple regression. Your instructor may assign one or more of them, or you may decide to download the ones that sound interesting.

Online **LearningCenter**

Topic	LearningStats Demonstrations
Multiple regression overview	▣ Multiple Regression Overview ▣ Violations of Assumptions
Simulation	▣ Effects of Collinearity ▣ Effects of Multicollinearity

Key: ▣ = PowerPoint   ▣ = Excel

1. Which statement is *correct* concerning one-factor ANOVA? Why not the others?

   a. The ANOVA is a test to see whether the variances of c groups are the same.
   b. In ANOVA, the k groups are compared two at a time, not simultaneously.
   c. ANOVA depends on the assumption of normality of the populations sampled.

2. Which statement is *incorrect*? Explain.

   a. We need a Tukey test because ANOVA doesn't tell *which* group means differ.
   b. Hartley's test is needed to determine whether the means of the groups differ.
   c. ANOVA assumes equal variances in the k groups being compared.

3. Given the following ANOVA table, find the F statistic and the critical value of $F_{.05}$.

Source	Sum of Squares	df	Mean Square	F
Treatment	744.00	4		
Error	751.50	15		
Total	1,495.50	19		

4. Given the following ANOVA: (a) How many ATM locations were there? (b) What was the sample size? (c) At $\alpha = .05$, is there a significant effect due to **Day of Week**? (d) At $\alpha = .05$, is there a significant interaction?

Source of Variation	SS	df	MS	F	P-Value	F Crit
ATM Location	41926.67	2	20963.33	9.133	0.0002	3.044
Day of Week	4909.52	6	818.25	0.356	0.9055	2.147
Interaction	29913.33	12	2492.78	1.086	0.3740	1.804
Error	433820.00	189	2295.34			
Total	510569.52	209				

5. Given a sample correlation coefficient $r = .373$ with $n = 30$, can you reject the hypothesis $\rho = 0$ for the population at $\alpha = .01$? Explain, stating the critical value you are using in the test.

6. Which statement is *incorrect*? Explain.

   a. Correlation uses a t-test with $n–2$ degrees of freedom.
   b. Correlation analysis assumes that X is independent and Y is dependent.
   c. Correlation analysis is a test for the degree of linearity between X and Y.

7. Based on the information in this ANOVA table, the coefficient of determination R^2 is

   a. 0.499   b. 0.501   c. 0.382

ANOVA Table					
Source	Sum of Squares	df	Mean Square	F	p-Value
Regression	158.3268	1	158.3268	24.88	0.00004
Residual	159.0806	25	6.3632		
Total	317.4074	26			

8. In a test of the regression model $Y = \beta_0 + \beta_1 X$ with 27 observations, what is the critical value of t to test the hypothesis that $\beta_1 = 0$ using $\alpha = .05$ in a two-tailed test?

   a. 1.960   b. 2.060   c. 1.708

9. Which statement is *correct* for a simple regression? Why not the others?

   a. A 95% confidence interval (CI) for the mean of Y is wider than the 95% CI for the predicted Y.
   b. A confidence interval for the predicted Y is widest when $X = \bar{x}$.
   c. The t test for zero slope always gives the same t_{calc} as the correlation test for $\rho = 0$.

10. Tell if each statement is *true* or *false* for a simple regression. If false, explain.

    a. If the standard error is $s_{yx} = 3,207$ then a residual $e_i = 4,327$ would be an outlier.
    b. In a regression with $n = 50$ then a leverage statistic $h_i = .10$ indicates unusual leverage.
    c. A decimal change is often used to improve data conditioning.

11. For a multiple regression, which statement is *true?* Why not the others?

    a. Evans' Rule suggests at least 10 observations for each predictor.
    b. The t_{calc} in a test for significance of a binary predictor can have only two values.
    c. Occam's Razor says we must prefer simple regression because it is simple.

12. For a multiple regression, which statement is *false?* Explain.

    a. If $R^2 = .752$ and $R^2_{adj} = .578$, the model probably has at least one weak predictor.
    b. R^2_{adj} can exceed R^2 if the model contains some very strong predictors.
    c. Deleting a predictor could increase the R^2_{adj} but will not increase R^2.

13. Which *predictor coefficients* differ significantly from zero at $\alpha = .05$?

    a. X3 and X5   b. X5 only   c. all but X1 and X3

	Coefficients	Std. Error	Lower 95%	Upper 95%
Intercept	22.47427	6.43282	9.40122	35.54733
X1	−0.243035	0.162983	−0.574256	0.088186
X2	0.187555	0.278185	−0.377784	0.752895
X3	−0.339730	0.063168	−0.468102	−0.211358
X4	0.001902	0.008016	−0.014389	0.018193
X5	1.602511	0.723290	0.132609	3.072413

14. Which predictors differ significantly from zero at $\alpha = .05$?

    a. X3 only   b. X4 only   c. both X3 and X4

	Coefficients	Std. Error	p-Value
Intercept	23.3015	4.1948	0.0000
X1	−0.227977	0.178227	0.2100
X2	0.218970	0.300784	0.4719
X3	−0.343658	0.059742	0.0000
X4	1.588353	0.742737	0.0402

15. In this regression with $n = 40$, which *predictor* differs significantly from zero at $\alpha = .01$?

    a. X2   b. X3   c. X5

	Coefficients	Std. Error
Intercept	3.210610	0.918974
X1	−0.034719	0.023283
X2	0.026794	0.039741
X3	−0.048533	0.009024
X4	0.000272	0.001145
X5	0.228930	0.103327

Time-Series Analysis

Chapter Learning Objectives

When you finish this chapter you should be able to

LO1 Define time-series data and its components.

LO2 Interpret a linear, exponential, or quadratic trend model.

LO3 Fit any common trend model and use it to make forecasts.

LO4 Know the definitions of common fit measures.

LO5 Interpret a moving average and use Excel to create it.

LO6 Use exponential smoothing to forecast trendless data.

LO7 Use software to deseasonalize a time-series.

LO8 Use regression with seasonal binaries to make forecasts.

LO9 Interpret index numbers.

Time-Series Data

Businesses must track their performance. By looking at their output over time, businesses can tell where they've been, whether they are performing poorly or satisfactorily, and how much improvement is needed, both in the short term and the long term. A **time-series variable** (denoted Y) consists of data observed over n periods of time. Consider a clothing retailer that specializes in blue jeans. Examples of time-series data this company might be interested in tracking would be the number of jeans sold and the company's market share. Or, from the manufacturing perspective, the company might track cost of raw materials over time.

Businesses also use time-series data to monitor whether a particular process is stable or unstable. And they use time-series data to help predict the future, a process we call *forecasting*. In addition to business time-series data we see economic time-series data in *The Wall Street Journal* or *BusinessWeek,* and also in *USA Today* or *Time,* or even when we browse the Web. Although business and economic time-series data are most common, we can see time-series data for population, health, crime, sports, and social problems. Usually, time-series data are presented in a graph, like Figures 14.1 and 14.2.

It is customary to plot time-series data either as a line graph or a bar graph, with time on the horizontal X-axis and the variable of interest on the vertical Y-axis to reveal how the variable changes over time. In a line graph, the X-Y data points are connected with line segments to make it easier to see fluctuations. While anyone can understand time-series graphs in a general way, this chapter explains how to interpret time-series data *statistically* and to make defensible forecasts. Our analysis begins with sample observations $y_1, y_2, \ldots, y_n$ covering n time periods. The following notation is used:

- y_t is the value of the time-series in period t.
- t is an index denoting the time period ($t = 1, 2, \ldots, n$).
- n is the number of time periods.
- $y_1, y_2, \ldots, y_n$ is the data set for analysis.

LO1

Define time-series data and its components.

FIGURE 14.1

U.S. Employment (monthly)

Source: www.clevelandfed.org.

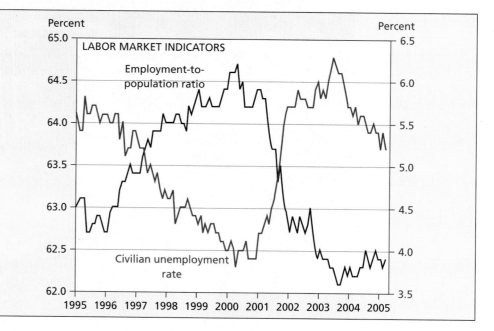

FIGURE 14.2

Exchange Rates (daily)

Source: www.clevelandfed.org.

To distinguish time-series data from cross-sectional data, we use y_t instead of x_i for an individual observation, and a subscript t instead of i.

Time-series data may be measured *at a point in time* or *over an interval of time*. For example, in accounting, balance sheet data are measured at the end of the fiscal year, while income statement data are measured over an entire fiscal year. The Gross Domestic Product (GDP) is a flow of goods and services measured *over an interval of time*, while the prime rate of interest is measured *at a point in time*. Your GPA is measured *at a point in time* while your weekly pay is measured *over an interval of time*. The distinction is sometimes vague in reported data, but a little thought will usually clarify matters. For example, Canada's 2006 unemployment rate (6.3 percent) would be measured at a point in time (e.g., at year's end) while Canada's 2006 hydroelectric production (341 terawatt-hours) would be measured over the entire year.

Periodicity

The **periodicity** is the time interval over which data are collected (decade, year, quarter, month, week, day, hour). For example, the U.S. population is measured each *decade,* your personal income tax is calculated *annually,* GDP is reported *quarterly,* the unemployment rate is estimated *monthly,* and *The Wall Street Journal* reports the closing price of General Motors stock *daily* (although stock prices are also monitored continuously on the Web). Firms typically report profits by quarter, but pension liabilities only at year's end. Any periodicity is possible, but the principles of time-series modeling can be understood with these three common data types:

- Annual data (1 observation per year)
- Quarterly data (4 observations per year)
- Monthly data (12 observations per year)

Additive versus Multiplicative Models

Time-series *decomposition* seeks to separate a time-series Y into four components: trend (T), cycle (C), seasonal (S), and irregular (I). These components are assumed to follow either an additive or a multiplicative model, as shown in Table 14.1.

TABLE 14.1

Components of a Time-Series

Model	Components	Used For
Additive	$Y = T + C + S + I$	Data of similar magnitude (short-run or trend-free data) with constant *absolute* growth or decline.
Multiplicative	$Y = T \times C \times S \times I$	Data of increasing or decreasing magnitude (long-run or trended data) with constant *percent* growth or decline.

The additive form is attractive for its simplicity, but the multiplicative model is often more useful for forecasting financial data, particularly when the data vary over a range of magnitudes. Especially in the short run, it may not matter greatly which form is assumed. In fact, the model forms are fundamentally equivalent because the multiplicative model becomes additive if logarithms are taken (as long as the data are nonnegative):

$$\log(Y) = \log(T \times C \times S \times I) = \log(T) + \log(C) + \log(S) + \log(I)$$

LO1

Define time-series data and its components.

A Graphical View

Figure 14.3 illustrates these four components in a hypothetical time-series. The four components may be thought of as layering atop one another to produce the actual time series. In this example, the irregular component (I) is large enough to obscure the cycle (C) and seasonal (S) components, but not the trend (T). However, we can usually extract the original components from the time series by using statistical methods.

Trend

Trend (T) is a general movement over all years ($t = 1, 2, \ldots, n$). Change over a few years is not a trend. Some trends are steady and predictable. For example, the data may be steadily growing (e.g., total U.S. population), neither growing nor declining (e.g., your current car's mpg), or steadily declining (infant mortality rates in a developing nation). Most of us think of three general patterns: growth, stability, or decline. But there are subtler trends within each category. A time-series can increase at a steady *linear* rate (e.g., the number of books you have read in your lifetime), at an *increasing* rate (e.g., Medicare costs for an aging population), or at a *decreasing* rate (e.g., live attendance at NFL football games). It can grow for awhile and then level off (e.g., sales of HDTV) or grow toward an asymptote (e.g., percent of adults owning a camera phone). A mathematical trend can be fitted to any data, but its predictive value depends on the situation.

FIGURE 14.3

Four Components of a Time-Series

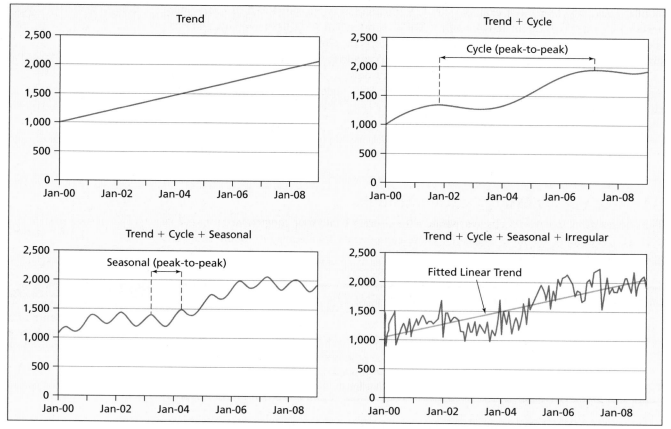

For example, to predict future organ transplants (Figure 14.4) a mathematical trend might be useful, but a mathematical model might not be very helpful for predicting space launches (Figure 14.5).

Cycle

Cycle (*C*) is a repetitive up-and-down movement around the trend that covers *several years*. For example, industry analysts have studied cycles for sales of new automobiles, new home construction, inventories, and business investment. These cycles are based primarily on product life and replacement cycles. In any market economy there are broad business cycles that affect employment and production. After we have extracted the trend and seasonal components of a time series, a cycle may be detected as autocorrelation in the residuals (see Chapter 12, Section 12.8). Although cycles are important, there is no general theory of cycles, and even those cycles that have been identified in specific industries have erratic timing and complex causes that defy generalization. Over a small number of time periods (a typical forecasting situation) cycles are undetectable or may resemble a trend. For this reason cycles are not discussed further in this chapter.

Seasonal

Seasonal (*S*) is a repetitive cyclical pattern *within a year*.* For example, many retail businesses experience strong sales during the fourth quarter because of Christmas. Automobile

---

*Repetitive patterns within a week, day, or other time period may also be considered seasonal. For example, mail volume in the U.S. Postal Service is higher on Monday. Emergency arrivals at hospitals are lower during the first shift (midnight and 6:00 A.M.). In this chapter, we will discuss only *monthly* and *quarterly* seasonal patterns, because these are most typical of business data.

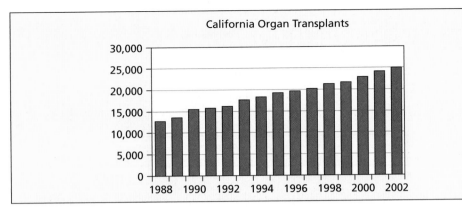

FIGURE 14.4

Steady Trend
Transplants

Source: www.gsds.org.
© Golden State Donor Services

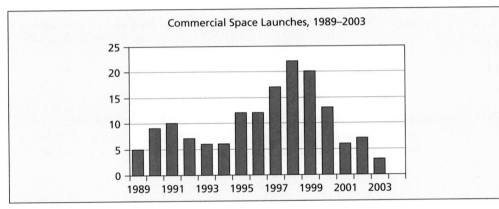

FIGURE 14.5

Erratic Pattern
SpaceLaunch

Source: http://www.faa.gov.

sales rise when new models are released. Peak demand for airline flights to Europe occurs during summer vacation travel. Although often imagined as sine waves, seasonal patterns may not be smooth. Peaks and valleys can occur in any month or quarter, and each industry may face its own unique seasonal pattern. For example, June weddings tend to create a "spike" in bridal sales, but there is no "sine wave" pattern in bridal sales. By definition, annual data have no seasonality.

Irregular

Irregular (I) is a random disturbance that follows no apparent pattern. It is also called the *error* component or *random noise* reflecting all factors other than trend, cycle, and seasonality. Large error components are not unusual. For example, daily prices of many common stocks fluctuate greatly. When the irregular component is large, it may be difficult to isolate other individual model components. Some data are pure I (lacking meaningful T or S or C components). In such cases, we use special techniques (e.g., **moving average** or **exponential smoothing**) to make short-run forecasts. Faced with erratic data, experts may use their own knowledge of a particular industry to make *judgment forecasts*. For example, monthly sales forecasts of a particular automobile may combine judgment forecasts from dealers, financial staff, and economists.

There are many forecasting methods designed for specific situations. Much of this chapter deals with *trend models* because they are so common in business. You will also learn to use *decomposition* to make adjustments for *seasonality,* and how to use *smoothing models.* The important topics of *ARIMA models* and *causal models* using regression are reserved for a more specialized class in forecasting. Figure 14.6 summarizes the main categories of forecasting models.

**14.2
TREND
FORECASTING**

FIGURE 14.6

Overview of Forecasting

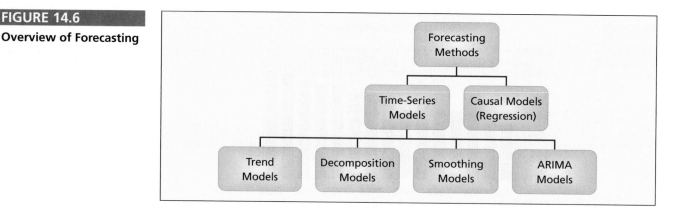

Three Trend Models

LO2

Interpret a linear,
exponential, or
quadratic trend model.

There are many possible trend models, but three of them are especially useful in business:

(14.1) $\qquad y_t = a + bt \qquad$ for $t = 1, 2, \ldots, n$ (linear trend)

(14.2) $\qquad y_t = ae^{bt} \qquad$ for $t = 1, 2, \ldots, n$ (exponential trend)

(14.3) $\qquad y_t = a + bt + ct^2 \quad$ for $t = 1, 2, \ldots, n$ (quadratic trend)

The linear and exponential models are widely used because they have only two parameters and are familiar to most business audiences. The quadratic model may be useful when the data have a turning point. All three can be fitted by Excel, MegaStat, or MINITAB. Each model will be examined in turn.

Linear Trend Model

The **linear trend** model has the form $y_t = a + bt$. It is useful for a time-series that grows or declines by the same amount (b) in each period, as shown in Figure 14.7. It is the simplest model and may suffice for short-run forecasting. It is generally preferred in business as a baseline forecasting model unless there are compelling reasons to consider a more complex model.

FIGURE 14.7

Linear Trend Models

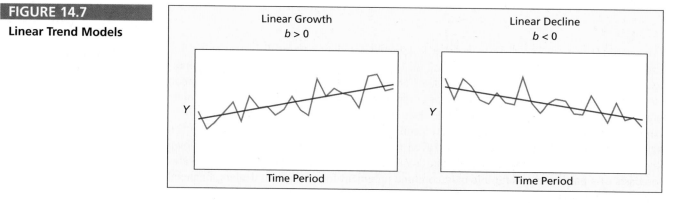

Illustration: Linear Trend

In recent years, the number of U.S. franchised new car dealerships has been declining, due to phasing out of low-volume dealerships and consolidation of market areas. What has been the average annual decline? Based on the line graph in Figure 14.8, the linear model seems appropriate to describe this trend. The slope of Excel's fitted trend indicates that, on average, 235 dealerships are being lost annually. However, in recent years, this downward trend has accelerated (see Section Exercise 14.4).

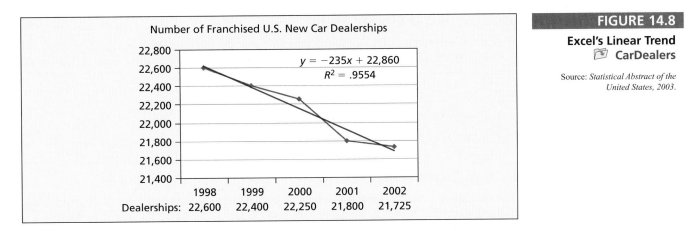

FIGURE 14.8

Excel's Linear Trend
📁 **CarDealers**

Source: *Statistical Abstract of the
United States, 2003.*

Linear Trend Calculations

The linear trend is fitted in the usual way by using the ordinary least squares formulas, as illustrated in Table 14.2. Because you are already familiar with regression, we will only point out the use of the index $t = 1, 2, 3, 4, 5$ as the independent variable (instead of using the years 1998, 1999, 2000, 2001, 2002). We use this time index to simplify the calculations and keep the data magnitudes under control (Excel uses this method too).

LO3

Fit any common trend model and use it to make forecasts.

$$\text{Slope:} \quad b = \frac{\sum_{t=1}^{n}(t - \bar{t})(y_t - \bar{y})}{\sum_{t=1}^{n}(t - \bar{t})^2} = \frac{-2,350}{10} = -235$$

$$\text{Intercept:} \quad a = \bar{y} - b\bar{t} = 22,155 - (-235)(3) = 22,860$$

The *slope* of the fitted trend $y_t = 22,860 - 235t$ says that we expect to lose 235 dealerships each year ($dy_t/dt = -235$). The *intercept* is the "starting point" for the time-series in period $t = 0$; that is, $y_0 = 22,860 - 235(0) = 22,860$.

Year	t	y_t	$t - \bar{t}$	$y_t - \bar{y}$	$(t - \bar{t})^2$	$(t - \bar{t})(y_t - \bar{y})$
1998	1	22,600	−2	445	4	−890
1999	2	22,400	−1	245	1	−245
2000	3	22,250	0	95	0	0
2001	4	21,800	1	−355	1	−355
2002	5	21,725	2	−430	4	−860
Sum	15	110,775	0	0	10	−2,350
Mean	3	22,155	0	0	2	−470

TABLE 14.2

Sums for Least Squares Calculations

Fitting and Interpreting an Annual Trend

In fitting a trend to annual data, the years (1998, 1999, 2000, 2001, 2002) are merely used as labels for the *X*-axis. The yearly labels should *not* be used in fitting the trend or calculating the forecast. To fit a trend to annual data, convert the labels to a time index ($t = 1, 2, \ldots$ etc.) To make a forecast, insert a value for the time index ($t = 1, 2, \ldots$ etc) into Excel's fitted trend.

Forecasting a Linear Trend

We can make a forecast for any future year by using the fitted model $y_t = 22,860 - 235t$. In the car dealer example, the fitted trend equation is based on only 5 years' data, so we should be wary of extrapolating very far ahead:

For 2003 $(t = 6)$: $y_6 = 22,860 - 235(6) = 21,450$

For 2004 $(t = 7)$: $y_7 = 22,860 - 235(7) = 21,215$

For 2005 $(t = 8)$: $y_8 = 22,860 - 235(8) = 20,980$

Linear Trend: Calculating R^2

The worksheet shown in Table 14.3 shows the calculation of the coefficient of determination. In this illustration, the linear model gives a good fit ($R^2 = .9554$) to the *past* data. However, a good fit to the past data does not guarantee good *future* forecasts. A deeper analysis of underlying causes of dealership consolidation is needed. What is causing the trend? Are the causal forces likely to remain the same in subsequent years? Could the current trend continue indefinitely, or will it approach an asymptote or limit of some kind? These are questions that forecasters must ask. The forecast is simply a projection of current trend assuming that nothing changes.

$$\text{Coefficient of determination:}\quad R^2 = 1 - \frac{\sum\limits_{t=1}^{n}(y_t - \hat{y}_t)^2}{\sum\limits_{t=1}^{n}(y_t - \bar{y})^2} = 1 - \frac{25,750}{578,000} = .9554$$

TABLE 14.3

Sums for R^2 Calculations

Year	t	y_t	$\hat{y}_t = 22,860 - 235t$	$y_t - \hat{y}_t$	$(y_t - \hat{y}_t)^2$	$(y_t - \bar{y})^2$
1998	1	22,600	22,625	−25	625	198,025
1999	2	22,400	22,390	10	100	60,025
2000	3	22,250	22,155	95	9,025	9,025
2001	4	21,800	21,920	−120	14,400	126,025
2002	5	21,725	21,685	40	1,600	184,900
Sum	15		110,775	0	25,750	578,000

Exponential Trend Model

The **exponential trend** model has the form $y_t = ae^{bt}$. It is useful for a time-series that grows or declines at the same *rate* (b) in each period, as shown in Figure 14.9. When the growth rate is positive ($b > 0$), then Y grows by an *increasing* amount each period (unlike the linear model, which assumes a *constant* increment each period). If the growth rate is negative ($b < 0$), then Y declines by a *decreasing* amount each period (unlike the linear model, which assumes a *constant* decrement each period).

FIGURE 14.9

Exponential Trend Models

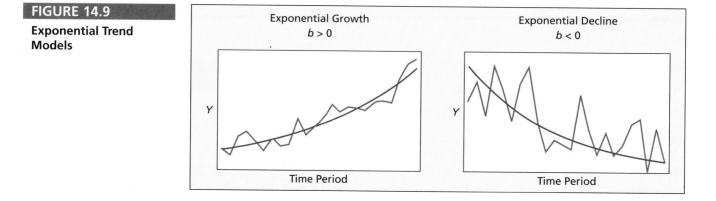

When to Use the Exponential Model

The exponential model is often preferred for financial data or data that cover a longer period of time. When you invest money in a commercial bank savings account, interest accrues at a given percent. Your savings grow faster than a linear rate because you earn interest on the accumulated interest. Banks use the exponential formula to calculate interest on CDs. Financial analysts often find the exponential model attractive because costs, revenue, and salaries are best projected under assumed *percent* growth rates.

Another nice feature of the exponential model is that you can compare two growth rates in two time-series variables with dissimilar data units (i.e., a percent growth rate is *unit-free*). For example, between 1990 and 2000 the number of Medicare enrollees grew from 34.3 million persons to 39.6 million persons (1.45 percent growth per annum), while Medicare payments to hospitals grew from $65.7 billion to $126.0 billion (6.73 percent growth per annum). Comparing the percents, we see that Medicare insurance payments have been growing more than four times as fast as the Medicare head count. These facts underlie the ongoing debate about Medicare spending in the United States.

There may not be much difference between a linear and exponential model when the growth rate is small and the data set covers only a few time periods. For example, suppose your starting salary is $50,000. Table 14.4 compares salary increases of $2,500 each year ($y_t = 50,000 + 2,500t$) with a continuously compounded 4.879 percent salary growth ($y_t = 50,000e^{.04879t}$). Over the first few years, there is little difference. But after 20 years, the difference is obvious, as shown in Figure 14.10. Despite its attractive simplicity* the linear model's assumptions may be inappropriate for some financial variables.

t	$y_t = 50,000 + 2,500t$ **Linear**	$y_t = 50,000e^{.04879t}$ **Exponential**
0	50,000	50,000
5	62,500	63,814
10	75,000	81,445
15	87,500	103,946
20	100,000	132,665

TABLE 14.4

Two Models of Salary Growth

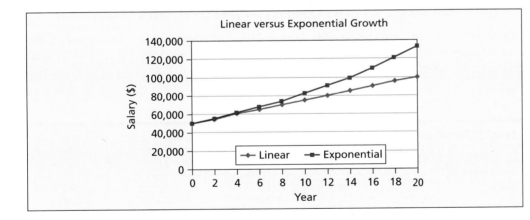

FIGURE 14.10

Linear and Exponential Growth Compared

Illustration: Exponential Trend

Spending on Internet security in the United States has shown explosive growth, as indicated in Figure 14.11. Clearly, a linear trend (constant *dollar* growth) would be inadequate. It is more reasonable to assume a constant *percent* rate of growth and fit an exponential

---

*In a sense, the linear model ($y_t = a + bt$) and the exponential model ($y_t = ae^{bt}$) are equally simple because they are two-parameter models, and a log-transformed exponential model $\ln(y_t) = \ln(a) + bt$ is actually linear.

FIGURE 14.11

Excel's Exponential Trend
📁 DolonCorp

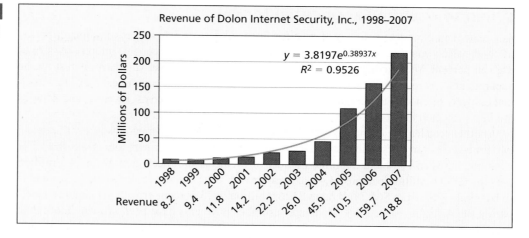

model. For the Dolon company's revenue, the fitted exponential trend is $y_t = 3.8197e^{.3894t}$. The value of b in the exponential model $y_t = ae^{bt}$ is the continuously compounded growth rate, so we can say that Dolon's revenue is growing at an astonishing rate of 38.94 percent per year. A negative value of b in the equation $y_t = ae^{bt}$ would indicate *decline* instead of growth. The intercept a is the "starting point" in period $t = 0$. For example, $y_0 = 3.8197e^{.3894(0)} = 3.8197$.

Exponential Trend Calculations

Table 14.5 shows the worksheet for the required sums. Calculations of the exponential trend are done by using a transformed variable $z_t = \ln(y_t)$ instead of y_t, to produce a linear equation so that we can use the least squares formulas.

$$\text{Slope:} \quad b = \frac{\sum_{t=1}^{n}(t - \bar{t})(z_t - \bar{z})}{\sum_{t=1}^{n}(t - \bar{t})^2} = \frac{32.12329}{82.5} = .3893732$$

$$\text{Intercept:} \quad a = \bar{z} - b\bar{t} = 3.481731 - (.3893732)(5.5) = 1.340178$$

When the least squares calculations are completed, we must transform the intercept back to the original units by exponentiation to get the correct intercept $a = e^{1.340178} = 3.8197$. In final form, the fitted trend equation is

$$y_t = ae^{bt} = 3.8197e^{.38937t}$$

TABLE 14.5			Least Squares Sums for the Exponential Model	📁 DolonCorp			
Year	**t**	**y_t**	**$z_t = \ln(y_t)$**	**$t - \bar{t}$**	**$z_t - \bar{z}$**	**$(t - \bar{t})^2$**	**$(t - \bar{t})(z_t - \bar{z})$**
1998	1	8.2	2.10413	−4.5	−1.37760	20.25	6.19919
1999	2	9.4	2.24071	−3.5	−1.24102	12.25	4.34357
2000	3	11.8	2.46810	−2.5	−1.01363	6.25	2.53408
2001	4	14.2	2.65324	−1.5	−0.82849	2.25	1.24273
2002	5	22.2	3.10009	−0.5	−0.38164	0.25	0.19082
2003	6	26.0	3.25810	0.5	−0.22363	0.25	−0.11182
2004	7	45.9	3.82647	1.5	0.34473	2.25	0.51710
2005	8	110.5	4.70502	2.5	1.22328	6.25	3.05821
2006	9	159.7	5.07330	3.5	1.59157	12.25	5.57048
2007	10	218.8	5.38816	4.5	1.90643	20.25	8.57892
Sum	55	626.7	34.81731	0.0	0.00000	82.5	32.12329
Mean	5.5	62.67	3.481731				

Forecasting an Exponential Trend

We can make a forecast of debit card usage for any future year by using the fitted model*:

For 2008 ($t = 11$): $y_{11} = 3.8197e^{.38937(11)} = 276.8$

For 2009 ($t = 12$): $y_{12} = 3.8197e^{.38937(12)} = 408.5$

For 2010 ($t = 13$): $y_{13} = 3.8197e^{.38937(13)} = 603.0$

Can Dolon's revenue actually continue to grow at a rate of 38.937 percent? It seems unlikely. Typically, when a new product is introduced, its growth rate at first is very strong, but eventually slows down as the market becomes saturated and/or as competitors arise.

Exponential Trend: Calculating R^2

As shown in Table 14.6, we calculate R^2 the same way as for the linear trend, except that we replace the dependent variable y_t with $z_t = \ln(y_t)$ and the fitted value with $\hat{z}_t = 1.340178 + .389373t$. This is necessary because Excel's trend-fitting calculations are done in logarithms in an exponential model:

$$\text{Coefficient of determination:} \quad R^2 = 1 - \frac{\sum_{t=1}^{n}(z_t - \hat{z}_t)^2}{\sum_{t=1}^{n}(z_t - \bar{z})^2} = 1 - \frac{0.62228}{13.13021} = .9526$$

In this example, the exponential trend gives a very good fit ($R^2 = .9526$) to the past data. Although a high R^2 does not guarantee good forecasts, Internet security protection is expected to reach a wider consumer audience in the future, so the high growth rate could continue if the firm is able to manage its expansion.

Sums for R^2 Calculations in Exponential Model DolonCorp   **TABLE 14.6**

t	$z_t = \ln(y_t)$	$\hat{z}_t = 1.340178 + .389373t$	$z_t - \hat{z}_t$	$(z_t - \hat{z}_t)^2$	$(z_t - \bar{z})^2$
1	2.10413	1.72955	0.37458	0.14031	1.89777
2	2.24071	2.11892	0.12178	0.01483	1.54013
3	2.46810	2.50830	−0.04020	0.00162	1.02745
4	2.65324	2.89767	−0.24443	0.05975	0.68639
5	3.10009	3.28704	−0.18695	0.03495	0.14565
6	3.25810	3.67642	−0.41832	0.17499	0.05001
7	3.82647	4.06579	−0.23933	0.05728	0.11884
8	4.70502	4.45516	0.24985	0.06243	1.49643
9	5.07330	4.84454	0.22876	0.05233	2.53308
10	5.38816	5.23391	0.15425	0.02379	3.63446
Sum	34.81731	34.81731	0	0.62228	13.13021
Mean	3.48173				

Quadratic Trend Model

The **quadratic trend** model has the form $y_t = a + bt + ct^2$. The t^2 term allows a nonlinear shape. It is useful for a time series that has a turning point or that is not captured by the

---

*Excel uses the exponential formula $y_t = ae^{bt}$ in which the coefficient b is the *continuously compounded* growth rate. But MINITAB uses an equivalent formula $y_t = y_0(1 + r)^t$, which you may recognize as the formula for compound interest. Although the formulas appear different, they give identical forecasts. For example, for the debit card data, MINITAB's fitted trend is $y_t = 3.81972(1.47606)^t$ so the forecasts are

For 2008 ($t = 11$): $y_{11} = 3.81972(1.47606)^{11} = 276.8$

For 2009 ($t = 12$): $y_{12} = 3.81972(1.47606)^{12} = 408.5$

For 2010 ($t = 13$): $y_{13} = 3.81972(1.47606)^{13} = 603.0$

To convert MINITAB's fitted equation to Excel's, set $a = y_0$ and $b = \ln(1 + r)$. To convert Excel's fitted equation to MINITAB's, set $y_0 = a$ and $r = e^b - 1$.

exponential model. If $c = 0$, the quadratic model $y_t = a + bt + ct^2$ becomes a linear model because the term ct^2 drops out of the equation (i.e., the linear model is a special case of the quadratic model). Some forecasters fit a quadratic model as a way of checking for nonlinearity. If the coefficient c does not differ significantly from zero, then the linear model would suffice. Depending on the values of b and c, the quadratic model can assume any of four shapes, as shown in Figure 14.12.

FIGURE 14.12

Four Quadratic Trend Models

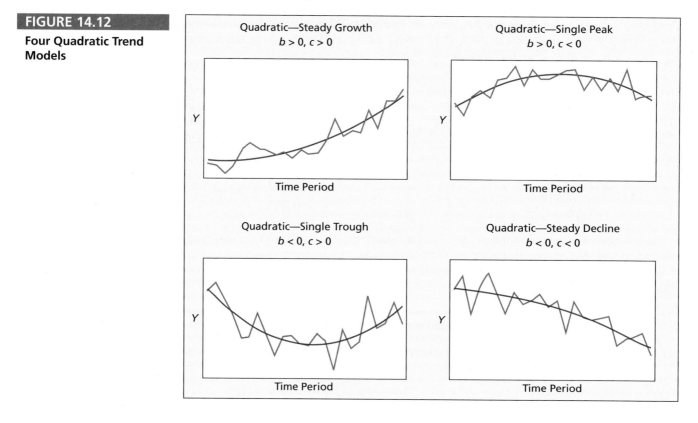

Illustration: Quadratic Trend

The number of hospital beds (Table 14.7) in the United States declined during the late 1990s, showed signs of leveling out, and then declined again. What trend would we choose if the objective is to make a realistic 1-year forecast?

TABLE 14.7

U.S. Hospital Beds (thousands), 1995–2004
🗀 HospitalBeds

Source: *Statistical Abstract of the United States, 2007*, p. 114.

Year	Beds	Year	Beds
1995	1,081	2000	984
1996	1,062	2001	987
1997	1,035	2002	976
1998	1,013	2003	965
1999	994	2004	956

Figure 14.13 shows 1-year projections using the linear and quadratic models. Many observers would think that the quadratic model offers a more believable prediction, because the quadratic model is able to capture the slight curvature in the data pattern. But this gain in forecast credibility must be weighed against the added complexity of the quadratic model. It appears that the forecasts would turn upward if projected more than 1 year ahead. We should be especially skeptical of any polynomial model that is projected more than one or two periods into the future.

Because the quadratic trend model $y_t = a + bt + ct^2$ is a multiple regression with two predictors (t and t^2), the least squares calculations are not shown. However, Figure 14.14 shows the MINITAB fitted regression. Note that both t and t^2 are significant predictors (large t, small p).

FIGURE 14.13

Two Trend Models for U.S. Hospital Beds HospitalBeds

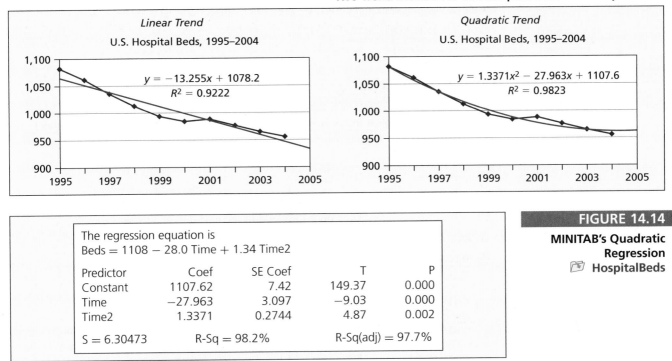

Linear Trend
U.S. Hospital Beds, 1995–2004

$y = -13.255x + 1078.2$
$R^2 = 0.9222$

Quadratic Trend
U.S. Hospital Beds, 1995–2004

$y = 1.3371x^2 - 27.963x + 1107.6$
$R^2 = 0.9823$

FIGURE 14.14

MINITAB's Quadratic Regression
HospitalBeds

The regression equation is
Beds = 1108 − 28.0 Time + 1.34 Time2

Predictor	Coef	SE Coef	T	P
Constant	1107.62	7.42	149.37	0.000
Time	−27.963	3.097	−9.03	0.000
Time2	1.3371	0.2744	4.87	0.002

S = 6.30473   R-Sq = 98.2%   R-Sq(adj) = 97.7%

Using Excel for Trend Fitting

Plot the data, right-click on the data, and choose a trend. Figure 14.15 shows Excel's menu of six trend options. The menu includes a sketch of each trend type. Click the Options tab if you want to display the R^2 and fitted equation on the graph, or if you want to plot forecasts (trend extrapolations) on the graph. The quadratic model is a **polynomial model** of order 2. Despite the many choices, some patterns cannot be captured by any of the common trend models. By default, Excel only reports four decimal accuracy. However, you can click on Excel's fitted trend equation, choose Format Data Labels, choose Number, and set the number of decimal places you want to see.

LO3

Fit any common trend model and use it to make forecasts.

FIGURE 14.15

Excel's Trend-Fitting Menus
WomenPilots

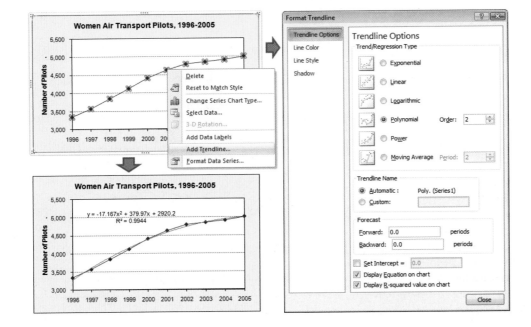

Principle of Occam's Razor

Given two *sufficient* explanations, we prefer the simpler one.
        —*William of Occam (1285–1347)*

Trend-Fitting Criteria

It is so easy to fit a trend in Excel that it is tempting to "shop around" for the best fit. But forecasters prefer the simplest trend model that adequately matches the trend. Simple models are easier to interpret and explain to others. Criteria for selecting a trend model for forecasting include:

Criterion	*Ask Yourself*
• Occam's Razor	Would a simpler model suffice?
• Overall fit	How does the trend fit the past data?
• Believability	Does the extrapolated trend "look right"?
• Fit to recent data	Does the fitted trend match the last few data points?

EXAMPLE

Comparing Trends

You can usually increase the R^2 by choosing a more complex model. But if you are making a *forecast,* this is not the only relevant issue, because R^2 measures the fit to the *past* data. Figure 14.16 shows four fitted trends using the same data, with three-period forecasts. For

FIGURE 14.16

Four Fitted Trends Using the Same Data

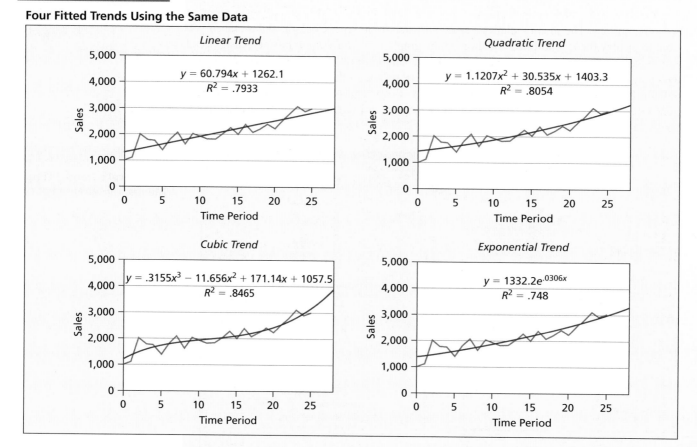

Linear Trend
$$y = 60.794x + 1262.1$$
$$R^2 = .7933$$

Quadratic Trend
$$y = 1.1207x^2 + 30.535x + 1403.3$$
$$R^2 = .8054$$

Cubic Trend
$$y = .3155x^3 - 11.656x^2 + 171.14x + 1057.5$$
$$R^2 = .8465$$

Exponential Trend
$$y = 1332.2e^{.0306x}$$
$$R^2 = .748$$

this data set, the linear model may be inadequate because its fit to recent periods is marginal (we prefer the simplest model *only if* it "does the job"). Here, the cubic trend yields the highest R^2, but the fitted equation is nonintuitive and would be hard to explain or defend. Also, its forecasts appear to be increasing too rapidly. In this example, the exponential model has the lowest R^2, yet matches the recent data fairly well and its forecasts appear credible when projected a few periods ahead.

Any trend model's forecasts become less reliable as they are extrapolated farther into the future. The quadratic trend, the simplest of Excel's polynomial models, is sometimes acceptable for short-term forecasting. However, forecasters avoid higher-order polynomial models (cubic and higher) not only because they are complex, but also because they can give bizarre forecasts when extrapolated more than one period ahead. Table 14.8 compares the features of the three most common trend models.

TABLE 14.8   **Comparison of Three Trend Models**

Model	Pro	Con
Linear	1. Simple, familiar to everyone. 2. May suffice for short-run data.	1. Assumes constant slope. 2. Cannot capture nonlinear change.
Exponential	1. Familiar to financial analysts. 2. Shows compound percent growth rate.	1. Some managers are unfamiliar with e^x. 2. Data values must be positive.
Quadratic	1. Useful for data with a turning point. 2. Useful test for nonlinearity.	1. Complex and no intuitive interpretation. 2. Can give untrustworthy forecasts if extrapolated too far.

LO2

Interpret a linear, exponential, or quadratic trend model.

SECTION EXERCISES

connect

14.1 In 2009, US Airways Flight 1549 made a successful emergency landing in the Hudson River, after striking birds shortly after takeoff. Are bird strikes an increasing threat to planes? (a) Make an Excel graph of the data on bird strikes. (b) Discuss the underlying causes that might explain the trend. (c) Use Excel, MegaStat, or MINITAB to fit three trends (linear, quadratic, and exponential) to the time series. (d) Which trend model do you think is best to make forecasts for the next 3 years? Why? (e) Use *each* of the three fitted trend equations to make numerical forecasts for 2008, 2009, and 2010. How much difference does the choice of model make? Which forecasts do you trust the most, and why? (f) If you have access to the Web, check your forecasts. How accurate were they?   **BirdStrikes**

Number of Reported Bird Strikes to Civil Aircraft in U.S., 1997–2007
  BirdStrikes

Year	Strikes	Year	Strikes
1990	1,738	1999	5,002
1991	2,252	2000	5,872
1992	2,351	2001	5,644
1993	2,395	2002	6,044
1994	2,459	2003	5,854
1995	2,643	2004	6,398
1996	2,840	2005	7,036
1997	3,351	2006	6,996
1998	3,658	2007	7,439

Source: http://wildlife-mitigation.tc.faa.gov.

14.2 (a) Make an Excel graph of the data on U.S. online advertising spending. (b) Discuss the underlying causes that might explain the trend or pattern. (c) Use Excel, MegaStat, or MINITAB to fit three trends (linear, quadratic, exponential) to the time-series. (d) Which trend model do you think is best to make forecasts for the next 3 years? Why? (e) Use *each* of the three fitted trend equations to make a numerical forecast for 2007. How similar are the three models' forecasts? 📷 **Online**

U.S. Online Advertising, 2000–2006 (billions)

Year	Spending
2000	8.1
2001	7.1
2002	6.0
2003	6.3
2004	6.8
2005	7.2
2006	8.1

Source: William F. Arens, *Contemporary Advertising,* 9th ed. (McGraw-Hill, 2004), p. 549.

14.3 (a) Make an Excel line graph of the data on employee work stoppages. (b) Discuss the underlying causes that might explain the trend or pattern. (c) Fit three trends (linear, exponential, quadratic). (d) Which trend model is best, and why? If none is satisfactory, explain. (e) Make a forecast for 2007, using a trend model of your choice or a judgment forecast. 📷 **Strikers**

U.S. Workers Involved in Work Stoppages (thousands)

Year	Strikers	Year	Strikers
1997	339	2002	46
1998	387	2003	129
1999	73	2004	171
2000	394	2005	100
2001	99	2006	70

Source: http://data.bls.gov.

14.4 (a) Make an Excel line graph of the car dealership data. (b) Discuss the underlying causes that might explain the trend or pattern. (c) Fit three trends (linear, exponential, quadratic). (d) Which trend model is best, and why? If none is satisfactory, explain. (e) Make forecasts for 2009, 2010, and 2011, using a trend model of your choice or a judgment forecast. 📷 **Dealerships**

Number of U.S. New Car Dealerships, 1998–2008 📷 **Dealerships**

Year	Dealerships
1998	22,600
1999	22,400
2000	22,250
2001	22,150
2002	21,800
2003	21,725
2004	21,650
2005	21,640
2006	21,495
2007	21,200
2008	20,700

Source: www.nada.org

14.5 (a) Plot the data on fruit and vegetable consumption. (b) Discuss the underlying causes that might explain the trend or pattern. (c) Fit a linear trend to the data. (d) Interpret the trend equation. What are its implications for producers? (e) Make a forecast for 2010. *Note:* Time increments are 5 years, so use $t = 6$ for your 2010 forecast. 📷 **Fruits**

U.S. Per Capita Consumption of Commercially Produced Fruits and Vegetables (pounds)

Year	Total
1980	608.8
1985	632.2
1990	660.2
1995	692.5
2000	711.7
2005	694.3

Source: *Statistical Abstract of the United States, 2007,* p. 134.

Mini Case   14.1

U.S. Trade Deficit

The imbalance between imports and exports (Table 14.9) has been a vexing policy problem for U.S. policymakers for decades. The last time the United States had a trade surplus was in 1975, partly due to reduced dependency on foreign oil through conservation measures enacted after the oil crisis (shortages and gas lines) in the early 1970s. However, the trade deficit has become more acute over time, due partly to continued oil imports, and, more recently, to availability of cheaper goods from China and other emerging economies.

TABLE 14.9   **U.S. Balance of Trade, 1992–2006**   TradeDeficit

Year	t	Exports	Imports
1992	1	635.3	668.6
1993	2	655.8	720.9
1994	3	720.9	814.5
1995	4	812.2	903.6
1996	5	868.6	964.8
1997	6	955.3	1,056.9
1998	7	955.9	1,115.9
1999	8	991.2	1,251.7
2000	9	1,096.3	1,475.8
2001	10	1,032.8	1,399.8
2002	11	1,005.9	1,430.3
2003	12	1,040.8	1,540.2
2004	13	1,178.1	1,791.4
2005	14	1,303.1	2,019.9
2006	15	1,468.2	2,260.0

Source: *Economic Report of the President, 2007.* Figures are in billions of dollars.

Figure 14.17 shows the data graphically, with fitted exponential trends. Imports fell in the recession that began in 2001, but then began to pick up, while exports remained weak. The fitted trend equations reveal that imports have been growing at a compound annual rate of 8.14 percent, while exports have only grown at a compound annual rate of 5.06 percent. Recent data exceed the fitted trends.

If we project these disparate growth rates, we would predict a widening trade deficit (calculations shown below). Of course, the assumption of *ceteris paribus* may not hold. Policymakers may seek to weaken the dollar or to change fuel efficiency of U.S. vehicles, or there could be changes in foreign economies (e.g., China). Forecasts are less a way of predicting the future than of showing where we are heading *if* nothing changes. A paradox of forecasting is that, as soon as decision makers see the implications of the forecast, they take steps to make sure the forecast is wrong!

FIGURE 14.17 **U.S. Trade, 1992–2006**

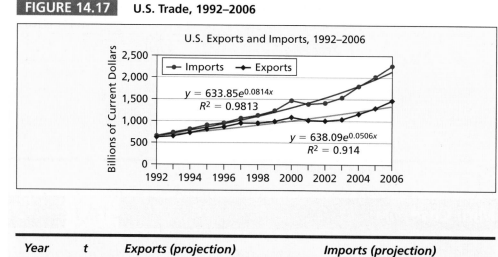

LO2

Interpret a linear,
exponential,
or quadratic trend
model.

Year	t	Exports (projection)	Imports (projection)
2007	16	$y_{16} = 638.09e^{0.0506(16)} = 1{,}434$	$y_{16} = 633.85e^{0.0814(16)} = 2{,}331$
2008	17	$y_{17} = 638.09e^{0.0506(17)} = 1{,}508$	$y_{17} = 633.85e^{0.0814(17)} = 2{,}529$
2009	18	$y_{18} = 638.09e^{0.0506(18)} = 1{,}586$	$y_{18} = 633.85e^{0.0814(18)} = 2{,}744$
2010	19	$y_{19} = 638.09e^{0.0506(19)} = 1{,}669$	$y_{19} = 633.85e^{0.0814(19)} = 2{,}976$

14.3 ASSESSING FIT

Five Measures of Fit

In time-series analysis, you are likely to encounter several different measures of "fit" that show how well the estimated trend model matches the observed time series. "Fit" refers to historical data, and you should bear in mind that a good fit is no guarantee of good forecasts—the usual goal. Five common measures of fit are shown in Table 14.10.

LO4

Know the definitions of
common fit measures.

TABLE 14.10 **Five Measures of Fit**

Statistic	Description	Pro	Con
(14.4) $R^2 = 1 - \dfrac{\sum_{t=1}^{n}(y_t - \hat{y}_t)^2}{\sum_{t=1}^{n}(y_t - \bar{y}_t)^2}$	Coefficient of Determination	1. Unit-free measure. 2. Very common.	1. Often interpreted incorrectly (e.g., "percent of correct predictions").
(14.5) $MAPE = \dfrac{100}{n}\sum_{t=1}^{n}\dfrac{|y_t - \hat{y}_t|}{y_t}$	Mean Absolute Percent Error (MAPE)	1. Unit-free measure (%). 2. Intuitive meaning.	1. Requires $y_t > 0$. 2. Lacks nice math properties.
(14.6) $MAD = \dfrac{1}{n}\sum_{t=1}^{n}|y_t - \hat{y}_t|$	Mean Absolute Deviation (MAD)	1. Intuitive meaning. 2. Same units as y_t.	1. Not unit-free. 2. Lacks nice math properties.
(14.7) $MSD = \dfrac{1}{n}\sum_{t=1}^{n}(y_t - \hat{y}_t)^2$	Mean Squared Deviation (MSD)	1. Nice math properties. 2. Penalizes big errors more.	1. Nonintuitive meaning. 2. Rarely reported.
(14.8) $SE = \sqrt{\sum_{t=1}^{n}\dfrac{(y_t - \hat{y}_t)^2}{n-2}}$	Standard Error (SE)	1. Same units as y_t. 2. For confidence intervals.	1. Nonintuitive meaning.

Figure 14.18 shows a MINITAB graph with fitted linear trend and 3-year forecasts for aggregate U.S. fire losses between 1997 and 2007. Notice that, instead of R^2, MINITAB displays *MAPE, MAD,* and *MSD* statistics. Table 14.11 shows the calculations for these statistics of fit. Because the residuals $y_t - \hat{y}_t$ sum to zero, we see why it's necessary to sum either their absolute values or their squares to obtain a measure of fit. *MAPE, MAD, MSD* and SE would be zero if the trend provided a perfect fit to the time series.

EXAMPLE

Fire Losses

FIGURE 14.18   **MINITAB's Time-Series Trend–Linear Model**   📄 **FireLosses**

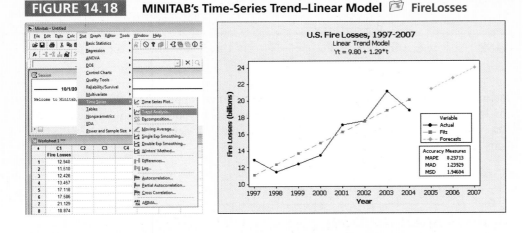

Sums for *MAD, MAPE, MSD*, and Standard Error   📄 **FireLosses**   **TABLE 14.11**

Period	Year	Losses	$\hat{y}_t = 9.8034 + 1.2949t$	$y_t - \hat{y}_t$	$\lvert y_t - \hat{y}_t \rvert$	$\lvert y_t - \hat{y}_t \rvert / y_t$	$(y_t - \hat{y}_t)^2$
1	1997	12.940	11.0983	1.8417	1.8417	0.1423	3.3919
2	1998	11.510	12.3932	−0.8832	0.8832	0.0767	0.7800
3	1999	12.428	13.6881	−1.2601	1.2601	0.1014	1.5879
4	2000	13.457	14.9830	−1.5260	1.5260	0.1134	2.3287
5	2001	17.118	16.2779	0.8401	0.8401	0.0491	0.7058
6	2002	17.586	17.5728	0.0132	0.0132	0.0008	0.0002
7	2003	21.129	18.8677	2.2613	2.2613	0.1070	5.1135
8	2004	18.874	20.1626	−1.2886	1.2886	0.0683	1.6605
			Sum	0.00	9.9142	0.6590	15.5683
			Mean	0.00	1.2393	0.0824	1.9460

Source: *Statistical Abstract of the United States, 2007*, p. 212. Losses are in billions of dollars.

Calculations

Using the sums in Table 14.11, we can apply the formulas for each fit statistic:

$$MAPE = \frac{100}{n} \sum_{t=1}^{n} \frac{\lvert y_t - \hat{y}_t \rvert}{y_t} = \frac{100}{8}(0.6590) = 8.24\%$$

$$MAD = \frac{1}{n} \sum_{t=1}^{n} \lvert y_t - \hat{y}_t \rvert = \frac{1}{8}(9.9142) = 1.239$$

$$MSD = \frac{1}{n} \sum_{t=1}^{n} (y_t - \hat{y}_t)^2 = \frac{1}{8}(15.5683) = 1.946$$

$$SE = \sqrt{\sum_{t=1}^{n} \frac{(y_t - \hat{y}_t)^2}{n-2}} = \sqrt{\frac{15.5683}{8-2}} = 1.611$$

Interpretation

The *MAPE* says that our fitted trend has a mean absolute error of 8.24 percent. The *MAD* says that the average error is 1.239 billion dollars (ignoring the sign). The *MSD* lacks a simple interpretation. These fit statistics are most useful in comparing different trend models for the same data. All the statistics (especially the *MSD*) are affected by the unusual residual in 1997, when fire losses greatly exceeded the trend. The standard error is useful if we want to make a prediction interval for a forecast, using formula 14.9. It is the same formula you saw in Chapter 12.

$$(14.9) \qquad \hat{y}_t \pm t_{n-2}\text{SE} \sqrt{1 + \frac{1}{n} + \frac{(t - \bar{t})^2}{\sum_{t=1}^{n}(t - \bar{t})^2}} \qquad \text{(prediction interval for future } y_t)$$

You may recall from Chapter 12 that you can get a "quick" approximate 95 percent prediction interval by using $\hat{y}_t \pm 2$ SE. However, for forecasts beyond the range of the observed data, you should use formula 14.9, which widens the confidence intervals when the time index is far from its historic mean.

14.4 MOVING AVERAGES

Trendless or Erratic Data

What if the time series $y_1, y_2, \ldots, y_n$ is erratic or has no consistent trend? In such cases, there may be little point in fitting a trend, and if the mean is changing over time, we cannot just "take the average" over the entire data set. Instead, a conservative approach is to calculate a *moving average*. There are two main types of moving averages: trailing or centered. We will illustrate each.

LO5

Interpret a moving average and use Excel to create it.

Trailing Moving Average (*TMA*)

The simplest kind of moving average is the **trailing moving average** (*TMA*) over the last m periods.

$$(14.10) \qquad \hat{y}_t = \frac{y_t + y_{t-1} + \cdots + y_{t-m+1}}{m} \qquad \text{(trailing moving average over } m \text{ periods)}$$

The *TMA* smoothes the past fluctuations in the time-series, helping us see the pattern more clearly. The choice of m depends on the situation. A larger m yields a "smoother" *TMA*, but requires more data. The value of $\hat{y}_t$ may also be used as a forecast for period $t + 1$. Beyond the range of the observed data $y_1, y_2, \ldots, y_n$ there is no way to update the moving average, so it is best regarded as a *one-period-ahead forecast*.

EXAMPLE

Fuel Economy

Many drivers keep track of their fuel economy. For a given vehicle, there is likely to be little trend over time, but there is always random fluctuation. Also, current driving conditions (e.g., snow, hot weather, road trips) could temporarily affect mileage over several consecutive time periods. In this situation, a moving average might be considered. Table 14.12 shows Andrew's fuel economy data set. Column six shows a three-period *TMA*. For example, for period 6 (yellow-shaded cells) the *TMA* is

$$\hat{y}_6 = \frac{24.392 + 21.458 + 24.128}{3} = 23.326$$

It is easiest to appreciate the moving average's "smoothing" of the data when it is displayed on a graph, as in Figure 14.19. It is clear that Andrew's mean is around 23 mpg, though the moving average fluctuates over a range of approximately ± 2 mpg.

TABLE 14.12	Andrew's Miles Per Gallon ($n = 20$) AndrewsMPG					
Obs	**Date**	**Miles Driven**	**Gallons**	**MPG**	**TMA**	**CMA**
1	5-Jan	285	11.324	25.168		
2	7-Jan	185	8.731	21.189		23.074
3	11-Jan	250	10.934	22.864	23.074	22.815
4	15-Jan	296	12.135	24.392	22.815	22.905
5	19-Jan	232	10.812	21.458	22.905	23.326
6	25-Jan	301	12.475	24.128	23.326	22.158
7	30-Jan	285	13.645	20.887	22.158	22.581
8	3-Feb	263	11.572	22.727	22.581	22.747
9	7-Feb	250	10.152	24.626	22.747	23.856
10	14-Feb	307	12.678	24.215	23.856	23.283
11	22-Feb	242	11.520	21.007	23.283	22.942
12	29-Feb	288	12.201	23.605	22.942	22.937
13	5-Mar	285	11.778	24.198	22.937	24.103
14	8-Mar	313	12.773	24.505	24.103	22.638
15	13-Mar	283	14.732	19.210	22.638	23.330
16	18-Mar	318	12.103	26.274	23.330	21.620
17	22-Mar	195	10.064	19.376	21.620	23.746
18	28-Mar	320	12.506	25.588	23.746	22.904
19	2-Apr	270	11.369	23.749	22.904	23.910
20	12-Apr	259	11.566	22.393	23.910	

Example:
TMA

Example:
CMA

Source: Data were collected by statistics student Andrew Fincher for his 11-year-old Pontiac Bonneville 3.8L V6.

FIGURE 14.19 **Three-Period Moving Average of MPG**

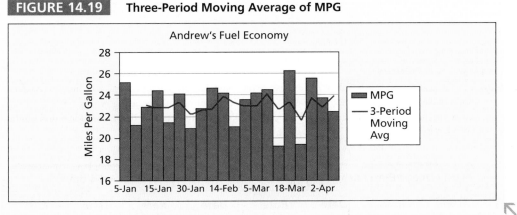

Centered Moving Average (*CMA*)

Another moving average is the **centered moving average (*CMA*)**. Formula 14.11 shows a *CMA* for $m = 3$ periods. The formula looks both forward *and* backward in time, to express the current "forecast" as the mean of the current observation *and* observations on either side of the current data.

$$\hat{y}_t = \frac{y_{t-1} + y_t + y_{t+1}}{3} \qquad \text{(centered moving average over } m \text{ periods)} \qquad \textbf{(14.11)}$$

This is not really a forecast at all, but merely a way of smoothing the data. In Table 14.12, column seven shows the *CMA* for Andrew's MPG data. For example, for period 14 (blue-shaded cells) the *CMA* is

$$\hat{y}_t = \frac{24.198 + 24.505 + 19.210}{3} = 22.638$$

When n is odd ($m = 3, 5$, etc.) the *CMA* is easy to calculate. When m is even, the formula is more complex, because the mean of an even number of data points would lie *between* two data points and would not be correctly centered. Instead, we take a double moving average (yipe!) to get the resulting *CMA* centered properly. For example, for $m = 4$, we would average y_{t-2} through y_{t+1}, then average y_{t-1} through y_{t+2}, and finally average the two averages! You need not worry about this formula for now. It will be illustrated shortly in the context of seasonal data.

Using Excel for a TMA

Excel offers a *TMA* in its Add Trendline option when you click on a time-series line graph or bar chart. Its menus are displayed in Figure 14.20. The *TMA* is a conservative choice whenever you doubt that one of Excel's five other trend models (linear, logarithmic, polynomial, power, exponential) would be appropriate. However, Excel does *not* give you the option of making any forecasts with its moving average model.

FIGURE 14.20

Excel's Moving Average Menus

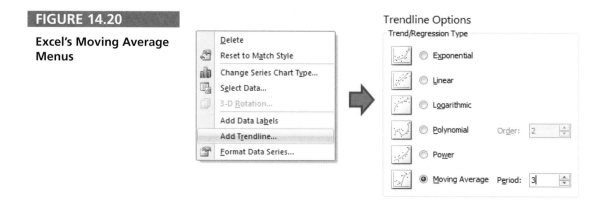

SECTION EXERCISES

connect

14.6 (a) Make an Excel line graph of the exchange rate data. Describe the pattern. (b) Click on the data and choose Add Trendline > Moving Average. Describe the effect of increasing m (e.g., $m = 2, 4, 6$, etc.). Include a copy of each graph with your answer. (c) Discuss how this moving average might help a currency speculator. **DollarEuro**

Daily Dollar/Euro Exchange Rate for First 3 Months of 2005 ($n = 64$ days)

Date	Rate	Date	Rate	Date	Rate	Date	Rate
3-Jan	1.3476	25-Jan	1.2954	16-Feb	1.2994	10-Mar	1.3409
4-Jan	1.3295	26-Jan	1.3081	17-Feb	1.3083	11-Mar	1.3465
5-Jan	1.3292	27-Jan	1.3032	18-Feb	1.3075	14-Mar	1.3346
6-Jan	1.3187	28-Jan	1.3033	21-Feb	1.3153	15-Mar	1.3315
7-Jan	1.3062	31-Jan	1.3049	22-Feb	1.3230	16-Mar	1.3423
10-Jan	1.3109	1-Feb	1.3017	23-Feb	1.3208	17-Mar	1.3373
11-Jan	1.3161	2-Feb	1.3015	24-Feb	1.3205	18-Mar	1.3311
12-Jan	1.3281	3-Feb	1.2959	25-Feb	1.3195	21-Mar	1.3165
13-Jan	1.3207	4-Feb	1.2927	28-Feb	1.3274	22-Mar	1.3210
14-Jan	1.3106	7-Feb	1.2773	1-Mar	1.3189	23-Mar	1.3005
17-Jan	1.3075	8-Feb	1.2783	2-Mar	1.3127	24-Mar	1.2957
18-Jan	1.3043	9-Feb	1.2797	3-Mar	1.3130	25-Mar	1.2954
19-Jan	1.3036	10-Feb	1.2882	4-Mar	1.3244	28-Mar	1.2877
20-Jan	1.2959	11-Feb	1.2864	7-Mar	1.3203	29-Mar	1.2913
21-Jan	1.3049	14-Feb	1.2981	8-Mar	1.3342	30-Mar	1.2944
24-Jan	1.3041	15-Feb	1.2986	9-Mar	1.3384	31-Mar	1.2969

Source: www.federalreserve.gov.

Forecast Updating

The *exponential smoothing* model is a special kind of moving average. It is used for ongoing one-period-ahead forecasting for data that has up-and-down movements but no consistent trend. For example, a retail outlet may place orders for thousands of different stock-keeping units (SKUs) each week, so as to maintain its inventory of each item at the desired level (to avoid emergency calls to warehouses or suppliers). For such forecasts, many firms choose exponential smoothing, a simple forecasting model with only two inputs and one constant. The updating formula for the forecasts is

$$F_{t+1} = \alpha y_t + (1 - \alpha)F_t \quad \text{(smoothing update)} \tag{14.12}$$

where

F_{t+1} = the forecast for the next period

α = the "smoothing constant" ($0 \le \alpha \le 1$)

y_t = the actual data value in period t

F_t = the previous forecast for period t

Smoothing Constant (α)

The next forecast F_{t+1} is a weighted average of y_t (the current data) and F_t (the previous forecast). The value of α, called the **smoothing constant**, is the weight given to the latest data. A small value of α would give low weight to the most recent observation and heavy weight $1 - \alpha$ to the previous forecast (a "heavily smoothed" series). The larger the value of α, the more quickly the forecasts adapt to recent data. For example,

If $\alpha = .05$, then $F_{t+1} = .05y_t + .95F_t$ (heavy smoothing, slow adaptation)

If $\alpha = .20$, then $F_{t+1} = .20y_t + .80F_t$ (moderate smoothing, moderate adaptation)

If $\alpha = .50$, then $F_{t+1} = .50y_t + .50F_t$ (little smoothing, quick adaptation)

Choosing the Value of α

If $\alpha = 1$, there is no smoothing at all, and the forecast for next period is the same as the latest data point, which basically defeats the purpose of exponential smoothing. MINITAB uses $\alpha = .20$ (i.e., moderate smoothing) as its default, which is a fairly common choice of α. The fit of the forecasts to the data will change as you try different values of α. Most computer packages can, as an option, solve for the "best" α using a criterion such as minimum *SSE*.

Over time, earlier data values have less effect on the exponential smoothing forecasts than more recent *y*-values. To see this, we can replace F_t in formula 14.12 with the prior forecast F_{t-1}, and repeat this type of substitution indefinitely to obtain this result:

$$F_{t+1} = \alpha y_t + \alpha(1 - \alpha)y_{t-1} + \alpha(1 - \alpha)^2 y_{t-2} + \alpha(1 - \alpha)^3 y_{t-3} + \cdots \tag{14.13}$$

We see that the next forecast F_{t+1} depends on *all* the prior data (y_{t-1}, y_{t-2}, etc). As long as $\alpha < 1$, as we go farther into the past, each prior data value has less and less impact on the current forecast.

Initializing the Process

From formula 14.12, we see that F_{t+1} depends on F_t, which in turn depends on F_{t-1}, and so on, all the way back to F_1. But where do we get F_1 (the initial forecast)? There are many ways to initialize the forecasting process. For example, Excel simply sets the initial forecast equal to the first actual data value:

Method A

Set $F_1 = y_1$ (use the first data value)

This method has the advantage of simplicity, but if y_1 happens to be unusual, it could take a few iterations for the forecasts to stabilize. Another approach is to set the initial forecast equal to the average of the first several observed data values. For example, MINITAB uses the first six data values:

Method B

$$\text{Set } F_1 = \frac{y_1 + y_2 + y_3 + y_4 + y_5 + y_6}{n} \quad \text{(average of first 6 data values)}$$

This method tends to iron out the effects of unusual y-values, but it consumes more data and is still vulnerable to unusual y-values.

Method C

Set $F_1 = $ prediction from *backcasting* (backward extrapolation)

You may think of this method as fitting a trend to the data *in reverse time order* and extrapolating the trend to "predict" the initial value in the series. This method is common because it tends to generate a more appropriate initial forecast F_1. However, backcasting requires special software, so it will not be discussed here.

EXAMPLE ↘

Weekly Sales Data

Table 14.13 shows weekly sales of deck sealer (a paint product sold in gallon containers) at a large do-it-yourself warehouse-style retailer. For exponential smoothing forecasts, the company uses $\alpha = .10$. Its choice of α is based on experience. Because α is fairly small, it will provide strong smoothing. The last two columns compare the two methods of initializing the forecasts. Unusually high sales in week 5 have a strong effect on method B's starting point. At first, the difference in forecasts is striking, but over time the methods converge.

TABLE 14.13 **Deck Sealer Sales: Exponential Smoothing ($n = 18$ weeks)**
📁 **DeckSealer**

Week	Sales in Gallons	Method A: $F_1 = y_1$	Method B: $F_1 = $ Average (1st 6)
1	106	106.000	127.833
2	110	106.000	125.650
3	108	106.400	124.085
4	97	106.560	122.477
5	210	105.604	119.929
6	136	116.044	128.936
7	128	118.039	129.642
8	134	119.035	129.478
9	107	120.532	129.930
10	123	119.179	127.637
11	139	119.561	127.174
12	140	121.505	128.356
13	144	123.354	129.521
14	94	125.419	130.969
15	108	122.277	127.272
16	168	120.849	125.344
17	179	125.564	129.610
18	120	130.908	134.549

Smoothed forecasts using $\alpha = .10$.

Using Method A:

$$F_2 = \alpha y_1 + (1 - \alpha)F_1 = (.10)(106) + (.90)(106) = 106$$
$$F_3 = \alpha y_2 + (1 - \alpha)F_2 = (.10)(110) + (.90)(106) = 106.4$$
$$F_4 = \alpha y_3 + (1 - \alpha)F_3 = (.10)(108) + (.90)(106.4) = 106.56$$
$$\vdots$$
$$F_{19} = \alpha y_{18} + (1 - \alpha)F_{18} = (.10)(120) + (.90)(130.908) = 129.82$$

Using Method B:

$$F_2 = \alpha y_1 + (1 - \alpha)F_1 = (.10)(106) + (.90)(127.833) = 125.650$$
$$F_3 = \alpha y_2 + (1 - \alpha)F_2 = (.10)(110) + (.90)(125.650) = 124.085$$
$$F_4 = \alpha y_3 + (1 - \alpha)F_3 = (.10)(108) + (.90)(124.085) = 122.477$$
$$\vdots$$
$$F_{19} = \alpha y_{18} + (1 - \alpha)F_{18} = (.10)(120) + (.90)(134.549) = 133.094$$

Despite their different starting points, the forecasts for period 19 do not differ greatly. Rounding to the next higher integer, for week 19, the firm would order 130 gallons (using method *A*) or 134 gallons (using method *B*). Figures 14.21 and 14.22 show the similarity in *patterns* of the forecasts, although the *level* of forecasts is always higher in method *B* because of its higher initial value. This demonstrates that the choice of starting values *does* affect the forecasts.

FIGURE 14.21   **Using the First *y*-Value**

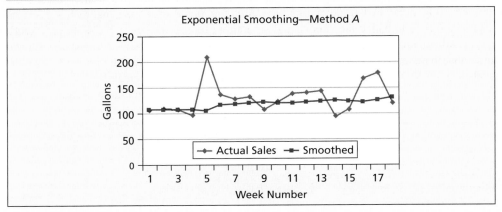

FIGURE 14.22   **Averaging the First Six *y*-Values**

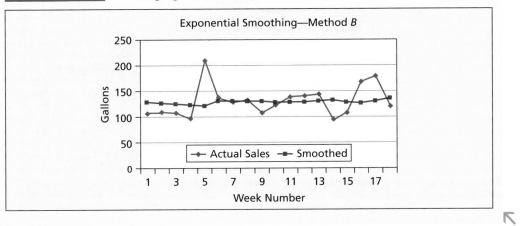

Using MINITAB

Figure 14.23 shows MINITAB's single exponential smoothing and 4 weeks' forecasts. After week 18, the exponential smoothing method cannot be updated with actual data, so the forecasts are constant. The wide 95 percent confidence intervals reflect the rather erratic past sales pattern.

FIGURE 14.23

MINITAB's Exponential Smoothing

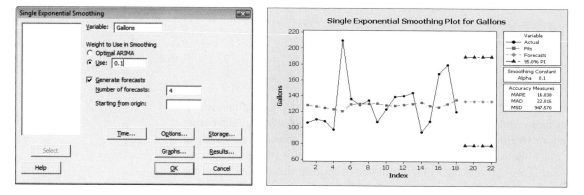

Using Excel

Excel also has an exponential smoothing option. It is found in the Data Analysis menu. One difference to be noted is that Excel asks for a *damping factor,* which is equal to $1 - \alpha$. Excel uses method *A* to initialize the exponential smoothing forecasts. Figure 14.24 shows Excel's exponential smoothing dialogue box and a line chart of the actual values and forecast values. Notice that there are no forecast values beyond period 18 and that there are no confidence intervals as with MINITAB. Excel's default chart doesn't show the original data, so you should expect to make your own "improved" line chart, like the one shown in Figure 14.24.

FIGURE 14.24

Excel's Exponential Smoothing

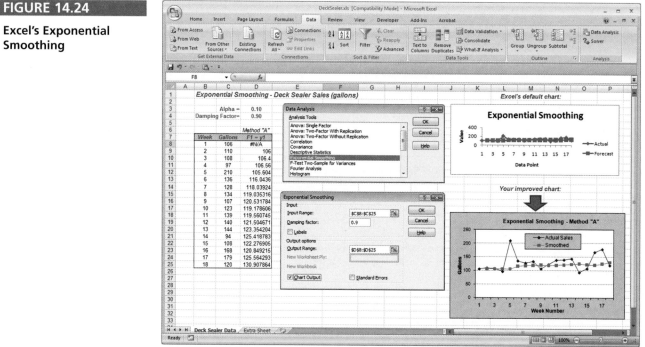

Smoothing with Trend and Seasonality

Single exponential smoothing is intended for *trendless* data. If your data have a trend, you can try *Holt's method* with *two* smoothing constants (one for *trend,* one for *level*). If you have both trend and seasonality, you can try *Winters's method* with *three* smoothing constants (one for *trend,* one for *level,* one for *seasonality*). These advanced methods are similar to single smoothing in that they use simple formulas to update the forecasts, and you may use them without special caution. These topics are usually reserved for a class in forecasting, so they will not be explained here.

Mini Case   14.2

Exchange Rates

We have data for March 1 to March 30 and want to forecast 1 day ahead to March 31 by using exponential smoothing. We choose a smoothing constant value of $\alpha = .20$ and set the initial forecast F_1 to the average of the first six data values. Table 14.14 shows the actual data (y_t) and MINITAB's forecasts (F_t) for each date. The March 31 forecast is $F_{23} = \alpha y_{22} + (1 - \alpha) F_{22} = (.20)(1.2164) + (.80)(1.21395) = 1.2144$.

TABLE 14.14	**Exchange Rate Canada/U.S. Dollar** 🖙 **Canada**		
t	*Date*	*Actual* y_t	*Forecast* F_t	*Error* $e_t = y_t - F_t$
1	1-Mar-05	1.2425	1.23450	0.0080
2	2-Mar-05	1.2395	1.23610	0.0034
3	3-Mar-05	1.2463	1.23678	0.0095
4	4-Mar-05	1.2324	1.23868	−0.0063
5	7-Mar-05	1.2300	1.23743	−0.0074
6	8-Mar-05	1.2163	1.23594	−0.0196
7	9-Mar-05	1.2064	1.23201	−0.0256
8	10-Mar-05	1.2050	1.22689	−0.0219
9	11-Mar-05	1.2041	1.22251	−0.0184
10	14-Mar-05	1.2087	1.21883	−0.0101
11	15-Mar-05	1.2064	1.21680	−0.0104
12	16-Mar-05	1.2038	1.21472	−0.0109
13	17-Mar-05	1.2028	1.21254	−0.0097
14	18-Mar-05	1.2027	1.21059	−0.0079
15	21-Mar-05	1.2110	1.20901	0.0020
16	22-Mar-05	1.2017	1.20941	−0.0077
17	23-Mar-05	1.2133	1.20787	0.0054
18	24-Mar-05	1.2150	1.20895	0.0061
19	25-Mar-05	1.2180	1.21016	0.0078
20	28-Mar-05	1.2234	1.21173	0.0117
21	29-Mar-05	1.2135	1.21406	−0.0006
22	30-Mar-05	1.2164	1.21395	0.0024
23	31-Mar-05		1.21444	

Source: Data from www.federalreserve.gov.

The column of errors (e_t) shown in Table 14.14 is used to calculate the measures of fit (e.g., *MAPE, MAD, MSE*) as shown on the spreadsheet 🖙 **Canada**. The resulting measures of fit are displayed in Figure 14.25 along with the MINITAB plot of the data and forecasts. The forecasts adapt, but always with a lag. The actual exchange rate on March 31 was 1.2094, slightly lower than the forecast, but well within the 95 percent prediction limits.

FIGURE 14.25	**MINITAB's Exponential Smoothing ($\alpha = .20$)**

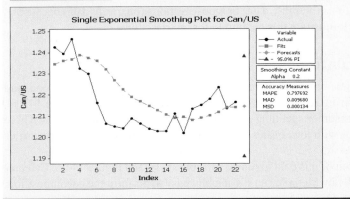

SECTION EXERCISES   **14.7**   (a) Make an Excel line graph of the following bond yield data. Describe the pattern. Is there a consistent trend? (b) Use exponential smoothing (MegaStat, MINITAB, or Excel) with $\alpha = .20$. Use both methods A and B to initialize the forecast (the default in both MegaStat and MINITAB). (c) Record the statistics of fit (MegaStat uses MSE and MSD, MINITAB uses MSD and $MAPE$). With Excel you will have to calculate these by creating cell formulas). (d) Do the smoothing again with $\alpha = .10$ and then with $\alpha = .30$, recording the statistics of fit. (e) Compare the statistics of fit for the three values of α. (f) Make a one-period forecast (i.e., $t = 53$) using each of the three α values. How did α affect your forecasts?   📷 **BondYield**

U.S. Treasury 10-Year Bond Yields at Week's End ($n = 52$ weeks)							
Week	**Yield**	**Week**	**Yield**	**Week**	**Yield**	**Week**	**Yield**
4/2/04	3.95	7/2/04	4.63	10/1/04	4.10	12/31/04	4.29
4/9/04	4.21	7/9/04	4.49	10/8/04	4.20	1/7/05	4.28
4/16/04	4.36	7/16/04	4.47	10/15/04	4.08	1/14/05	4.25
4/23/04	4.43	7/23/04	4.46	10/22/04	4.03	1/21/05	4.19
4/30/04	4.49	7/30/04	4.56	10/29/04	4.05	1/28/05	4.19
5/7/04	4.62	8/6/04	4.41	11/5/04	4.12	2/4/05	4.14
5/14/04	4.81	8/13/04	4.28	11/12/04	4.22	2/11/05	4.06
5/21/04	4.74	8/20/04	4.23	11/19/04	4.17	2/18/05	4.16
5/28/04	4.68	8/27/04	4.25	11/26/04	4.20	2/25/05	4.28
6/4/04	4.74	9/3/04	4.19	12/3/04	4.35	3/4/05	4.37
6/11/04	4.80	9/10/04	4.21	12/10/04	4.19	3/11/05	4.45
6/18/04	4.75	9/17/04	4.14	12/17/04	4.16	3/18/05	4.51
6/25/04	4.69	9/24/04	4.04	12/24/04	4.21	3/25/05	4.59

Source: www.federalreserve.gov.

14.6 SEASONALITY

LO7

Use software to deseasonalize a time-series.

When and How to Deseasonalize

When the data periodicity is monthly or quarterly we should calculate a seasonal index and use it to **deseasonalize** the data (annual data have no seasonality). For a multiplicative model (the usual assumption) a seasonal index is a *ratio*. For example, if the seasonal index for July is 1.25, it means that July is 125 percent of the monthly average. If the seasonal index for January is 0.84, it means that January is 84 percent of the monthly average. If the seasonal index for October is 1.00, it means that October is an average month. The seasonal indexes must sum to 12 for monthly data or 4 for quarterly data. The following steps are used to deseasonalize data for time-series observations:

- Step 1   Calculate a centered moving average (*CMA*) for each month (quarter).
- Step 2   Divide each observed y_t value by the *CMA* to obtain seasonal ratios.
- Step 3   Average the seasonal ratios by month (quarter) to get raw seasonal indexes.
- Step 4   Adjust the raw seasonal indexes so they sum to 12 (monthly) or 4 (quarterly).
- Step 5   Divide each y_t by its seasonal index to get deseasonalized data.

In step 1, we lose 12 observations (monthly data) or 4 observations (quarterly data) because of the centering process. We will illustrate this technique for quarterly data.

Illustration of Calculations

Table 14.15 shows 6 years' data on quarterly revenue from sales of carpeting, tile, wood, and vinyl flooring by a floor-covering retailer. The data have an upward trend (see Figure 14.26), perhaps due to a boom in consumer spending on home improvement and new homes. There also appears to be seasonality, with lower sales in the third quarter (summer) and higher sales in the first quarter (winter).

The seasonal decomposition of this data is shown in Table 14.16 and Figure 14.26. Calculations are handled automatically by MegaStat so it's actually easy to perform the decomposition.

TABLE 14.15

Sales of Floor Covering Materials ($ thousands)
    FloorSales

Quarter	2002	2003	2004	2005	2006	2007
1	259	306	379	369	515	626
2	236	300	262	373	373	535
3	164	189	242	255	339	397
4	222	275	296	374	519	488

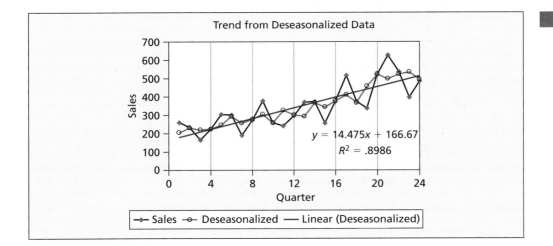

FIGURE 14.26

MegaStat's Deseasonalized Trend

Because the number of subperiods (quarters) is even ($m = 4$), each value of the *CMA* is the average of two averages. For example, the first *CMA* value 226.125 is the average of $(259 + 236 + 164 + 222)/4$ and $(236 + 164 + 222 + 306)/4$. Table 14.17 shows how the indexes are averaged. The *CMA* loses two quarters at the beginning and two quarters at the end, so each seasonal index is an average of only five quarters (instead of six). Each mean is then adjusted to force the sum to be 4.000, and these become the seasonal indexes. If we had monthly data, the indexes would be adjusted so that their sum would be 12.000.

Obs	Year	Quarter	Sales	CMA	Sales/CMA	Seasonal Index	Deseasonalized
1	2002	1	259			1.252	206.9
2		2	236			1.021	231.1
3		3	164	226.125	0.725	0.740	221.7
4		4	222	240.000	0.925	0.987	224.9
5	2003	1	306	251.125	1.219	1.252	244.4
6		2	300	260.875	1.150	1.021	293.8
7		3	189	276.625	0.683	0.740	255.5
8		4	275	281.000	0.979	0.987	278.6
9	2004	1	379	282.875	1.340	1.252	302.7
10		2	262	292.125	0.897	1.021	256.6
11		3	242	293.500	0.825	0.740	327.2
12		4	296	306.125	0.967	0.987	299.8
13	2005	1	369	321.625	1.147	1.252	294.7
14		2	373	333.000	1.120	1.021	365.3
15		3	255	361.000	0.706	0.740	344.7
16		4	374	379.250	0.986	0.987	378.8
17	2006	1	515	389.750	1.321	1.252	411.3
18		2	373	418.375	0.892	1.021	365.3
19		3	339	450.375	0.753	0.740	458.3
20		4	519	484.500	1.071	0.987	525.7
21	2007	1	626	512.000	1.223	1.252	500.0
22		2	535	515.375	1.038	1.021	524.0
23		3	397			0.740	536.7
24		4	488			0.987	494.3

TABLE 14.17

Calculation of
Seasonal Indexes
🖝 FloorSales

Quarter	2002	2003	2004	2005	2006	2007	Mean	Adjusted
1		1.219	1.340	1.147	1.321	1.223	1.250	1.252
2		1.150	0.897	1.120	0.892	1.038	1.019	1.021
3	0.725	0.683	0.825	0.706	0.753		0.738	0.740
4	0.925	0.979	0.967	0.986	1.071		0.986	0.987
							3.993	4.000

Due to rounding, details may not yield the result shown.

After the data have been deseasonalized, the trend is fitted. Figure 14.26 shows the fitted trend from MegaStat, based on the deseasonalized data. The sharper peaks and valleys in the original time-series (Y) have been smoothed by removing the seasonality (S). Any remaining variation about the trend (T) is irregular (I) or "random noise."

LO7

Use software to
deseasonalize a time-
series.

Using MINITAB to Deseasonalize

MINITAB performs its deseasonalization in a similar way, although it averages the seasonal factors using *medians* instead of *means,* so the results are not exactly the same as MegaStat's. For example, using the same floor covering sales data:

Quarter	MegaStat's Seasonal Index	MINITAB's Seasonal Index
1	1.252	1.234
2	1.021	1.047
3	0.740	0.732
4	0.987	0.987
Sum	4.000	4.000
Fitted trend	$y_t = 166.67 + 14.475t$	$y_t = 166.62 + 14.483t$

MINITAB offers nice graphical displays for decomposition, as well as forecasts, as shown in Figure 14.27. MINITAB also offers additive as well as multiplicative seasonality. In an additive model, the *CMA* is calculated in the same way, but the raw seasonals are *differences* (instead of ratios) and the seasonal indexes are forced to sum to *zero* (e.g., months with higher sales must exactly balance months with lower sales). Most analysts prefer multiplicative models (assuming trended data), so the additive model is not discussed in detail here.

FIGURE 14.27

MINITAB's Graphs for Floor Covering Sales

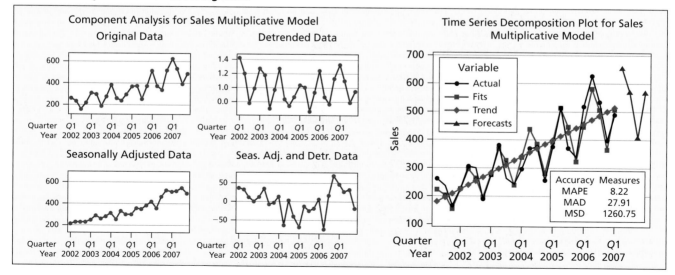

Seasonal Forecasts Using Binary Predictors

Another way to address seasonality is to estimate a regression model using **seasonal binaries** as predictors. For quarterly data, for example, the data set would look as shown in Table 14.18. When we have four binaries (i.e., four quarters) we must exclude one binary to prevent perfect multicollinearity (see Chapter 13, Section 13.5). Arbitrarily, we exclude the fourth quarter binary *Qtr4* (it will be a portion of the intercept when $Qtr1 = 0$ and $Qtr2 = 0$ and $Qtr3 = 0$).

Year	Quarter	Sales	Time	Qtr1	Qtr2	Qtr3
2002	1	259	1	1	0	0
	2	236	2	0	1	0
	3	164	3	0	0	1
	4	222	4	0	0	0
2003	1	306	5	1	0	0
	2	300	6	0	1	0
	3	189	7	0	0	1
	4	275	8	0	0	0
2004	1	379	9	1	0	0
	2	262	10	0	1	0
	3	242	11	0	0	1
	4	296	12	0	0	0
2005	1	369	13	1	0	0
	2	373	14	0	1	0
	3	255	15	0	0	1
	4	374	16	0	0	0
2006	1	515	17	1	0	0
	2	373	18	0	1	0
	3	339	19	0	0	1
	4	519	20	0	0	0
2007	1	626	21	1	0	0
	2	535	22	0	1	0
	3	397	23	0	0	1
	4	488	24	0	0	0

TABLE 14.18

Sales Data with Seasonal Binaries
📁 **FloorSales**

LO8

Use regression with seasonal binaries to make forecasts.

We assume a linear trend, and specify the regression model *Sales* = *f*(*Time, Qtr1, Qtr2, Qtr3*). MINITAB's estimated regression is shown in Figure 14.28. This is an additive model of the form $Y = T + S + I$ (recall that we omit the cycle C in practice). The fitted equation is

$$Sales = 161 + 14.4 \ Time + 89.8 \ Qtr1 + 12.9 \ Qtr2 - 83.6 \ Qtr3$$

FIGURE 14.28

MINITAB's Fitted Regression for Seasonal Binaries

```
The regression equation is
Sales = 161 + 14.4 Time + 89.8 Qtr1 + 12.9 Qtr2 − 83.6 Qtr3

Predictor         Coef        SE Coef          T          P
Constant        161.21         24.33        6.62      0.000
Time            14.366          1.244       11.55      0.000
Qtr1             89.76         24.32         3.69      0.002
Qtr2             12.90         24.16         0.53      0.600
Qtr3            −83.63         24.07        −3.47      0.003

S = 41.6313        R-Sq = 90.0%           R-Sq(adj) = 87.9%
```

Time is a significant predictor ($p = .000$) indicating significant linear trend. Two of the binaries are significant: *Qtr1* ($p = .002$) and *Qtr3* ($p = .003$). The second quarter binary *Qtr2* ($p = .600$) is not significant. The model gives a good overall fit ($R^2 = .90$). The main virtue of the seasonal regression model is its versatility. We can plug in future values of *Time* and the seasonal binaries to create forecasts as far ahead as we wish. For example, the forecasts for 2006 are

$$Period\ 25: Sales = 161 + 14.4(25) + 89.8(1) + 12.9(0) - 83.6(0) = 610.8$$
$$Period\ 26: Sales = 161 + 14.4(26) + 89.8(0) + 12.9(1) - 83.6(0) = 548.3$$
$$Period\ 27: Sales = 161 + 14.4(27) + 89.8(0) + 12.9(0) - 83.6(1) = 466.2$$
$$Period\ 28: Sales = 161 + 14.4(28) + 89.8(0) + 12.9(0) - 83.6(0) = 564.2$$

SECTION EXERCISES

connect

14.8 (a) Use MegaStat or MINITAB to deseasonalize the quarterly data on PepsiCo's revenues and fit a trend. Interpret the results. (b) Use MegaStat or MINITAB to perform a regression using seasonal binaries. Interpret the results. (c) Use the regression equation to make a prediction for each quarter in 2009. (d) If you have access to http://finance.yahoo.com, check your forecasts. How accurate were they? 📁 **PepsiCo**

PepsiCo Revenues ($ millions), 2003–2008

Quarter	2003	2004	2005	2006	2007	2008
Qtr1	5,530	6,131	6,585	7,205	7,350	8,332
Qtr2	6,538	7,070	7,697	8,599	9,607	10,945
Qtr3	6,830	7,257	8,184	8,950	10,171	11,244
Qtr4	8,073	8,803	10,096	10,383	12,346	12,729

Source: *Standard & Poor's Stock Reports*, March 2007, and http://finance.yahoo.com.

14.9 (a) Use MegaStat or MINITAB to deseasonalize the monthly Corvette sales data and fit a trend. Interpret the results. (b) Use MegaStat or MINITAB to perform a regression using seasonal binaries. Interpret the results. (c) Use the regression equation to make a prediction for each month in 2004. (d) If you have access to *Ward's Automotive Yearbook, 2005* (67th edition), check your forecasts. How accurate were they? 📁 **Corvette**

U.S. Corvette Sales, 2000–2004 (number of cars sold)

Month	2000	2001	2002	2003
Jan	1,863	2,252	2,443	1,468
Feb	2,765	2,766	3,354	1,724
Mar	3,440	2,923	1,877	2,792
Apr	3,018	2,713	2,176	6,249
May	2,725	2,847	3,049	2,441
Jun	2,538	2,521	2,708	2,272
Jul	1,598	2,000	2,960	2,007
Aug	2,861	2,789	2,912	2,107
Sep	2,942	3,639	2,960	1,615
Oct	2,748	4,647	3,094	1,878
Nov	2,376	2,910	2,163	1,596
Dec	2,334	1,648	2,859	1,825
Total	31,208	33,655	32,555	27,974

Source: *Ward's Automotive Yearbook, 2001–2004.*

Mini Case   14.3

Using Seasonal Binaries 📎 Beer

Figure 14.29 shows monthly U.S. shipments of bottled beer for 2001–2006. A strong seasonal pattern is evident, presumably because people drink more beer in the warmer months. How can we describe the pattern statistically?

FIGURE 14.29   **U.S. Bottled Beer Shipments, 2001–2006**

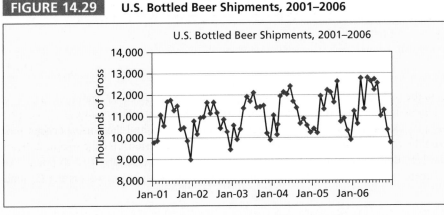

Source: www.census.gov.

LO8

Use regression with seasonal binaries to make forecasts.

We create a regression data set with linear trend (Time = 1, 2, . . . , 72) and 11 seasonal binaries (Feb–Dec). The January binary is omitted to prevent perfect multicollinearity. The regression results, shown in Figure 14.30, indicate a good fit ($R^2 = .857$), significant upward trend ($p = 0.000$ for Time), and several seasonal binaries that differ significantly from zero (*p*-values near zero). Binary predictor coefficients indicate that shipments are above the January average during the spring and summer (Mar–Aug), below the January average in the winter (Nov–Feb), and near the January average in the fall (Sep–Oct). The fitted regression equation can be used to forecast any future months' shipments.

FIGURE 14.30   **MINITAB's Fitted Regression for Seasonal Binaries**

```
The regression equation is
Beer = 10164 + 16.9 Time − 484 Feb + 768 Mar + 579 Apr
       + 1311 May + 1182 Jun + 975 Jul + 892 Aug − 99 Sep
       + 107 Oct − 644 Nov − 1089 Dec
```

Predictor	Coef	SE Coef	T	P
Constant	10163.7	161.4	62.97	0.000
Time	16.9	2.1	8.11	0.000
Feb	−483.9	209.2	−2.31	0.024
Mar	767.5	209.2	3.67	0.001
Apr	579.0	209.3	2.77	0.008
May	1310.7	209.3	6.26	0.000
Jun	1182.0	209.4	5.64	0.000
Jul	975.3	209.5	4.65	0.000
Aug	892.2	209.7	4.26	0.000
Sep	−99.3	209.8	−0.47	0.638
Oct	106.9	210.0	0.51	0.613
Nov	−644.1	210.2	−3.06	0.003
Dec	−1089.0	210.4	−5.18	0.000

```
   S = 362.302  R-Sq = 85.7%      R-Sq (adj) = 82.8%
```

14.7

INDEX NUMBERS

A simple way to measure changes over time (and especially to compare two or more variables) is to convert time-series data into **index numbers**. The idea is to create an index that starts at 100 in a *base period,* so we can see *relative changes* in the data regardless of the original data units. Indexes are most often used for financial data (e.g., prices, wages, costs) but can be used with any numerical data (e.g., number of units sold, warranty claims, computer spam).

Relative Indexes

LO9

Interpret index numbers.

To convert a time series $y_1, y_2, \ldots, y_n$ into a *relative index,* (sometimes called a *simple index*) we divide each data value y_t by the data value y_1 in a base period and multiply by 100. The relative index I_t for period t is

$$I_t = 100 \times \frac{y_t}{y_1} \tag{14.14}$$

The index in the base period is always $I_1 = 100$, so the index $I_1, I_2, \ldots, I_n$ makes it easy to see *relative changes* in the data, regardless of the original data units. For example, Table 14.19 shows six-years' of daily U.S. dollar exchange rates (on the left) and the corresponding index numbers (on the right) using January 3, 2000 = 100 as a base period. By the end of 2006, we see that the U.S. dollar fell to 83.1 percent of its starting value versus the British pound, rose to 114.9 percent versus the Mexican peso, and dropped to 80.6 percent versus the Canadian dollar.

TABLE 14.19

U.S. Foreign Exchange Rates, 2000–2006
 Currency

	Foreign Currency per Dollar			Index Numbers (Jan 3, 2000 = 100)		
Date	*U.K.*	*Mexico*	*Canada*	*U.K.*	*Mexico*	*Canada*
3-Jan-00	0.61463	9.4015	1.4465	100.0	100.0	100.0
4-Jan-00	0.61087	9.4570	1.4518	99.4	100.6	100.4
5-Jan-00	0.60920	9.5350	1.4518	99.1	101.4	100.4
⋮	⋮	⋮	⋮	⋮	⋮	⋮
27-Dec-06	0.51109	10.8820	1.1610	83.2	115.7	80.3
28-Dec-06	0.50966	10.8740	1.1599	82.9	115.7	80.2
29-Dec-06	0.51057	10.7995	1.1652	83.1	114.9	80.6

Source: www.federalreserve.gov.

A graph like Figure 14.31 allows us to display seven years (1,759 days) of data. Since each index starts at the same point (100), we can easily see the fluctuations and trends. We could fit a moving average, if we wanted to smooth the data. Speculators who engage in currency arbitrage would use even more-sophisticated tools to analyze movements in currency indexes.

FIGURE 14.31

U.S. Foreign Exchange Rates, 2000–2006
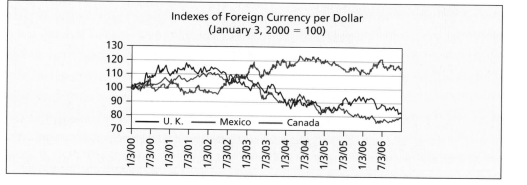 Currency

Weighted Indexes

A different calculation is required for a *weighted index* such as the Consumer Price Index for all urban consumers (CPI-U). The CPI-U is a measure of the relative prices paid by urban consumers for a market basket of goods and services, based on prices of hundreds of goods and services in eight major groups. The goal is to make the CPI-U representative of the prices paid for all goods and services purchased by all urban consumers. This requires assigning weights to each consumer good or service to reflect its importance relative to all the other goods and services in the market basket (e.g., housing gets a higher weight because it is a larger proportion of total spending). The basic formula for a simple weighted price index is

$$I_t = 100 \times \frac{\sum\limits_{i=1}^{m} p_{it}q_i}{\sum\limits_{i=1}^{m} p_{i1}q_i} = 100 \times \frac{p_{1t}q_1 + p_{2t}q_2 + \cdots + p_{mt}q_m}{p_{11}q_1 + p_{21}q_2 + \cdots + p_{m1}q_m} \qquad (14.15)$$

where
I_t = weighted index for period t ($t = 1, 2, \ldots, n$)
p_{it} = price of good i in period t ($t = 1, 2, \ldots, n$)
q_i = weight assigned to good i ($i = 1, 2, \ldots m$)

The numerator is the cost of buying a given market basket of goods and services at today's prices (period t) relative to the cost of the same market basket in the base period (period 1). The weight q_i represents the relative quantity of the item in the consumer's budget. For example, suppose there is a price increase of 5 percent for food and beverages and a 10 percent increase for medical care costs, with no price changes for the other expenditure categories. This would result in an increase of 1.4 percent in the CPI, as shown in Table 14.20.

Illustrative Calculation of Price Index				**TABLE 14.20**		
	Base Year (*t* = 1)			Current Year (*t* = 2)		
Expenditure Category	Weight (q_i)	Relative Price (p_{i1})	Relative Spending ($p_{i1}q_i$)	Weight (q_i)	Relative Price (p_{i2})	Relative Spending ($p_{i2}q_i$)
Food and beverages	15.7 ×	1.00 =	15.7	15.7 ×	1.05 =	16.5
Housing	40.9 ×	1.00 =	40.9	40.9 ×	1.00 =	40.9
Apparel	4.4 ×	1.00 =	4.4	4.4 ×	1.00 =	4.4
Transportation	17.1 ×	1.00 =	17.1	17.1 ×	1.00 =	17.1
Medical care	5.8 ×	1.00 =	5.8	5.8 ×	1.10 =	6.4
Recreation	6.0 ×	1.00 =	6.0	6.0 ×	1.00 =	6.0
Education/communication	5.8 ×	1.00 =	5.8	5.8 ×	1.00 =	5.8
Other goods and services	4.3 ×	1.00 =	4.3	4.3 ×	1.00 =	4.3
Sum	100.0	$\sum\limits_{i=1}^{n} p_{i1}q_i$ =	100.0	100.0	$\sum\limits_{i=1}^{n} p_{i2}q_i$ =	101.4

From Table 14.20, the price index rose from 100.0 to 101.4, or a 1.4 percent increase:

$$I_2 = 100 \times \frac{\sum\limits_{i=1}^{n} p_{i2}q_i}{\sum\limits_{i=1}^{n} p_{i1}q_i} = 100 \times \frac{101.4}{100.0} = 101.4$$

Formula (14.15) is called a *Laspeyres index.* It treats the base year quantity weights as constant. Weights are based on the *Survey of Consumer Expenditures.* In your economics classes, you may learn more sophisticated methods that take into account the fact that expenditure weights do change over time. One such method is the *Paasche index,* which uses a formula similar to the Laspeyres index, except that quantity weights are adjusted for each period.

Importance of Index Numbers

The CPI affects nearly all Americans because it is used to adjust things like retirement benefits, food stamps, school lunch benefits, alimony, and tax brackets. The CPI-U could be compared with an index of salary growth for workers, or to measure current-dollar salaries in "real dollars." The Bureau of Labor Statistics (www.bls.gov) publishes CPI historical statistics for each of the eight categories shown in Table 14.20. The most widely used CPI-U uses 1982–84 as a reference. That is, the Bureau of Labor Statistics sets the CPI-U (the average price level) for the 36-month period covering the years 1982, 1983, and 1984 equal to 100, and then measures changes in relation to that figure. As of May 2007, for example, the CPI-U was 207.9, meaning that, on average, prices had slightly more than doubled over the previous 25 years (about a 3.1 percent annual increase, applying the geometric mean formula 4.6 with $n = 25$). The CPI is based on the buying habits of the "average" consumer, so it may not be a perfect reflection of anyone's individual price experience.

Other familiar price indexes, such as the Dow Jones Industrial Average (DJIA), have their own unique methodologies. Originally a simple arithmetic mean of stock prices, the DJIA now is the sum of the 30 stock prices divided by a "divisor" to compensate for stock splits and other changes over time. The divisor is revised periodically. Because high-priced stocks comprise a larger proportion of the sum, the DJIA is more strongly affected by changes in high-priced stocks. A little Web research can tell you a lot about how stock price indexes are calculated, their strengths and weaknesses, and some alternative indexes that finance experts have invented.

14.8
FORECASTING: FINAL THOUGHTS

Role of Forecasting

In many ways, forecasting resembles planning. *Forecasting* is an analytical way to describe a "what-if" future that might confront the organization. *Planning* is the organization's attempt to determine actions it will take under each foreseeable contingency. Forecasts help decision makers become aware of trends or patterns that require a response. Actions taken by the decision makers may actually head off the contingency envisioned in the forecast. Thus, forecasts tend to be self-defeating because they trigger homeostatic organizational responses.

Behavioral Aspects of Forecasting

Forecasts can facilitate organizational communication. The forecast (or even just a nicely prepared time-series chart) lets everyone examine the same facts concurrently, and perhaps argue with the data or the assumptions that underlie the forecast or its relevance to the organization. A quantitative forecast helps *make assumptions explicit*. Those who prepare the forecast must explain and defend their assumptions, while others must challenge them. In the process, everyone gains understanding of the data, the underlying realities, and the imperfections in the data. Forecasts *focus the dialogue* and can make it more productive.

Of course, this assumes a certain maturity among the individuals around the table. Strong leaders (or possibly meeting facilitators) can play a role in guiding the discourse to produce a positive result. The danger is that people may try to find scapegoats (yes, they do tend to blame the forecaster), deny facts, or avoid responsibility for tough decisions. But one premise of this book is that statistics, when done well, can strengthen any dialogue and lead to better decisions.

Forecasts Are Always Wrong

We discussed several measures to use to determine if a forecast model fits the time series. Successful forecasters understand that a forecast is never precise. There is always some error, but we can *use* the error measures to track forecast error. Many companies use several different forecasting models and rely on the model that has had the least error over some time period. We have described simple models in this chapter. You may take a class specifically focusing on forecasting in which you will learn about other time-series models including AR (autoregressive) and ARIMA (autoregressive integrated moving average) models. Such models take advantage of the dependency that might exist between values in the time series.

To ensure good forecast outcomes

- Maintain up-to-date databases of *relevant* data.
- Allow sufficient lead time to analyze the data.
- State several alternative forecasts or scenarios.
- Track forecast errors over time.
- State your assumptions and qualifications and consider your time horizon.
- Don't underestimate the power of a good graph.

Mini Case   14.4

How Does Noodles & Company Ensure Its Ingredients Are as Fresh as Possible?

Using only fresh ingredients is key for great food and success for restaurants like Noodles & Company. To be sure that the restaurants are serving only the freshest ingredients, while also reducing food waste, Noodles & Company turned to statistical forecasting for ordering ingredients and daily food preparation. The challenge was to create a forecast that is sophisticated enough to be accurate, yet simple enough for new restaurant employees to understand.

Noodles & Company uses a food management software system to forecast the demand for its menu items based on the moving average of the previous four weeks' sales. This simple forecasting technique has been very accurate. The automated process also uses the forecast of each item to estimate how many ingredients to order as well as how much to prepare each day. For example, the system might forecast that during next Wednesday's lunch, the location in Longmont, Colorado, will sell 55 Pesto Cavatappi's. After forecasting the demand for each menu item, the system then specifies exactly how much of each ingredient to prepare for that lunch period.

For the restaurant teams, the old manual process of estimating and guessing how much of each ingredient to prepare is now replaced with an automated prep sheet. Noodles & Company has reduced food waste because restaurants are less likely to over order ingredients and overprepare menu items. The restaurant teams are more efficient and customers are served meals made with the freshest ingredients possible.

CHAPTER SUMMARY

A **time series** is assumed to have four components. For most business data, **trend** is the general pattern of change over all years observed while **cycle** is a repetitive pattern of change around the trend over several years and **seasonality** is a repetitive pattern within a year. The **irregular** component is a random disturbance that follows no pattern. The **additive model** is adequate in the short run because the four components' magnitude does not change much, but for observations over longer periods of time, the **multiplicative model** is preferred. Common trend models include **linear** (constant slope and no turning point), **quadratic** (one turning point), and **exponential** (constant percent growth or decline). Higher polynomial models are untrustworthy and liable to give strange forecasts, though any trend model is less reliable the farther out it is projected. In forecasting, forecasters use fit measures besides R^2, such as mean absolute percent error (**MAPE**), mean absolute deviation (**MAD**), and mean squared deviation (**MSD**). For trendless or erratic data, we use a **moving average** over m periods or **exponential smoothing**. Forecasts adapt rapidly to changing data when the **smoothing constant** α is large (near 1) and conversely for a small α (near 0). For monthly or quarterly data, a **seasonal adjustment** is required before extracting the trend. Alternatively, regression with **seasonal binaries** can be used to capture seasonality and make forecasts. **Index numbers** are used to show changes relative to a base period.

KEY TERMS

Commonly Used Formulas

Additive time-series model: $Y = T + C + S + I$

Multiplicative time-series model: $Y = T \times C \times S \times I$

Linear trend model: $y_t = a + bt$

Exponential trend model: $y_t = ae^{bt}$

Quadratic trend model: $y_t = a + bt + ct^2$

Coefficient of determination: $R^2 = 1 - \dfrac{\sum\limits_{t=1}^{n}(y_t - \hat{y}_t)^2}{\sum\limits_{t=1}^{n}(y_t - \bar{y})^2}$

Mean absolute percent error: $MAPE = \dfrac{100}{n} \sum\limits_{t=1}^{n} \dfrac{|y_t - \hat{y}_t|}{y_t}$

Mean absolute deviation: $MAD = \dfrac{1}{n} \sum\limits_{t=1}^{n} |y_t - \hat{y}_t|$

Mean squared deviation: $MSD = \dfrac{1}{n} \sum\limits_{t=1}^{n} (y_t - \hat{y}_t)^2$

Standard error: $SE = \sqrt{\sum\limits_{t=1}^{n} \dfrac{(y_t - \hat{y}_t)^2}{n - 2}}$

Forecast updating equation for exponential smoothing: $F_{t+1} = \alpha y_t + (1 - \alpha)F_t$

CHAPTER REVIEW

1. Explain the difference between (a) stocks and flows; (b) cross-sectional and time-series data; (c) additive and multiplicative models.

2. (a) What is periodicity? (b) Give original examples of data with different periodicity.

3. (a) What are the distinguishing features of each component of a time series (trend, cycle, seasonal, irregular)? (b) Why is cycle usually ignored in time-series modeling?

4. Name four criteria for assessing a trend forecast.

5. Name two advantages and two disadvantages of each of the common trend models (linear, exponential, quadratic).

6. When would the exponential trend model be preferred to a linear trend model?

7. Explain how to obtain the compound percent growth rate from a fitted exponential model.

8. (a) When might a quadratic model be useful? (b) What precautions must be taken when forecasting with a quadratic model? (c) Why are higher-order polynomial models dangerous?

9. Name five measures of fit for a trend, and state their advantages and disadvantages.

10. (a) When do we use a moving average? (b) Name two types of moving averages. (c) When is a centered moving average harder to calculate?

11. (a) When is exponential smoothing most useful? (b) Interpret the smoothing constant α. What is its range? (c) What does a small α say about the degree of smoothing? A large α?

12. (a) Explain two ways to initialize the forecasts in an exponential smoothing process. (b) Name an advantage and a disadvantage of each method.

13. (a) Why is seasonality irrelevant for annual data? (b) List the steps in deseasonalizing a monthly time series. (c) What is the sum of a monthly seasonal index? A quarterly index?

14. (a) How can forecasting improve communication within an organization? (b) List five tips for ensuring effective forecasting outcomes.

15. (a) Explain how seasonal binaries can be used to model seasonal data. (b) What is the advantage of using seasonal binaries?

16. Explain the equivalency between the two forms of an exponential trend model.

17. What is the purpose of index numbers?

Instructions: For each exercise, use Excel, MegaStat, or MINITAB to make an attractive, well-labeled time-series line chart. Adjust the *Y*-axis scale if necessary to show more detail (because Excel usually starts the scale at zero). If a fitted trend is called for, use Excel's option to display the equation and R^2 statistic (or *MAPE, MAD,* and *MSD* in MINITAB). Include printed copies of all relevant graphs with your answers to each exercise. Exercises marked with * are based on harder material.

14.10 (a) Make a line chart for JetBlue's revenue. (b) Describe the trend (if any) and discuss possible causes. (c) Fit both a linear and an exponential trend to the data. (d) Which model is preferred? Why? (e) Make a forecast for 2009, using a trend model of your choice (or a judgment forecast). 🗁 **JetBlue**

JetBlue Airlines Revenue, 2002–2008 (millions)

Year	Revenue		Year	Revenue
2002	635		2006	2,363
2003	998		2007	2,842
2004	1,265		2008	3,388
2005	1,701			

Source: *Standard & Poor's Stock Reports,* February 2007 and http://finance.yahoo.com.

14.11 (a) Plot both Swiss watch time series on the same graph. (b) Describe the trend (if any) and discuss possible causes. (c) Fit an exponential trend to each time series. (d) Interpret each fitted trend carefully. What conclusion do you draw? (e) Make forecasts for 2003, using the linear trend model. Do you feel confident in your forecasts? Explain. 🗁 **Swiss**

Swiss Watch Exports (thousands of units), 1998–2003

Year	Mechanical	Electronic
1998	2,558	29,678
1999	2,526	28,766
2000	2,549	27,313
2001	2,580	23,811
2002	2,722	24,107
2003	2,718	21,864

Source: Fédération de L'Industrie Horlogère Suisse, Swiss Watch Exports, www.fhs.ch.

14.12 (a) Plot the total minutes of TV viewing time per household. (b) Describe the trend (if any) and discuss possible causes. (c) Fit a linear trend to the data. (d) Would this model give reasonable forecasts? Would another trend model be better? Explain. (e) Make a forecast for 2010. Check the forecast if you have access to the Web. Show the forecast calculations. (f) Would this data ever approach an asymptote? Explain. *Note:* Time is in 5-year increments, so use $t = 13$ for the 2010 forecast. 🗁 **Television**

Average Daily TV Viewing Time Per U.S. Household

Year	Hours	Min	Total Min
1950	4	35	275
1955	4	51	291
1960	5	6	306
1965	5	29	329
1970	5	56	356
1975	6	7	367
1980	6	36	396
1985	7	10	430
1990	6	53	413
1995	7	17	437
2000	7	35	455
2005	8	11	491

Source: As published by the TVB based on Nielsen Media Research data. Used with permission.

14.13 (a) Plot the voter participation rate. (b) Describe the trend (if any) and discuss possible causes. (c) Fit both a linear and a quadratic trend to the data. (d) Which model is preferred? Why? (e) Make a forecast for 2008, using a trend model of your choice (or a judgment forecast). (f) Check the Web for the actual 2008 voter participation rate. How close was your forecast? *Note:* Time is in 4-year increments, so use $t = 15$ for the 2008 forecast. 🖾 **Voters**

U.S. Presidential Election Voter Participation, 1952–2004

Year	Voting Age Population	Voted for President	% Voting Pres
1952	99,929	61,551	61.6
1956	104,515	62,027	59.3
1960	109,672	68,838	62.8
1964	114,090	70,645	61.9
1968	120,285	73,212	60.9
1972	140,777	77,719	55.2
1976	152,308	81,556	53.5
1980	163,945	86,515	52.8
1984	173,995	92,653	53.3
1988	181,956	91,595	50.3
1992	189,524	104,425	55.1
1996	196,928	96,278	49.0
2000	207,884	105,397	50.7
2004	220,377	122,349	55.5

Source: *Statistical Abstract of the United States, 2007,* www.census.gov. Voters are in thousands.

14.14 Data centers use lots of electricity to power the Web searches and online shopping that we enjoy. (a) Plot the electricity data. (b) Describe the trend (if any) and discuss possible causes. (c) Fit three trends (linear, exponential, quadratic). (d) Which trend model is best, and why? If none is satisfactory, explain. (e) Make a forecast for 2007 by using a trend model of your choice or a judgment forecast. 🖾 **DataCenters**

Annual Usage of Electricity in U.S. Data Center Servers

Year	Billions of KwH
2000	11.6
2001	13.9
2002	15.6
2003	17.4
2004	19.8
2005	22.6
2006	24.5

Source: U.S. EPA www.energystar.gov/.

14.15 (a) Choose *one* category of consumer credit and plot it. (b) Describe the trend (if any) and discuss possible causes. (c) Fit a trend model of your choice. (d) Make a forecast for 2006, using a trend model of your choice. *Note:* Revolving credit is mostly credit card and home equity loans, while nonrevolving credit is for a specific purchase such as a car. 🖾 **Consumer**

Consumer Credit Outstanding, 2000–2005 ($ billions)

Year	Total	Revolving	Nonrevolving
2000	1,722	683	1,039
2001	1,872	716	1,155
2002	1,984	749	1,235
2003	2,088	771	1,317
2004	2,202	801	1,401
2005	2,296	827	1,469

Source: *Economic Report of the President,* 2007.

14.16 (a) Plot the data on U.S. general aviation shipments. (b) Describe the pattern and discuss possible causes. (c) Would a fitted trend be helpful? Explain. (d) Make a similar graph for 1993–2008 only. Would a fitted trend be helpful in making a prediction for 2009? (e) Fit a trend model of your choice to the 1993–2008 data. (f) Make a forecast for 2009, using either a fitted trend model or a judgment forecast. (g) Might it be best to ignore earlier years in this data set? 📁 **Airplanes**

U.S. Manufactured General Aviation Shipments, 1977–2008

Year	Planes	Year	Planes	Year	Planes	Year	Planes
1977	16,904	1985	2,029	1993	964	2001	2,634
1978	17,811	1986	1,495	1994	928	2002	2,207
1979	17,048	1987	1,085	1995	1,077	2003	2,137
1980	11,877	1988	1,212	1996	1,115	2004	2,355
1981	9,457	1989	1,535	1997	1,549	2005	2,857
1982	4,266	1990	1,144	1998	2,200	2006	3,147
1983	2,691	1991	1,021	1999	2,504	2007	3,279
1984	2,431	1992	941	2000	2,816	2008	3,079

Source: U.S. Manufactured General Aviation Shipments, *Statistical Databook 2008,* General Aviation Manufacturers Association, used with permission.

14.17 (a) Choose *one* beverage category and plot the data. (b) Describe the trend (if any) and discuss possible causes. (c) Would a fitted trend be helpful? Explain. (d) Fit several trend models. Which is best, and why? If none is satisfactory, explain. (e) Make a forecast for 2005, using a trend model of your choice or a judgment forecast. Discuss. *Note:* Time increments are 5 years, so use $t = 6$ for your 2005 forecast. 📁 **Beverages**

U.S. Per Capita Annual Consumption of Selected Beverages (gallons)

Beverage	1980	1985	1990	1995	2000
Milk	27.6	26.7	25.7	23.9	22.5
Whole	17.0	14.3	10.5	8.6	8.1
Reduced-fat	10.5	12.3	15.2	15.3	14.4
Carbonated soft drinks	35.1	35.7	46.2	47.4	49.3
Diet	5.1	7.1	10.7	10.9	11.6
Regular	29.9	28.7	35.6	36.5	37.7
Fruit juices	7.4	7.8	7.8	8.3	8.7
Alcoholic	28.3	28.0	27.5	24.7	24.9
Beer	24.3	23.8	23.9	21.8	21.7
Wine	2.1	2.4	2.0	1.7	2.0
Distilled spirits	2.0	1.8	1.5	1.2	1.3

Source: *Statistical Abstract of the United States, 2003.*

14.18 (a) Plot *either* receipts and outlays *or* federal debt and GDP (plot both time series on the same graph). (b) Describe the trend (if any) and discuss possible causes. (c) Fit an exponential trend to each. (d) Interpret each fitted trend equation, explaining its implications. (e) To whom is this issue relevant? 📁 **FedBudget**

U.S. Federal Finances, 2000-2009 ($ billions current)

Year	Receipts	Outlays	Federal Debt	GDP
2000	2,026	1,789	5,629	9,710
2001	1,991	1,863	5,770	10,058
2002	1,853	2,011	6,198	10,377
2003	1,783	2,160	6,760	10,809
2004	1,880	2,293	7,355	11,500
2005	2,154	2,472	7,905	12,238
2006	2,407	2,655	8,451	13,016
2007	2,568	2,730	8,951	13,671
2008	2,524	2,979	9,623	14,248
2009	2,651	3,133	10,438	14,822

Source: *Economic Report of the President, 2009.*

14.19 (a) Plot both men's and women's winning times on the same graph. (b) Fit a linear trend model to each series. From the fitted trends, will the times eventually converge? *Hint:* Ask Excel for forecasts (e.g., 20 years ahead). (c) Make a copy of your graph, and click each fitted trend and change it to a moving average trend type. (d) Would a moving average be a reasonable approach to modeling these data sets? *Note:* The data file 📆 **Boston** has the data converted to decimal minutes.

Boston Marathon Champions, 1980–2009

Men			Women		
Year	Name of Winner	Time	Year	Name of Winner	Time
1980	Bill Rodgers	2:12:11	1980	Jacqueline Gareau	2:34:28
1981	Toshihiko Seko	2:09:26	1981	Allison Roe	2:26:46
1982	Alberto Salazar	2:08:52	1982	Charlotte Teske	2:29:33
⋮	⋮	⋮	⋮	⋮	⋮
2007	Robert Cheruiyot	2:14:13	2007	Lidiya Grigoryeva	2:29:18
2008	Robert Cheruiyot	2:07:46	2008	Dire Tune	2:25:25
2009	Deriba Marga	2:08:42	2009	Salina Kosgei	2:32:16

Source: www.boston.com/marathon/history.

14.20 (a) Plot the data on leisure and hospitality employment. (b) Describe the trend (if any) and discuss possible causes. (c) Fit the linear and exponential trends. Would these trend models give credible forecasts? Explain. (d) Make a forecast for 2008, using any method (including your own judgment). 📆 **Leisure**

Leisure and Hospitality Employment, 1998–2007 (thousands)

Year	Employees	Year	Employees	Year	Employees	Year	Employees
1998	11,232	2001	12,032	2004	12,495	2006	13,139
1999	11,544	2002	11,986	2005	12,814	2007	13,448
2000	11,860	2003	12,173				

Source: http://data.bls.gov.

14.21 (a) Plot the data on law enforcement officers killed. (b) Describe the trend (if any) and discuss possible causes. (c) Would a fitted trend be helpful? Explain. (c) Make a forecast for 2008 using any method you like (including judgment). 📆 **LawOfficers**

U.S. Law Enforcement Officers Killed, 1994–2007

Year	Killed	Year	Killed	Year	Killed	Year	Killed
1994	141	1998	142	2002	132	2005	122
1995	133	1999	107	2003	133	2006	114
1996	113	2000	134	2004	139	2007	140
1997	133	2001	218				

Source: *Statistical Abstract of the United States, 2009*, p. 200.

14.22 (a) Plot the data on lightning deaths. (b) Describe the trend (if any) and discuss possible causes. (c) Fit an exponential trend to the data. Interpret the fitted equation. (d) Make a forecast for 2010, using a trend model of your choice (or a judgment forecast). Explain the basis for your forecast. *Note:* Time is in 5-year increments, so use $t = 15$ for your 2010 forecast. 📆 **Lightning**

U.S. Lightning Deaths, 1940–2005

Year	Deaths	Year	Deaths	Year	Deaths	Year	Deaths
1940	340	1960	129	1980	74	1995	85
1945	268	1965	149	1985	74	2000	51
1950	219	1970	122	1990	74	2005	38
1955	181	1975	91				

Source: *Statistical Abstract of the United States, 2007*, p. 228 and www.nws.noaa.gov.

14.23 (a) Plot the data on skier/snowboard visits. (b) Would a fitted trend be helpful? Explain. (c) Make a forecast for 2007–2008, using a trend model of your choice (or a judgment forecast).
📂 **SnowBoards**

U.S. Skier/Snowboarder Visits, 1984–2007 (millions)

Season	Visits	Season	Visits	Season	Visits
1984–1985	51.354	1992–1993	54.032	2000–2001	57.337
1985–1986	51.921	1993–1994	54.637	2001–2002	54.411
1986–1987	53.749	1994–1995	52.677	2002–2003	57.594
1987–1988	53.908	1995–1996	53.983	2003–2004	57.067
1988–1989	53.335	1996–1997	52.520	2004–2005	56.882
1989–1990	50.020	1997–1998	54.122	2005–2006	58.897
1990–1991	46.722	1998–1999	52.089	2006–2007	55.068
1991–1992	50.835	1999–2000	52.198		

Source: www.nsaa.org/nsaa/press/industryStats.asp

14.24 (a) Plot both men's and women's winning times on the same graph. (b) Fit a linear trend model to each series (men, women). (c) Use Excel's option to forecast each trend graphically to 2040 (i.e., to period $t = 27$ periods, because observations are in 4-year increments). From these projections, does it appear that the times will eventually converge? *(d) Set the fitted trends equal, solve for x (the time period when the trends will cross), and convert x to a year. Is the result plausible? Explain. (e) Use the Web to check your 2004 and 2008 forecasts. 📂 **Olympic**

Summer Olympics 100-Meter Winning Times

Year	Men's 100-Meter Winner	Seconds	Women's 100-Meter Winner	Seconds
1928	Percy Williams, Canada	10.80	Elizabeth Robinson, United States	12.20
1932	Eddie Tolan, United States	10.30	Stella Walsh, Poland	11.90
1936	Jesse Owens, United States	10.30	Helen Stephens, United States	11.50
1948	Harrison Dillard, United States	10.30	Fanny Blankers-Koen, Netherlands	11.90
1952	Lindy Remigino, United States	10.40	Marjorie Jackson, United States	11.50
1956	Bobby Morrow, United States	10.50	Betty Cuthbert, Australia	11.50
1960	Armin Hary, West Germany	10.20	Wilma Rudolph, United States	11.00
1964	Bob Hayes, United States	10.00	Wyomia Tyus, United States	11.40
1968	Jim Hines, United States	9.95	Wyomia Tyus, United States	11.00
1972	Valery Borzov, USSR	10.14	Renate Stecher, East Germany	11.07
1976	Hasely Crawford, Trinidad	10.06	Annegret Richter, West Germany	11.08
1980	Allan Wells, Great Britain	10.25	Lyudmila Kondratyeva, USSR	11.06
1984	Carl Lewis, United States	9.99	Evelyn Ashford, United States	10.97
1988	Carl Lewis, United States	9.92	Florence Griffith-Joyner, United States	10.54
1992	Linford Christie, Great Britain	9.96	Gail Devers, United States	10.82
1996	Donovan Bailey, Canada	9.84	Gail Devers, United States	10.94
2000	Maurice Greene, United States	9.87	Marion Jones, United States	10.75

Source: Summer Olympics 100-meter times, *The World Almanac, 2002*, pp. 900–904.

14.25 (a) Plot U.S. petroleum imports on a graph. (b) Describe the trend (if any) and discuss possible causes. (c) Fit both a linear and an exponential trend. (c) Interpret each fitted trend equation, explaining the implications. (d) Make a projection for 2010. Do you believe it? (e) To whom is this issue relevant? *Note:* Time increments are 5 years, so use $t = 11$ for the 2010 forecast.
📂 **Petroleum**

U.S. Annual Petroleum Imports, 1960–2005 (billions of barrels)

Year	Imports	Year	Imports
1960	664	1985	1,850
1965	901	1990	2,926
1970	1,248	1995	3,225
1975	2,210	2000	4,194
1980	2,529	2005	4,937

Source: www.eia.doe.gov.

14.26 (a) Use Excel, MegaStat, or MINITAB to fit an m-period moving average to the exchange rate data shown below with $m = 2, 3, 4$, and 5 periods. Make a line chart. (b) Which value of m do you prefer? Why? (c) Is a moving average appropriate for this kind of data? Include a chart for each value of m. 🗐 **Sterling**

Daily Spot Exchange Rate, U.S. Dollars per Pound Sterling

Date	Rate	Date	Rate	Date	Rate
1-Apr-04	1.8564	21-Apr-04	1.7720	11-May-04	1.7544
2-Apr-04	1.8293	22-Apr-04	1.7684	12-May-04	1.7743
5-Apr-04	1.8140	23-Apr-04	1.7674	13-May-04	1.7584
6-Apr-04	1.8374	26-Apr-04	1.7857	14-May-04	1.7572
7-Apr-04	1.8410	27-Apr-04	1.7925	17-May-04	1.7695
8-Apr-04	1.8325	28-Apr-04	1.7720	18-May-04	1.7695
9-Apr-04	1.8322	29-Apr-04	1.7751	19-May-04	1.7827
12-Apr-04	1.8358	30-Apr-04	1.7744	20-May-04	1.7710
13-Apr-04	1.8160	3-May-04	1.7720	21-May-04	1.7880
14-Apr-04	1.7902	4-May-04	1.7907	24-May-04	1.7908
15-Apr-04	1.7785	5-May-04	1.7932	25-May-04	1.8135
16-Apr-04	1.8004	6-May-04	1.7941	26-May-04	1.8142
19-Apr-04	1.8055	7-May-04	1.7842	27-May-04	1.8369
20-Apr-04	1.7914	10-May-04	1.7723	28-May-04	1.8330

Source: Federal Reserve Board of Governors.

14.27 Refer to exercise 14.26. (a) Plot the dollar/pound exchange rate data. Make the graph nice, then copy and paste it so you have four copies. (b) Use MegaStat or MINITAB to perform a simple exponential smoothing using $\alpha = .05, .10, .20$, and $.50$, using a different line chart for each. (c) Which value of α do you prefer? Why? (d) Is an exponential smoothing process appropriate for this kind of data? 🗐 **Sterling**

14.28 (a) Plot the data on gas bills. (b) Can you see seasonal patterns? Explain. (c) Use MegaStat or MINITAB to calculate estimated seasonal indexes and trend. (d) Which months are the most expensive? The least expensive? Can you explain this pattern? (e) Is there a trend in the deseasonalized data? *(f) Use MegaStat or MINITAB to perform a regression using seasonal binaries. Interpret the results. 🗐 **GasBills**

Natural Gas Bills for a Residence, 2000–2003

Month	2000	2001	2002	2003
Jan	78.98	118.86	101.44	155.37
Feb	84.44	111.31	122.20	148.77
Mar	65.54	75.62	99.49	115.12
Apr	62.60	77.47	55.85	85.89
May	29.24	29.23	44.94	46.84
Jun	18.10	17.10	19.57	24.93
Jul	91.57	16.59	15.98	20.84
Aug	6.48	27.64	14.97	26.94
Sep	19.35	28.86	18.03	34.17
Oct	29.02	48.21	56.98	88.58
Nov	94.09	67.15	115.27	100.63
Dec	101.65	125.18	130.95	174.63

Source: Homeowner's records.

14.29 (a) Plot the data on air travel delays. (b) Can you see seasonal patterns? Explain. (c) Use MegaStat or MINITAB to calculate estimated seasonal indexes and trend. (d) Which months have the most permits? The fewest? Is this logical? (e) Is there a trend in the deseasonalized data? 🗐 **Delays**

U.S. Airspace Total System Delays, 2002–2006

Month	2002	2003	2004	2005	2006
Jan	14,158	16,159	28,104	32,121	29,463
Feb	13,821	18,260	32,274	30,176	24,705
Mar	20,020	25,387	34,001	34,633	37,218
Apr	24,027	17,474	32,459	25,887	35,132
May	28,533	26,544	50,800	30,920	40,669
Jun	33,770	27,413	52,121	48,922	48,096
Jul	32,304	32,833	46,894	58,471	47,606
Aug	29,056	37,066	43,770	45,328	46,547
Sep	24,493	28,882	30,412	32,949	48,092
Oct	25,266	21,422	37,271	34,221	51,053
Nov	17,712	34,116	35,234	34,273	43,482
Dec	22,489	31,332	32,446	29,766	39,797

Source: www.faa.gov.

14.30 (a) Plot the data on airplane shipments. (b) Can you see seasonal patterns? Explain. (c) Use MegaStat or MINITAB to calculate estimated seasonal indexes and trend. Is there a trend in the deseasonalized data? 📂 **AirplanesQtr**

U.S. Manufactured General Aviation Shipments, 1995–2003

Year	Qtr 1	Qtr 2	Qtr 3	Qtr 4	Total
1995	208	248	257	315	1,077
1996	229	284	230	310	1,115
1997	253	337	367	525	1,549
1998	481	486	546	602	2,200
1999	502	611	606	702	2,504
2000	613	704	685	712	2,816
2001	568	711	586	673	2,632
2002	442	576	510	641	2,207
2003	393	526	492	679	2,137

Note: Quarterly shipments may not add to annual total because some manufacturers report only annual totals.

Source: U.S. Manufactured General Aviation Shipments, *Statistical Databook 2003,* General Aviation Manufacturers Association, used with permission.

14.31 (a) Plot the data on revolving credit (credit cards and home equity lines of credit are the two major types of revolving credit). (b) Use MegaStat or MINITAB to calculate estimated seasonal indexes and trend. Is there a trend in the deseasonalized data? (c) Which months have the most borrowing? The least? Is this logical? 📂 **Revolving**

U.S. Consumers Revolving Credit (billions)

Month	2001	2002	2003	2004
Jan	223.2	232.5	240.6	276.7
Feb	221.5	229.7	239.7	272.8
Mar	220.1	230.2	234.0	268.3
Apr	227.7	235.6	235.4	270.6
May	229.1	233.1	240.4	278.0
Jun	225.7	231.0	240.7	275.6
Jul	222.1	229.9	238.6	278.7
Aug	219.6	241.1	240.7	286.4
Sep	216.3	243.1	239.9	286.7
Oct	223.3	242.4	235.8	286.1
Nov	233.2	244.2	269.5	285.8
Dec	238.3	250.2	284.7	315.8

Source: www.federalreserve.gov.

14.32 (a) In Excel, convert each time-series variable into index numbers (1990 = 100). (b) What is the 2004 index value for each time series? What does this tell you? (c) Plot all four series of index numbers on the same graph. Describe what you see. (d) What is the advantage of using index numbers in plotting and comparing these data over time? 📁 **Prisons**

U.S. Adults on Probation, in Jail or Prison, or on Parole, 1990–2004 (thousands)

Year	Probation	Jail	Prison	Parole
1990	2,670	403	743	531
1991	2,728	424	793	590
1992	2,812	442	851	659
1993	2,903	456	909	676
1994	2,981	480	990	690
1995	3,078	507	1,079	679
1996	3,165	510	1,128	680
1997	3,297	558	1,177	695
1998	3,670	584	1,224	696
1999	3,780	596	1,287	714
2000	3,826	621	1,316	724
2001	3,932	631	1,330	732
2002	4,024	665	1,368	751
2003	4,145	691	1,393	745
2004	4,151	714	1,422	765

Source: *Statistical Abstract of the United States, 2007*, p. 209.

14.33 (a) Plot the data on M1 money stock. (b) Use MegaStat or MINITAB to calculate estimated seasonal indexes and trend. Is there a trend in the deseasonalized data? (c) Make monthly forecasts for 2007. *Note:* M1 includes currency, travelers checks, demand deposits, and other checkable deposits. 📁 **MoneyStock**

U.S. Money Stock M1 Component, 2000–2006 ($ billions)

Month	2000	2001	2002	2003	2004	2005	2006
Jan	1,127	1,100	1,191	1,225	1,302	1,361	1,375
Feb	1,097	1,090	1,178	1,225	1,306	1,355	1,362
Mar	1,109	1,111	1,196	1,245	1,338	1,382	1,394
Apr	1,126	1,127	1,197	1,259	1,343	1,369	1,393
May	1,100	1,115	1,186	1,266	1,333	1,369	1,391
Jun	1,102	1,126	1,194	1,284	1,348	1,384	1,378
Jul	1,103	1,140	1,200	1,287	1,339	1,365	1,367
Aug	1,094	1,145	1,182	1,292	1,352	1,377	1,370
Sep	1,089	1,194	1,185	1,286	1,349	1,363	1,347
Oct	1,092	1,159	1,196	1,288	1,351	1,365	1,360
Nov	1,092	1,169	1,205	1,293	1,371	1,373	1,368
Dec	1,112	1,208	1,245	1,332	1,401	1,396	1,388

Source: Federal Reserve Board of Governors, www.federalreserve.gov. Data not seasonally adjusted.

14.34 (a) Use MegaStat or MINITAB to deseasonalize the quarterly data on Coca-Cola's revenues and fit a trend. Interpret the results. (b) Use MegaStat or MINITAB to perform a regression using seasonal binaries. Interpret the results. (c) Use the regression equation to make a prediction for each quarter in 2009. (d) If you have access to http://finance.yahoo.com, check your forecasts. How accurate were they? 📁 **CocaCola**

Coca-Cola Revenues ($ millions), 2003–2008

Quarter	2003	2004	2005	2006	2007	2008
Qtr1	4,502	5,078	5,206	5,226	6,103	7,379
Qtr2	5,695	5,965	6,310	6,476	7,733	9,046
Qtr3	5,671	5,622	6,037	6,454	7,690	8,393
Qtr4	5,176	5,257	5,551	5,932	7,331	7,126

Source: *Standard & Poor's Stock Reports*, March 2007, and http://finance.yahoo.com.

14.35 (a) Use MegaStat or MINITAB to perform a regression using seasonal binaries. Interpret the results. (b) Make monthly forecasts for 2006. If you can find data on the Web, check your forecasts.
📁 **StudentPilots**

Student Pilot Certificates Issued by Month, 2000–2005

Month	2000	2001	2002	2003	2004	2005
Jan	4,248	4,747	5,346	4,954	4,883	4,234
Feb	3,824	4,317	4,114	4,602	4,442	5,846
Mar	4,687	4,853	4,306	4,897	5,273	5,063
Apr	4,486	4,616	4,294	5,313	4,584	4,001
May	4,706	4,613	4,982	5,196	5,644	4,697
Jun	5,509	5,485	5,531	6,197	6,560	5,182
Jul	5,306	6,130	6,046	7,151	6,560	5,037
Aug	6,284	6,145	6,216	7,278	7,355	6,401
Sep	4,698	5,524	5,592	6,204	4,643	5,216
Oct	3,985	4,800	5,201	5,621	5,029	4,958
Nov	3,443	4,353	3,818	4,287	4,095	4,130
Dec	2,400	2,779	2,990	3,721	2,771	3,277

Source: www.faa.gov/data_statistics/aviation_data_statistics.

*14.36 Translate each of the following fitted exponential trend models into a compound interest model of the form $y_t = y_0(1 + r)^t$. *Hint:* See footnote on p. 605.

   a. $y_t = 456e^{.123t}$ b. $y_t = 228e^{.075t}$ c. $y_t = 456e^{-.038t}$

*14.37 Translate each of the following fitted compound interest trend models into an exponential model of the form $y_t = ae^{bt}$. *Hint:* See footnote on p. 605.

   a. $y_t = 123(1.089)^t$ b. $y_t = 654(1.217)^t$ c. $y_t = 308(.942)^t$

RELATED READING

DeLurgio, Stephen A. *Forecasting Principles and Applications*. Irwin/McGraw-Hill, 1998.

Diebold, Francis X. *Elements of Forecasting*. 3rd ed. South-Western, 2004.

Granger, C. W. J. *Forecasting in Business and Economics*. 2nd ed. Academic Press, 1989.

Hanke, John E., and Dean W. Wichern. *Business Forecasting*. 8th ed. Prentice-Hall, 2005.

Wilson, J. Holton, and Barry Keating. *Business Forecasting*. 4th ed. Irwin, 2002.

Makridakis, Spyros; Steven C. Wheelwright; and Rob J. Hyndman. *Forecasting: Methods and Applications*. 4th ed. Wiley, 2006.

CHAPTER 14   Online Learning Resources

The Online Learning Center (OLC) at www.mhhe.com/doane3e has several *LearningStats* demonstrations to help you understand time series analysis. Your instructor may assign one or more of them, or you may decide to download the ones that sound interesting.

Topic	LearningStats Demonstrations
Trends and forecasting	🔲 Trend Forecasting ❎ Exponential Smoothing ❎ Measures of Fit ❎ Exponential Trend Formula
Simulations	❎ Time-Series Components ❎ Trend Simulator ❎ Seasonal Time-Series Generator

Key: 🔲 = PowerPoint   📘 = Word   ❎ = Excel

Chi-Square Tests

Chapter Contents

Chapter Learning Objectives

When you finish this chapter you should be able to

LO1 Recognize a contingency table.

LO2 Find degrees of freedom and use the chi-square table of critical values.

LO3 Perform a chi-square test for independence on a contingency table.

LO4 Perform a goodness-of-fit (GOF) test for a uniform distribution.

LO5 Explain the GOF test for a Poisson distribution.

LO6 Use computer software to perform a chi-square GOF test for normality.

LO7 State advantages of ECDF tests as compared to chi-square GOF tests.

Not all information pertaining to business can be summarized numerically. We are often interested in answers to questions such as: Do employees in different age groups choose different types of health plans? Do consumers prefer red, yellow, or blue package lettering on our bread bags? Does the name of our new lawn mower influence how we perceive the quality? Answers to questions such as these are not measurements on a numerical scale. Rather, the variables that we are interested in learning about may be *categorical* or *ordinal*. Health plans are categorized by the way services are paid, so the variable *health plan* might have four different categories: Catastrophic, HMO (health maintenance organization), POS (point of service), and CDHP (consumer-driven health plan). The variable *package lettering color* would have categories red, yellow, and blue, and the variable *perceived quality* might have categories excellent, satisfactory, and poor.

We can collect observations on these variables to answer the types of questions posed either by surveying our customers and employees or by conducting carefully designed experiments. Once our data have been collected we summarize by tallying response frequencies on a table that we call a *contingency table*. A **contingency table** is a cross-tabulation of *n* paired observations into categories. Each cell shows the count of observations that fall into the category defined by its row and column heading.

15.1 CHI-SQUARE TEST FOR INDEPENDENCE

EXAMPLE

Web Pages(4 × 3 Table)

As online shopping has grown, opportunity has also grown for personal data collection and invasion of privacy. Mainstream online retailers have policies known as "privacy disclaimers" that define the rules regarding their uses of information collected, the customer's right to refuse third-party promotional offers, and so on. You can access these policies through a Web link, found either on the Web site's home page, on the order page (i.e., as you enter your credit card information), on a client Web page, or on some other Web page. In the United States, such links are voluntary, while in the European Union (EU) they are mandated by law. Location of the privacy disclaimer is considered to be a measure of the degree of consumer protection (the farther the link is from the home page, the less likely it is to be noticed). Marketing researchers did a survey of 291 Web sites in three nations (France, U.K., U.S.) and obtained the *contingency table* shown here as Table 15.1. Is location of the privacy disclaimer *independent* of the Web site's nationality? This question can be answered by using a test based on the frequencies in this contingency table.

TABLE 15.1   **Privacy Disclaimer Location and Web Site Nationality**   WebSites

| | Nationality of Web Site | | | |
Location of Disclaimer	France	U.K.	U.S.	Row Total
Home page	56	68	35	159
Order page	19	19	28	66
Client page	6	10	16	32
Other page	12	9	13	34
Col Total	93	106	92	291

Source: Calin Gurau, Ashok Ranchhod, and Claire Gauzente, "To Legislate or Not to Legislate: A Comparative Exploratory Study of Privacy/Personalisation Factors Affecting French, UK, and US Web Sites," *Journal of Consumer Marketing* 20, no. 7 (2003), p. 659. Used with permission, Emerald Group Publishing Limited.

LO1

Recognize a contingency table.

Table 15.2 illustrates the terminology of a contingency table. Variable A has r levels (rows) and variable B has c levels (columns) so we call this an $r \times c$ contingency table. Each cell shows the observed frequency f_{jk} in row j and column k.

TABLE 15.2

Table of Observed Frequencies

| | Variable B | | | | |
Variable A	1	2	. . .	c	Row Total
1	f_{11}	f_{12}	. . .	f_{1c}	R_1
2	f_{21}	f_{22}	. . .	f_{2c}	R_2
. . .	.	.	.	.	.
r	f_{r1}	f_{r2}	. . .	f_{rc}	R_r
Col Total	C_1	C_2	. . .	C_c	n

LO3

Perform a chi-square test for independence on a contingency table.

Chi-Square Test

In a test of independence for an $r \times c$ contingency table, the hypotheses are:

H_0: Variable A is independent of variable B

H_1: Variable A is not independent of variable B

To test these hypotheses, we use the **chi-square test** *for independence,* developed by Karl Pearson (1857–1936). It is a test based on *frequencies.* It measures the association between the two variables A and B in the contingency table. The chi-square test for independence is called a *distribution-free test* because it requires no assumptions about the shape of the populations from which the samples are drawn. The only operation performed is classifying the n data pairs into r rows (variable A) and c columns (variable B), and then comparing the **observed frequency** f_{jk} in each cell of the contingency table with the **expected frequency** e_{jk} under the assumption of independence. The chi-square test statistic measures the *relative* difference between expected and observed frequencies:

$$\chi^2_{calc} = \sum_{j=1}^{r} \sum_{k=1}^{c} \frac{[f_{jk} - e_{jk}]^2}{e_{jk}} \qquad \textbf{(15.1)}$$

If the two variables are **independent**, then f_{jk} should be close to e_{jk}, leading to a chi-square test statistic near zero. Conversely, large differences between f_{jk} and e_{jk} will lead to a large chi-square test statistic. The chi-square test statistic cannot be negative (due to squaring) so it is always a right-tailed test. If the test statistic is far enough in the right tail, we will reject the hypothesis of independence. Squaring each difference removes the sign, so it doesn't matter whether e_{jk} is greater than or less than f_{jk}. Each squared difference is expressed *relative to* e_{jk}.

Chi-Square Distribution

The test statistic is compared with a critical value from the **chi-square probability distribution**. It has one parameter called **degrees of freedom**. For the $r \times c$ contingency table, the degrees of freedom are:

$$d.f. = \text{degrees of freedom} = (r - 1)(c - 1) \qquad \textbf{(15.2)}$$

where

    r = the number of rows in the contingency table

    c = the number of columns in the contingency table

The parameter $d.f.$ is the number of non-redundant cells in the contingency table. There is a different chi-square distribution for each value of $d.f.$ Appendix E contains critical values for right-tail areas of the chi-square distribution. Its mean is $d.f.$ and its variance is $2d.f.$ As illustrated in Figure 15.1, all chi-square distributions are skewed to the right, but become more symmetric as $d.f.$ increases. For $d.f. = 1$ the distribution is discontinuous at the origin. As $d.f.$ increases the shape begins to resemble a normal, bell-shaped curve. However, for any contingency table you are likely to encounter, degrees of freedom will not be large enough to assume normality.

LO2

Find degrees of freedom and use the chi-square table of critical values.

FIGURE 15.1

Various Chi-Square Distributions

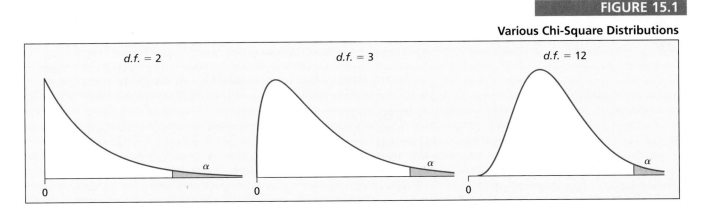

Expected Frequencies

Assuming that H_0 is true, the expected frequency of row j and column k is

$$e_{jk} = R_j C_k / n \qquad \text{(expected frequency in row } j \text{ and column } k) \qquad \textbf{(15.3)}$$

where

    R_j = total for row j $(j = 1, 2, \ldots, r)$

    C_k = total for column k $(k = 1, 2, \ldots, c)$

    n = sample size (or number of responses)

This formula for expected frequencies stems from the definition of independent events (see Chapter 5). When two events are independent, their *joint* probability is the product of their marginal probabilities, so for a cell in row j and column k the joint probability would be $(R_j/n)(C_k/n)$. To get the expected cell frequency, we multiply this joint probability by the sample size n to obtain $e_{jk} = R_j C_k/n$. The e_{jk} always sum to the same row and column frequencies as the observed frequencies. Expected frequencies will not, in general, be integers.

Illustration of the Chi-Square Calculations

We will illustrate the chi-square test by using the Web page frequencies from the contingency table (Table 15.1). We follow the usual five-step hypothesis testing procedure:

Step 1: State the Hypotheses   For the Web page example, the hypotheses are:

H_0: Privacy disclaimer location is independent of Web site nationality

H_1: Privacy disclaimer location is dependent on Web site nationality

Step 2: Specify the Decision Rule   For the Web page contingency table, we have $r = 4$ rows and $c = 3$ columns, so degrees of freedom are $d.f. = (r-1)(c-1) = (4-1)(3-1) = 6$. We will choose $\alpha = .05$ for the test. Figure 15.2 shows that the right-tail critical value from Appendix E with $d.f. = 6$ is $\chi^2_{.05} = 12.59$. This critical value could also be obtained from Excel using =CHIINV(.05,6) = 12.59159.

FIGURE 15.2

Critical Value of Chi-Square from Appendix E for *d.f.* = 6 and $\alpha = .05$

APPENDIX E

Example for *d.f.* = 6

.05

0   12.59

CHI-SQUARE CRITICAL VALUES

This table shows the critical value of chi-square for each desired tail area and degrees of freedom (*d.f.*).

						Area in Upper Tail				
d.f.	.995	.990	.975	.95	.90	.10	.05	.025	.01	.005
1	0.000	0.000	0.001	0.004	0.016	2.706	3.841	5.024	6.635	7.879
2	0.010	0.020	0.051	0.103	0.211	4.605	5.991	7.378	9.210	10.60
3	0.072	0.115	0.216	0.352	0.584	6.251	7.815	9.348	11.34	12.84
4	0.207	0.297	0.484	0.711	1.064	7.779	9.488	11.14	13.28	14.86
5	0.412	0.554	0.831	1.145	1.610	9.236	11.07	12.83	15.09	16.75
6	0.676	0.872	1.237	1.635	2.204	10.64	12.59	14.45	16.81	18.55
7	0.989	1.239	1.690	2.167	2.833	12.02	14.07	16.01	18.48	20.28
8	1.344	1.646	2.180	2.733	3.490	13.36	15.51	17.53	20.09	21.95
9	1.735	2.088	2.700	3.325	4.168	14.68	16.92	19.02	21.67	23.59
10	2.156	2.558	3.247	3.940	4.865	15.99	18.31	20.48	23.21	25.19
.	.	.	.	.	.	.	.	.	.	.
.	.	.	.	.	.	.	.	.	.	.
100	67.33	70.06	74.22	77.93	82.36	118.5	124.3	129.6	135.8	140.2

For $\alpha = .05$ in this right-tailed test, the decision rule is:

Reject H_0 if $\chi^2_{calc} > 12.59$

Otherwise do no reject H_0

The decision rule is illustrated in Figure 15.3.

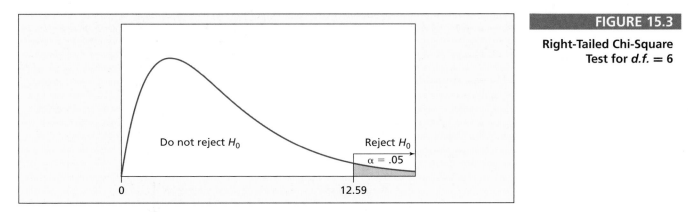

FIGURE 15.3

Right-Tailed Chi-Square Test for *d.f.* = 6

Step 3: Calculate the Expected Frequencies   The expected frequency in row j and column k is $e_{jk} = R_j C_k / n$. The calculations are illustrated in Table 15.3. The expected frequencies (lower part of Table 15.3) must sum to the same row and column frequencies at the observed frequencies (upper part of Table 15.3).

Observed and Expected Frequencies 🖅 WebSites				**TABLE 15.3**
Observed Frequencies				
Location	France	UK	USA	Row Total
Home	56	68	35	159
Order	19	19	28	66
Client	6	10	16	32
Other	12	9	13	34
Col Total	93	106	92	291
Expected Frequencies (assuming independence)				
Location	France	UK	USA	Row Total
Home	(159 × 93)/291 = 50.81	(159 × 106)/291 = 57.92	(159 × 92)/291 = 50.27	159
Order	(66 × 93)/291 = 21.09	(66 × 106)/291 = 24.04	(66 × 92)/291 = 20.87	66
Client	(32 × 93)/291 = 10.23	(32 × 106)/291 = 11.66	(32 × 92)/291 = 10.12	32
Other	(34 × 93)/291 = 10.87	(34 × 106)/291 = 12.38	(34 × 92)/291 = 10.75	34
Col Total	93	106	92	291

Step 4: Calculate the Test Statistic   The chi-square test statistic is

$$\chi^2_{calc} = \sum_{j=1}^{r} \sum_{k=1}^{c} \frac{[f_{jk} - e_{jk}]^2}{e_{jk}} = \frac{(56 - 50.81)^2}{50.81} + \cdots + \frac{(13 - 10.75)^2}{10.75}$$

$$= 0.53 + \cdots + 0.47 = 17.54$$

Even for this simple problem, the calculations are too lengthy to show in full. In fact, few would choose to do the calculations of the expected frequencies and chi-square test statistic without a spreadsheet. Fortunately, any statistical package will do a chi-square test. MegaStat's setup and output are shown in Figure 15.4. As you can see, MegaStat's calculations are arranged in a tabular form.

FIGURE 15.4

MegaStat's Chi-Square Test for Web Page Data

FIGURE 15.4

MegaStat's Chi-Square Test for Web Page Data

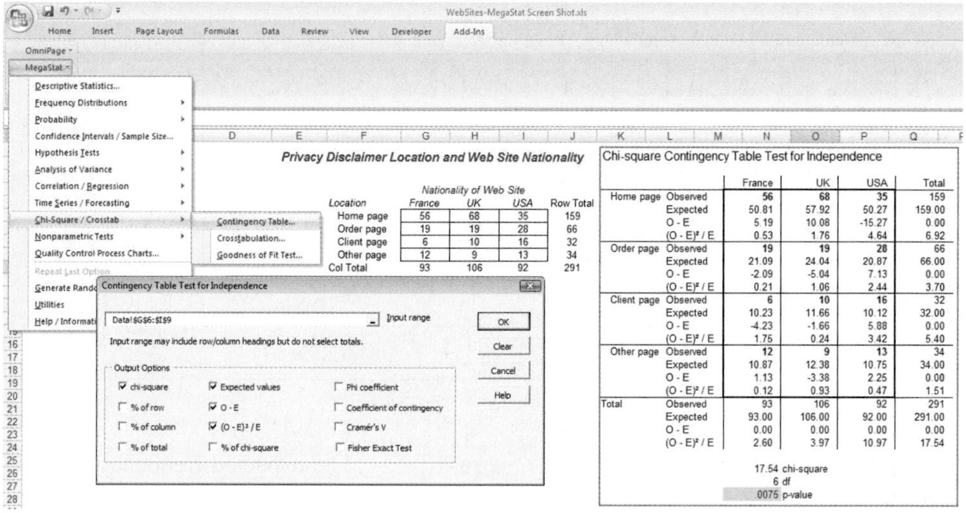

Step 5: Make the Decision Since the test statistic $\chi^2_{calc} = 17.54$ exceeds 12.59, we conclude that the observed differences between expected and observed frequencies differ significantly at $\alpha = .05$. The p-value (.0075) indicates that H_0 should be rejected at $\alpha = .05$. You can obtain this same p-value using Excel's function =CHIDIST(χ^2, $d.f.$) or in this case =CHIDIST(17.54,6), which gives a right-tail area of .0075. This p-value indicates that privacy disclaimer location is *not* independent of nationality at $\alpha = .05$, based on this sample of 291 Web sites.

Discussion MegaStat rounds things off for display purposes, though it maintains full internal accuracy in the calculations (as you must, if you do these calculations by hand). Differences between observed and expected frequencies O–E must sum to zero across each row and down each column. If you are doing these calculations by hand, check these sums (if they are not zero, you have made an error). From Figure 15.4 we see that only three cells (column 3, rows 1, 2, and 3) contribute a majority (4.64, 2.44, 3.42) of the chi-square sum (17.54). The hypothesis of independence fails largely because of these three cells.

EXAMPLE

*Night Flying
(2 × 2 Table)*

After the accident in which U.S. Senator John F. Kennedy, Jr., died while piloting his airplane at night from New York to Cape Cod, a random telephone poll was taken in which 409 New Yorkers were asked, "Should private pilots be allowed to fly at night without an instrument rating?" The same question was posed to 70 aviation experts. Results are shown in Table 15.4. The totals exclude those who had "No Opinion" (1 expert and 25 general public).

TABLE 15.4	Should Noninstrument Rated Pilots Fly at Night? 🖫 Pilots		
Opinion	*Experienced Pilots*	*General Public*	*Row Total*
Yes	40	61	101
No	29	323	352
Col Total	69	384	453

Source: Siena College Research Institute.

The hypotheses are:

H_0: Opinion is independent of aviation expertise

H_1: Opinion is not independent of aviation expertise

The test results from MegaStat are shown in Figure 15.5. Degrees of freedom are $d.f. = (r - 1)(c - 1) = (2 - 1)(2 - 1) = 1$. Appendix E shows that the critical value of chi-square for $\alpha = .005$ is 7.879. Since the test statistic $\chi^2 = 59.80$ greatly exceeds 7.879, we firmly reject the hypothesis. The p-value (.0000) confirms that opinion is *not* independent of aviation experience.

FIGURE 15.5   MegaStat Chi-Square Test with *d.f.* = 1

Chi-square Contingency Table Test for Independence

	Col 1	Col 2	Total
Row 1 Observed	**40**	**61**	101
Expected	15.38	85.62	101.00
O − E	24.62	−24.62	0.00
$(O − E)^2/E$	39.39	7.08	46.47
Row 2 Observed	**29**	**323**	352
Expected	53.62	298.38	352.00
O − E	−24.62	24.62	0.00
$(O − E)^2/E$	11.30	2.03	13.33
Total Observed	69	384	453
Expected	69.00	384.00	453.00
O − E	0.00	0.00	0.00
$(O − E)^2/E$	50.69	9.11	59.80

59.80	chi-square
1	df
1.05E-14	p-value
1.38E-12	Fisher Exact Probability

Test of Two Proportions

For a 2 × 2 contingency table, the chi-square test is equivalent to a two-tailed *z* test for two proportions, if the samples are large enough to ensure normality. The hypotheses are:

$$H_0: \pi_1 - \pi_2 = 0$$
$$H_1: \pi_1 - \pi_2 \neq 0$$

In the aviation survey example, the proportion of aviation experts who said yes on the survey is $p_1 = x_1/n_1 = 40/69 = .57971$, or 58.0 percent, compared to the proportion of the general public $p_2 = x_2/n_2 = 61/384 = .15885$, or 15.9 percent. The pooled proportion is $\bar{p} = (x_1 + x_2)/(n_1 + n_2) = 101/453 = .22296$. The *z* test statistic is then

$$z_{calc} = \frac{p_1 - p_2}{\sqrt{\bar{p}(1-\bar{p})\left(\frac{1}{n_1} + \frac{1}{n_2}\right)}} = \frac{.57971 - .15885}{\sqrt{.22296(1 - .22296)\left(\frac{1}{69} + \frac{1}{384}\right)}} = 7.7329$$

Using Excel's function =NORMSDIST(7.7329) we find the *p*-value =.0000. The square of the *z* test statistic for the two-tailed test of proportions is the same as the chi-square test statistic for the corresponding 2 × 2 contingency table. In the aviation example, $z^2 = 7.7329^2 = 59.80 = \chi^2$. Our conclusion is identical whether we used the chi-square test or the test for two proportions.

Small Expected Frequencies

The chi-square test is unreliable if the *expected* frequencies are too small. As you can see from the formula for the test statistic, when e_{jk} in the denominator is small, the chi-square statistic may be inflated. A commonly used rule of thumb known as **Cochran's Rule** requires that $e_{jk} > 5$ for all cells. Another rule of thumb says that up to 20 percent of the cells may have $e_{jk} < 5$. Statisticians generally become quite nervous when $e_{jk} < 2$, and there is agreement that a chi-square test is infeasible if $e_{jk} < 1$ in any cell. Computer packages may offer warnings or refuse to proceed when expected frequencies are too small. When this happens, it may be possible to salvage the test by combining adjacent rows or columns to enlarge the expected frequencies. In the Web page example, all the expected frequencies are safely greater than 5.

Cross-Tabulating Raw Data

Chi-square tests for independence are quite flexible. Although most often used with nominal data such as gender (male, female), we can also analyze quantitative variables (such as salary) by coding them into categories (e.g., under \$25,000; \$25,000 to \$50,000; \$50,000 and over). Open-ended classes are acceptable. We can mix data types as required (nominal, ordinal, interval, ratio) by defining the bins appropriately. Few statistical tests are so versatile. Continuous data may be classified into any categories that make sense. To tabulate a continuous variable into two classes, we would make the cut at the median. For three bins, we would use the 33rd and 67th percentiles as cutpoints. For four bins, we would use the 25th, 50th, and 75th percentiles as cutpoints. We prefer classes that yield approximately equal frequencies for each cell to help protect against small expected frequencies (recall that Cochran's Rule requires expected frequencies be at least 5). Our bin choices are limited when we have integer data with a small range (e.g., a Likert scale with responses 1, 2, 3, 4, 5), but we can still define classes however we wish (e.g., 1 or 2, 3, 4 or 5).

EXAMPLE

Doctors and Infant Mortality 🗁 **Doctors**

Let $X =$ doctors per 100,000 residents of a state, and $Y =$ infant deaths per 1,000 births in the state. We might reasonably hypothesize that states with more doctors relative to population would have lower infant mortality, but do they? We are reluctant to assume normality and equal variances, so we prefer to avoid a t test. Instead, we hypothesize:

H_0: Infant mortality rate is independent of doctors per 100,000 population

H_1: Infant mortality rate is not independent of doctors per 100,000 population

Depending on how we form the contingency table, we could get different results. Figure 15.6 shows 2×2 and 3×3 tables. Each table shows both actual and expected frequencies assuming the null hypothesis. Neither p-value indicates a very strong relationship. Since we cannot reject H_0 at these customary levels of significance, we conclude that doctors and infant mortality are not strongly related. A *multivariate* regression model might be the next step, to explore other predictors (e.g., per capita income, per capita Medicaid spending, percent of college graduates) that might be related to infant mortality in a state.

FIGURE 15.6

Two Cross-Tabulations of Same Raw Data

2 × 2 Table				
		Doctors per 100,000		
Infant Deaths per 1,000 Births		Low	High	Total
Low	Obs	**10**	**14**	24
	Exp	12.00	12.00	
High	Obs	**15**	**11**	26
	Exp	13.00	13.00	
Total		25	25	50

1.28 chi-square (*d.f.* = 1)
.2575 p-value

3 × 3 Table					
		Doctors per 100,000			
Infant Deaths per 1,000 Births		Low	Med	High	Total
Low	Obs	**4**	**6**	**6**	16
	Exp	5.44	5.44	5.12	
Med	Obs	**5**	**6**	**6**	17
	Exp	5.78	5.78	5.44	
High	Obs	**8**	**5**	**4**	17
	Exp	5.78	5.78	5.44	
Total		17	17	16	50

2.10 chi-square (*d.f.* = 4)
.7173 p-value

Why Do a Chi-Square Test on Numerical Data?

Why would anyone convert numerical data (X, Y) into categorical data in order to make a contingency table and do a chi-square test? Why not use the (X, Y) data to calculate a correlation coefficient or fit a regression? Here are three reasons:

- The researcher may believe there is a relationship between X and Y, but does not want to make an assumption about its form (linear, curvilinear, etc.) as required in a regression.

- There are outliers or other anomalies that prevent us from assuming that the data came from a normal population. Unlike correlation and regression, the chi-square test does *not* require any normality assumptions.

- The researcher has numerical data for one variable but not the other. A chi-square test can be used if we convert the numerical variable into categories.

3-Way Tables and Higher

There is no conceptual reason to limit ourselves to two-way contingency tables comparing two variables. However, such tables become rather hard to visualize, even when they are "sliced" into a series of 2-way tables. A table comparing three variables can be visualized as a *cube* or as a stack of tiled 2-way contingency tables. Major computer packages (SAS, SPSS, and others) permit 3-way contingency tables. For four or more variables, there is no physical analog to aid us, and their cumbersome nature would suggest analytical methods other than chi-square tests.

Instructions: For each exercise, include MegaStat or Excel exhibits to support your chi-square calculations. (a) State the hypotheses. (b) Show how the degrees of freedom are calculated for the contingency table. (c) Using the level of significance specified in the exercise, find the critical value of chi-square from Appendix E or from Excel's function =CHIINV(alpha, deg_freedom). (d) Carry out the calculations for a chi-square test for independence and draw a conclusion. (e) Which cells of the contingency table contribute the most to the chi-square test statistic? (f) Are any of the expected frequencies too small? (g) Interpret the *p*-value. If necessary, you can calculate the *p*-value using Excel's function =CHIDIST(test statistic, deg_freedom). *(h) If it is a 2 × 2 table, perform a two-tailed two-sample *z* test for $\pi_1 = \pi_2$ and verify that z^2 is the same as your chi-square statistic. *Note:* Exercises marked with an asterisk (*) are more difficult.

SECTION EXERCISES

connect

15.1 In a study of how managers attempt to manage earnings, researchers analyzed a sample of 515 earnings-management attempts from a survey of experienced auditors. The frequency of effects is summarized in the table shown. *Research question:* At $\alpha = .01$, is the effect on earnings independent of the approach used? (Data are from Mark W. Nelson, John A. Elliott, and Robin L. Tarpley, "How Are Earnings Managed? Examples from Auditors," *Accounting Horizons,* Supplement, 2003, pp. 17–35.) 🗁 **Earnings**

Current-Period Income Effect of Four Earnings Management Approaches

Approach Used	Increase	Decrease	No Clear Effect	Row Total
Expenses and Other Losses	133	113	23	269
Revenue and Other Gains	86	20	8	114
Business Combinations	12	22	33	67
Other Approaches	41	4	20	65
Col Total	272	159	84	515

15.2 Teenagers make up a large percentage of the market for clothing. Below are data on running shoe ownership in four world regions (excluding China). *Research question:* At $\alpha = .01$, does this sample show that running shoe ownership depends on world region? (See J. Paul Peter and Jerry C. Olson, *Consumer Behavior and Marketing Strategy,* 9th ed. [McGraw-Hill, 2004], p. 64.) 🗁 **Running**

Running Shoe Ownership in World Regions

Owned By	U.S.	Europe	Asia	Latin America	Row Total
Teens	80	89	69	65	303
Adults	20	11	31	35	97
Col Total	100	100	100	100	400

15.3 Students applying for admission to an MBA program must submit scores from the GMAT test, which includes a verbal and a quantitative component. Shown here are raw scores for 100 randomly chosen MBA applicants at a Midwestern, public, AACSB-accredited business school. *Research question:* At $\alpha = .005$, is the quantitative score independent of the verbal score? 📷 **GMAT**

Verbal	Quantitative			Row Total
	Under 25	25 to 35	35 or More	
Under 25	25	9	1	35
25 to 35	4	28	18	50
35 or More	1	3	11	15
Col Total	30	40	30	100

15.4 Computer abuse by employees is an ongoing worry to businesses. A study revealed the data shown below. *Research question:* At $\alpha = .01$, is the frequency of disciplinary action independent of the abuser's level of privilege? (Data are from Detmar W. Straub and William D. Nance, "Discovering and Disciplining Computer Abuse in Organizations," *MIS Quarterly* 14, no. 1 [March 1990], pp. 45–60.) 📷 **Abuse**

Computer Abuse Incidents Cross-Tabulated by Privilege and Punishment

Level of Privilege	Disciplined	Not Disciplined	Row Total
Low	20	11	31
Medium	42	3	45
High	33	3	36
Col Total	95	17	112

15.5 Marketing researchers prepared an advance notification card announcing an upcoming mail survey and describing the purpose of their research. Half the target customers received the prenotification, followed by the survey. The other half received only the survey. The survey return rates are shown below. *Research question:* At $\alpha = .025$, is return rate independent of prenotification? (Data are from Paul R. Murphy, Douglas R. Dalenberg, and James M. Daley, "Improving Survey Responses with Postcards," *Industrial Marketing Management* 19, no. 4 [November 1990], pp. 349–355.) 📷 **Advance**

Cross-Tabulation of Returns by Notification

Pre-Notified?	Returned	Not Returned	Row Total
Yes	39	155	194
No	22	170	192
Col Total	61	325	386

Mini Case 15.1

Student Work and Car Age

Do students work longer hours to pay for newer cars? This hypothesis was tested using data from a 2001 survey of introductory business statistics students at a large commuter university campus. The survey contained these two fill-in-the-blank questions:

About how many hours per week do you expect to work at an outside job this semester?

What is the age (in years) of the car you usually drive?

The contingency table shown in Table 15.5 summarizes the responses of 162 students. Very few students worked less than 15 hours, and a majority worked 25 hours or more. Most drove cars less than 3 years old, although a few drove cars 10 years old or more. Neither

TABLE 15.5   **Frequency Classification for Work Hours and Car Age**   CarAge

Hours of Outside Work Per Week	Age of Car Usually Driven				Row Total
	Less than 3	3 to 6	6 to 10	10 or More	
Under 15	9	8	8	4	29
15 to 25	34	17	11	9	71
25 or More	28	20	8	6	62
Col Total	71	45	27	19	162

variable was normally distributed (and there were outliers) so a chi-square test was preferable to a correlation or regression model. The hypotheses to be tested are:

H_0: Car age is independent of work hours

H_1: Car age is not independent of work hours

Figure 15.7 shows MegaStat's analysis of the 3 × 4 contingency table. Two expected frequencies (upper right) are below 5, so Cochran's Rule is not quite met. MegaStat has highlighted these cells to call attention to this concern. But the most striking feature of this table is that almost all of the actual frequencies are very close to the frequencies expected under the hypothesis of independence, leading to a very small chi-square test statistic (5.24). The test requires six degrees of freedom, i.e. $(r - 1)(c - 1) = (3 - 1)(4 - 1) = 6$. From Appendix E we obtain the right-tail critical value $\chi^2_{.10} = 10.64$ at $\alpha = .10$. Even at this rather weak level of significance, we cannot reject H_0. MegaStat's p-value (.5132) says that a test statistic of this magnitude could arise by chance more than half the time in samples from a population in which the two variables really were independent. Hence, the data lend no support to the hypothesis that students work longer hours to support newer cars.

FIGURE 15.7   **MegaStat's Analysis of Car Age Data**

Chi-square Contingency Table Test for Independence

		Less than 3	3 to 6	6 to 10	10 or More	Total
Under 15	Observed	**9**	**8**	**8**	**4**	29
	Expected	12.71	8.06	4.83	3.40	29.00
	O − E	−3.71	−0.06	3.17	0.60	0.00
	$(O - E)^2/E$	1.08	0.00	2.07	0.11	3.26
15 to 25	Observed	**34**	**17**	**11**	**9**	71
	Expected	31.12	19.72	11.83	8.33	71.00
	O − E	2.88	−2.72	−0.83	0.67	0.00
	$(O - E)^2/E$	0.27	0.38	0.06	0.05	0.76
25 or More	Observed	**28**	**20**	**8**	**6**	62
	Expected	27.17	17.22	10.33	7.27	62.00
	O − E	0.83	2.78	−2.33	−1.27	0.00
	$(O - E)^2/E$	0.03	0.45	0.53	0.22	1.22
Total	Observed	71	45	27	19	162
	Expected	71.00	45.00	27.00	19.00	162.00
	O − E	0.00	0.00	0.00	0.00	0.00
	$(O - E)^2/E$	1.38	0.82	2.66	0.38	5.24

5.24   chi-square
6   df
.5132   p-value

15.2

CHI-SQUARE TESTS FOR GOODNESS-OF-FIT

Purpose of the Test

A **goodness-of-fit test** (or GOF test) is used to help you decide whether your sample resembles a particular kind of population. The chi-square test can be used to compare sample frequencies with any probability distribution. Tests for goodness-of-fit are easy to understand, but until spreadsheets came along, the calculations were tedious. Today, computers make it easy, and tests for departure from normality or any other distribution are routine. We will first illustrate the GOF test using a general type of distribution. A **multinomial distribution** is defined by any k probabilities $\pi_1, \pi_2, \ldots, \pi_k$ that sum to one. You can apply this same technique for the three familiar distributions we have already studied (uniform, Poisson, and normal). Although there are many tests for goodness-of-fit, the chi-square test is attractive because it is versatile and easy to understand.

Multinomial GOF Test: M&M Colors

According to the "official" M&M Web site* the distribution of M&M colors is:

Brown (13%)	Red (13%)	Blue (24%)
Orange (20%)	Yellow (16%)	Green (14%)

But do bags of M&Ms shipped to retailers actually follow this distribution? We will use a sample of four bags of candy and conduct a chi-square GOF test. We will assume the distribution is the same as stated on the Web site *unless the sample shows us otherwise.*

Hypotheses

The hypotheses are:

H_0: $\pi_{brown} = .13$, $\pi_{red} = .13$, $\pi_{blue} = .24$, $\pi_{orange} = .20$, $\pi_{yellow} = .16$, $\pi_{green} = .14$

H_1: At least one of the π's differs from the hypothesized value

To test these hypotheses, statistics students opened four bags of M&Ms ($n = 220$ pieces) and counted the number of each color, with the results shown in Table 15.6. We assign an index to each of the six colors ($j = 1, 2, \ldots, 6$) and define:

f_j = the actual frequency of M&Ms of color j

e_j = the expected frequency of M&Ms of color j assuming that H_0 is true

Each expected frequency (e_j) is calculated by multiplying the sample size (n) by the hypothesized proportion (π_j). We can now calculate a chi-square test statistic that compares the actual and expected frequencies:

(15.4)
$$\chi^2_{calc} = \sum_{j=1}^{c} \frac{[f_j - e_j]^2}{e_j}$$

TABLE 15.6

Hypothesis Test of M&M Proportions
  MM

Color	Official π_j	Observed f_j	Expected $e_j = n \times \pi_j$	$f_j - e_j$	$(f_j - e_j)^2/e_j$
Brown	0.13	38	28.6	+9.4	3.0895
Red	0.13	30	28.6	+1.4	0.0685
Blue	0.24	44	52.8	−8.8	1.4667
Orange	0.20	52	44.0	+8.0	1.4545
Green	0.16	30	35.2	−5.2	0.7682
Yellow	0.14	26	30.8	−4.8	0.7481
Sum	1.00	220	220.0	0.0	$\chi^2_{calc} = 7.5955$

*The official Web site for M&M candies is http://us.mms.com/. These proportions were taken from their Web site during June 2006.

If the proposed distribution gives a good fit to the sample, the chi-square statistic will be near zero because f_j and e_j will be approximately equal. Conversely, if f_j and e_j differ greatly, the chi-square statistic will be large. It is always a right-tail test. We will reject H_0 if the test statistic exceeds the chi-square critical value chosen from Appendix E. For any GOF test, the rule for degrees of freedom is:

$$d.f. = c - m - 1 \qquad\qquad (15.5)$$

where c is the number of classes used in the test and m is the number of parameters estimated.

Results of the Test

Table 15.6 summarizes the calculations in a worksheet. No parameters were estimated ($m = 0$) and we have six classes ($c = 6$), so degrees of freedom are:

$$d.f. = c - m - 1 = 6 - 0 - 1 = 5$$

From Appendix E, the critical value of chi-square for $\alpha = .01$ is $\chi^2_{.01} = 15.09$. Since the test statistic $\chi^2_{calc} = 7.5955$ (from Table 15.6) is smaller than the critical value, we cannot reject the hypothesis that the M&M's color distribution is as stated on the M&M Web site. Notice that the f_j and e_j *always* sum exactly to the sample size ($n = 220$ in this example) and the differences $f_j - e_j$ must sum to zero. If not, you have made a mistake in your calculations—a useful way to check your work.

Small Expected Frequencies

Goodness-of-fit tests may lack power in small samples. Further, small expected frequencies tend to inflate the χ^2 test statistic because e_j is in the denominator of formula 15.4. The minimum necessary sample size depends on the type of test being employed. As a guideline, a chi-square goodness-of-fit test should be avoided if $n < 25$ (some experts would suggest a higher number). Cochran's Rule that expected frequencies should be at least 5 (i.e., all $e_j \geq 5$) also provides a guideline, although some experts would weaken the rule to require only $e_j \geq 2$. In the M&M example, the expected frequencies are all large, so there is no reason to doubt the test.

GOF Tests for Other Distributions

We can also use the chi-square GOF test to compare a sample of data with a familiar distribution such as the uniform, Poisson, or normal. We would state the hypotheses as below:

> H_0: The population follows a _____ distribution.
>
> H_1: The population doesn't follow a _____ distribution.

The blank may contain the name of any theoretical distribution. Assuming that we have n observations, we group the observations into c classes and then find the *chi-square test statistic* using formula 15.4. In a GOF test, if we use sample data to *estimate* the distribution's parameters then our degrees of freedom would be as follows:

Uniform: $d.f. = c - m - 1 = c - 0 - 1 = c - 1$ (no parameters are estimated)   **(15.6)**

Poisson: $d.f. = c - m - 1 = c - 1 - 1 = c - 2$ (if λ is estimated)   **(15.7)**

Normal: $d.f. = c - m - 1 = c - 2 - 1 = c - 3$ (if μ and σ are estimated)   **(15.8)**

Data-Generating Situations

"Fishing" for a good-fitting model is inappropriate. Instead, we visualize *a priori* the characteristics of the underlying *data-generating process*. It is undoubtedly true that the most common GOF test is for the normal distribution, simply because so many parametric tests assume normality, and that assumption must be tested. Also, the normal distribution may be used as a default benchmark for any mound-shaped data that has centrality and tapering tails, as long as you have reason to believe that a constant mean and variance would be reasonable (e.g., weights of circulated dimes). However, you would not consider a Poisson distribution for continuous data (e.g., gasoline price per liter) or certain integer variables (e.g., exam scores) because a Poisson model only applies to integer data on arrivals or rare, independent events (e.g., number of paint defects per square meter). We remind you of this because software makes it possible to fit inappropriate distributions all too easily.

Mixtures: A Problem

Your sample may not resemble any known distribution. One common problem is *mixtures*. A sample may have been created by more than one data-generating process superimposed on top of one another. For example, adult heights of either sex would follow a normal distribution, but a combined sample of both genders will be bimodal, and its mean and standard deviation may be unrepresentative of either sex. Obtaining a good fit is not *per se* sufficient justification for assuming a particular model. Each probability distribution has its own logic about the nature of the underlying process, so we must also examine the data-generating situation and be convinced that the proposed model is both logical *and* empirically apt.

Eyeball Tests

A simple "eyeball" inspection of the histogram or dot plot may suffice to rule out a hypothesized population. For example, if the sample is strongly bimodal or skewed, or if outliers are present, we would anticipate a poor fit to a normal distribution. The shape of the histogram can give you a rough idea whether a normal distribution is a likely candidate for a good fit. You can be fairly sure that a formal test will agree with what your common sense tells you, as long as the sample size is not too small.

Yet a limitation of eyeball tests is that we may be unsure just how much variation is expected for a given sample size. If anything, the human eye is overly sensitive, causing us to commit α error (rejecting a true null hypothesis) too often. People are sometimes unduly impressed by a small departure from the hypothesized distribution, when actually it is within chance. We will see examples of this.

15.3 UNIFORM GOODNESS-OF-FIT TEST

The uniform goodness-of-fit test is a special case of the multinomial in which every value has the same chance of occurrence. Uniform data-generating situations are rare, but some data *must* be from a **uniform distribution**, such as winning lottery numbers or random digits generated by a computer for random sampling. Another use of the uniform distribution is as a worst case scenario for an unknown distribution whose range is specified in a what-if analysis.

The chi-square test for a uniform distribution is a generalization of the test for equality of two proportions. The hypotheses are:

H_0: $\pi_1 = \pi_2 = \cdots = \pi_c = 1/c$

H_1: Not all the π_j are equal

LO4

Perform a goodness-of-fit (GOF) test for a uniform distribution.

The chi-square test compares all c groups *simultaneously*. Each discrete outcome should have probability $1/c$, so the test is very easy to perform. Evidence against H_0 would consist of sample frequencies that were not the same for all categories.

Classes need not represent numerical values. For example, we might compare the total number of items scanned per hour by four supermarket checkers (Bob, Frieda, Sam, and Wanda). The uniform test is quite versatile. For numerical variables, bins do not have to be of equal width and can be open-ended. For example, we might be interested in the ages of X-ray machines in a hospital (under 2 years, 2 to 5 years, 5 to 10 years, 10 years and over). In a uniform population, each category would be expected to have $e_j = n/c$ observations, so the calculation of expected frequencies is simple.

Uniform GOF Test: Grouped Data

The test is easiest if data are already tabulated into groups, which saves us the effort of defining the groups. For example, one year, a certain state had 756 traffic fatalities. Table 15.7 suggests that fatalities are not uniformly distributed by day of week, being higher on weekends. Can we reject the hypothesis of a uniform distribution, say, at $\alpha = .005$? The hypotheses are:

H_0: Traffic fatalities are uniformly distributed by day of the week

H_1: Traffic fatalities are not uniformly distributed by day of the week

Day	f_j	e_j	$f_j - e_j$	$(f_j - e_j)^2$	$(f_j - e_j)^2/e_j$
Sun	121	108	13	169	1.565
Mon	96	108	−12	144	1.333
Tue	91	108	−17	289	2.676
Wed	92	108	−16	256	2.370
Thu	96	108	−12	144	1.333
Fri	122	108	14	196	1.815
Sat	138	108	30	900	8.333
Total	756	756	0		$\chi^2_{calc} = 19.426$

Source: Based on www-nrd.nhtsa.dot.gov.

TABLE 15.7

Traffic Fatalities by Day of Week 🖾 **Traffic**

Under H_0 the expected frequency for each weekday is $e_j = n/c = 756/7 = 108$. The expected frequencies happen to be integers, although this is not true in general. Since no parameters were estimated ($m = 0$) to form the seven classes ($c = 7$) the chi-square test will have $d.f. = c - m - 1 = 7 - 0 - 1 = 6$ degrees of freedom. From Appendix E the critical value of chi-square for the 1 percent level of significance is $\chi^2_{.01} = 16.81$, so the hypothesis of a rectangular or uniform population can be rejected. The p-value (.0035) can be obtained from the Excel function =CHIDIST(19.426,6). The p-value tells us that such a sample result would occur by chance only about 35 times in 10,000 samples. There is a believable underlying causal mechanism at work (e.g., people may drink and drive more often on weekends).

Uniform GOF Test: Raw Data

When we are using raw data, we must form c bins of equal width and create our own frequency distribution. For example, suppose an auditor is checking the fairness of a state's "Daily 3" lottery. Table 15.8 shows winning three-digit lottery numbers for 100 consecutive days. All numbers from 000 to 999 are supposed to be equally likely, so the auditor is testing these hypotheses:

H_0: Lottery numbers are uniformly distributed
H_1: Lottery numbers are not uniformly distributed

TABLE 15.8

100 Consecutive Winning Three-Digit Lottery Numbers 🖾 **Lottery-A**

367	865	438	437	596	567	121	244	036	337
152	260	470	821	452	606	417	674	786	311
739	611	359	739	184	229	418	565	547	403
103	344	303	531	054	496	167	550	403	785
341	237	913	991	656	661	178	983	431	472
315	792	676	299	738	080	450	991	673	846
500	001	016	581	154	677	457	617	261	807
452	048	052	018	037	517	760	522	711	898
294	605	135	333	886	257	533	119	882	899
814	490	490	885	329	033	033	707	551	651

We know that three-digit lottery numbers must lie in the range 000 to 999, so there are many ways we could define our classes (e.g., 5 bins of width 200, 10 bins of width 100, 20 bins of width 50). We will use 10 bins, with the realization that we might get a different result if we chose different bins. The steps are:

- Step 1   Divide the range into 10 bins of equal width.
- Step 2   Calculate the observed frequency f_j for each bin.
- Step 3   Define $e_j = n/c = 100/10 = 10$.
- Step 4   Perform the chi-square calculations (see Table 15.9).
- Step 5   Make the decision.

TABLE 15.9

Uniform GOF Test for Lottery Numbers

Bin	f_j	e_j	$f_j - e_j$	$(f_j - e_j)^2$	$(f_j - e_j)^2/e_j$
0 < 100	11	10	1	1	0.100
100 < 200	9	10	−1	1	0.100
200 < 300	8	10	−2	4	0.400
300 < 400	10	10	0	0	0.000
400 < 500	16	10	6	36	3.600
500 < 600	12	10	2	4	0.400
600 < 700	11	10	1	1	0.100
700 < 800	9	10	−1	1	0.100
800 < 900	10	10	0	0	0.000
900 < 1,000	4	10	−6	36	3.600
Total	100	100	0		$\chi^2_{calc} = 8.400$

Since no parameters were estimated ($m = 0$) to form the 10 classes ($c = 10$) we have $d.f. = c - m - 1 = 10 - 0 - 1 = 9$ degrees of freedom. From Appendix E the critical value of chi-square for the 10 percent level of significance is $\chi^2_{.10} = 14.684$. Since the test statistic is 8.400, the hypothesis of a uniform distribution cannot be rejected.

If the bin limits cannot be set using *a priori* knowledge (as was possible in the lottery example), we maximize the test's power by defining bin width as the range divided by the number of classes:

(15.9) $\text{Bin width} = \dfrac{x_{max} - x_{min}}{c}$ (setting bin width from sample data)

The resulting bin limits may not be aesthetically pleasing, but the expected frequencies will be as large as possible (you might be able to round the bin limits to a "nice" number without affecting the calculations very much). If the sample size is small, small expected frequencies could be a problem. Since all expected frequencies are the same in a uniform model, this problem will exist in all classes simultaneously. For example, we could not classify 25 observations into 10 classes without violating Cochran's Rule (although the more relaxed rule $e_j \geq 2$ would be satisfied).

FIGURE 15.8

Ten-Bin Histogram

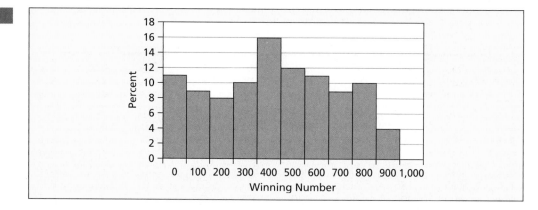

The histograms in Figures 15.8 and 15.9 suggest too many winning lottery numbers in the middle and too few at the top. But histogram appearance is affected by the way we define our bins and the number of classes, so the chi-square test is a more reliable guide. Humans are adept at finding patterns in sample distributions that actually are within the realm of chance.

As you learned in Chapter 6, a discrete uniform distribution $U(a, b)$ is symmetric with mean $\mu = (a + b)/2$ and $\sigma = \sqrt{[(b - a + 1)^2 - 1]/12}$. For the lottery, we have $a = 000$ and $b = 999$, so we expect the mean to be $\mu = (0 + 999)/2 = 499.5$ and $\sigma = \sqrt{[(999 - 0 + 1)^2 - 1]/12} = 288.7$. For the sample, Table 15.10 shows that the low (001) and high (991) are near their theoretical values, as are the sample mean (472.2), standard deviation (271.0), and skewness coefficient (.01). The first quartile (260.5) is close to its expected value (.25 × 999 = 249.8), while the third quartile (675.5) is smaller than expected (.75 × 999 = 749.3).

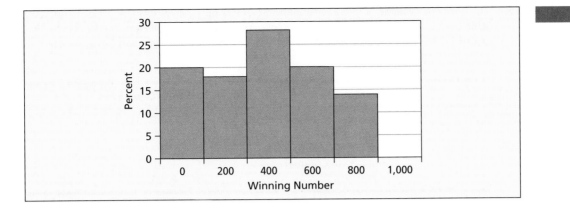

FIGURE 15.9

Five-Bin Histogram

TABLE 15.10

Descriptive Statistics
🖘 **Lottery-A**

Statistic	Sample	If Uniform
Minimum	001	000
Maximum	991	999
Mean	472.2	499.5
Median	471.0	499.5
Standard Deviation	271.0	288.7
Quartile 1	260.5	249.8
Quartile 3	675.5	749.3
Skewness	0.01	0.00

Since the data are not skewed (mean ≈ median) and the sample size is large ($n \geq 30$), the mean is approximately normally distributed, so we can use the normal distribution to test the sample mean for a significant difference from the hypothesized uniform mean, assuming that $\sigma = 288.7$ as would be true if the data were uniform:

$$z = \frac{\bar{x} - \mu}{\frac{\sigma}{\sqrt{n}}} = \frac{472.2 - 499.5}{\frac{288.7}{\sqrt{100}}} = -0.95 \qquad \text{(two-tail } p\text{-value} = .34)$$

The difference is not significant at any common level of α. Overall, these statistics show no convincing evidence of departure from a uniform distribution, thereby confirming the chi-square test's conclusion i.e., the lottery is fair.

SECTION EXERCISES

connect

15.6 Advertisers need to know which age groups are likely to see their ads. Purchasers of 120 copies of *Cosmopolitan* are shown by age group. (a) Make a bar chart and describe it. (b) Calculate expected frequencies for each class. (c) Perform the chi-square test for a uniform distribution. At $\alpha = .01$, does this sample contradict the assumption that readership is uniformly distributed among these six age groups? (See J. Paul Peter and Jerry C. Olson, *Consumer Behavior and Marketing Strategy,* 9th ed. [McGraw-Hill, 2004], p. 300.) 🖘 **Cosmo**

Purchaser Age	Units Sold
18–24	38
25–34	28
35–44	19
45–54	16
55–64	10
65+	9
Total	120

15.7 One-year sales volume of four similar 20-oz. beverages on a college campus is shown. (a) Make a bar chart and describe it. (b) Calculate expected frequencies for each class. (c) Perform the chi-square test for a uniform distribution. At $\alpha = .05$, does this sample contradict the assumption that sales are the same for each beverage? 📀 **Frapp**

Beverage	Sales (Cases)
Frappuccino Coffee	18
Frappuccino Mocha	23
Frappuccino Vanilla	23
Frappuccino Caramel	20
Total	84

15.8 In a three-digit lottery, each of the three digits is supposed to have the same probability of occurrence (counting initial blanks as zeros, e.g., 32 is treated as 032). The table shows the frequency of occurrence of each digit for 90 consecutive daily three-digit drawings. (a) Make a bar chart and describe it. (b) Calculate expected frequencies for each class. (c) Perform the chi-square test for a uniform distribution. At $\alpha = .05$, can you reject the hypothesis that the digits are from a uniform population? 📀 **Lottery3**

Digit	Frequency
0	33
1	17
2	25
3	30
4	31
5	28
6	24
7	25
8	32
9	25
Total	270

15.9 Ages of 56 attendees of a Harry Potter movie are shown. (a) Form seven age classes (10 to 20, 20 to 30, etc.). Tabulate the frequency of attendees in each class. (b) Calculate expected frequencies for each class. (c) Perform a chi-square GOF test for a uniform distribution, using the 5 percent level of significance. 📀 **Harry**

10	22	58	11	73	22	57
35	33	33	59	54	55	75
79	24	13	73	52	69	30
71	64	17	50	72	67	50
72	35	26	59	47	65	35
64	34	39	66	37	41	58
51	43	29	74	73	50	62
58	34	50	27	13	67	67

15.4 POISSON GOODNESS-OF-FIT TEST

Poisson Data-Generating Situations

In a **Poisson distribution** model, X represents the number of events per unit of time or space. By definition, X is a discrete nonnegative random variable with integer values (0, 1, 2, . . .). Event arrivals must be independent of one another. Events that tend to fit this definition might include customer arrivals per minute at an ATM, calls per minute at Ticketmaster, or alarms per hour at a fire station. In such cases, the mean arrival rate would vary by time of day, day of the week, and so on. The Poisson has been demonstrated to apply to scores in some sports events (goals scored per soccer game, goals in hockey games) and to defects in manufactured components such as LCDs, printed circuits, and automobile paint jobs. Typically X has a fairly small mean, which is why the Poisson is sometimes called a model of *rare events*. If the mean is large, we might fit a normal distribution instead. Poisson random number generators are used by researchers who model queues, an important application in dense urban cultures. The Poisson distribution is inappropriate for noninteger data or financial data such as you would find in company annual reports. Remembering these facts can spare you from wasted time trying to fit a Poisson model when it is inappropriate.

Poisson Goodness-of-Fit Test

A Poisson model is completely described by its one parameter, the mean λ. Assuming that λ is unknown and must be estimated from the sample, the initial steps are:

- Step 1   Tally the observed frequency f_j of each x-value.
- Step 2   Estimate the mean λ from the sample.
- Step 3   Use the estimated λ to find the Poisson probability $P(X = x)$ for each x-value.
- Step 4   Multiply $P(X = x)$ by the sample size n to get expected Poisson frequencies e_j.
- Step 5   Perform the chi-square calculations.
- Step 6   Make the decision.

If the data are already tabulated, we can skip the first step. A Poisson test always has an open-ended class on the high end, since technically X has no upper limit. Unfortunately, Poisson tail probabilities are very small, and so will be the corresponding expected frequencies. But classes can be combined from each end inward until expected frequencies become large enough for the test (at least until $e_j \geq 2$). Combining classes implies using fewer classes than you would wish, but a more detailed breakdown isn't justified unless the sample is very large.

Poisson GOF Test: Tabulated Data

The number of U.S. Supreme Court appointments in a given year might be hypothesized to be a Poisson variable, since rare events that occur independently over time are often well approximated by the Poisson model. We formulate these hypotheses:

H_0: Supreme Court appointments follow a Poisson distribution

H_1: Supreme Court appointments do not follow a Poisson distribution

The frequency of U.S. Supreme Court appointments for the period 1900 through 1999 is summarized in Table 15.11. This sample of 100 years should be large enough to obtain a valid hypothesis test. In a typical year, there are no appointments, and only twice have there been three or four appointments (1910 and 1941).

x	f_j	$x_j f_j$
0	59	0
1	31	31
2	8	16
3	1	3
4	1	4
Total	100	54

TABLE 15.11

Number of Annual U.S. Supreme Court Appointments, 1900–1999
📷 **Supreme**

The total number of appointments is

$$\sum_{j=1}^{c} x_j f_j = (0)(59) + (1)(31) + (2)(8) + (3)(1) + (4)(1) = 54$$

so the sample mean is

$$\hat{\lambda} = \frac{54}{100} = 0.54 \text{ appointments per year}$$

Using the estimated mean $\hat{\lambda} = 0.54$ we can calculate the Poisson probabilities, either by using the Poisson formula $P(X = x) = (\lambda^x e^{-\lambda})/x!$ or Excel's function =POISSON(x,mean,0). We multiply $P(X = x)$ by n to get the expected frequencies, with $n = 100$ years, as shown in Table 15.12.

TABLE 15.12

Fitted Poisson Probabilities
📂 Supreme

x	P(X = x)	$e_j = nP(X = x)$
0	0.58275	$100 \times 0.58275 = 58.275$
1	0.31468	$100 \times 0.31468 = 31.468$
2	0.08496	$100 \times 0.08496 = 8.496$
3	0.01529	$100 \times 0.01529 = 1.529$
4	0.00206	$100 \times 0.00206 = 0.206$
5	0.00022	$100 \times 0.00022 = 0.022$
6 or more	0.00004	$100 \times 0.00004 = 0.004$
Sum	1.00000	100.00

The probabilities rapidly become small as X increases. To ensure that $e_j \geq 2$ it is necessary to combine the top classes to end up with only three classes, the top class being "2 or more" before doing the chi-square calculations shown in Table 15.13. Since f_j and e_j are almost identical, the Poisson distribution obviously gives an excellent fit, so we are not surprised that the test statistic (0.022) is very near zero.

TABLE 15.13

Chi-Square Test for Supreme Court Data

x	f_j	e_j	$f_j - e_j$	$(f_j - e_j)^2$	$(f_j - e_j)^2/e_j$
0	59	58.275	0.725	0.525625	0.009
1	31	31.468	−0.468	0.219024	0.007
2 or more	10	10.257	−0.257	0.066049	0.006
Total	100	100			$\chi^2_{calc} = 0.022$

Using $c = 3$ classes in the test and with $m = 1$ parameter estimated, the degrees of freedom are $c - m - 1 = 3 - 1 - 1 = 1$. From Appendix E, we see that the critical value for $\alpha = .10$ is $\chi^2_{.10} = 2.706$, so we clearly cannot reject the hypothesis of a Poisson distribution, even at a modest level of significance. Excel's function =CHIDIST(.022,1) gives the p-value .882, which indicates an excellent fit. Although we can never *prove* that the annual U.S. Supreme Court appointments follow a Poisson distribution, we can see that the Poisson distribution fits the sample well, as in the graph in Figure 15.10 (orange bar is actual, green line is fitted Poisson).

FIGURE 15.10

Supreme Court Vacancy Poisson GOF Test

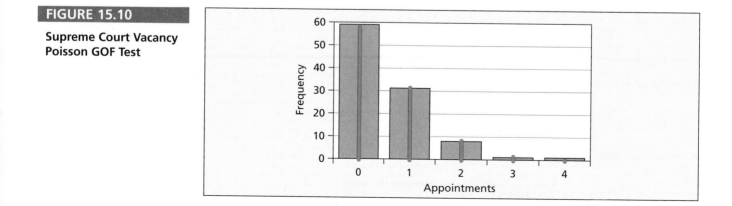

Poisson GOF Test: Raw Data

Figure 15.11 shows the menu from Excel's Data Analysis > Random Number Generation, which was used to create 100 Poisson random numbers with a mean of $\lambda = 4.0$. We would like to test this generator's accuracy.

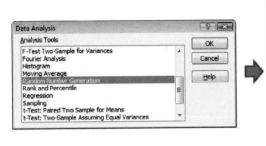

FIGURE 15.11

Excel's Poisson Random Number Generator

Table 15.14 shows 100 Excel-generated Poisson arrivals whose mean is supposed to be $\lambda = 4.0$ arrivals per minute. Is Excel's simulation algorithm working properly? A visual inspection shows two possibly unusual observations (two 11s) but beyond that it is hard to tell.

TABLE 15.14

100 Random Poisson Arrivals with $\lambda = 4$
RandPoisson

5	3	11	4	5	1	7	4	4	5
3	2	5	7	4	4	6	5	5	7
2	4	9	7	5	5	4	5	4	3
4	6	3	3	3	4	6	2	6	7
6	2	7	3	6	6	4	4	2	0
4	8	4	4	4	2	5	2	5	4
3	6	7	8	4	5	4	3	7	5
2	3	2	4	3	5	2	6	5	7
2	3	7	2	1	4	2	3	4	5
0	3	3	7	3	8	5	5	6	11

The hypotheses are:

H_0: Excel's random data are from a Poisson distribution

H_1: Excel's random data are not from a Poisson distribution

Figure 15.12 shows the chi-square test for this data set. To ensure that all expected frequencies are at least 2, the 0s and 1s have been combined into one category, and all values of 9 or more have been combined.

FIGURE 15.12

Chi-Square Test

Arrivals	Obs	Exp	Obs-Exp	Chi-Square
1 or less	4	9.158	−5.158	2.905
2	13	14.653	−1.653	0.186
3	16	19.537	−3.537	0.640
4	22	19.537	2.463	0.311
5	18	15.629	2.371	0.360
6	10	10.420	−0.420	0.017
7	11	5.954	5.046	4.276
8	3	2.977	0.023	0.000
9 or more	3	2.136	0.864	0.349
Total	100	100.000	0.000	9.044
Assuming known $\lambda = 4.0$			d.f. = 8	*p*-value = 0.339

No parameters were estimated, since we specified *a priori* the value $\lambda = 4$. For $c = 9$ classes and $m = 0$ parameters estimated, the degrees of freedom are $c - m - 1 = c - 1 = 8$. At $\alpha = .10$, the test statistic (9.044) does not exceed the critical value from Appendix E for $d.f. = 8$ ($\chi^2_{.10} = 13.36$) so we do not reject the hypothesis of a Poisson distribution despite the surfeit of 7s ($f = 11, e = 5.954$) and dearth of 0s or 1s ($f = 4, e = 9.158$). Presumably, this peculiarity of our sample would not be repeated if we took another sample of 100. The *p*-value (.339) suggests that such a result would occur about 339 times in 1,000 samples if the population we are sampling were Poisson, which suggests that any differences are within the realm of chance. Figure 15.13 shows a histogram of actual frequencies (orange bars) and expected frequencies (green lines).

FIGURE 15.13

Histogram

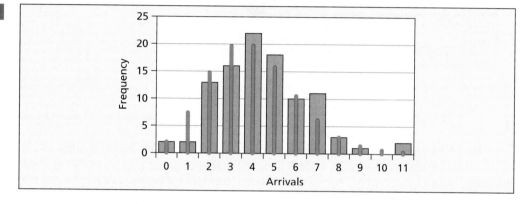

In addition to a chi-square GOF test, we can examine the sample statistics to see if they resemble what would be expected for a Poisson distribution. In a Poisson distribution, the mean is λ, the standard deviation is $\sqrt{\lambda}$, and the skewness is $1/\sqrt{\lambda}$. Table 15.15 shows that the sample mean (4.46) is a little larger than expected ($\mu = \lambda = 4.0$), but the sample standard deviation (2.072) is very close to the expected Poisson standard deviation ($\sigma = \sqrt{\lambda} = \sqrt{4} = 2$). The sample skewness (0.57) is close to the expected skewness ($1/\sqrt{4} = 0.50$). All in all, the evidence is compatible with the hypothesis that Excel's data follow a Poisson distribution.

TABLE 15.15

Statistics for Excel Sample 🗁 RandPoisson

Statistic	Sample	If Poisson
Mean	4.460	4.000
Standard Deviation	2.072	2.000
Skewness	0.57	0.50

As a last check, since the sample is large enough ($n \geq 30$) to assume normality of the mean, we can do a *z* test to see whether the sample mean equals the theoretical mean $\lambda = 4.0$. Interestingly, the *z* test does indicate a potentially significant difference in the sample mean from the intended mean:

$$z = \frac{\bar{x} - \mu}{\frac{\sigma}{\sqrt{n}}} = \frac{4.460 - 4.000}{\frac{2}{\sqrt{100}}} = 2.300 \qquad (p = .021 \text{ in a two-tailed test})$$

The *p*-value says that such a difference could occur about 21 times in 1,000 samples if the null hypothesis is true. Depending on our α, this could be a significant difference. This difference between the sample mean and the theoretical mean arises from the two outliers (at $x = 11$), which did not have much effect on the chi-square test.

SECTION EXERCISES

connect

15.10 Excel was asked to generate 50 Poisson random numbers with mean $\lambda = 5$. (a) Calculate the sample mean. How close is it to the desired value? (b) Calculate the expected frequencies assuming a Poisson distribution with $\lambda = 5$. Show your calculations in a spreadsheet format. (c) Carry out the chi-square test at $\alpha = .05$, combining end categories as needed to ensure that all expected frequencies are at least five. Show your degrees of freedom calculation. (d) Do you think your calculations would have been materially different if you had used the sample mean instead of $\lambda = 5.0$? Explain. 🗁 **RandPoisB**

x	Frequency
0	1
1	1
2	4
3	7
4	7
5	8
6	10
7	3
8	3
9	4
10	1
11	1

15.11 During the 1973–74 hockey season, the Boston Bruins played 39 home games and scored 193 points, as shown below. (a) Estimate the mean from the sample. (b) Calculate the expected frequencies assuming a Poisson distribution. Show your calculations in a spreadsheet format. (c) Carry out the chi-square test, combining end categories as needed to ensure that all expected frequencies are at least five. Show your degrees of freedom calculation. (d) At $\alpha = .05$, can you reject the hypothesis that goals per game follow a Poisson process? (Data are from Gary M. Mullett, "Simeon Poisson and the National Hockey League," *The American Statistician* 31, no. 1 [1977], p. 9.) 🖰 **Boston**

Number of Goals Scored (per game) by Boston Bruins, 1973–74

	Number of Goals											
	0	**1**	**2**	**3**	**4**	**5**	**6**	**7**	**8**	**9**	**10**	**Total**
Frequency	0	1	2	5	9	10	5	2	3	1	1	39

15.12 At a local supermarket receiving dock, the number of truck arrivals per day is recorded for 100 days. (a) Estimate the mean from the sample. (b) Calculate the expected frequencies assuming a Poisson distribution. Show your calculations in a spreadsheet format. (c) Carry out the chi-square test, combining end categories as needed to ensure that all expected frequencies are at least five. Show your degrees of freedom calculation. (d) At $\alpha = .05$, can you reject the hypothesis that arrivals per day follow a Poisson process? 🖰 **Trucks**

Arrivals per Day at a Loading Dock

	Number of Arrivals								
	0	**1**	**2**	**3**	**4**	**5**	**6**	**7**	**Total**
Frequency	4	23	28	22	8	9	4	2	100

Normal Data-Generating Situations

Any normal population is fully described by the two parameters μ and σ. Many data-generating situations could be compatible with a **normal distribution**, if the data possess a reasonable degree of central tendency and are not badly skewed. Measurements of continuous variables such as physical attributes (e.g., weight, size, travel time) may have a constant mean and variance if the underlying process is stable and the population is homogeneous. The normal model might apply to discrete or integer data if the range is relatively large, such as the number of successes in a large binomial sample or Poisson occurrences if the mean is large. Unless μ and

15.5

NORMAL CHI-SQUARE GOODNESS-OF-FIT TEST

σ parameters are known *a priori* (a rare circumstance) they must be estimated from a sample by using $\bar{x}$ and s. Using these statistics, we can set up the chi-square goodness-of-fit test. There are several ways this could be done.

Method 1: Standardizing the Data

There are various ways to calculate the frequencies for a chi-square test. One way is to transform the sample observations $x_1, x_2, \ldots, x_n$ into standardized values:

(15.10)
$$z = \frac{x_i - \bar{x}}{s}$$
(standardized data transformation)

We could count the sample observations f_j within intervals of the form $\bar{x} \pm ks$ and compare them with the known frequencies e_j based on the normal distribution, as illustrated in Figure 15.14. We could break the intervals down into more classes if we wish. This method has the advantage of using a standardized scale, but the disadvantage that data no longer are in the original units of measurement (e.g., kilograms) plus the effort required to standardize the data.

FIGURE 15.14

Normal Areas

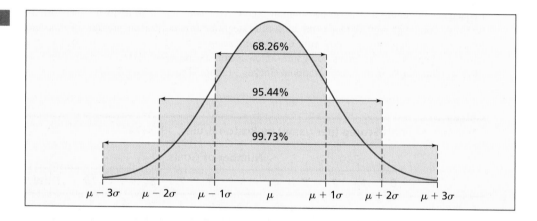

Method 2: Equal Bin Widths

An alternative approach is to create a histogram for the original data with equal-width bins. Rather than using "nice" bin limits (as we often do for histograms) we divide the *exact data range* into c groups of equal width.

(15.11)
$$\text{Bin width} = \frac{x_{\max} - x_{\min}}{c}$$
(setting bin width from sample data)

This avoids "empty" space within histogram intervals. We then proceed as follows:

- Step 1   Count the sample observations in each bin to get observed frequencies f_j.
- Step 2   Convert the bin limits into standardized z-values by using formula 15.10.
- Step 3   Find the area within each bin assuming a normal distribution.
- Step 4   Find expected frequencies e_j by multiplying each normal area by the sample size n.

An advantage of this test is that it corresponds directly to the histogram. Its disadvantage is that, in the end classes, very few observations would be expected. Since small expected frequencies can cause trouble for a chi-square test, classes may need to be collapsed from the ends inward, to enlarge the expected frequencies.

Method 3: Equal Expected Frequencies

A third method is to define histogram bins in such a way that an equal number of observations would be *expected* within each bin under the null hypothesis. That is, define bin limits so that

(15.12) $e_j = n/c$ (define bins to get equal expected frequencies)

We want a normal area of $1/c$ in each of the c bins. The first and last classes must be open-ended for a normal distribution, so to define c bins we need $c - 1$ cutpoints. The upper limit of bin j can be found directly by using Excel's function =NORMINV(j/c, $\bar{x}$, s). Alternatively, we can find z_j for bin j with Excel's standard normal function =NORMSINV(j/c,0,1) and then calculate the upper limit for bin j as $\bar{x} + z_j s$. Table 15.16 shows some typical z-values to put an area of $1/c$ in each bin.

Bin	3 Bins	4 Bins	5 Bins	6 Bins	7 Bins	8 Bins
1	−0.431	−0.675	−0.842	−0.967	−1.068	−1.150
2	0.431	0.000	−0.253	−0.431	−0.566	−0.675
3		0.675	0.253	0.000	−0.180	−0.319
4			0.842	0.431	0.180	0.000
5				0.967	0.566	0.319
6					1.068	0.675
						1.150

TABLE 15.16

Standard Normal Cutpoints for Equal Area Bins

Once the bins are defined, we count the observations f_j within each bin and compare them with the expected frequencies $e_j = n/c$. Although the bin limits will not be "nice," the compelling advantage of this method is that it guarantees the largest possible expected frequencies, and hence the most powerful test for c bins. MegaStat uses this method (Descriptive Statistics > Normal Curve Goodness of Fit) and calculations are automatic, but you cannot vary the number of bins. MegaStat always uses the number of bins suggested by Sturges' Rule $k = 1 + 3.3 \log_{10}(n)$.

Application: Quality Management

A sample of 35 Hershey's Milk Chocolate Kisses was taken from a bag containing 84 Kisses. The population is assumed infinite. After removing the foil wrapper, each Kiss was weighed. The weights are shown in Table 15.17. Are these weights from a normal population?

4.666	4.854	4.868	4.849	4.700	4.683	5.064
4.800	4.694	4.760	5.075	4.780	4.781	5.103
4.568	4.983	5.076	4.808	5.084	4.749	5.092
4.783	4.520	4.698	5.084	4.880	4.883	4.880
4.928	4.651	4.797	4.682	4.756	5.041	4.906

TABLE 15.17

Weights of 35 Hershey's Milk Chocolate Kisses (in grams) 🖅 **Kisses**

Source: An independent project by MBA student Frances Williams. Kisses were weighed on an American Scientific Model S/P 120 analytical balance accurate to 0.0001 gm.

It might be supposed *a priori* that Kiss weights would be normally distributed, since the manufacturing process should have a single, constant mean and standard deviation. Variation is inevitable in any manufacturing process. Chocolate is especially difficult to handle, because liquid chocolate must be dropped in precisely measured amounts, solidified, wrapped, and bagged. Since chocolate is soft and crumbles easily, even the process of weighing the Kisses may abrade some chocolate and introduce measurement error. We will test the following hypotheses:

H_0: Kisses' weights are from a normal distribution

H_1: Kisses' weights aren't from a normal distribution

Before undertaking a GOF test, consider the histograms in Figure 15.15. The graphs show fitted normal distributions, based on the estimated mean and standard deviation from the data. Although it is only a visual aid, the fitted normal gives you a clue as to the likely outcome of the test. The histograms reveal no apparent outliers, and nothing in conflict with the idea of a normal population except a second mode toward the high end of the scale and perhaps a flatter appearance than normal. Since histogram appearance can vary, depending on the number of classes and the way the bin limits are specified, further tests are needed.

FIGURE 15.15

Histograms of 35 Hershey's Kiss Weights

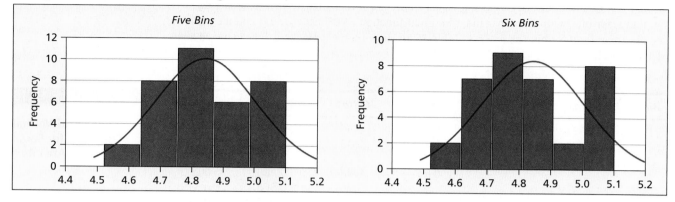

Table 15.18 compares the sample statistics with parameters expected for a normal distribution. Since the mean and standard deviation were fitted from the data, they tell us nothing. The median (4.808) is slightly less than the mean (4.844), but the skewness coefficient (0.14) is fairly close to the value (0.00) that would be expected in a symmetric normal distribution. The sample quartiles (4.700 and 4.983) are nearly what we expect for a normal distribution using the 25th and 75th percentiles ($\bar{x} \pm 0.675s$). There are no outliers, as the smallest Kiss (4.520 grams) is 2.01 standard deviations below the mean, while the largest Kiss (5.103 grams) is 1.61 standard deviations above the mean.

TABLE 15.18

Sample vs. Normal
Kisses

Statistic	Kiss Weight	If Normal
Mean	4.844	4.844
Standard Deviation	0.161	0.161
Quartile 1	4.700	4.735
Median	4.808	4.844
Quartile 3	4.983	4.952
Skewness	0.14	0.00

For a chi-square GOF test, degrees of freedom are $d.f. = c - m - 1$, where c is the number of classes used in the test and m is the number of parameters estimated. Since two parameters, μ and σ, are estimated from the sample, $m = 2$. The degrees of freedom and critical values for various numbers of bins are shown in Table 15.19. We need at least four bins to ensure at least 1 degree of freedom, while Cochran's Rule (at least 5 *expected* observations per bin) suggests a maximum of 7 bins for $n = 35$ data points (since $35/7 = 5$).

TABLE 15.19

Critical Values for Normal GOF Test

Number of Bins	Degrees of Freedom	$\chi^2_{.10}$	$\chi^2_{.05}$
4	$d.f. = c - m - 1 = c - 2 - 1 = 4 - 3 = 1$	2.706	3.841
5	$d.f. = c - m - 1 = c - 2 - 1 = 5 - 3 = 2$	4.605	5.991
6	$d.f. = c - m - 1 = c - 2 - 1 = 6 - 3 = 3$	6.251	7.815
7	$d.f. = c - m - 1 = c - 2 - 1 = 7 - 3 = 4$	7.779	9.488

Because we anticipate that the number of bins may affect the results, we will vary the number of bins from 4 to 7. We will concentrate on seeing whether the result is affected by the number of bins, and whether certain bins have a disproportionate effect on the chi-square test statistic. We will use method 3 (equal expected frequencies) because it is the most powerful.

Using four bins (Figure 15.16) the chi-square test statistic (0.086) is not significant at $\alpha = .10$ ($\chi^2_{.10} = 2.706$) and its p-value (.770) indicates that such a result would be expected

Kiss Weight	Obs	Exp	Obs-Exp	Chi-Square
Under 4.735	9	8.75	0.25	0.007
4.735 < 4.844	9	8.75	0.25	0.007
4.844 < 4.952	8	8.75	−0.75	0.064
4.952 or more	9	8.75	0.25	0.007
Total	35	35	0	0.086
Parameters from sample			d.f. = 1	p < 0.770

FIGURE 15.16

Four Bins (c = 4)

Kiss Weight	Obs	Exp	Obs-Exp	Chi-Square
Under 4.708	9	7.00	2.00	0.571
4.708 < 4.803	8	7.00	1.00	0.143
4.803 < 4.884	7	7.00	0.00	0.000
4.884 < 4.979	2	7.00	−5.00	3.571
4.979 or more	9	7.00	2.00	0.571
Total	35	35	0	4.857
Parameters from sample			d.f. = 2	p < 0.088

FIGURE 15.17

Five Bins (c = 5)

about 770 times in 1,000 samples if the population were normal. Using five bins (Figure 15.17) the chi-square test statistic (4.857) is barely significant at $\alpha = .10$ ($\chi^2_{.10} = 4.605$) and its *p*-value (.088) indicates that such a result would be expected about 88 times in 1,000 samples if the population were normal. Bin four (highlighted) contributes heavily to the chi-square statistic. In these GOF tests, a low *p*-value indicates *less* resemblance to a normal.

Using six bins (Figure 15.18), the chi-square test statistic (3.571) is not significant at $\alpha = .10$ ($\chi^2_{.10} = 6.251$) and its *p*-value (.312) indicates that such a result would be expected about 312 times in 1,000 samples if the population were normal. Bin five (highlighted) contributes heavily to the chi-square statistic. Using seven bins (Figure 15.19), the chi-square test statistic (8.000) is not quite significant at $\alpha = .10$ ($\chi^2_{.10} = 7.779$) and its *p*-value (.092) indicates that such a result would be expected about 92 times in 1,000 samples if the population were normal. Bin six (highlighted) contributes heavily to the chi-square statistic.

Kiss Weight	Obs	Exp	Obs-Exp	Chi-Square
Under 4.688	6	5.83	0.17	0.005
4.688 < 4.774	6	5.83	0.17	0.005
4.774 < 4.844	6	5.83	0.17	0.005
4.844 < 4.913	7	5.83	1.17	0.233
4.913 < 4.999	2	5.83	−3.83	2.519
4.999 or more	8	5.83	2.17	0.805
Total	35	35	0	3.571
Parameters from sample			d.f. = 3	p < 0.312

FIGURE 5.18

Six Bins (c = 6)

Kiss Weight	Obs	Exp	Obs-Exp	Chi-Square
Under 4.672	4	5.00	−1.00	0.200
4.672 < 4.752	6	5.00	1.00	0.200
4.752 < 4.815	8	5.00	3.00	1.800
4.815 < 4.873	3	5.00	−2.00	0.800
4.873 < 4.935	5	5.00	0.00	0.000
4.935 < 5.015	1	5.00	−4.00	3.200
5.015 or more	8	5.00	3.00	1.800
Total	35	35	0	8.000
Parameters from sample			d.f. = 4	p < 0.092

FIGURE 15.19

Seven Bins (c = 7)

Interpretation   Depending on the number of bins, the chi-square tests either fail to reject the hypothesis of normality or reject it at a weak level of significance. These results fail to *disprove* normality convincingly. However, the histograms do suggest a bimodal shape. This could occur if the Kisses were molded by two or more different machines. If each machine has a different μ and σ, this could lead to the "mixture of distributions" problem mentioned earlier. If so, a platykurtic distribution (flatter than normal) would be likely. This issue bears further investigation. A quality control analyst would probably take a larger sample and study the manufacturing methods to see what could be learned.

SECTION EXERCISES

Hint: Check your work using MegaStat's Descriptive Statistics > Normal curve goodness of fit test.

connect

15.13 Exam scores of 40 students in a statistics class are shown. (a) Estimate the mean and standard deviation from the sample. (b) Assuming that the data are from a normal distribution, define bins by using method 3 (equal expected frequencies). Use 8 bins. (c) Set up an Excel worksheet for your chi-square calculations, with a column showing the expected frequency for each bin (they must add to 40). (d) Tabulate the observed frequency for each bin and record it in the next column. (e) Carry out the chi-square test, using $\alpha = .05$. Can you reject the hypothesis that the exam scores came from a normal population? 📂 **ExamScores**

79	75	77	57	81	70	83	66
81	89	59	83	75	60	96	86
78	76	71	78	78	70	54	60
71	81	79	88	77	82	75	68
77	69	83	79	79	76	78	71

15.14 One Friday night, there were 42 carry-out orders at Ashoka Curry Express. (a) Estimate the mean and standard deviation from the sample. (b) Assuming that the data are from a normal distribution, define bins by using method 3 (equal expected frequencies). Use 8 bins. (c) Set up an Excel worksheet for your chi-square calculations, with a column showing the expected frequency for each bin (they must add to 42). (d) Tabulate the observed frequency for each bin and record it in the next column. (e) Do the chi-square test at $\alpha = .025$. Can you reject the hypothesis that carry-out orders follow a normal population? 📂 **TakeOut**

18.74	21.05	31.19	23.06	20.17	25.12	24.30
46.04	33.96	45.04	34.63	35.24	30.13	29.93
52.33	26.52	19.68	19.62	32.96	42.07	47.82
38.62	31.88	44.97	36.35	21.50	41.42	33.87
26.43	35.28	21.88	24.80	27.49	18.30	44.47
28.40	36.72	26.30	47.08	34.33	13.15	15.51

15.6
ECDF TESTS (OPTIONAL)

Kolmogorov-Smirnov and Lilliefors Tests

There are many alternatives to the chi-square test, based on the **empirical cumulative distribution function (ECDF)**. One such test is the **Kolmogorov-Smirnov test**. The K-S test statistic D is the largest absolute difference between the actual and expected cumulative relative frequency of the n data values:

LO7

State advantages of ECDF tests as compared to chi-square GOF tests.

(15.13)
$$D = \text{Max} \, |F_a - F_e|$$

The K-S test is not recommended for grouped data, as it may be less powerful than the chi-square test.

   F_a is the actual cumulative frequency at observation i, and F_e is the expected cumulative frequency at observation i under the assumption that the data came from the hypothesized distribution. The K-S test assumes that no parameters are estimated. If they are (e.g., the mean and variance may be estimated) we use a **Lilliefors test**, whose test statistic is the same, but with a different table of critical values. Since these tests are always done by computer (F_e

requires the inverse CDF for the hypothesized distribution), we will omit further details and merely illustrate the test visually. Because observations are treated individually, information is not lost by combining categories, as in a chi-square test. Thus, ECDF tests may surpass the chi-square test in their ability to detect departures from the distribution specified in the null hypothesis, if raw data are available.

Illustrations: Lottery Numbers and Kiss Weights

Figure 15.20 shows the Kolmogorov-Smirnov test for *uniformity* in the 100 lottery numbers tested earlier in a chi-square test. The largest difference (.087) occurs at observation 77, but the large *p*-value does not warrant rejection of the hypothesis of a uniform distribution. The CDF under the hypothesis of uniformity is a straight line, while for a normal distribution, the CDF would be *S*-shaped. Figure 15.21 shows a *normality* test for weights of Hershey's Kisses. The largest difference occurs at observation 28, but the *p*-value does not warrant rejection of the hypothesis of normality. For this data set, the K-S test lacks sufficient power to reject *either* a uniform *or* a normal distribution.

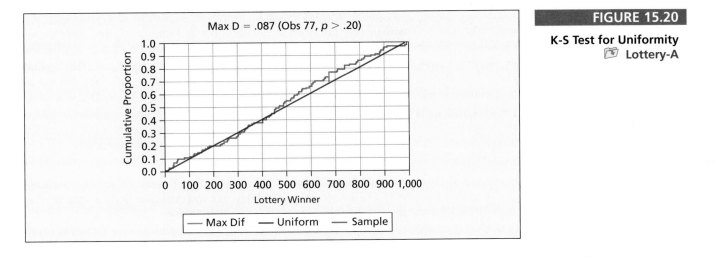

FIGURE 15.20

K-S Test for Uniformity
Lottery-A

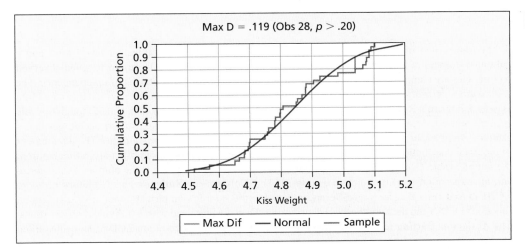

FIGURE 15.21

K-S Test for Normality
Kisses

Anderson-Darling Test

The **Anderson-Darling test**, another ECDF test, is perhaps the most widely used test for non-normality because of its power. It is always done on a computer since it requires the inverse CDF for the hypothesized distribution. The A-D test is based on a **probability plot**. When the data fit the hypothesized distribution closely, the probability plot will be close to a straight line. The A-D test statistic measures the overall distance between the actual and the hypothesized

FIGURE 15.22

MINITAB's Probability Plot and Anderson-Darling Test for Kiss Weights

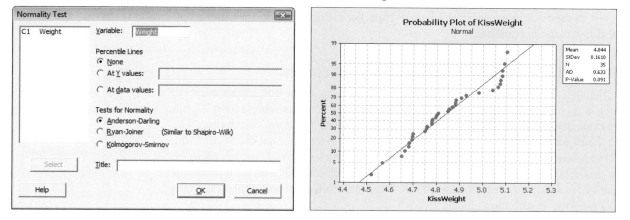

distributions, using a weighted squared distance. It provides a *p*-value to complement the visual plot. The A-D statistic is not difficult to calculate, but its formula is rather complex, so it is omitted. Figure 15.22 shows a graph displaying the probability plot and A-D statistic for the Hershey's Kiss data using MINITAB's Stats > Basic Statistics > Normality Test. The *p*-value (.091) suggests a departure from normality at the 10 percent level of significance, but not at the 5 percent level. This result is consistent with our previous findings. The A-D test is more powerful than a chi-square test if raw data are available, because it treats the observations individually. Also, the probability plot has the attraction of revealing discrepancies between the sample and the hypothesized distribution, and it is usually easy to spot outliers.

SECTION EXERCISES

connect

*15.15 Use MINITAB's Stat > Basic Statistics > Normality Test to obtain a probability plot for the exam score data (see Exercise 15.13). Interpret the probability plot and Anderson-Darling statistic. Was MINITAB easier to use than the chi-square test? 📂 **ExamScores**

*15.16 Use MINITAB's Stat > Basic Statistics > Normality Test to obtain a probability plot for the Ashoka Curry House carry-out order data (see Exercise 15.14). Interpret the probability plot and Anderson-Darling statistic. Was MINITAB easier to use than the chi-square test? 📂 **TakeOut**

CHAPTER SUMMARY

A **chi-square test of independence** requires an $r \times c$ **contingency table** that has r rows and c columns. Degrees of freedom for the chi-square test will be $(r - 1)(c - 1)$. In this test, the **observed frequencies** are compared with the **expected frequencies** under the hypothesis of independence. The test assumes categorical data (attribute data) but can also be used with numerical data grouped into classes. **Cochran's Rule** requires that expected frequencies be at least 5 in each cell, although this rule is often relaxed. A test for **goodness-of-fit (GOF)** uses the chi-square statistic to decide whether a sample is from a specified distribution (e.g., multinomial, uniform, Poisson, normal). The **parameters** of the fitted distribution (e.g., the mean) may be specified *a priori,* but more often are estimated from the sample. Degrees of freedom for the GOF test are $c - m - 1$ where c is the number of categories and m is the number of parameters estimated. The **Kolmogorov-Smirnov** and **Lilliefors** tests are **ECDF-based tests** that look at differences between the sample's empirical cumulative distribution function (ECDF) and the hypothesized distribution. They are best used with n individual observations. The **Anderson-Darling** test and the **probability plot** are the most common ECDF tests, most often used to test for normality.

KEY TERMS

Anderson-Darling test, *671*
chi-square probability
distribution, *645*
chi-square test, *644*
Cochran's Rule, *649*
contingency table, *643*
degrees of freedom, *645*

empirical cumulative
distribution function
(ECDF), *670*
expected frequency, *644*
goodness-of-fit test, *654*
independent, *645*
Kolmogorov-Smirnov test, *670*

Lilliefors test, *670*
multinomial distribution, *654*
normal distribution, *665*
observed frequency, *644*
Poisson distribution, *660*
probability plot, *671*
uniform distribution, *656*

Commonly Used Formulas

Chi-Square Test for Independence

Test statistic for independence in a contingency table with r rows

and c columns: $\chi^2_{calc} = \sum_{j=1}^{r} \sum_{k=1}^{c} \frac{[f_{jk} - e_{jk}]^2}{e_{jk}}$

Degrees of freedom for a contingency table with r rows
and c columns: $d.f. = (r - 1)(c - 1)$

Expected frequency in row j and column k: $e_{jk} = R_j C_k / n$

Chi-Square Test for Goodness-of-Fit

Test statistic for observed frequencies in c classes under an hypothesized distribution

H_0 (e.g., uniform, Poisson, normal): $\chi^2_{calc} = \sum_{j=1}^{c} \frac{[f_j - e_j]^2}{e_j}$

where

f_j = the observed frequency in class j

e_j = the expected frequency in class j

Degrees of freedom for the chi-square GOF test: $d.f. = c - m - 1$

where

c = the number of classes used in the test

m = the number of parameters estimated

Estimated mean of Poisson distribution with c classes: $\lambda = \sum_{j=1}^{c} x_j f_j$

where

x_j = the value of X in class j

f_j = the observed frequency in class j

Expected frequency in class j assuming a uniform distribution with c classes: $e_j = n/c$

Note: Questions labeled * are based on optional material from this chapter.

CHAPTER REVIEW

1. (a) What are the hypotheses in a chi-square test for independence? (b) Why do we call it a test of frequencies? (c) What distribution is used in this test? (d) How do we calculate the degrees of freedom for an $r \times c$ contingency table?

2. How do we calculate the expected frequencies for each cell of the contingency table?

3. What is Cochran's Rule, and why is it needed? Why do we call it a "rule of thumb"?

4. (a) Explain why the 2×2 table is analogous to a z test for two proportions. (b) What is the relationship between z and χ^2 in the 2×2 table?

5. (a) What are the hypotheses for a GOF test? (b) Explain how a chi-square GOF test is carried out in general.

6. What is the general formula for degrees of freedom in a chi-square GOF test?

7. (a) In a uniform GOF test, how do we calculate the expected frequencies? (b) Why is the test easier if the data are already grouped?

8. (a) In a Poisson GOF test, how do we calculate the expected frequencies? (b) Why do we need the mean λ before carrying out the chi-square test?

9. (a) Very briefly describe three ways of calculating expected frequencies for a normal GOF test. (b) Name advantages and disadvantages of each way. (c) Why is a normal GOF test almost always done on a computer?

*10. What is an ECDF test? Give an example.

*11. (a) Name potential advantages of the Kolmogorov-Smirnov or Lilliefors tests. (b) Why would this type of test almost always be done on a computer?

*12. (a) What does a probability plot show? (b) If the hypothesized distribution is a good fit to the data, what would be the appearance of the probability plot? (c) What are the advantages and disadvantages of a probability plot?

*13. (a) Name two advantages of the Anderson-Darling test. (b) Why is it almost always done on a computer?

CHAPTER EXERCISES

connect

Instructions: In all exercises, include MegaStat, Excel, or MINITAB exhibits to support your calculations. State the hypotheses, show how the degrees of freedom are calculated, find the critical value of chi-square from Appendix E or from Excel's function =CHIINV(alpha, deg_freedom), and interpret the *p*-value. Tell whether the conclusion is sensitive to the level of significance chosen, identify cells that contribute the most to the chi-square test statistic, and check for small expected frequencies. If necessary, you can calculate the *p*-value by using Excel's function =CHIDIST(test statistic, deg_freedom). *Note:* Exercises marked * are harder or require optional material.

15.17 Employees of Axolotl Corporation were sampled at random from pay records and asked to complete an anonymous job satisfaction survey, yielding the tabulation shown. *Research question:* At $\alpha = .05$, is job satisfaction independent of pay category? 📂 **Employees**

Pay Type	Satisfied	Neutral	Dissatisfied	Total
Salaried	20	13	2	35
Hourly	135	127	58	320
Total	155	140	60	355

15.18 Sixty-four students in an introductory college economics class were asked how many credits they had earned in college, and how certain they were about their choice of major. *Research question:* At $\alpha = .01$, is the degree of certainty independent of credits earned? 📂 **Certainty**

Credits Earned	Very Uncertain	Somewhat Certain	Very Certain	Row Total
0–9	12	8	3	23
10–59	8	4	10	22
60 or more	1	7	11	19
Col Total	21	19	24	64

15.19 To see whether students who finish an exam first get the same grades as those who finish later, a professor kept track of the order in which papers were handed in. Of the first 25 papers, 10 received a "B" or better compared with 8 of the last 24 papers handed in. *Research question:* At $\alpha = .10$, is the grade independent of the order handed in? Since it is a 2 × 2 table, try also a two-tailed two-sample *z* test for $\pi_1 = \pi_2$ (see Chapter 10) and verify that z^2 is the same as your chi-square statistic. Which test do you prefer? Why? 📂 **Grades**

Grade	Earlier Hand-In	Later Hand-In	Row Total
"B" or better	10	8	18
"C" or worse	15	16	31
Col Total	25	24	49

15.20 From 74 of its restaurants, Noodles & Company managers collected data on per-person sales and the percent of sales due to "potstickers" (a popular food item). Both numerical variables failed tests for normality, so they tried a chi-square test. Each variable was converted into ordinal categories (low, medium, high) using cutoff points that produced roughly equal group sizes. *Research question:* At $\alpha = .05$, is per-person spending independent of percent of sales from potstickers? 📂 **Noodles**

Per person Spending	Potsticker % of Sales			Row Total
	Low	Medium	High	
Low	14	7	3	24
Medium	7	15	6	28
High	3	4	15	22
Col Total	24	26	24	74

15.21 A Web-based anonymous survey of students asked for a self-rating on proficiency in a language other than English and the student's frequency of newspaper reading. *Research question:* At $\alpha = .10$, is frequency of newspaper reading independent of foreign language proficiency? 📂 **WebSurvey**

Non-English Proficiency	Daily Newspaper Reading			Row Total
	Never	*Occasionally*	*Regularly*	
None	4	13	5	22
Slight	11	45	9	65
Moderate	6	33	7	46
Fluent	5	19	1	25
Col Total	26	110	22	158

15.22 A student team examined parked cars in four different suburban shopping malls. One hundred vehicles were examined in each location. *Research question:* At $\alpha = .05$, does vehicle type vary by mall location? (Data are from a project by MBA students Steve Bennett, Alicia Morais, Steve Olson, and Greg Corda.) 📂 **Vehicles**

Vehicle Type	Somerset	Oakland	Great Lakes	Jamestown	Row Total
Car	44	49	36	64	193
Minivan	21	15	18	13	67
Full-sized Van	2	3	3	2	10
SUV	19	27	26	12	84
Truck	14	6	17	9	46
Col Total	100	100	100	100	400

15.23 Choose either 2×2 contingency table shown below (males *or* females). *Research question:* At $\alpha = .005$, is smoking independent of race? (Smoking rates are from *Statistical Abstract of the United States, 2001*, pp. 16 and 12, applied to hypothetical samples of 500.) 📂 **Smoking**

Smoking by Race for Males Aged 18–24

Race	Smoker	Nonsmoker	Row Total
White	145	280	425
Black	15	60	75
Col Total	160	340	500

Smoking by Race for Females Aged 18–24

Race	Smoker	Nonsmoker	Row Total
White	116	299	415
Black	7	78	85
Col Total	123	377	500

15.24 High levels of cockpit noise in an aircraft can damage the hearing of pilots who are exposed to this hazard for many hours. A Boeing 727 co-pilot collected 61 noise observations using a handheld sound meter. Noise level is defined as "Low" (under 88 decibels), "Medium" (88 to 91 decibels), or "High" (92 decibels or more). There are three flight phases (Climb, Cruise, Descent). *Research question:* At $\alpha = .05$, is the cockpit noise level independent of flight phase? (Data are from Capt. Robert E. Hartl, retired.) 🖅 **Noise**

Noise Level	Climb	Cruise	Descent	Row Total
Low	6	2	6	14
Medium	18	3	8	29
High	1	3	14	18
Col Total	25	8	28	61

15.25 Forecasters' interest rate predictions over the period 1982–1990 were studied to see whether the predictions corresponded to what actually happened. The 2×2 contingency table below shows the frequencies of actual and predicted interest rate movements. *Research question:* At $\alpha = .10$, is the actual change independent of the predicted change? (Data are from R. A. Kolb and H. O. Steckler, "How Well Do Analysts Forecast Interest Rates?" *Journal of Forecasting* 15, no. 15 [1996], pp. 385–394.) 🖅 **Forecasts**

Forecasted Change	Rates Fell	Rates Rose	Row Total
Rates would fall	7	12	19
Rates would rise	9	6	15
Col Total	16	18	34

15.26 In a study of childhood asthma, 4,317 observations were collected on education and smoking during pregnancy, shown in the 4×3 contingency table below. *Research question:* At $\alpha = .005$, is smoking during pregnancy independent of education level? (Data are from Michael Weitzman and Deborah Klein Walker, "Maternal Smoking and Asthma," *Pediatrics* 85, no. 4 [April 1990], p. 507.) 🖅 **Pregnancy**

Education	No Smoking	$<\frac{1}{2}$ Pack	$\geq\frac{1}{2}$ Pack	Row Total
<High School	641	196	196	1,033
High School	1,370	290	270	1,930
Some College	635	68	53	756
College	550	30	18	598
Col Total	3,196	584	537	4,317

15.27 Two contingency tables below show return on investment (ROI) and percent of sales growth over the previous 5 years for 85 U.S. firms. ROI is defined as percentage of return on a combination of stockholders' equity (both common and preferred) plus capital from long-term debt including current maturities, minority stockholders' equity in consolidated subsidiaries, and accumulated deferred taxes and investment tax credits. *Research question:* At $\alpha = .05$, is ROI independent of sales growth? Would you expect it to be? Do the two tables (2×2 and 3×3) agree? Are small expected frequencies a problem? (Data are adapted from a research project by MBA student B. J. Oline.) 🖅 **ROI**

2 × 2 Cross-Tabulation of Companies

ROI	Low Growth	High Growth	Row Total
Low ROI	24	16	40
High ROI	14	31	45
Col Total	38	47	85

3 × 3 Cross-Tabulation of Companies

ROI	Low Growth	Medium Growth	High Growth	Row Total
Low ROI	9	12	7	28
Medium ROI	6	14	7	27
High ROI	1	12	17	30
Col Total	16	38	31	85

15.28 Can people really identify their favorite brand of cola? Volunteers tasted Coca-Cola Classic, Pepsi, Diet Coke, and Diet Pepsi, with the results shown below. *Research question:* At $\alpha = .05$, is the correctness of the prediction different for the two types of cola drinkers? Could *you* identify your favorite brand in this kind of test? Since it is a 2 × 2 table, try also a two-tailed two-sample *z* test for $\pi_1 = \pi_2$ (see Chapter 10) and verify that z^2 is the same as your chi-square statistic. Which test do you prefer? Why? (Data are from *Consumer Reports* 56, no. 8 [August 1991], p. 519.) **Cola**

Correct?	Regular Cola	Diet Cola	Row Total
Yes, got it right	7	7	14
No, got it wrong	12	20	32
Col Total	19	27	46

15.29 A survey of randomly chosen new students at a certain university revealed the data below concerning the main reason for choosing this university instead of another. *Research question:* At $\alpha = .01$, is the main reason for choosing the university independent of student type? **Students**

New Student	Tuition	Location	Reputation	Row Total
Freshmen	50	30	35	115
Transfers	15	29	20	64
MBAs	5	20	60	85
Col Total	70	79	115	264

15.30 A survey of 189 statistics students asked the age of car usually driven and the student's political orientation. The car age was a numerical variable, which was converted into ordinal categories. *Research question:* At $\alpha = .10$, are students' political views independent of the age of car they usually drive? **Politics**

	Age of Car Usually Driven			
Politics	Under 3	3–6	7 or More	Row Total
Liberal	19	12	13	44
Middle-of-Road	33	31	28	92
Conservative	16	24	13	53
Col Total	68	67	54	189

15.31 Here is a table showing the season in which the first 36 U.S. presidents died. *Research question:* At $\alpha = .10$, can you reject the hypothesis that presidents' deaths are uniformly distributed by season? (Data are from *The World Almanac and Book of Facts, 2002,* pp. 545–556.) **Presidents-A**

Month of Demise	Deaths
January–March	11
April–June	9
July–September	10
October–December	6
Total	36

15.32 Prof. Green's multiple-choice exam had 50 questions with the distribution of correct answers shown below. *Research question:* At $\alpha = .05$, can you reject the hypothesis that Green's exam answers came from a uniform population? 📁 **Correct**

Correct Answer	Frequency
A	8
B	8
C	9
D	11
E	14
Total	50

15.33 Oxnard Kortholt, Ltd., employs 50 workers. During the last year, the company noted the number of visits with health care professionals (doctor, emergency, home) for each of its employees. U.S. national averages are shown. *Research question:* At $\alpha = .05$, do Oxnard employees differ significantly from the national percent distribution? (National averages are from *The World Almanac and Book of Facts, 2005* [World Almanac Education Group, Inc., 2005], p. 180.) 📁 **Oxnard**

Health Care Visits	National Average (%)	Oxnard Employees (%)
No visits	16.5	4
1–3 visits	45.8	20
4–9 visits	24.4	15
10 or more visits	13.3	11
Total	100.0	50

15.34 In a four-digit lottery, each of the four digits is supposed to have the same probability of occurrence. The table shows the frequency of occurrence of each digit for 89 consecutive daily four-digit drawings. *Research question:* At $\alpha = .01$, can you reject the hypothesis that the digits are from a uniform population? Why do the frequencies add to 356? 📁 **Lottery4**

Digit	Frequency
0	39
1	27
2	35
3	39
4	35
5	35
6	27
7	42
8	36
9	41
Total	356

15.35 A student rolled a supposedly fair die 60 times, resulting in the distribution of dots shown. *Research question:* At $\alpha = .10$, can you reject the hypothesis that the die is fair? 📁 **Dice**

	Number of Dots						
	1	2	3	4	5	6	Total
Frequency	7	14	9	13	7	10	60

15.36 The World Cup soccer tournament is held every 4 years, with 32 teams from various nations competing. In the World Cup tournaments between 1990 and 2002, there were 232 games with the distribution of goals shown in this worksheet. *Research question:* At $\alpha = .025$, can you reject the hypothesis that goals per game follow a Poisson process? *Hint:* You must calculate the mean and look up the Poisson probabilities in Appendix B or Excel. (Data are from Singfat Chu, "Using Soccer Goals to Motivate the Poisson Process," *INFORMS Transactions on Education* 3, no. 2, pp. 62–68.) ☞ **WorldCup**

Goals	f_j	P(X)	e_j	$f_j - e_j$	$(f_j - e_j)^2$	$(f_j - e_j)^2/e_j$
0	19					
1	49					
2	60					
3	47					
4	32					
5	18					
6 or more	7					
Total games	232					
Total goals	575					
Mean goals/game						

*15.37 The table below shows the number of ATM customer arrivals per minute in 60 randomly chosen minutes. *Research question:* At $\alpha = .025$, can you reject the hypothesis that the number of arrivals per minute follows a Poisson process? ☞ **ATM**

0	0	0	1	3	0	0	0	2	5	2	0	1	1	1	2	1	1	0	2
3	0	0	3	0	1	0	1	1	1	1	2	0	2	0	3	0	2	0	1
1	0	0	0	0	1	3	2	1	0	0	0	4	1	0	1	0	3	3	1

15.38 Pick *one* Excel data set (A through F) and investigate whether the data could have come from a normal population using $\alpha = .01$. Use any test you wish, including a histogram, or MegaStat's **Descriptive Statistics > Normal curve goodness of fit test**, or MINITAB's **Stats > Basic Statistics > Normality Test** to obtain a probability plot with the Anderson-Darling statistic. Interpret the *p*-value from your tests. For larger data sets, only the first three and last three observations are shown.

DATA SET A   **Kentucky Derby Winning Time (Seconds), 1950–2006 ($n = 57$)**
☞ **Derby**

Year	Derby Winner	Time
1950	Middleground	121.6
1951	Count Turf	122.6
1952	Hill Gail	121.6
⋮	⋮	⋮
2004	Smarty Jones	124.1
2005	Giacomo	122.8
2006	Barbaro	121.4

Source: *Information Please Sports Almanac* (ESPN Books, 1998), *Facts on File, Detroit Free Press,* and *The New York Times,* selected issues.

DATA SET B   **National League Runs Scored Leader, 1900–2004 ($n = 105$)**
☞ **Runs**

Year	Player	Runs
1900	Roy Thomas, Phil	131
1901	Jesse Burkett, StL	139
1902	Honus Wagner, Pitt	105
⋮	⋮	⋮
2002	Sammy Sosa, Chi	122
2003	Albert Pujols, StL	137
2004	Albert Pujols, StL	133

Source: *Sports Illustrated 2003 Almanac,* pp. 100–113, www.baseball-almanac.com, and www.hickoksports.com.

DATA SET C   Weight (in grams) of Pieces of Halloween Candy (*n* = 78)
Candy

1.6931	1.8320	1.3167	0.5031	0.7097	1.4358
1.8851	1.6695	1.6101	1.6506	1.2105	1.4074
1.5836	1.1164	1.2953	1.4107	1.3212	1.6353
1.5435	1.7175	1.3489	1.1688	1.5543	1.3566
1.4844	1.4636	1.1701	1.5238	1.7346	1.1981
1.6601	1.8359	1.1334	1.7030	1.2481	1.4356
1.3756	1.3172	1.3700	1.0145	1.0062	0.9409
1.4942	1.2316	1.6505	1.7088	1.1850	1.3583
1.5188	1.3460	1.3928	1.6522	0.5303	1.6301
1.0474	1.4664	1.2902	1.9638	1.9687	1.2406
1.6759	1.6989	1.4959	1.4180	1.5218	2.1064
1.3213	1.1116	1.4535	1.4289	1.9156	1.8142
1.3676	1.7157	1.4493	1.4303	1.2912	1.7137

Source: Independent project by statistics student Frances Williams. Weighed on an American Scientific Model S/P 120 analytical balance accurate to 0.0001 gram.

DATA SET D   Price/Earnings Ratios for Specialty Retailers (*n* = 58)
PERatios

Company	PE Ratio
Abercrombie and Fitch	19
Advance AutoParts	16
American Eagle Outfitters	30
⋮	⋮
United Auto Group	12
Williams-Sonoma	28
Zale	15

Source: *BusinessWeek,* November 22, 2004, pp. 95–98.

DATA SET E   U.S. Presidents' Ages at Inauguration (*n* = 43)   Presidents-B

President	Age
Washington	57
J. Adams	61
Jefferson	57
⋮	⋮
Clinton	46
G. W. Bush	54
Obama	47

Source: *The World Almanac and Book of Facts,* 2002, p. 545.

DATA SET F   Weights of 31 Randomly Chosen Circulated Nickels (*n* = 31)
Nickels

5.043	4.980	4.967	5.043	4.956	4.999	4.917	4.927
4.893	5.003	4.951	5.040	5.043	5.004	5.014	5.035
4.883	5.022	4.932	4.998	5.032	4.948	5.001	4.983
4.912	4.796	4.970	4.956	5.036	5.045	4.801	

Note: Weighed by statistics student Dorothy Duffy as an independent project. Nickels were weighed on a Mettler PE 360 Delta Range scale, accurate to 0.001 gram.

INTEGRATIVE PROJECTS

*15.39 In 2002, the Anaheim Angels defeated the San Francisco Giants in the World Series 4 games to 3. The table below shows the inning-by-inning breakdown of runs by each team ($\times$ indicates unnecessary last half of inning). (a) Estimate λ (the mean runs per game). (b) Use Excel's function =POISSON(x,mean,0) to fill in the $P(X = x)$ column. (c) Multiply $P(X = x)$ by 121 to obtain the expected frequencies. (d) Carry out the chi-square test at $\alpha = .05$, combining classes as needed to enlarge expected frequencies. (e) Explain how you obtained the degrees of freedom. (f) Which cells show the largest contribution to the chi-square test statistic? (g) Obtain the *p*-value using Excel's function =CHIDIST(test statistic,deg_freedom). (h) Why is the Poisson distribution a poor fit for baseball runs, even though it fits hockey goals pretty well? WorldSeries

2002 World Series Runs by Inning

		Inning									
		1	*2*	*3*	*4*	*5*	*6*	*7*	*8*	*9*	*Score*
1	San Fran	0	2	0	0	0	2	0	0	0	4
	Anaheim	0	1	0	0	0	2	0	0	0	3
2	San Fran	0	4	1	0	4	0	0	0	1	10
	Anaheim	5	2	0	0	1	1	0	2	$\times$	11
3	Anaheim	0	0	4	4	0	1	0	1	0	10
	San Fran	1	0	0	0	3	0	0	0	0	4
4	Anaheim	0	1	2	0	0	0	0	0	0	3
	San Fran	0	0	0	0	3	0	0	1	$\times$	4
5	Anaheim	0	0	0	0	3	1	0	0	0	4
	San Fran	3	3	0	0	0	2	4	4	$\times$	16
6	San Fran	0	0	0	0	3	1	1	0	0	5
	Anaheim	0	0	0	0	0	0	3	3	$\times$	6
7	San Fran	0	1	0	0	0	0	0	0	0	1
	Anaheim	0	1	3	0	0	0	0	0	$\times$	4

Source: *The Baseball Encyclopedia,* 10th ed. (Macmillan, 1996), and *Baseball Almanac* at www.cnnsi.com.

Runs (x)	f_j	$P(X = x)$	e_j	$f_j - e_j$	$(f_j - e_j)^2$	$(f_j - e_j)^2/e_j$
0	83					
1	15					
2	7					
3	9					
4	6					
5 or more	1					
Total ½ innings	121					
Total runs	85					
Mean runs/inning						

*15.40 Refer to the previous problem. In the 2002 World Series, a total of 85 runs were scored. (a) Before doing any calculations, based on your understanding of baseball, why might runs per inning *not* be uniform? (b) Complete the tabulation below, by counting the frequency of runs in each of the nine innings with all games combined. (c) Calculate the frequency of runs per inning by dividing the total number of runs by 9. (d) Perform the chi-square goodness-of-fit test and obtain a *p*-value using Excel's function =CHIDIST(test statistic,deg_freedom). (e) State your conclusions plainly. WorldSeries

Inning	f_j	e_j	$f_j - e_j$	$(f_j - e_j)^2$	$(f_j - e_j)^2/e_j$
1					
2					
3					
4					
5					
6					
7					
8					
9					
Total					

*15.41 (a) Use either MINITAB or MegaStat or Excel's function =NORMINV(RAND(),0,1) or Excel's Data Analysis > Random Numbers to generate 100 normally distributed random numbers with a mean of 0 and a standard deviation of 1. (b) Make a histogram of your sample and assess its shape. Are there outliers? (c) Calculate descriptive statistics. Are the sample mean and standard deviation close to their intended values? (d) See if the first and third quartiles are approximately -0.675 and $+0.675$, as they should be. (e) Use a z test

$$z = \frac{\bar{x} - \mu}{\sigma/\sqrt{n}} = \frac{\bar{x} - 0}{1/\sqrt{100}} = 10\bar{x}$$

to compare the sample mean to the desired mean. *Note:* Use z instead of t because the hypothesized mean $\mu = 0$ and standard deviation $\sigma = 1$ are known. (f) What would happen if 100 statistics students performed similar experiments, assuming that the random number generator is working correctly?

*15.42 (a) Use either MegaStat or Excel's function =RAND() or Excel's Data Analysis > Random Numbers to generate 100 uniformly distributed random numbers between 0 and 1. (b) Make a histogram of your sample and assess its shape. (c) Calculate descriptive statistics. Are the sample mean and standard deviation close to their intended values $\mu = (0 + 1)/2 = 0.5000$ and $\sigma = \sqrt{1/12} = 0.288675$? (d) See if the first and third quartiles are approximately 0.25 and 0.75, as they should be. (e) Use a z test

$$z = \frac{\bar{x} - \mu}{\sigma/\sqrt{n}} = \frac{\bar{x} - 0.5000}{(0.288675)/\sqrt{100}}$$

to compare the sample mean to the desired mean. *Note:* Use z instead of t because the hypothesized mean $\mu = 0.5000$ and standard deviation $\sigma = 0.288675$ are known. (f) What would happen if 100 statistics students performed similar experiments, assuming that the random number generator is working correctly?

*15.43 (a) Use Excel's Data Analysis > Random Numbers to generate 100 Poisson-distributed random numbers with a mean of $\lambda = 4$. (b) Make a histogram of your sample and assess its shape. (c) Calculate descriptive statistics. Are the sample mean and standard deviation close to their intended values $\lambda = 4$ and $\sigma = \sqrt{\lambda} = \sqrt{4} = 2$? (d) Use a z test

$$z = \frac{\bar{x} - \mu}{\sigma/\sqrt{n}} = \frac{\bar{x} - 4}{2/\sqrt{100}} = 5\bar{x} - 20$$

to compare the sample mean to the desired mean. *Note:* Use z instead of t because the hypothesized mean $\mu = 0.5000$ and standard deviation $\sigma = 0.2887$ are known. (e) What would happen if 100 statistics students performed similar experiments, assuming that Excel's random number generator is working correctly?

RELATED READINGS

Bowman, K. O., and L. R. Shenton. "Omnibus Test Contours for Departures from Normality Based on β_1 and β_2." *Biometrika* 62, no. 2 (1975), pp. 243–50.

Conover, William J. "Some Reasons for Not Using the Yates Continuity Correction on 2×2 Contingency Tables." *Journal of the American Statistical Association* 69 (1974), pp. 374–76.

D'Agostino, Ralph B., and Michael A. Stephens. *Goodness-of-Fit Techniques.* Marcel Dekker, 1986.

Haber, Michael. "A Comparison of Some Continuity Corrections for the Chi-Squared Test on 2×2 Tables." *Journal of the American Statistical Association* 75, no. 371 (1980), pp. 510–15.

Mantel, Nathan. "The Continuity Correction." *The American Statistician* 30, no. 2 (May 1976), pp. 103–104.

Thode, Henry C., Jr. *Testing for Normality.* Marcel Dekker, 2002.

CHAPTER 15   Online Learning Resources

The Online Learning Center (OLC) at www.mhhe.com/doane3e has several *LearningStats* demonstrations to help you understand chi-square tests. Your instructor may assign one or more of them, or you may decide to download the ones that sound interesting.

Topic	LearningStats Demonstrations
Goodness-of-fit tests	☒ Normal and Uniform Tests
	☒ ECDF Plots Illustrated
	☒ Contingency Tables: A Simulation
	☒ Probability Plots: A Simulation
	☒ CDF Normality Test
	☒ Degrees of Freedom
	☒ How Big a Sample

Key: ☒ = Excel

Nonparametric Tests

Chapter Contents

Chapter Learning Objectives

When you finish this chapter you should be able to

LO1 Define nonparametric tests and explain when they may be desirable.

LO2 Use the one-sample runs test.

LO3 Use the Wilcoxon signed-rank test.

LO4 Use the Mann-Whitney test.

LO5 Use the Kruskal-Wallis test for independent samples.

LO6 Use the Friedman test for related samples.

LO7 Use the Spearman rank correlation test.

LO8 Use computer software to perform the tests and obtain p-values.

The hypothesis tests in previous chapters require the estimation of one or more unknown parameters (for example, the population mean or variance). These tests often make unrealistic assumptions about the normality of the underlying population or require large samples to invoke the Central Limit Theorem. In contrast, **nonparametric tests** or distribution-free tests usually focus on the sign or rank of the data rather than the exact numerical value of the variable, do not specify the shape of the parent population, can often be used in smaller samples, and can be used for ordinal data (when the measurement scale is not interval or ratio). Table 16.1 highlights the advantages and disadvantages of nonparametric tests.

TABLE 16.1

Advantages and Disadvantages of Nonparametric Tests

Advantages	Disadvantages
1. Can often be used in small samples.	1. Require special tables for small samples.
2. Generally more powerful than parametric tests when normality cannot be assumed.	2. If normality *can* be assumed, parametric tests are generally more powerful.
3. Can be used for ordinal data.	

Rejection of a hypothesis using a nonparametric test is especially convincing, because non-parametric tests generally make fewer assumptions about the population. If two methods are justified and have similar **power**, the principle of Occam's Razor favors the simpler method. For this reason, statisticians are attracted to nonparametric tests, particularly in applications where data are likely to be ill-behaved and when samples are small.

You might expect that nonparametric tests would primarily be used in areas of business where nominal or ordinal data are common (e.g., human resources, marketing). Yet business analysts who mostly use ratio data (e.g., accounting, finance) may encounter skewed populations that render parametric tests unreliable. These analysts might use nonparametric tests as a *complement* to their customary **parametric tests**. Figure 16.1 shows common nonparametric tests and their parametric counterparts, which you have seen in earlier chapters.

LO1

Define nonparametric tests and explain when they may be desirable.

FIGURE 16.1

Some Common Nonparametric Tests

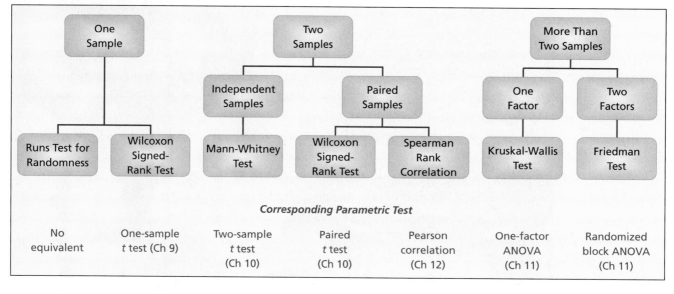

This chapter illustrates only a few of the many nonparametric techniques that are available. The selections are those you are most likely to encounter. Small-sample nonparametric tests are omitted, but references are shown at the end of the chapter for those who need them.

16.2
ONE-SAMPLE RUNS TEST

Use the one-sample runs test.

The one-sample **runs test** is also called the **Wald-Wolfowitz test** after its inventor Abraham Wald (1902–1950) and his student Jacob Wolfowitz. Its purpose is to detect nonrandomness. A nonrandom pattern suggests that the observations are not *independent*—a fundamental assumption of many statistical tests. We are asking whether each observation in a sequence is independent of its predecessor. In a time series, a nonrandom pattern of residuals indicates *autocorrelation* (as in Chapters 12 and 13). In quality control, a nonrandom pattern of deviations from the design specification may indicate an *out-of-control* process. We will illustrate only the large sample version of this test (defined as samples of 10 or more).

Runs Test

This test is to determine whether a sequence of binary events follows a random pattern. A nonrandom sequence suggests nonindependent observations.

The hypotheses are:

H_0: Events follow a random pattern

H_1: Events do not follow a random pattern

To test the hypothesis of randomness we first count the number of outcomes of each type:

n_1 = number of outcomes of the first type

n_2 = number of outcomes of the second type

n = total sample size = $n_1 + n_2$

Application: Quality Inspection Defects

Inspection of 44 computer chips reveals the following sequence of defective (*D*) or acceptable (*A*) chips:

DAAAAAAADDDDAAAAAAAADDAAAAAAAADDDDAAAAAAAAAA

Do defective chips appear at random? A pattern could indicate that the assembly process has a cyclic problem due to unknown causes. The hypotheses are:

H_0: Defects follow a random sequence

H_1: Defects follow a nonrandom sequence

A *run* is a series of consecutive outcomes of the same type, surrounded by a sequence of outcomes of the other type. We group sequences of similar outcomes and count the runs:

D	AAAAAAA	DDDD	AAAAAAAA	DD	AAAAAAAA	DDDD	AAAAAAAAAA
1	2	3	4	5	6	7	8

A run can be a single outcome if it is preceded and followed by outcomes of the other type. There are 8 runs in our sample ($R = 8$). The number of outcomes of each type is:

n_1 = number of defective chips $(D) = 11$

n_2 = number of acceptable chips $(A) = 33$

n = total sample size = $n_1 + n_2 = 11 + 33 = 44$

In a large-sample situation (when $n_1 \geq 10$ and $n_2 \geq 10$), the number of runs R may be assumed to be normally distributed with mean μ_R and standard deviation σ_R.

$$z_{calc} = \frac{R - \mu_R}{\sigma_R} \qquad \text{(test statistic comparing } R \text{ with its expected value } \mu_R) \qquad \textbf{(16.1)}$$

$$\mu_R = \frac{2n_1 n_2}{n} + 1 \qquad \text{(expected value of } R \text{ if } H_0 \text{ is true)} \qquad \textbf{(16.2)}$$

$$\sigma_R = \sqrt{\frac{2n_1 n_2(2n_1 n_2 - n)}{n^2(n - 1)}} \qquad \text{(standard error of } R \text{ if } H_0 \text{ is true)} \qquad \textbf{(16.3)}$$

For our data, the expected number of runs would be

$$\mu_R = \frac{2n_1 n_2}{n} + 1 = \frac{2(11)(33)}{44} + 1 = 17.5$$

Because the actual number of runs ($R = 8$) is far less than expected ($\mu_R = 17.5$) our sample suggests that the null hypothesis may be false, depending on the standard deviation. For our data, the standard deviation is

$$\sigma_R = \sqrt{\frac{2n_1 n_2(2n_1 n_2 - n)}{n^2(n - 1)}} = \sqrt{\frac{2(11)(33)[2(11)(33) - 44]}{44^2(44 - 1)}} = 2.438785$$

The actual number of runs is $R = 8$, so the test statistic is

$$z_{calc} = \frac{R - \mu_R}{\sigma_R} = \frac{8 - 17.5}{2.438785} = -3.90$$

Since either too many runs or too few runs would be nonrandom, we choose a two-tailed test. The critical value $z_{.005}$ for a two-tailed test at $\alpha = .01$ is ± 2.576 so the decision rule is:

Reject the hypothesis of a random pattern if $z < -2.576$ or $z > +2.576$

Otherwise the observed difference is attributable to chance

The test statistic $z = -3.90$ is well below the lower critical limit, as shown in Figure 16.2, so we can easily reject the hypothesis of randomness. The difference between the observed number of runs and the expected number of runs is too great to be due to chance ($p = .0001$).

Figure 16.3 shows the MegaStat output for this problem, which also includes the p-value and the entire distribution for various values of R (not shown because it is lengthy). As with

FIGURE 16.2

Decision Rule for Large-Sample Runs Test

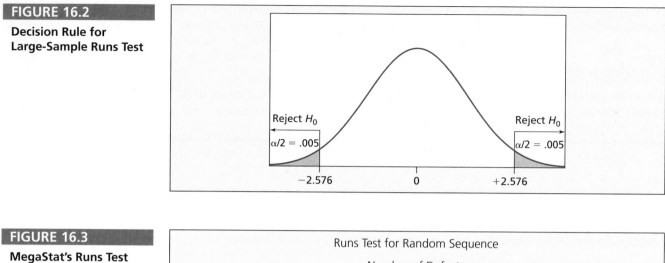

FIGURE 16.3

MegaStat's Runs Test

LO8

Use computer software to perform the tests and obtain p-values.

Runs Test for Random Sequence

Number of Defects

n	runs	
11	4	D
33	4	A
44	8	total

17.50 expected value
2.44 standard deviation
−3.895 z
.0001 p-value (two-tailed)

any hypothesis test, the smaller the *p*-value, the stronger the evidence against H_0. Here, the small *p*-value provides very strong evidence that H_0 is false (i.e., that the sequence is not random).

Small Samples

See end-of-chapter RELATED READINGS for small sample procedures and tables of critical values that extend the test to small samples ($n < 10$). The problem with small samples is that they lack power. That is, in a small sample, it would take an extremely small or large number of runs to convince us that the sequence is nonrandom. While some researchers must deal with small samples, business analysts (e.g., quality control) often have hundreds of observations, so small samples rarely pose a problem.

SECTION EXERCISES

connect

16.1 Using $\alpha = .05$, perform a runs test for randomness on the sample data ($n = 27$).

$A\,A\,B\,B\,A\,A\,B\,B\,A\,B\,A\,A\,B\,B\,A\,A\,B\,B\,B\,B\,A\,A\,B\,A\,B\,B$

16.2 Using $\alpha = .10$, perform a runs test for randomness on the sample data ($n = 24$).

$X\,O\,X\,X\,X\,O\,O\,O\,O\,X\,O\,O\,O\,X\,O\,O\,O\,X\,O\,O\,X\,X\,O$

16.3 On a professional certifying exam there are 25 true-false questions. The correct answers are $T\,F\,T$ $T\,F\,F\,F\,T\,T\,F\,T\,F\,T\,T\,T\,F\,F\,T\,T\,F\,F\,T\,T\,F\,T$. *Research question:* At $\alpha = .05$, is the *T/F* pattern random? **TrueFalse**

16.4 A baseball player was at bat 33 times during preseason exhibition games. His pattern of hits (H) and nonhits (N) is shown (a nonhit is a walk or a strikeout). *Research question:* At $\alpha = .01$, is the pattern of hits random? **Hits**

$N\,N\,H\,N\,H\,N\,N\,H\,N\,N\,H\,H\,N\,N\,N\,H\,N\,H\,N\,N\,N\,H\,N\,N\,H\,N\,H\,N\,N\,H\,H$

The **Wilcoxon signed-rank test** was developed by Frank Wilcoxon (1892–1965) to compare a single sample with a benchmark using only **ranks** of the data instead of the original observations, as in a one-sample t test. It is more often used to compare *paired* observations, as an alternative to the paired-sample t test, which is a special case of the one-sample t test. The advantages of the Wilcoxon test are its freedom from the normality assumption, its robustness to outliers, and its applicability to ordinal data. Although the test does require the population to be roughly symmetric, it has fairly good power over a range of possible non-normal population shapes. It is slightly less powerful than the one-sample t test when the population is normal.

Wilcoxon Signed-Rank Test

The Wilcoxon signed-rank test is a nonparametric test to compare a sample median with a benchmark or to test the median difference in paired samples. It does not require normality but does assume symmetric populations. It corresponds to the parametric t test for one mean.

LO3

Use the Wilcoxon signed-rank test.

If we denote the hypothesized benchmark median as M_0, the hypotheses about the population median M are:

Left-Tailed Test	*Two-Tailed Test*	*Right-Tailed Test*
$H_0: M \geq M_0$	$H_0: M = M_0$	$H_0: M \leq M_0$
$H_1: M < M_0$	$H_1: M \neq M_0$	$H_1: M > M_0$

When the variable of interest is the median difference between paired observations, the test is the same, but we use the symbol M_d for the population median *difference* and (generally) use zero as the benchmark:

Left-Tailed Test	*Two-Tailed Test*	*Right-Tailed Test*
$H_0: M_d \geq 0$	$H_0: M_d = 0$	$H_0: M_d \leq 0$
$H_1: M_d < 0$	$H_1: M_d \neq 0$	$H_1: M_d > 0$

We calculate the difference between each observation and the hypothesized median (or the differences between the paired observations), rank them from smallest to largest by absolute value, and add the ranks of the *positive* differences to obtain the Wilcoxon signed-rank test statistic W. Its expected value and variance depend only on the sample size n.

$$W = \sum_{i=1}^{n} R^+ \qquad \text{(the sum of all positive ranks)} \qquad \textbf{(16.4)}$$

$$\mu_W = \frac{n(n+1)}{4} \qquad \text{(expected value of the } W \text{ statistic)} \qquad \textbf{(16.5)}$$

$$\sigma_W = \sqrt{\frac{n(n+1)(2n+1)}{24}} \qquad \text{(standard deviation of the } W \text{ statistic)} \qquad \textbf{(16.6)}$$

For large samples ($n \geq 20$) the test statistic is approximately normal:

$$z_{\text{calc}} = \frac{W - \dfrac{n(n+1)}{4}}{\sqrt{\dfrac{n(n+1)(2n+1)}{24}}} \qquad \text{(Wilcoxon test statistic for large } n) \qquad \textbf{(16.7)}$$

Application: Median versus Benchmark

Are price-earnings (P/E) ratios of stocks in *specialty* retail stores (e.g., Abercrombie & Fitch) the same as P/E ratios for stocks of *multiline* retail stores (e.g., Target)? Table 16.2 shows P/E ratios for a random sample of 21 specialty stores. The median P/E ratio for all multiline retail stores for the same date was $M_0 = 20.2$ (our benchmark). Our hypotheses are:

$H_0: M = 20.2$ (the median P/E ratio for specialty stores is 20.2)

$H_1: M \neq 20.2$ (the median P/E ratio for specialty stores is not 20.2)

TABLE 16.2		Wilcoxon Signed-Rank Test of P/E Ratios ($n = 21$ firms) WilcoxonA				
Company	X	X − 20.2	| X − 20.2 |	Rank	R^+	R^-
Bebe Stores Inc	19.8	−0.4	0.4	1.5		1.5
Barnes & Noble Inc	19.8	−0.4	0.4	1.5		1.5
Aeropostale Inc	20.6	0.4	0.4	3	3	
Deb Shops	18.7	−1.5	1.5	4		4
Gap Inc	22.0	1.8	1.8	5	5	
PETsMART Inc	17.9	−2.3	2.3	6		6
Payless Shoesource	17.0	−3.2	3.2	7		7
Abercrombie & Fitch Co	16.8	−3.4	3.4	8.5		8.5
AutoZone Inc	16.8	−3.4	3.4	8.5		8.5
Lithia Motors Inc A	16.3	−3.9	3.9	10		10
Genesco Inc	24.3	4.1	4.1	11	11	
Sherwin-Williams Co	16.0	−4.2	4.2	12		12
CSK Auto Corp	14.5	−5.7	5.7	13		13
Tiffany & Co	26.2	6.0	6.0	14	14	
Rex Stores	14.0	−6.2	6.2	15		15
Casual Male Retail Group	12.6	−7.6	7.6	16		16
Sally Beauty Co Inc	28.9	8.7	8.7	17	17	
Syms Corp	32.1	11.9	11.9	18	18	
Zale Corp	40.4	20.2	20.2	19	19	
Coldwater Creek Inc	41.0	20.8	20.8	20	20	
Talbots Inc	124.7	104.5	104.5	21	21	
			Sum	231.0	128.0	103.0

Source: http://investing.businessweek.com, accessed on June 19, 2007. Companies are sorted by rank of absolute differences.

To perform the test, we subtract 20.2 (the benchmark) from each specialty store's P/E ratio, take absolute values, convert to ranks, and sum the *positive* ranks. Negative ranks are shown, but are not used. We assign tie ranks so that the sum of the tied values is the same as if they were not tied. For example, 3.4 occurs twice (Abercrombie & Fitch and AutoZone). If not tied, these data values would have ranks 8 and 9, so we assign a "tie" rank of 8.5 to each. Companies are shown in rank order of absolute differences.

The test statistic is:

$$z_{calc} = \frac{W - \dfrac{n(n+1)}{4}}{\sqrt{\dfrac{n(n+1)(2n+1)}{24}}} = \frac{128.0 - \dfrac{21(21+1)}{4}}{\sqrt{\dfrac{21(21+1)(42+1)}{24}}} = \frac{128.0 - 115.5}{28.770645} = 0.43447$$

Using Excel, the two-tailed *p*-value is $p = .6639$ (or $p = .6672$ if we use Appendix C with $z = 0.43$). At any customary level of significance, we cannot reject the hypothesis that specialty retail stores have the same median P/E as multiline retail stores. Although we use the *z* table for the *test statistic* (because $n \geq 20$), the P/E *data* do not seem to be from a normal population (for example, look at Talbot's extreme P/E ratio of 124.7). Thus, Wilcoxon's nonparametric test of the *median* is preferred to a one-sample *t* test of the *mean* (Chapter 9).

Application: Paired Data

Did P/E ratios decline between 2003 and 2007? We will perform a Wilcoxon test for *paired data* using a random sample of 23 common stocks. The parameter of interest is the median difference (M_d). Because the P/E ratios do not appear to be normally distributed (e.g., Rohm & Haas Co.'s 2003 P/E ratio) the Wilcoxon test of *medians* is attractive (instead of the paired *t* test for *means* in Chapter 10). Using $d = X_{2007} - X_{2003}$, a left-tailed test is appropriate:

$H_0: M_d \geq 0$ (the median difference is zero or positive)
$H_1: M_d < 0$ (the median difference is negative, i.e., 2007 P/E is less than 2003 P/E)

Table 16.3 shows the calculations for the Wilcoxon signed-rank statistic, with the companies in rank order of absolute differences. Because the first three have zero difference (neither positive nor negative), these three observations (highlighted) are *excluded* from the analysis.

Wilcoxon Signed-Rank Paired Test (*n* = 23 firms) WilcoxonB							TABLE 16.3
Company (Ticker Symbol)	2007 P/E	2003 P/E	d	|d|	Rank	R⁺	R⁻
FirstEnergy Corp (FE)	14	14	0	0	—		
Whirlpool Corp (WHR)	18	18	0	0	—		
Burlington/Santa (BNI)	14	14	0	0	—		
Constellation Energy (CEG)	16	15	1	1	1	1	
Mellon Financial (MEL)	17	19	−2	2	2.5		2.5
Yum! Brands Inc (YUM)	18	16	2	2	2.5	2.5	
Baxter International (BAX)	20	23	−3	3	5		5
Fluor Corp (FLR)	22	19	3	3	5	5	
Allied Waste Ind (AW)	21	18	3	3	5	5	
Ingersoll-Rand-A (IR)	12	16	−4	4	7.5		7.5
Lexmark Intl A (LXK)	17	21	−4	4	7.5		7.5
Moody's Corp (MCO)	29	24	5	5	9	9	
Electronic Data (EDS)	17	23	−6	6	10		10
Freeport-Mcmor-B (FCX)	11	18	−7	7	11		11
Family Dollar Stores (FDO)	19	27	−8	8	12.5		12.5
Leggett & Platt (LEG)	13	21	−8	8	12.5		12.5
Wendy's Intl Inc (WEN)	24	15	9	9	14	14	
Sara Lee Corp (SLE)	25	13	12	12	15	15	
Bed Bath & Beyond (BBBY)	20	37	−17	17	16		16
Ace Ltd (ACE)	8	26	−18	18	17.5		17.5
ConocoPhillips (COP)	8	26	−18	18	17.5		17.5
Baker Hughes Inc (BHI)	13	55	−42	42	19		19
Rohm & Haas Co (ROH)	15	68	−53	53	20		20
				Sum	210.0	51.5	158.5

Source: *The Wall Street Journal,* July 31, 2003, and Standard & Poors, *Security Owner's Stock Guide,* February 2007. P/E ratios were reported as integers in these publications. Companies are sorted by rank of absolute differences.

Despite losing three observations due to zero differences, we still have $n \geq 20$ so we can use the large-sample test statistic:

$$z_{calc} = \frac{W - \frac{n(n+1)}{4}}{\sqrt{\frac{n(n+1)(2n+1)}{24}}} = \frac{51.5 - \frac{20(20+1)}{4}}{\sqrt{\frac{20(20+1)(40+1)}{24}}} = \frac{51.5 - 105.0}{26.7862} = -1.9973$$

Using Excel, we find the left-tailed *p*-value to be $p = .0229$ (or $p = .0228$ if we use Appendix C with $z = -2.00$) so at $\alpha = .05$ we conclude that P/E ratios did decline between 2003 and 2007. Figure 16.4 shows that MegaStat confirms our calculations.

FIGURE 16.4

MegaStat Signed-Rank Test for Paired Data

LO8

Use computer software to perform the tests and obtain *p*-values.

Wilcoxon Signed-Rank Test

variables: 2007 P/E−2003 P/E
    51.5 sum of positive ranks
   158.5 sum of negative ranks

    20 n
105.00 expected value
  26.79 standard deviation
 −1.997 z
  .0229 p-value (one-tailed, lower)

SECTION EXERCISES

16.5 A sample of 28 student scores on the chemistry midterm exam is shown. (a) At $\alpha = .10$, does the population median differ from 50? Make a worksheet in Excel for your calculations. (b) Make a histogram of the data. Would you be justified in using a parametric t test that assumes normality? Explain. 📖 **Chemistry**

74	60	7	97	62	2	100
5	99	78	93	32	43	64
87	37	70	54	60	62	17
26	45	84	24	66	7	48

16.6 Final exam scores for a sample of 20 students in a managerial accounting class are shown. (a) At $\alpha = .05$, is there a difference in the population median scores on the two exams? Make an Excel worksheet for your Wilcoxon signed-rank test calculations and check your work by using MegaStat or a similar computer package. (b) Perform a two-tailed parametric t test for paired two-sample means by using Excel or MegaStat. Do you get the same decision? 📖 **Accounting**

Student	Exam 1	Exam 2	Student	Exam 1	Exam 2	Student	Exam 1	Exam 2
1	70	81	8	71	69	15	59	68
2	74	89	9	52	53	16	54	47
3	65	59	10	79	84	17	75	84
4	60	68	11	84	96	18	92	100
5	63	75	12	95	96	19	70	81
6	58	77	13	83	99	20	54	58
7	72	82	14	81	76			

16.4 MANN-WHITNEY TEST

The **Mann-Whitney test**, named after Henry B. Mann (1905–2000) and D. R. Whitney, is a nonparametric test that compares two populations. The Mann-Whitney test does not assume normality. Assuming that the populations differ only in centrality (i.e., location) it is a test for equality of *medians*. It is analogous to the t test for two independent sample means.

Mann-Whitney Test

The Mann-Whitney test is a nonparametric test to compare two populations, utilizing only the ranks of the data from two independent samples. It does not require normality, but does assume equal variances. It corresponds to the parametric t test for two means.

Studies suggest that the Mann-Whitney test has only slightly less power in distinguishing between centrality of two populations than the t test for two independent sample means, which you studied in Chapter 10. The Mann-Whitney test requires independent samples from populations with equal variances, but the populations need not be normal. To avoid the use of special tables, we will illustrate only a large-sample version of this test (defined as samples of 10 or more).*

Assuming that the only difference in the populations is in location, the hypotheses for a two-tailed test of the population medians would be:

LO4

Use the Mann-Whitney test.

H_0: $M_1 = M_2$ (no difference in medians)

H_1: $M_1 \neq M_2$ (medians differ for the two groups)

Application: Restaurant Quality 📖 Restaurants

Does spending more at a restaurant lead to greater customer satisfaction? Readers of *Consumer Reports* rated 29 American, Italian, and Mexican chain restaurants on a scale of 0 to 100, based mainly on the taste of the food. Results are shown in Table 16.4, sorted by

---

*If populations are normal but have unequal variances, the unpooled two-sample t-test with Welch's correction is preferred to the Mann-Whitney test. You can test for equal variances by using the F test discussed in Chapter 10. See end of chapter RELATED READINGS for small sample procedures and tables.

Obs	Satisfaction	Rank	Price	Obs	Satisfaction	Rank	Price
1	73	1	Low	16	81	16.5	Low
2	76	2.5	Low	17	81	16.5	Low
3	76	2.5	High	18	82	18.5	High
4	77	4.5	Low	19	82	18.5	High
5	77	4.5	Low	20	83	20.5	Low
6	78	7	Low	21	83	20.5	Low
7	78	7	High	22	84	22.5	High
8	78	7	High	23	84	22.5	High
9	79	10	Low	24	85	25	High
10	79	10	Low	25	85	25	High
11	79	10	Low	26	85	25	High
12	80	13.5	Low	27	86	28	High
13	80	13.5	Low	28	86	28	High
14	80	13.5	Low	29	86	28	High
15	80	13.5	High				

TABLE 16.4

Satisfaction and Ranks for 29 Chain Restaurants
Restaurants

Source: © 2003 by Consumers Union of U.S., Inc., Yonkers, NY 10703-1057, excerpted or adapted with permission from the July 2003 issue of *Consumer Reports* for educational purposes only.

satisfaction rating (note that, in this test, the lowest data value is assigned a rank of 1, which is rather counterintuitive for restaurant ratings). Each restaurant is assigned to one of two price groups: *Low* (under $15 per person) and *High* ($15 or more per person). Is there a significant difference in satisfaction between the higher-priced restaurants and the lower-priced ones? The parametric *t* test for two means would require that the variable be measured on a ratio or interval level. Because the satisfaction ratings are solely based on human perception, we are unwilling to assume the strong measurement properties associated with ratio or interval data. Instead, we treat these measurements as ordinal data (i.e., ranked data).

In Table 16.4, we convert the customer satisfaction ratings into ranks by sorting the *combined* samples from lowest to highest satisfaction, and then assigning a rank to each satisfaction score. If values are tied, the average of the ranks is assigned to each. Restaurants are then separated into two groups based on the price category (*Low, High*) as displayed in Table 16.5.

Low-Priced Restaurants ($n_1 = 15$)		High-Priced Restaurants ($n_2 = 14$)	
Satisfaction	Rank	Satisfaction	Rank
73	1	76	2.5
76	2.5	78	7
77	4.5	78	7
77	4.5	80	13.5
78	7	82	18.5
79	10	82	18.5
79	10	84	22.5
79	10	84	22.5
80	13.5	85	25
80	13.5	85	25
80	13.5	85	25
81	16.5	86	28
81	16.5	86	28
83	20.5	86	28
83	20.5		
Rank sum: $T_1 = 164$		Rank sum: $T_2 = 271$	
Sample size $n_1 = 15$		Sample size $n_2 = 14$	
Mean rank: $\bar{T}_1 = 164/15 = 10.93333$		Mean rank: $\bar{T}_2 = 271/14 = 19.35714$	

TABLE 16.5

Chain Restaurant Customer Satisfaction Score

The ranks are summed for each column to get $T_1 = 164$ and $T_2 = 271$. The sum $T_1 + T_2$ must be $n(n + 1)/2$ where $n = n_1 + n_2 = 15 + 14 = 29$. Because $n(n + 1)/2 = (29)(30)/2 = 435$

and the sample sums are $T_1 + T_2 = 164 + 271 = 435$, our calculations check.* Next, we calculate the mean rank sums $\bar{T}_1$ and $\bar{T}_2$. If there is no difference between groups, we would expect $\bar{T}_1 - \bar{T}_2$ to be near zero. For large samples ($n_1 \geq 10$, $n_2 \geq 10$) we can use a z test (see end-of-chapter RELATED READINGS for small sample tables and procedures). The test statistic is

(16.8)
$$z_{calc} = \frac{\bar{T}_1 - \bar{T}_2}{(n_1 + n_2)\sqrt{\dfrac{n_1 + n_2 + 1}{12 n_1 n_2}}}$$

For our data:

$$z_{calc} = \frac{10.93333 - 19.35714}{(15 + 14)\sqrt{\dfrac{15 + 14 + 1}{(12)(15)(14)}}} = -2.662$$

At $\alpha = .01$, rejection in a two-tailed test requires $z > +2.326$ or $z < -2.326$, so we would reject the hypothesis that the population medians are the same. From Appendix C the two-tail p-value is .0078, which says that a sample difference of this magnitude would be expected only about 8 times in 1,000 samples if the populations were the same. MegaStat uses a different version of this test,** but obtains a similar result, as shown in Figure 16.5.

FIGURE 16.5

MegaStat's Mann-Whitney Test

LO8

Use computer software to perform the tests and obtain p-values.

Wilcoxon Mann/Whitney Test

n	sum of ranks	
15	164	Group 1
14	271	Group 2
29	435	total

225.00 expected value
22.91 standard deviation
−2.662 z, corrected for ties
.0078 p-value (two-tailed)

SECTION EXERCISES

connect

16.7 Bob and Tom are "paper investors." They each "buy" stocks they think will rise in value and "hold" them for a year. At the end of the year, they compare their stocks' appreciation (percent). (a) At $\alpha = .05$, is there a difference in the medians (assume these are samples of Bob's and Tom's stock-picking skills). Use MegaStat or a similar computer package for the Mann-Whitney (Wilcoxon rank-sum test) calculations. (b) Perform a two-tailed parametric t test for two independent sample means by using Excel or MegaStat. Do you get the same decision? Investors

Bob's Portfolio (10 stocks)	7.0, 2.5, 6.2, 4.4, 4.2, 8.5, 10.0, 6.4, 3.6, 7.6
Tom's Portfolio (12 stocks)	5.2, 0.4, 2.6, −0.2, 4.0, 5.2, 8.6, 4.3, 3.0, 0.0, 8.6, 7.5

16.8 An experimental bumper was designed to reduce damage in low-speed collisions. This bumper was installed on an experimental group of vans in a large fleet, but not on a control group. At the end of a trial period, there were 12 repair incidents (a "repair incident" is an accident that resulted in a repair invoice) for the experimental group and 9 repair incidents for the control group. The dollar cost per repair incident is shown below. (a) Use MegaStat or MINITAB to perform a two-tailed Mann-Whitney test at $\alpha = .05$. (b) Perform a two-tailed parametric t test for two independent sample means by using Excel or MegaStat. Do you get the same

---

*If the sum $T_1 + T_2$ does not check, you have made an error in calculating the ranks. It is more reliable to use MINITAB's Calc function RANK() to convert a column of data into ranks. Avoid Excel's =RANK() function, because it does not adjust for ties.

**The *Mann-Whitney test* is also called the *Wilcoxon rank-sum test,* hence MegaStat's heading. When statistical tests were developed or popularized independently by more than one statistician, the names may vary.

decision? (Data are from Floyd G. Willoughby and Thomas W. Lauer, confidential case study.)

📁 **Damage**

> *Old bumper:* 1,185, 885, 2,955, 815, 2,852, 1,217, 1,762, 2,592, 1,632
>
> *New bumper:* 1,973, 403, 509, 2,103, 1,153, 292, 1,916, 1,602, 1,559, 547, 801, 359

16.5 KRUSKAL-WALLIS TEST FOR INDEPENDENT SAMPLES

William H. Kruskal and W. Allen Wallis proposed a test to compare c independent samples. It may be viewed as a generalization of the Mann-Whitney test, which compares two independent samples. Groups can be of different sizes if each has five or more observations. If we assume that the populations differ only in centrality (i.e., location), the **Kruskal-Wallis test** (K-W test) compares the medians of c independent samples. It is analogous to one-factor ANOVA (completely randomized model). The K-W test requires that the populations be of similar shape, but does not require normal populations as in ANOVA, making it an attractive alternative for applications in finance, engineering, and marketing.

Kruskal-Wallis Test

LO5

Use the Kruskal-Wallis test for independent samples.

The K-W test compares the medians of c independent samples. It may be viewed as a generalization of the Mann-Whitney test and is a nonparametric alternative to one-factor ANOVA.

Assuming that the populations are otherwise similar, the hypotheses to be tested are:

H_0: All c population medians are the same

H_1: Not all the population medians are the same

In testing for equality of location, the K-W test may be almost as powerful as one-factor ANOVA. It can even be useful for ratio or interval data when there are outliers or unequal group variances, or if the population is thought to be non-normal. For a completely randomized design with c groups the test statistic is

$$H_{calc} = \frac{12}{n(n+1)} \sum_{j=1}^{c} \frac{T_j^2}{n_j} - 3(n+1) \qquad \text{(Kruskal-Wallis test statistic)} \qquad \textbf{(16.9)}$$

where

$n = n_1 + n_2 + \cdots + n_c$

n_j = number of observations in group j

T_j = sum of ranks for group j

Application: Employee Absenteeism

The *XYZ* Corporation is interested in possible differences in days worked by salaried employees in three departments in the financial area. Table 16.6 shows annual days worked by 23 randomly chosen employees from these departments. Because the sampling methodology reflects the department sizes, the sample sizes are unequal.

TABLE 16.6

Annual Days Worked by Department
📁 **Days**

Department	Days Worked									
Budgets	278	260	265	245	258					
Payables	205	270	220	240	255	217	266	239	240	228
Pricing	240	258	233	256	233	242	244	249		

To get the test statistic, we combine the samples and assign a rank to each observation in each group, as shown in Table 16.7. We use a column worksheet so the calculations are easier to follow. When a tie occurs, each observation is assigned the average of the ranks.

TABLE 16.7

Merged Data Converted to Ranks

Obs	Rank	Days	Dept
1	1	205	Payables
2	2	217	Payables
3	3	220	Payables
4	4	228	Payables
5	5.5	233	Pricing
6	5.5	233	Pricing
7	7	239	Payables
8	9	240	Payables
9	9	240	Payables
10	9	240	Pricing
11	11	242	Pricing
12	12	244	Pricing
13	13	245	Budgets
14	14	249	Pricing
15	15	255	Payables
16	16	256	Pricing
17	17.5	258	Budgets
18	17.5	258	Pricing
19	19	260	Budgets
20	20	265	Budgets
21	21	266	Payables
22	22	270	Payables
23	23	278	Budgets

Next, the data are arranged by groups, as shown in Table 16.8, and the ranks are summed to give T_1, T_2, and T_3. As a check on our work, the sum of the ranks must be $n(n + 1)/2 = (23)(23 + 1)/2 = 276$. This is easily verified because $T_1 + T_2 + T_3 = 92.5 + 93.0 + 90.5 = 276$.

TABLE 16.8

Worksheet for Rank Sums

Budgets	Rank	Payables	Rank	Pricing	Rank
245	13	205	1	233	5.5
258	17.5	217	2	233	5.5
260	19	220	3	240	9
265	20	228	4	242	11
278	23	239	7	244	12
		240	9	249	14
		240	9	256	16
		255	15	258	17.5
		266	21		
		270	22		
Sum of ranks	92.5	Sum of ranks	93	Sum of ranks	90.5
Sample size	$n_1 = 5$	Sample size	$n_2 = 10$	Sample size	$n_3 = 8$

The value of the test statistic is

$$H_{\text{calc}} = \frac{12}{n(n + 1)} \sum_{j=1}^{c} \frac{T_j^2}{n_j} - 3(n + 1)$$

$$= \frac{12}{(23)(23 + 1)} \left[\frac{92.5^2}{5} + \frac{93^2}{10} + \frac{90.5^2}{8} \right] - 3(23 + 1) = 6.259$$

The H test statistic follows a chi-square distribution with degrees of freedom $d.f. = c - 1 = 3 - 1 = 2$. This is a right-tailed test (i.e., we will reject the null hypothesis of equal medians if H exceeds its critical value). Using $d.f. = 2$, from Appendix E we obtain critical values for various levels of significance:

α	χ^2_α	*Interpretation*
.10	4.605	Reject H_0—conclude that the means differ
.05	5.991	Reject H_0—conclude that the means differ
.025	7.378	Do not reject H_0—conclude that the means are not different

In this instance, our decision is sensitive to the level of significance chosen. The p-value is between .05 and .025, so it seems appropriate to conclude that the difference among the three groups is not overwhelming. MegaStat gives the exact p-value (.0437) as shown in Figure 16.6. We could also obtain this p-value from Excel's function =CHIDIST(6.259,2). The stacked dot plots in Figure 16.7 reveal that the three distributions overlap quite a bit, so there may be little practical difference in the distributions. The MINITAB K-W test is similar, but requires unstacked data (one column for the data, one column for the group name). MINITAB warns you if the sample size is too small.

Kruskal-Wallis Test

Median	n	Avg. Rank	
260.00	5	18.50	Budgets
239.50	10	9.30	Payables
243.00	8	11.31	Pricing
244.00	23		Total
		6.259	H
		2	d.f.
		.0437	p-value

FIGURE 16.6

MegaStat's Kruskal-Wallis Test

LO8

Use computer software to perform the tests and obtain p-values.

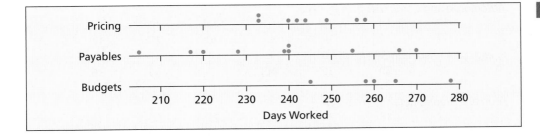

FIGURE 16.7

MINITAB's Stacked Dot Plots for Days Worked

SECTION EXERCISES

connect

16.9   Samples are shown of volatility (coefficient of variation) for sector stocks over a certain period of time. (a) At $\alpha = .05$, is there a difference in median volatility in these four portfolios? Use MegaStat, MINITAB, or a similar computer package for the calculations. (b) Use one-factor ANOVA to compare the means. Do you reach the same conclusion? (c) Make a histogram or other display of each sample. Would you be willing to assume normality?   **Volatile**

Health	Energy	Retail	Leisure
14.5	23.0	19.4	17.6
18.4	19.9	20.7	18.1
13.7	24.5	18.5	16.1
16.9	24.2	15.5	23.2
16.2	19.4	17.7	17.6
21.6	22.1	21.4	25.5
25.6	31.6	26.5	24.1
21.4	22.4	21.5	25.9
26.6	31.3	22.8	25.5
19.0	32.5	27.4	26.3
12.6	12.8	22.0	12.9
13.5	14.4	17.1	11.1
13.5		24.8	4.9
13.0		13.4	
13.6			

16.10 The results shown below are mean productivity measurements (average number of assemblies completed per hour) for a random sample of workers at each of three work stations. (a) At $\alpha = .05$, is there a difference in median productivity? Use MegaStat, MINITAB, or a similar computer package for the calculations. (b) Use one-factor ANOVA to compare the means. Do you reach the same conclusion? (c) Make a histogram or other display of the pooled data. Does the assumption of normality seem justified? 📁 **Workers**

Hourly Productivity of Assemblers in Plants

Work Station	Finished Units Produced Per Hour								
A (9 workers)	3.6	5.1	2.8	4.6	4.7	4.1	3.4	2.9	4.5
B (6 workers)	2.7	3.1	5.0	1.9	2.2	3.2			
C (10 workers)	6.8	2.5	5.4	6.7	4.6	3.9	5.4	4.9	7.1	8.4

Mini Case   16.1

Price/Earnings Ratios

Are price/earnings ratios different for firms in the five sectors shown in Table 16.9? Since the data are interval, we could try either one-factor ANOVA or a Kruskal-Wallis test. How can we decide?

TABLE 16.9   Common Stock P/E Ratios of Selected Companies 📁 **PERatios**

Automotive and Components (n = 17)

9	13	14	29	10	32	16	14	9
21	17	21	10	7	20	13	17	

Energy Equipment and Services (n = 12)

31	22	39	25	46	7	29	36	42
36	49	35						

Food and Staples Retailing (n = 22)

25	22	18	24	27	21	66	30	24
22	21	9	11	16	13	32	15	25
36	29	25	18					

Hotels, Restaurants, and Leisure (n = 18)

34	26	74	24	17	19	22	34	30
22	24	19	23	19	21	31	16	19

Multiline Retail Firms (n = 18)

16	29	22	19	20	14	22	18	28
13	16	20	21	23	20	3	14	27

Source: *BusinessWeek*, November 22, 2004.

Combining the samples, the histogram in Figure 16.8 and the probability plot in Figure 16.9 suggest non-normality, so instead of one-factor ANOVA we would prefer the nonparametric Kruskal-Wallis test with $d.f. = c - 1 = 5 - 1 = 4$ degrees of freedom. MINITAB's output in Figure 16.10 shows that the medians differ ($p = .000$). The test statistic ($H = 25.32$) exceeds the chi-square critical value for $\alpha = .01$ (13.28). We conclude that the P/E ratios are *not* the same for these five sectors.

FIGURE 16.8   **Histogram of Combined Samples ($n = 87$)**

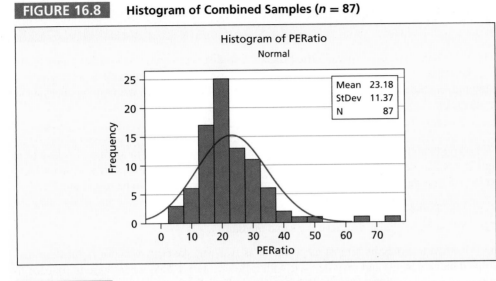

FIGURE 16.9   **Probability Plot of Combined Samples ($n = 87$)**

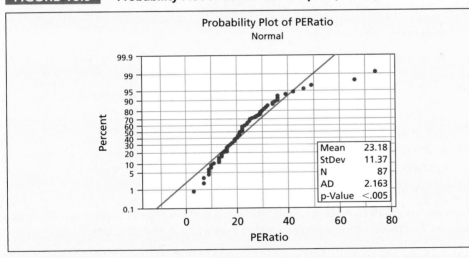

FIGURE 16.10   **MINITAB's Kruskal-Wallis Test**

Kruskal-Wallis Test: PERatio versus Sector

Sector	N	Median	Ave Rank	z
Auto	17	14.00	24.4	−3.58
EnergyEq	12	35.50	68.5	3.62
FoodDrug	22	23.00	46.9	0.62
Leisure	18	22.50	51.1	1.34
Retail	18	20.00	35.6	−1.58
Overall	87		44.0	

H = 25.27   DF = 4   P = 0.000
H = 25.32   DF = 4   P = 0.000   (adjusted for ties)

LO8

Use computer software to perform the tests and obtain *p*-values.

16.6
FRIEDMAN TEST FOR RELATED SAMPLES

The **Friedman test** is a nonparametric test that will reveal whether c treatments have the same central tendency when there is a second factor with r levels. If the populations are assumed the same except for centrality (location), the test is a comparison of medians. The test is analogous to two-factor ANOVA without replication (or randomized block design) with one observation for each cell. The groups must be of the same size, treatments should be randomly assigned within the blocks, and data should be at least interval scale.

LO6

Use the Friedman test for related samples.

Friedman Test

The Friedman test is a nonparametric procedure to discover whether c population medians are the same or different when classification is based on two factors. It is analogous to randomized block ANOVA (two-factor without replication) but without the normality assumption.

The Friedman test resembles the Kruskal-Wallis test except that, in addition to the c treatment levels that define the columns of the observation matrix, it also specifies r block factor levels to define each row of the observation matrix. The hypotheses to be tested are:

H_0: All c populations have the same median

H_1: Not all the populations have the same median

The Friedman test may be almost as powerful as two-way ANOVA without replication (randomized block design) and may be used with ratio or interval data when there is concern for outliers or non-normality of the underlying populations. It is a rare population that meets the normality requirement, so Friedman's test is quite useful.

Test Statistic

The test statistic is

(16.10) $$F_{calc} = \frac{12}{rc(c+1)} \sum_{j=1}^{c} T_j^2 - 3r(c+1) \qquad \text{(Friedman test statistic)}$$

where

r = the number of blocks (rows)

c = the number of treatments (columns)

T_j = the sum of ranks for treatment j

Although the Friedman formula resembles the Kruskal-Wallis formula, there is a difference: the ranks are computed *within each block* rather than within a pooled sample.

Application: Braking Effectiveness

Experiments are being conducted to test the effect of brake pad composition on stopping distance. Five prototype brake pads are prepared. Each pad is installed on the same automobile, which is accelerated to 100 kph and then braked to the shortest possible stop without loss of control. This test is repeated four times in rapid succession to reveal brake fade due to heating and lining abrasion. Car weight and balance are identical in all tests, and the same expert driver performs all tests. The pavement is dry and the outside air temperature is the same for all tests. To eliminate potential bias, the driver has no information about which pad is installed for a given test. The results are shown in Table 16.10.

The Friedman test requires that either the number of blocks or the number of treatments be at least 5. Our matrix meets this requirement because $r = 4$ and $c = 5$. Ranks are computed *within each row*. As a check on our arithmetic, we may utilize the fact that the ranks must sum to $rc(c + 1)/2 = (4)(5)(5 + 1)/2 = 60$. We see that our sums are correct because $T_1 + T_2 + T_3 + T_4 + T_5 = 15 + 14 + 5 + 19 + 7 = 60$.

TABLE 16.10

Stopping Distance from 100 kph
🖮 **Braking**

	Pad 1		Pad 2		Pad 3		Pad 4		Pad 5	
	Feet	*Rank*	*Feet*	*Rank*	*Feet*	*Rank*	*Feet*	*Rank*	*Feet*	*Rank*
Trial 1	166	3	176	4	152	2	198	5	148	1
Trial 2	174	4	170	3	148	1	206	5	152	2
Trial 3	184	3	186	4	160	1	212	5	168	2
Trial 4	220	5	204	3	184	1	216	4	196	2
Rank sum	$T_1 = 15$		$T_2 = 14$		$T_3 = 5$		$T_4 = 19$		$T_5 = 7$	

We now compute the test statistic:

$$F_{calc} = \frac{12}{rc(c+1)} \sum_{j=1}^{c} T_j^2 - 3r(c+1)$$

$$= \frac{12}{(4)(5)(5+1)}[15^2 + 14^2 + 5^2 + 19^2 + 7^2] - 3(4)(5+1) = 13.6$$

The Friedman test statistic follows a chi-square distribution with degrees of freedom $d.f. = c - 1 = 5 - 1 = 4$. Using $d.f. = 4$, from Appendix E we obtain the critical values for various α levels:

α	χ_α^2	*Interpretation*
.025	11.143	Reject H_0—conclude that the medians differ
.01	13.277	Reject H_0—conclude that the medians differ
.005	14.861	Do not reject H_0—the medians do not differ

The *p*-value is between .01 and .005, so we conclude that there is a significant difference in brake pads except at very strict Type I error levels. The results from MegaStat shown in Figure 16.11 show the exact *p*-value (.0087). We could also obtain this *p*-value by using Excel's function =CHIDIST(13.6,4).

FIGURE 16.11

MegaStat's Friedman Test for Brake Pads

LO8

Use computer software to perform the tests and obtain *p*-values.

Friedman Test

Sum of Ranks	Avg. Rank	
15.00	3.75	
14.00	3.50	
5.00	1.25	
19.00	4.75	
7.00	1.75	
60.00	3.00	Total
	4	n
	13.600	chi-square
	4	d.f.
	.0087	*p*-value

SECTION EXERCISES

16.11 Consumers are asked to rate the attractiveness of four potential dashboard surface textures on an interval scale (1 = least attractive, 10 = most attractive). Use MegaStat or another software package to perform a Friedman test to see whether the median ratings of surfaces differ at $\alpha = .05$, using age as the blocking factor. 🖮 **Texture**

	Shiny	Satin	Pebbled	Pattern	Embossed
Youth (Under 21)	6.7	6.6	5.5	4.3	4.4
Adult (21 to 39)	5.5	5.3	6.2	5.9	6.2
Middle-Age (40 to 61)	4.5	5.1	6.7	5.5	5.4
Senior (62 and over)	3.9	4.5	6.1	4.1	4.9

16.12 JavaMax is a neighborhood take-out coffee shop that offers three sizes. Yesterday's sales are shown. Use MegaStat or another software package to perform a Friedman test to see whether the median sales of coffee sizes differ at $\alpha = .05$, using time of day as the blocking factor. ⬆ **Coffee**

	Small	Medium	Large
6 A.M. to 8 A.M.	60	77	85
8 A.M. to 11 A.M.	65	74	76
11 A.M. to 3 P.M.	70	70	70
3 P.M. to 7 P.M.	61	60	55
7 P.M. to 11 P.M.	55	50	48

16.7
SPEARMAN RANK CORRELATION TEST

LO7

Use the Spearman rank correlation.

An overall nonparametric test of association between two variables can be performed by using **Spearman's rank correlation** coefficient (sometimes called **Spearman's rho**). This statistic is useful when it is inappropriate to assume an interval scale (a requirement of the Pearson correlation coefficient you learned in Chapter 12). The statistic is named for Charles E. Spearman (1863–1945), a British behavioral psychologist who was interested in assessment of human intelligence. The research question was the extent of agreement between different I.Q. tests (e.g., Stanford-Binet and Wechsler's WAIS). However, ordinal data are also common in business. For example, Moody's bond ratings (e.g., Aaa, Aa, A, Baa, Ba, B, etc.), bank safety ratings (e.g., by Veribanc or BankRate.com), or Morningstar's mutual fund ratings (e.g., 5/5, 5/4, 4/4, etc.) are ordinal (not interval) measurements. We could use Spearman's rank correlation to answer questions like these:

- When n corporate bonds are assigned a quality rating by two different agencies (e.g., Moody and Dominion), to what extent do the ratings agree?

- When creditworthiness scores are assigned to n individuals by different credit-rating agencies (e.g., Equifax and TransUnion), to what extent do the scores agree?

In cases like these, we would expect strong agreement, since presumably the rating agencies are trying to measure the same thing. In other cases, we may have ratio or interval data, but prefer to rely on rank-based tests because of serious non-normality or outliers. For example:

- To what extent do rankings of n companies based on revenues agree with their rankings based on profits?

- To what extent do rankings of n mutual funds based on 1-year rates of return agree with their rankings based on 5-year rates of return?

Spearman Rank Correlation

Spearman rank correlation is a nonparametric test that measures the strength of the association, if any, between two variables using only ranks. It does not assume interval measurement.

The formula for Spearman's rank correlation coefficient for a sample is

$$r_s = 1 - \frac{6 \sum\limits_{i=1}^{n} d_i^2}{n(n^2 - 1)} \qquad \text{(Spearman rank correlation)} \qquad \textbf{(16.11)}$$

where

d_i = difference in ranks for case i

n = sample size

The sample rank correlation coefficient r_s must fall in the range $-1 \le r_s \le +1$. Its sign tells whether the relationship is direct (ranks tend to vary in the same direction) or inverse (ranks tend to vary in opposite directions). If r_s is near zero, there is little or no agreement between the rankings. If r_s is near $+1$, there is strong agreement between the ranks, while if r_s is near -1, there is strong *inverse* agreement between the ranks.

Application: Calories and Fat

Calories come from fat, but also from carbohydrates. How closely related are fat calories and total calories? As an experiment, a student team examined a sample of 20 brands of pasta sauce, obtaining the data shown in Table 16.11. The serving sizes (in grams) varied, so we divided each product's total calories and fat calories by serving size to obtain a per-gram measurement. Ranks were then calculated for each measure of calories. If more than one value was the same, they were assigned the average of the ranks. As a check, the sums of ranks within each column must always be $n(n + 1)/2$, which in our case is $(20)(20 + 1)/2 = 210$. After checking the ranks, the difference in ranks d_i is computed for each observation. As a further check on our calculations, we verify that the rank differences sum to zero (if not, we have made an error somewhere). The sample rank correlation coefficient $r_s = .9109$ indicates positive agreement:

$$r_s = 1 - \frac{6 \sum\limits_{i=1}^{n} d_i^2}{n(n^2 - 1)} = 1 - \frac{(6)(118.5)}{(20)(20^2 - 1)} = .9109$$

	TABLE 16.11
	Calories Per Gram for 20 Pasta Sauces
	📁 **Pasta**
	Source: This data set was created by statistics students Donna Bennett, Nicole Cook, Latrice Haywood, and Robert Malcolm. It is intended for training purposes only and should not be viewed as a nutrition guide.

	Total Calories		Fat Calories			
Product	*Per Gram*	*Rank*	*Per Gram*	*Rank*	d_i	d_i^2
Barilla Roasted Garlic & Onion	0.64	10	0.20	8	2	4
Barilla Tomato & Basil	0.56	13	0.12	13.5	−0.5	0.25
Classico Tomato & Basil	0.40	19.5	0.08	17	2.5	6.25
Del Monte Mushroom	0.48	17	0.04	19	−2	4
Five Bros. Tomato & Basil	0.64	10	0.12	13.5	−3.5	12.25
Healthy Choice Traditional	0.40	19.5	0.00	20	−0.5	0.25
Master Choice Chunky Garden Veg.	0.56	13	0.08	17	−4	16
Meijer All Natural Meatless	0.55	15	0.08	17	−2	4
Newman's Own Traditional	0.48	17	0.12	13.5	3.5	12.25
Paul Newman Venetian	0.48	17	0.12	13.5	3.5	12.25
Prego Fresh Mushrooms	1.25	1	0.38	1	0	0
Prego Hearty Meat—Pepperoni	1.00	3.5	0.33	2.5	1	1
Prego Hearty Meat—Hamburger	1.00	3.5	0.29	4	−0.5	0.25
Prego Traditional	1.17	2	0.33	2.5	−0.5	0.25
Prego Roasted Red Pepper & Garlic	0.92	5	0.25	5.5	−0.5	0.25
Ragu Old World Style w/meat	0.67	8	0.25	5.5	2.5	6.25
Ragu Roasted Red Pepper & Onion	0.86	6	0.20	8	−2	4
Ragu Roasted Garlic	0.70	7	0.19	10	−3	9
Ragu Traditional	0.56	13	0.20	8	5	25
Sutter Home Tomato & Garlic	0.64	10	0.16	11	−1	1
Column Sum		210		210	0	118.5

Our sample correlation r_s is 0.9109. For a right-tailed test the hypotheses are:

H_0: True rank correlation is zero ($\rho_s \leq 0$)

H_1: True rank correlation is positive ($\rho_s > 0$)

In this case we choose a right-tailed test because *a priori* we would expect positive agreement. That is, a pasta sauce that ranks high in fat calories would be expected also to rank high in total calories. If the sample size is small, a special table is required (see end-of-chapter RELATED READINGS). If n is large (usually defined as at least 20 observations), then r_s may be assumed to follow the normal distribution using the test statistic

(16.12)
$$z_{\text{calc}} = r_s \sqrt{n-1}$$

To illustrate this formula, we will plug in our previous sample result:

$$z_{\text{calc}} = (.9109)\sqrt{20-1} = 3.971$$

Using Appendix C we obtain one-tail critical values of z for various levels of significance:

α	z_α	*Interpretation*
.025	1.960	Reject H_0
.01	2.326	Reject H_0
.005	2.576	Reject H_0

Clearly, we can reject the hypothesis of no correlation at any of the customary α levels. Using MegaStat, we can obtain equivalent results, as shown in Figure 16.12, except that the critical value of r_s is shown instead of the t statistic.

FIGURE 16.12

MegaStat's Rank Correlation Test

Spearman Coefficient of Rank Correlation

	Total Calories/gram	Fat Calories/gram
Total Calories/gram	1.000	
Fat Calories/gram	.911	1.000

20 sample size

±.444 critical value .05 (two-tail)
±.561 critical value .01 (two-tail)

Correlation versus Causation

One final word of caution: you should remember that correlation does not imply causation. Countless examples can be found of correlations that are "significant" even when there is no causal relation between the two variables. On the other hand, causation is not ruled out. More than one scientific discovery has occurred because of an unexpected correlation. Just bear in mind that if you look at 1,000 correlation coefficients in samples drawn from uncorrelated populations, approximately 50 will be "significant" at $\alpha = .05$, approximately 10 will be "significant" at $\alpha = .01$, and so on. Testing for significance is just one step in the scientific process.

Bear in mind also that multiple causes may be present. Correlation between X and Y could be caused by an unspecified third variable Z. Even more complex systems of causation may exist. Bivariate correlations of any kind must be regarded as potentially out of context if the true relationship is *multivariate* rather than *bivariate*.

16.13 Profits of 20 consumer food companies are shown. (a) Convert the data to ranks. Check the column sums. (b) Calculate Spearman's rank correlation coefficient. Show your calculations. (c) At $\alpha = .01$ can you reject the hypothesis of zero rank correlation? (d) Check your work by using MegaStat. (e) Calculate the Pearson correlation coefficient (using Excel). (f) Why might the rank correlation be preferred? 📂 **Food-B**

SECTION EXERCISES

connect

Profit of 20 Food Consumer Products Firms ($ millions)

Company	2004	2005
Campbell Soup	595	647
ConAgra Foods	775	880
Dean Foods	356	285
Del Monte Foods	134	165
Dole Food	105	134
Flowers Foods	15	51
General Mills	917	1,055
H. J. Heinz	566	804
Hershey Foods	458	591
Hormel Foods	186	232
Interstate Bakeries	27	−26
J. M. Smucker	96	111
Kellogg	787	891
Land O'Lakes	107	21
McCormick	211	215
PepsiCo	3,568	4,212
Ralcorp Holdings	7	65
Sara Lee	1,221	1,272
Smithfield Foods	26	227
Wm. Wrigley, Jr.	446	493

Source: *Fortune* 151, no. 8 (April 18, 2005), p. F-52.

16.14 Rates of return on 24 mutual funds are shown. (a) Convert the data to ranks. Check the column sums. (b) Calculate Spearman's rank correlation coefficient. Show your calculations. (c) At $\alpha = .01$ can you reject the hypothesis of zero rank correlation? (d) Check your work by using MegaStat. (e) Calculate the Pearson correlation coefficient (using Excel). (f) In this case, why might either test be used? 📂 **Funds**

Rates of Return on 24 Selected Mutual Funds (percent)

Fund	12-Mo.	5-Year	Fund	12-Mo.	5-Year
1	11.2	10.5	13	14.0	9.7
2	−2.4	5.0	14	11.6	14.7
3	8.6	8.6	15	13.2	11.8
4	3.4	3.7	16	−1.0	2.3
5	3.9	−2.9	17	6.2	10.5
6	10.3	9.6	18	21.1	9.0
7	16.1	14.1	19	−1.2	3.0
8	6.7	6.2	20	8.7	7.1
9	6.5	7.4	21	9.7	10.2
10	11.1	14.0	22	0.4	9.3
11	8.0	7.3	23	0.9	6.0
12	11.2	14.2	24	12.7	10.0

CHAPTER SUMMARY   Statisticians are attracted to **nonparametric tests** because they avoid the restrictive assumption of normality, although often there are still assumptions to be met (e.g., similar population shape). Many nonparametric tests have **similar power** to their **parametric** counterparts (and superior power when samples are small). The **runs test** (or **Wald-Wolfowitz** test) checks for random order in binary data. The **Wilcoxon signed-rank test** resembles a parametric one-sample t test, most often being used as a substitute for the parametric paired-difference t test. The **Mann-Whitney test** (also called the **Wilcoxon rank-sum test**) compares medians in independent samples, resembling a parametric two-sample t test. The **Kruskal-Wallis test** is a c-sample comparison of medians (similar to one-factor ANOVA). The **Friedman test** resembles a randomized block ANOVA except that it compares medians instead of means. **Spearman's rank correlation** is like the usual Pearson correlation except the data are ranks. Calculations of these tests are usually done by computer. Special tables are required when samples are small (see RELATED READINGS or check the internet for small-sample procedures and tables of critical values, e.g., http://en.wikipedia.org/wiki/Mann-Whitney_U_test).

KEY TERMS

Friedman test, *700*
Kruskal-Wallis test, *695*
Mann-Whitney test, *692*
nonparametric tests, *685*
parametric tests, *685*

power, *685*
ranks, *689*
runs test, *686*
Spearman's rank
   correlation, *702*

Spearman's rho, *702*
Wald-Wolfowitz test, *686*
Wilcoxon signed-rank
   test, *689*

Commonly Used Formulas

Wald-Wolfowitz one-sample runs test for randomness (for $n_1 \geq 10$, $n_2 \geq 10$):

$$z_{calc} = \frac{R - \dfrac{2n_1 n_2}{n} + 1}{\sqrt{\dfrac{2n_1 n_2 (2n_1 n_2 - n)}{n^2 (n-1)}}}$$

where

R = number of runs
n = total sample size = $n_1 + n_2$

Wilcoxon signed-rank test for one sample median (for $n \geq 20$):

$$z_{calc} = \frac{W - \dfrac{n(n+1)}{4}}{\sqrt{\dfrac{n(n+1)(2n+1)}{24}}}$$

where

W = sum of positive ranks

Mann-Whitney test for equality of two medians (for $n_1 \geq 10$, $n_2 \geq 10$):

$$z_{calc} = \frac{\bar{T}_1 - \bar{T}_2}{(n_1 + n_2)\sqrt{\dfrac{n_1 + n_2 + 1}{12 n_1 n_2}}}$$

where

T_1 = mean rank for sample 1
T_2 = mean rank for sample 2

Kruskal-Wallis test for equality of c medians: $H_{calc} = \dfrac{12}{n(n+1)} \displaystyle\sum_{j=1}^{c} \dfrac{T_j^2}{n_j} - 3(n+1)$ with $d.f. = c - 1$

where

n_j = number of observations in group j
T_j = sum of ranks for group j
$n = n_1 + n_2 + \cdots + n_c$

Friedman test for equality of medians in an array with r rows and c columns:

$$F_{calc} = \frac{12}{rc(c+1)} \sum_{j=1}^{c} T_j^2 - 3r(c+1) \quad \text{with } d.f. = c - 1$$

where

  $r =$ the number of blocks (rows)
  $c =$ the number of treatments (columns)
  $T_j =$ the sum of ranks for treatment j

Spearman's rank correlation coefficient for n paired observations (for $n \geq 20$).

$$r_s = 1 - \frac{6 \sum_{i=1}^{n} d_i^2}{n(n^2 - 1)} \quad \text{and } z_{calc} = r_s \sqrt{n-1}$$

CHAPTER REVIEW

1. (a) Name three advantages of nonparametric tests. (b) Name two deficiencies in data that might cause us to prefer a nonparametric test. (c) Why is significance in a nonparametric test especially convincing?

2. (a) What is the purpose of a runs test? (b) How many runs of each type are needed for a large-sample runs test? (c) Give an example of a sequence containing runs and count the runs. (d) What distribution do we use for the large-sample runs test?

3. (a) What is the purpose of a Wilcoxon signed-rank test? (b) How large a sample is needed to use a normal table for the test statistic? (c) The Wilcoxon signed-rank test resembles which parametric test(s)?

4. (a) What is the purpose of a Mann-Whitney test? (b) The M-W test is a test of two medians under what assumption? (c) What sample sizes are needed for the large-sample M-W test? (d) The M-W test is analogous to which parametric test?

5. (a) In the Mann-Whitney test, how are ranks assigned when there is a tie? (b) What distribution do we use for the large-sample M-W test?

6. (a) What is the purpose of a Kruskal-Wallis test? (b) The K-W test is a test of c medians under what assumption? (c) The K-W test is analogous to which parametric test?

7. (a) In the Kruskal-Wallis test, what is the procedure for assigning ranks to observations in each group? (b) What distribution do we use for the K-W test? (c) What are the degrees of freedom for the K-W test?

8. (a) What is the purpose of a Friedman test? (b) The Friedman test is analogous to what parametric test? (c) How does the Friedman test differ from the ANOVA test in the way it handles the blocking factor?

9. (a) Describe the assignment of ranks in the Friedman test. (b) What distribution do we use for the Friedman test? (c) What are the degrees of freedom for the Friedman test?

10. (a) What is the purpose of the Spearman rank correlation? (b) Describe the way in which ranks are assigned in calculating the Spearman rank correlation.

11. (a) Why is a significant correlation not proof of causation? (b) When might a bivariate correlation be misleading?

CHAPTER EXERCISES

connect

Instructions: In all exercises, use a computer package (e.g., MegaStat, MINITAB) or show the calculations in a worksheet, depending on your instructor's wishes. If you use the computer, include relevant output or screen shots. If you do the calculations manually, show your work. State the hypotheses and give the test statistic and its two-tailed p-value. Make the decision. If the decision is close, say so. Are there issues of sample size? Is non-normality a concern?

16.15 A supplier of laptop PC power supplies uses a control chart to track the output (in watts) of each unit produced. The pattern below shows whether each unit's output was above (A) or below (B) the desired specification. *Research question:* At $\alpha = .05$, do the deviations follow a random pattern? **Watts**

B A A B B B A B A B A A B A A B B A B B A A B A B A

A A B B A A A A B B A A B A A A A B B A A B A A

16.16 A basketball player took 35 free throws during the season. Her sequence of hits (H) and misses (M) is shown. *Research question:* At $\alpha = .01$, is her hit/miss sequence random? **FreeThrows**

H M M H H M H M M H H H H H H M M H H M M H M H H H H M H H H H H M M M H H

16.17 Thirty-four customers at Starbucks either ordered coffee (*C*) or did not order coffee (*X*). *Research question:* At $\alpha = .05$, is the sequence random? 📁 **Starbucks**

C X C X C C C C X X X X C X C X C X C C C X C X C X C C X C X X X C C X

16.18 The price of a particular stock over a period of 60 days rises (+) or declines (−) in the following pattern: *Research question:* At $\alpha = .05$, is the pattern random? 📁 **Stock**

+ + − − − + + + + + + + − − − − + + − + − + − + − − − − + + + +
− + + + + − + + + − + − + − + + + − − − − − − − + + + + + − −

16.19 A forecasting model is fitted to sales data over 24 months. Forecasting errors are tabulated to reveal whether the model provides an overestimate (+) or an underestimate (−) for each month's sales. The results are − − + + + − + − − + + − − − − − − + + + + + − −. *Research question:* At $\alpha = .05$, is the pattern random? 📁 **Forecast**

16.20 A cognitive retraining clinic assists outpatient victims of head injury, anoxia, or other conditions that result in cognitive impairment. Each incoming patient is evaluated to establish an appropriate treatment program and estimated length of stay (ELOS is always a multiple of 4 weeks because treatment sessions are scheduled on a monthly basis). To see if there is any difference in ELOS between the two clinics, a sample is taken, consisting of all patients evaluated at each clinic during October, with the results shown. *Research question:* At $\alpha = .10$, do the medians differ? 📁 **Cognitive**

Clinic A (10 patients): 24, 24, 52, 30, 40, 40, 18, 30, 18, 40
Clinic B (12 patients): 20, 20, 52, 36, 36, 36, 24, 32, 16, 40, 24, 16

16.21 Two manufacturing facilities produce 1280 × 1024 LED (light-emitting diode) displays. Twelve shipments are tested at random from each lab, and the number of bad pixels per billion is noted for each shipment. *Research question:* At $\alpha = .05$, do the medians differ? 📁 **LED**

Defects in Randomly Inspected LED Displays

Facility	Number of Bad Pixels per billion											
Lab *A*	422	319	326	410	393	368	497	381	515	472	423	355
Lab *B*	497	421	408	375	410	489	389	418	447	429	404	477

16.22 In the 1996 Super Bowl, Dallas beat Pittsburgh 27-17. The weights of the linemen on each team are shown below. *Research question:* At $\alpha = .01$, do the medians differ? 📁 **Linemen**

Weights of Linemen in 1996 Super Bowl

Dallas Cowboys		Pittsburgh Steelers	
Player	**Weight**	**Player**	**Weight**
Derek Kennard	300	Kendall Gammon	288
Nate Newton	320	Dermontti Dawson	288
Ron Stone	309	John Jackson	297
Russell Maryland	279	Thomas Newberry	285
Michael Batiste	305	Brenden Stai	297
George Hegamin	338	Ariel Solomon	290
Dale Hellestrae	286	Leon Searcy	304
Mark Tuinei	305	Justin Strzelczyk	302
Larry Allen	326	Taase Faumui	278
Leon Lett	288	James Parrish	310
Erik Williams	322	Bill Johnson	300
Darren Benson	308	Joel Steed	300
Chad Hennings	288	Oliver Gibson	283
Hurvin McCormack	274		

Source: *Detroit Free Press,* January 28, 1996, pp. 6D–7D.

16.23 Does a class break stimulate the pulse? Here are heart rates for a sample of 30 students before and after a class break. *Research question:* At $\alpha = .05$, do the medians differ? 📁 **HeartRate**

Heart Rate before and after Class Break

Student	Before	After	Student	Before	After
1	60	62	16	70	64
2	70	76	17	69	66
3	77	78	18	64	69
4	80	83	19	70	73
5	82	82	20	59	58
6	82	83	21	62	65
7	41	66	22	66	68
8	65	63	23	81	77
9	58	60	24	56	57
10	50	54	25	64	62
11	82	93	26	78	79
12	56	55	27	75	74
13	71	67	28	66	67
14	67	68	29	59	63
15	66	75	30	98	82

Thanks to colleague Gene Fliedner for having his evening students take their own pulses before and after the 10-minute class break.

16.24 An experimental bumper was designed to reduce damage in low-speed collisions. This bumper was installed on an experimental group of vans in a large fleet, but not on a control group. At the end of a trial period, accident data showed 12 repair incidents for the experimental group and 9 repair incidents for the control group. The vehicle downtime (in days) per repair incident is shown. *Research question:* At $\alpha = .05$, do the medians differ? (Data are from Floyd G. Willoughby and Thomas W. Lauer, confidential case study.) 📁 **Downtime**

New bumper: 9, 2, 5, 12, 5, 4, 7, 5, 11, 3, 7, 1

Old bumper: 7, 5, 7, 4, 18, 4, 8, 14, 13

16.25 The square footage of each of the last 11 homes sold in each of two suburban neighborhoods is noted. *Research question:* At $\alpha = .01$, do the medians differ? 📁 **SqFt**

Square Footage of Homes Sold

Grosse Hills (Built in 1985)	Haut Nez Estates (Built in 2003)
3,220	3,850
3,450	3,560
3,270	4,300
3,200	4,100
4,850	3,750
3,150	3,450
2,800	3,400
3,050	3,550
2,950	3,750
3,430	4,150
3,220	3,850

16.26 Below are grade point averages for 25 randomly chosen university business students during a recent semester. *Research question:* At $\alpha = .01$, are the median grade point averages the same for students in these four class levels? 📁 **GPA**

Grade Point Averages of 25 Business Students

Freshman (5 students)	Sophomore (7 students)	Junior (7 students)	Senior (6 students)
1.91	3.89	3.01	3.32
2.14	2.02	2.89	2.45
3.47	2.96	3.45	3.81
2.19	3.32	3.67	3.02
2.71	2.29	3.33	3.01
	2.82	2.98	3.17
	3.11	3.26	

16.27 In a bumper test, three types of autos were deliberately crashed into a barrier at 5 mph, and the resulting damage (in dollars) was estimated. Five test vehicles of each type were crashed, with the results shown below. *Research question:* At $\alpha = .01$, are the median crash damages the same for these three vehicles? 🗂 **Crash**

Crash Damage in Dollars

Goliath	Varmint	Weasel
1,600	1,290	1,090
760	1,400	2,100
880	1,390	1,830
1,950	1,850	1,250
1,220	950	1,920

16.28 The waiting time (in minutes) for emergency room patients with non-life-threatening injuries was measured at four hospitals for all patients who arrived between 6:00 and 6:30 P.M. on a certain Wednesday. The results are shown below. *Research question:* At $\alpha = .05$, are the median waiting times the same for emergency patients in these four hospitals? 🗂 **Emergency**

Emergency Room Waiting Time (minutes)

Hospital A (5 patients)	Hospital B (4 patients)	Hospital C (7 patients)	Hospital D (6 patients)
10	8	5	0
19	25	11	20
5	17	24	9
26	36	16	5
11		18	10
		29	12
		15	

16.29 Mean output of arrays of solar cells of three types are measured four times under random light intensity over a period of 5 minutes, yielding the results shown below. *Research question:* At $\alpha = .05$, is the median solar cell output the same for all three types? 🗂 **Solar**

Solar Cell Output (Watts)

Cell Type	Output (Watts)					
A	123	121	123	124	125	127
B	125	122	122	121	122	126
C	126	128	125	129	131	128

16.30 Below are results of braking tests of the Ford Explorer on glare ice, packed snow, and split traction (one set of wheels on ice, the other on dry pavement), using three braking methods. *Research question:* At $\alpha = .01$, is braking method related to stopping distance? 🗂 **Stopping**

Stopping Distance from 40 mph to Zero

Road Condition	Pumping	Locked	ABS
Glare Ice	441	455	460
Split Traction	223	148	183
Packed Snow	149	146	167

Source: *Popular Science* 252, no. 6 (June 1998), p. 78.

16.31 In a call center, the average waiting time for an answer (in seconds) is shown below by time of day. *Research question:* At $\alpha = .01$, does the waiting time differ by day of the week? *Note:* Only the first 3 and last 3 observations are shown. ✉ **Wait**

Average Waiting Time (in Seconds) for Answer ($n = 26$)

Time	Mon	Tue	Wed	Thu	Fri
06:00	34	71	33	39	39
06:30	52	70	88	53	49
07:00	36	103	47	32	91
⋮	⋮	⋮	⋮	⋮	⋮
17:30	28	31	27	22	26
18:00	35	14	115	26	22
18:30	25	34	9	5	47

16.32 The table below shows annual financial data for a sample of 20 companies in the food consumer products sector. *Research question:* At $\alpha = .01$, is there a significant correlation between revenue and profit? Why is a rank correlation preferred? What factors might result in a less-than-perfect correlation? *Note:* Only the first 3 and last 3 companies are shown. ✉ **Food-A**

Food Consumer Products Companies' 2004 Revenue and Profit ($ millions)

Obs	Company	Revenue	Profit
1	Campbell Soup	7,109	647
2	ConAgra Foods	18,179	880
3	Dean Foods	10,822	285
⋮	⋮	⋮	⋮
18	Sara Lee	19,556	1,272
19	Smithfield Foods	10,107	227
20	Wm. Wrigley, Jr.	3,649	493

Source: *Fortune* 151, no. 8, April 18, 2005, p. F-52.

16.33 Fertility rates (children born per woman) are shown for 15 EU nations in 2 years a decade apart. *Research question:* At $\alpha = .05$, is there a significant rank correlation? *Note:* Only the first 3 and last 3 nations are shown. ✉ **Fertility**

Fertility Rates in EU Nations ($n = 15$)

Nation	1990	2000
Austria	1.5	1.3
Belgium	1.6	1.5
Denmark	1.6	1.7
⋮	⋮	⋮
Spain	1.4	1.1
Sweden	2.0	1.4
United Kingdom	1.8	1.7

Source: World Health Organization.

16.34 A newspaper article listed nutritional facts for 56 frozen dinners. From that list, 16 frozen dinners were randomly selected by using the random number method. *Research question:* Choose any two variables. At $\alpha = .01$, based on this sample, is there a significant rank correlation between the two variables? *Note:* Only the first 3 and last 3 observations are shown. 📁 **Dinners**

Frozen Dinner Nutritional Information (n = 16)

Company	Dinner/Entree	Fat (g)	Calories	Sodium (mg)
Budget Gourmet	French Recipe Chicken	9	240	1,000
Budget Gourmet	Chicken au Gratin	11	250	870
Budget Gourmet Light	Stuffed Turkey Breast	6	230	520
⋮	⋮	⋮	⋮	⋮
Weight Watchers	Filet of Fish au Gratin	6	200	700
Weight Watchers	Beef Sirloin Tips	7	220	540
Weight Watchers	Lasagna with Meat Sauce	10	320	630

Source: *Detroit Free Press,* April 10, 1991, p. 2F. This information is intended solely to illustrate statistical concepts, and should not be used as a guide to nutrition. Nutritional content of frozen dinners may have changed since the newspaper article was written.

16.35 The table below shows annual incidence of cancer of the colon in women of different nations (cases per 100,000) and average meat consumption (grams per person per day). *Research question:* At $\alpha = .05$, based on this data, is there a significant rank correlation between colon cancer and meat consumption? *Note:* Only the first 3 and last 3 nations are shown. 📁 **Cancer**

Women's Colon Cancer Rates and Meat Consumption in Various Nations (n = 23)

Nation	Colon Cancer Rate	Per Capita Meat (gm)
Canada	29.5	229
Chile	7.1	81
Colombia	3.9	80
⋮	⋮	⋮
USA	33.2	274
W. Germany	15.5	177
Yugoslavia	8.6	71

Source: Ian Spratley, *Living With Technology and Numeracy,* p. 7, copyright © 1982 The Open University, used with permission.

16.36 Are gasoline prices a potential policy tool in controlling carbon emissions? The table below shows 2001 gasoline prices (dollars per liter) and carbon dioxide emissions per dollar of GDP. *Research question:* At $\alpha = .05$, based on this data, is there a significant rank correlation between these two variables? *Note:* Only the first 3 and last 3 observations are shown. 📁 **Emissions**

Gasoline Prices and Carbon Emissions for Selected Nations (n = 31)

Nation	Gas Price ($/L)	CO_2/GDP (kg/$)
Australia	0.489	0.79
Austria	0.888	0.25
Belgium	0.984	0.37
⋮	⋮	⋮
Turkey	1.003	0.99
United Kingdom	1.165	0.41
United States	0.381	0.63

Source: International Energy Agency, www.iea.org.

16.37 Below are the top 20 U.S. football teams in the seventh and eighth weeks of the 2003 season, along with the points awarded to each team by the *ESPN/USA Today* coaches poll. *Research question:* At $\alpha = .01$, based on this data, is there a significant rank correlation between these two variables? 📁 **Teams**

Football Ratings in *ESPN/USA Today* Coaches Poll (*n* = 20)

Team	This Week	Last Week
Oklahoma	1575	1622
Southern Cal	1502	1470
Florida State	1412	1320
LSU	1337	1241
Virginia Tech	1281	1026
Miami	1263	1563
Ohio State	1208	1226
Michigan	1135	938
Georgia	951	1378
Iowa	932	762
Texas	881	605
TCU	875	727
Wash State	827	1260
Purdue	667	487
Michigan State	645	1041
Nebraska	558	924
Tennessee	544	449
Minnesota	490	149
Florida	480	246
Bowling Green	369	577

Source: *Detroit Free Press.*

RELATED READING

Corder, Gregory W., and Dale I. Foreman. *Nonparametric Statistics for Non-Statisticians: A Step-by-Step Approach* (Wiley, 2009).

Conover, William J. *Practical Nonparametric Statistics.* 3rd ed. (Wiley, 1998).

Higgins, James J. *Introduction to Modern Nonparametric Statistics* (Brooks/Cole, 2004).

Gibbons, Jean D. *Nonparametric Statistics: An Introduction* (Sage, 1999).

Huber, Peter J. *Robust Statistics* (Wiley, 2003).

Lehmann, Erich L. *Nonparametrics: Statistical Methods Based on Ranks.* Rev. ed. (Springer, 2006).

CHAPTER 16   Online Learning Resources

The Online Learning Center (OLC) at www.mhhe.com/doane3e has several *LearningStats* demonstrations to help you understand nonparametric tests. Your instructor may assign one or more of them, or you may decide to download the ones that sound interesting.

Online **Learning**Center

Topic	LearningStats Demonstrations
Overview	What Are Nonparametric Tests?
Case studies	Runs Test: Baseball Streaks
	Wilcoxon Signed-Rank: Exam Scores
	Mann-Whitney: ATM Withdrawals
	Kruskal-Wallis: DVD Prices
	Friedman Test: Freeway Pollution
	Spearman's Rho: EU Nations Fertility
Tables	Chi-Square Critical Values

Key: = PowerPoint   = Excel

Quality Management

Chapter Learning Objectives

When you finish this chapter you should be able to

LO1   Define quality and explain how it may be measured.

LO2   Distinguish between common cause variation and special cause variation.

LO3   Name key individuals and their contributions to the quality movement.

LO4   List common statistical tools used in quality improvement.

LO5   List steps toward continuous quality improvement and variance reduction.

LO6   Make and interpret common control charts ($\bar{x}$, R, and p).

LO7   Recognize abnormal patterns in control charts and their potential causes.

LO8   Assess the capability of a process.

What Is Quality?

Quality can be measured in many ways. Quality may be a *physical* metric, such as the number of bad sectors on a computer hard disk or the quietness of an air conditioning fan. Quality may be an *aesthetic* attribute such as the ripeness of a banana or cleanliness of a clinic waiting room. (Does the fig bar turned in the wrong direction in Figure 17.1 affect the aesthetic quality of the product?) Quality may be a *functional* characteristic such as ergonomic accessibility of car radio controls or convenience of hours that a bank is open. It may be a *personal* attribute such as friendliness of service at a restaurant or diligence of follow-up by a veterinary clinic. It may be an *efficiency* attribute such as promptness in delivery of an order or the waiting time at a dentist's. Quality is generally understood to include these attributes:

LO1

Define quality and explain how it may be measured.

- Conformance to specifications.
- Performance in the intended use.
- As near to zero defects as possible.
- Reliability and durability.
- Serviceability when needed.
- Favorable customer perceptions.

Measurement of quality is specific to the organization and its products. To improve quality, we must undertake systematic data collection and careful measurement of key metrics that

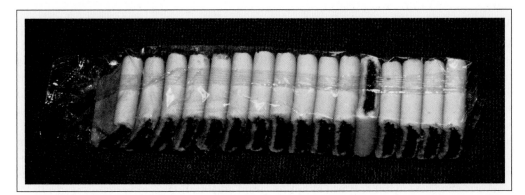

FIGURE 17.1

Unopened Fig Bars: Quality as an Aesthetic Attribute

describe the product or service that is valued by customers. In manufacturing, the focus is likely to be on physical characteristics (e.g., defects, reliability, consistency), while in services, the focus is likely to be on customer perceptions (e.g., courtesy, responsiveness, competence). Table 17.1 lists some typical quality indicators that might be important to firms engaged in manufacturing as compared to firms that deliver services.

TABLE 7.1

Typical Quality Indicators

Manufacturing	Services
Proportion of nonconforming output	Proportion of satisfied customers
Warranty claim costs	Average customer waiting time
Repeat purchase rate (loyalty)	Repeat client base (loyalty)

Productivity, Processes, and Quality

Productivity (output per unit of input) is a measure of efficiency. High productivity lowers cost per unit, increases profit, and supports higher wages and salaries. Productivity, like quality, can be measured in various ways. In service industries, productivity is difficult to define. What is the productivity of an investment banker, a CEO, a kindergarten teacher, a college professor, a tax analyst, or a design engineer? Service organizations often rely on quasi-financial measurements, such as average daily sales per field representative, hours billed per attorney, or patients seen by a physician. These are imperfect proxies for productivity, but may be the best that can be devised.

In the past, many companies assumed an inverse relationship between quality and productivity. This view was based on a short-term perspective. The belief was that the only way to truly improve quality was to slow down and put more time into each product. While slowing or stopping an assembly line does imply less output today, defective products lead to waste, rework, and lost customers. In the modern view, quality and productivity move in the same direction, because doing it right the first time saves time and money in the long run. Similarly, in services (e.g., health care) reducing delays and avoiding errors will make customers happier and will reduce the burden of follow-up to fix problems. Our focus in the 21st century is on designing and operating effective business processes to meet customer requirements consistently.

A **process** is a sequence of interconnected tasks that result in the creation of a product or in the delivery of a service. Manufacturing, assembly, or packaging operations usually come to mind when we hear the term "process." Yet service operations such as filling mail orders, providing customer support, handling loan applications, delivering health services, and meeting payrolls are also processes. Since a majority of workers are in the service sector, it is reasonable to say that nonmanufacturing processes are predominant in today's economy. **Quality control** refers to methods used by organizations to ensure that their products and services meet customer expectations and to ensure that there is improvement over time.

Variance Reduction

Where does statistics enter the quality picture? Statistics can help the company choose appropriate metrics, set up a system to collect valid data, track variation in the chosen metric(s), and tell when variation is increasing or decreasing. Statistics focuses on the phenomenon of *variation*. Processes that produce, package, and deliver supposedly identical products and services cannot eliminate all sources of variation around the target specification(s). Although some degree of variation is normal and expected, firms do try to attain consistency in their products and services, because excessive variation is often a sign of poor quality. Although slight variation may not affect customer satisfaction, variation that affects real or perceived performance of the product or service clearly requires attention. The quest for **reduced variation** is a never-ending activity for any firm or not-for-profit organization. *Zero variation* is an elusive goal that can be approached only asymptotically, because each successive improvement usually comes at an increasing cost.

Common Cause versus Special Cause

Statisticians define two categories of variation. **Common cause variation** (random "noise") is normal and expected, and is present in any stable, in-control process. **Special cause variation** is due to factors that are abnormal and require investigation. Special cause variation will produce observations that are not from the same population as the majority of observations. Until special cause variation is eliminated, a process is not in control. For example, waiting time at a ski lift is a random variable that follows a predictable pattern at different times of day (common cause variation, normal and expected). But when there is an equipment malfunction, waiting times may change dramatically (special cause variation).

Sources of variation in processes include human abilities, training, motivation, technology, materials, management, and organization. Some of these factors are under the control of the organization, while others cannot easily be changed. Most factors are fixed in the short run but may be changed in the long run. For example, technology can be changed through research and development and capital spending on new equipment, but such changes may take years. Human performance can change over time through education and training, but usually not in hours or days.

LO2

Distinguish between common cause variation and special cause variation.

Role of Management

Management is expected to find ways to maintain process control in the short run and to reduce variation in the long run. The degree to which variance can be reduced depends on equipment, technology, and worker training. Managers may call upon statistical specialists for advice and to train nonstatisticians who comprise the majority of the workforce. Training requirements depend on the type of organization. A manufacturing firm may require broad-based statistical training for engineers, plant managers, supervisors, and even assembly workers. But financial, purchasing, marketing, and sales managers must also understand statistics, because they interact with technical experts on cost control, waste management, and quality improvement. Even in banks or health care, broad-based training in statistical methods can be helpful in increasing efficiency and improving quality.

Role of Statisticians

We use statistics to measure variation, set attainable limits for variation, and establish rules to decide whether processes are in control. Trained statisticians may perceive problems that are not immediately apparent to those who manage day-to-day business activities. Statisticians have made many contributions to quality management and play an active consulting role.

SECTION EXERCISES

17.1   Define (a) process, (b) quality, and (c) variation.

17.2   Distinguish between common cause variation and special cause variation.

17.3   Can zero variation be achieved? Explain.

Who Is a Customer?

17.2
CUSTOMER ORIENTATION

One initial step in setting up a quality management system is defining the clients or customers who are being served. A **customer** is whoever consumes what you produce. *Internal customers* are employees of another branch of your organization. For example, the Accounts Payable Department provides services consumed by the Cost Department and the Purchasing Department. *External customers* are outside the organization. Vendors get paid, thereby consuming services provided by the Accounts Payable Department. Employees may be less aware of external customers because most of their dealings are with other employees of the company, but it is the external customers who provide the revenue that supports the organization.

Measuring Quality

Each customer category has its own viewpoint, so we may have to measure several aspects of the product or service to assess quality. Different customer groups may require unique quality measurements, while sometimes a single quality measurement may apply to several customer groups. Observers may not agree on the interpretation of quality measures, so planning and training are essential to ensure that employees collect meaningful data. Table 17.2 gives examples of customers and measurable aspects of quality.

TABLE 17.2	Examples of Customers and Measurable Aspects of Quality	
Department or Process	**Possible Customers (Type)**	**Measurable Aspects**
Payroll department in a large hospital	Hourly and salaried employees who are to be paid on time (internal).	Percent of employees paid incorrectly or late each month.
	Federal and state tax agencies that withhold taxes (external).	Percent of employees with insufficient taxes withheld each year.
	Creditors and courts seeking to garnish employee wages for child support (external).	Number of weekly creditor telephone complaints.
Aluminum beverage container manufacturing plant	Bottling plant awaiting shipments of containers (internal).	Monthly hours of downtime due to delayed shipments.
	Staff design engineers seeking to reduce can weight while maintaining strength (internal).	Thickness and weight of alloy or number of structurally defective cans per 100,000.
	State and federal health and safety agencies such as OSHA (external).	Number of worker injuries per month.
Retail pharmacy	Individuals needing prescription filled (external).	Percent of prescriptions filled within 15 minutes.
	Doctors, HMOs, and customers phoning in prescriptions (external).	Average wait for phone to be answered or percent of callers getting a busy signal.
	Cashier waiting for pharmacist to fill prescription (internal).	Time (in minutes) a cashier must wait for pharmacist.

SECTION EXERCISES

17.4 Distinguish between internal and external customers, giving an example of each within an organization with which you are familiar.

17.5 Define a measurable aspect of quality for (a) the car dealership where you bought your car; (b) the bank or credit union where you usually make personal transactions; and (c) the movie theater where you usually go.

17.3
BEHAVIORAL ASPECTS OF QUALITY

Blame versus Solutions

Employees tend to think about their own job performance problems or the immediate demands of co-workers and internal customers, losing sight of the fact that their jobs and department budget ultimately depend on serving customers well. To succeed, management must create an atmosphere and incentives that support and reward customer orientation. Employees must take seriously quality indicators that tell whether they are doing a good job. Sometimes this is painful, since it means acknowledging bad outcomes and signs of weakening quality.

In a quality-driven organization, problems do not lead to *blame,* but to a search for *solutions.* What happens if a manager blames an employee for a quality problem? That employee is likely to quit reporting quality problems. Other employees will hear about it and adopt a negative attitude toward quality tracking. If quality problems are covered up, matters can only get worse.

W. Edwards Deming, a famous quality expert, believed that most employees want to do a good job. He found that most of quality problems do not stem from willful disregard of quality, but from flaws in the process or system, such as

- Inadequate equipment
- Inadequate maintenance
- Inadequate training
- Inadequate supervision
- Inadequate support systems
- Inadequate task design

Employee Involvement

Good solutions to quality problems will be more likely if employee representatives from each area are brought together as a *team* to address the quality problem. Team-building activities can help establish group goals, values, and communication. The team then begins the process of problem solving as a group. Teamwork is an important part of the strategy of the quality-driven organization. This goes far beyond statistics.

But organizations have finite resources. Not all problems can be solved. Which problems are most urgent? Which ones can we live with for awhile? Which solutions would have the greatest impact on improving customer satisfaction? Trade-offs must be made. This is an economic problem. There is also a behavioral aspect of resource constraints. Research shows that employee involvement is necessary to create changes that will be accepted, to ensure "buy-in" to change, and to ensure that viable options are not overlooked. Top-down decisions without employee input can create new problems, such as resentment or unworkable processes. That is why we must study organizational behavior, as well as statistics.

SECTION EXERCISES

17.6 On the Web, look up the following terms (e.g., in Google) and print *two* interesting quotations for each. (a) quality; (b) quality improvement; (c) common cause variation.

17.7 What did Deming say about blaming employees for poor quality?

Brief History of Quality Control

During the early 1900s, quality control took the form of improved inspection and improvement in the methods of mass production, under the leadership of American experts. From about 1920 to just after World War II, techniques such as process control charts (Walter A. Shewhart) and acceptance sampling from lots (Harold F. Dodge and Harry G. Romig) were perfected and were widely applied in North America. But during the 1950s and 1960s, Japanese manufacturers (particularly automotive) shed their previous image as low-quality producers and began to apply American quality control techniques. The Japanese based their efforts largely on ideas and training from American statisticians W. Edwards Deming and Joseph M. Juran, as well as Japanese statisticians Genichi Taguchi and Kaoru Ishikawa. They developed new approaches that focused on customer satisfaction and costs of quality. By the 1970s, despite exhortation by Deming and others, North American firms had lost their initial leadership in quality control, while the Japanese devised and perfected new quality improvement methods, soon adopted by the Europeans.

During the 1980s, North American firms began a process of recommitment to quality improvement and Japanese production methods. In their quest for quality improvement, these firms sought training and advice by experts such as Deming, Juran, and Armand Feigenbaum. The Japanese, however, continued to push the quality frontier forward, under the teachings of Taguchi and the perfection of the Kaizen philosophy of continuous improvement. The Europeans articulated the ISO 9000 standards, now adopted by most world-class firms.

17.4
PIONEERS IN QUALITY MANAGEMENT

LO3

Name key individuals and their contributions to the quality movement.

North American firms have implemented their own style of total quality management. Manufacturers now seek to build *quality* into their products and services, all the way down the supply chain. Quality is best viewed as a *management system* rather than purely as an application of statistics.

W. Edwards Deming

The late **W. Edwards Deming** (1900–1993) deserves special mention as an influential thinker. He was widely honored in his lifetime. Many know him primarily for his contributions to improving productivity and quality in Japan. In 1950, at the invitation of the Union of Japanese Scientists and Engineers, Deming gave a series of lectures to 230 leading Japanese industrialists who together controlled 80 percent of Japan's capital. His message was the same as to Americans he had taught during the previous decades. The Japanese listened carefully to his message, and their success in implementing Deming's ideas is a matter of historical record.

Deming said that *profound knowledge* of a system is needed for an individual to become a good listener who can teach others. He emphasized that all people are different, that management is not about ranking people, and that anyone's performance is governed largely by the system that he/she works in. He said that fear invites presentation of bad data. If bearers of bad news fare badly, the boss will hear only good news—guaranteeing bad management decisions.

It is difficult to encapsulate Deming's many ideas succinctly, but most observers would agree that his philosophy is reflected in his widely reproduced *14 Points,* which can be found in full on the Web or in abbreviated form here. The 14 Points are primarily statements about management, not statistics. They ask that management take responsibility for improving quality and avoid blaming workers. Deming spent much of his long life explaining these and other of his ideas, through a series of seminars aimed initially at management, an activity that continues today through the work of his followers at The W. Edwards Deming Institute (www.deming.org). Deming's impact was a function of his philosophy, his stature as a statistician, and his absorbing personal presence, not just his list of 14 points.

Deming's 14 Points (abbreviated)

1. Maintain constancy of purpose.
2. Adopt a new philosophy.
3. Don't rely on inspection—design quality in.
4. Don't award contracts just on the basis of price.
5. Continuous improvement.
6. Institute training on the job.
7. Supervision should help people do a better job.
8. Drive out fear and create trust.
9. Break down barriers between departments.
10. Eliminate slogans, exhortations, and targets.
11. Eliminate numerical goals.
12. Remove barriers to pride in work.
13. Continuing education for all.
14. Act to accomplish the transformation.

Source: W. Edwards Deming, *Out of the Crisis,* copyright © 1986 W. Edwards Deming. Reprinted by permission of MIT Press.

Modern business students may find some of his recommendations simplistic. For example, "drive out fear" is an elusive goal in a large, complex organization. Deming was not unaware of the behavioral difficulty of achieving his goals. He believed that one major difficulty lay in obtaining commitment from the top leadership, and was impatient when organizations did not demonstrate sufficient resolve to implement his ideas. Deming's ideas are a required subset of the broader principles of quality management.

Other Influential Thinkers

Walter A. Shewhart (1891–1967) invented the control chart and the concepts of special cause and common cause (assignable cause). Shewhart's charts were adopted by the American Society for Testing Materials (ASTM) in 1933 and were used to improve production during World War II. *Joseph M. Juran* (1904–2008) also taught quality education in Japan, contemporaneously with Deming. Like Deming, he became more influential with North American management in the 1980s. He felt that 80 percent of quality defects arise from management actions, and therefore that quality control was management's responsibility. This may seem obvious today, but before the 1980s there was a tendency to blame labor for quality problems and to assume that not much could be done about it. Juran articulated the idea of the *vital few*—a handful of causes that account for a vast majority of quality problems (the principle behind the **Pareto chart**). Effort, he said, should be concentrated on key problems, rather than diffused over many less-important problems.

Kaoru Ishikawa is a Japanese quality expert who is associated with the idea of *quality circles,* which characterize the Japanese approach. He also pioneered the idea of company-wide quality control and was influential in popularizing statistical tools for quality control. His textbook on statistical methods still is used in training, though many competitors now exist. He taught that elementary statistical tools (Pareto charts, histograms, scatter diagrams, and control charts) should be understood by everyone, while advanced tools (experimental design, regression) might best be left to specialists.

Armand V. Feigenbaum first used the term *total quality control* in 1951. He favored broad sharing of responsibility for quality assurance. This was at a time when many companies assumed that quality was the responsibility of the Quality Assurance Department alone. He felt that quality is an essential element of modern management, like marketing or finance. *Philip B. Crosby* is the author of an important book that argues that efforts at improving quality pay for themselves, and was among the first to popularize the catch-phrase "zero defects." *Genichi Taguchi* is a pioneer whose contributions are discussed further at the end of this chapter.

Other quality gurus include *Claus Moller,* whose European company specializes in management training. Moller believes that people can be inspired to do their best through development of the individual's self-esteem. Moller is known for his 12 Golden Rules and 17 hallmarks of a quality company. *Shigeo Shingo* has had great impact on Japanese industry. His basic idea (the "poka-yoke" system) is to stop a process whenever a defect occurs, define the cause, and prevent future occurrences. If source inspections are used, statistical sampling becomes unnecessary, because the worker is prevented from making errors in the first place. *Tom Peters* is an American who studied successful American companies to define a philosophy of quality improvement that discards "management" in favor of "leadership." He emphasizes customer orientation and his 12 keys to a quality revolution.

SECTION EXERCISES

17.8   On the Internet, look up *two* influential thinkers in quality control, and briefly state their contributions.

17.9   Look them up *two* of Deming's 14 points on the Internet and explain their meaning.

**17.5
QUALITY
IMPROVEMENT**

Acronyms abound in quality management (TQM, BPR, SQC, SPC, etc.). The following are only a few that you should know before you enter the workplace.

Business Quality Philosophies

Total quality management or **TQM** requires that all business activities should be oriented toward meeting and exceeding customer needs, empowering employees, eliminating waste or rework, and ensuring the long-run viability of the enterprise through continuous quality improvement. TQM encompasses a broad spectrum of behavioral, managerial, and technical approaches. It includes diverse but complementary elements such as statistics, benchmarking, process redesign, team building, group communications, quality function deployment, and cross-functional management.

Like TQM, **business process redesign** or **BPR** has a cross-functional orientation. But instead of focusing on incremental change and gradual improvement of processes, BPR seeks radical redesign of processes to achieve breakthrough improvement in performance measures—a lofty goal that is easier to state than to achieve. Business schools typically incorporate TQM and/or BPR concepts into a variety of nonstatistics core classes.

Statistical Quality Control (SQC)

LO4

List common statistical tools used in quality improvement.

Statistical quality control or **SQC** refers to a subset of quality improvement techniques that rely on statistics. A few of the descriptive tools (see Figure 17.2) have already been covered in earlier chapters, while others (e.g., control charts) will be discussed in this chapter.

Descriptive Tools	*Analytic Methods*
• Pareto diagrams	• Control charts
• Scatter plots	• Lot and batch inspection plans
• Box plots	• Acceptance sampling
• Fishbone diagrams	• Experimental design
• Check sheets	• Taguchi robust design

FIGURE 17.2

Three Descriptive SQC Tools

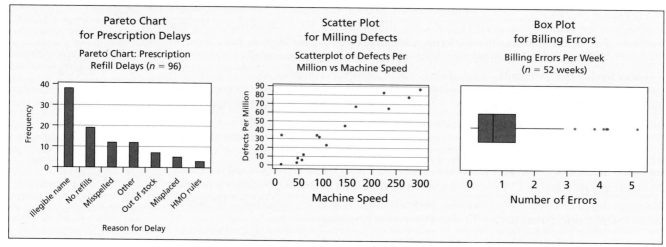

A *check sheet* is a form for counting the frequency of sources of nonconformance. The **fishbone chart** (also called a *cause-and-effect diagram*) is a visual display that summarizes the factors that increase process variation or adversely affect achievement of the target. For example, Figure 17.3 shows a fishbone chart for factors affecting patient length of stay in a hospital. The six main categories (materials, methods, people, management, measurement, technology) are general and may apply to almost any process. You can insert as many verbal descriptions ("fishbones") as you need to identify the causes of variation. The fishbone chart is not, strictly speaking, a statistical tool, but is helpful in thinking about root causes. MINITAB will make fishbone charts.

Statistical Process Control (SPC)

Statistical process control or **SPC** refers specifically to the monitoring of ongoing repetitive processes to ensure conformance to standards by using methods of statistics. Its main tools are *capability analysis* and *control charts*. Because this is a statistics textbook, we will focus on SPC tools, leaving SQC and TQM to other courses that you may take.

FIGURE 17.3

Fishbone (Cause-and-Effect) Chart for Patient Length of Stay

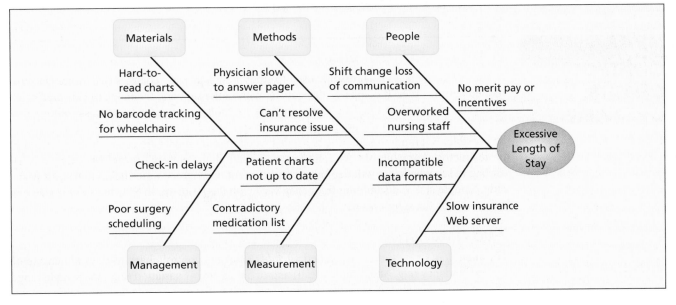

Continuous Quality Improvement (CQI)

Quality improvement begins with measurement of a *variable* (e.g., dimensions of an automobile door panel) or an *attribute* (e.g., number of emergency patients who wait more than 30 minutes). For a variable, quality improvement means reducing variation from the target specification. For an attribute, quality improvement means decreasing the rate of nonconformance. Statistical methods are used to ensure that the process is stable and in control by eliminating sources of *special cause* (nonrandom) variation, as opposed to *common cause* (random) variation that is normal and inherent in the process. We change the process whenever a way is discovered to reduce variation or to decrease nonconformance (especially if the process is incapable of meeting the target specifications). We continue to seek ways to reduce variation and/or nonconformance to even lower levels. The never-ending cycle is repeated indefinitely, giving rise to the concept of **CQI**. In the **Six Sigma** school of thought (see Section 17.12), the steps to quality improvement are abbreviated as **DMAIC** (define, measure, analyze, improve, control).

LO5

List steps toward continuous quality improvement and variance reduction.

Steps to Continuous Quality Improvement

- Step 1:   Define a relevant, measurable parameter of the product or service.
- Step 2:   Establish targets or desired specifications for the product or service.
- Step 3:   Monitor the process to be sure it is stable and in control.
- Step 4:   Is the process capable of meeting the desired specifications?
- Step 5:   Identify sources of variation or nonconformance.
- Step 6:   Change the process (technology, training, management, materials).
- Step 7:   Repeat steps 3–6 indefinitely.

The Japanese are credited with perfecting and implementing the philosophy of continuous improvement, along with the related concepts of quality circles, just-in-time inventory, and robust design of products and processes (the **Taguchi method**). Different social, economic, and geographic factors prevent adoption of some Japanese approaches by North American firms, but there is general agreement on their main points. Continuous improvement now is a guiding principle for automobile manufacturers, health care providers, insurance companies, computer software designers, fast-food restaurants, and even universities, churches, entertainment, and sports teams. Permanent change and a continuous search for better ways of doing things cascade down the organizational chart and across departmental lines.

SECTION EXERCISES

17.10 How does SPC differ from TQM and CQI?

17.11 On the Internet (e.g., using Google) search for these terms and print *two* interesting quotes on each. (a) fishbone chart; (b) statistical quality control.

17.6
CONTROL CHARTS: OVERVIEW

What Is a Control Chart?

A **control chart** is a visual display used to study how a process changes over time. Data are plotted in time order. It compares the statistic with limits showing the range of expected common cause variation in the data. Control charts are tools for monitoring process stability and for alerting managers if the process changes. In some processes, inspection of every item may be possible. But random sampling is needed when measurements are costly, time-consuming, or destructive. For example, we can't test every cell phone battery's useful life, trigger every air bag to see whether it will deploy correctly, or cut open every watermelon to test for pesticide. Sample size and sampling frequency vary with the problem. In SPC the sample size n is referred to as the *subgroup size*.

Two Data Types

For *numerical* data (sometimes called *variable* data) the control chart displays a measure of central tendency (e.g., the sample mean) and/or a measure of variation (e.g., the sample range or standard deviation). A *variable control chart* is used for measurable quantities like weight, diameter, or time. Typically, such data are found in manufacturing (e.g., dimensions of a metal fastener) but sometimes also in services (e.g., client waiting time). The subgroup size for numerical data may be quite small (e.g., under 10) or even a single item.

For *attribute* data (sometimes called *qualitative* data), the focus is on counting nonconforming items (those that do not meet the target specification). An *attribute control chart* may show the proportion nonconforming (assumed binomial process) or the total number nonconforming (assumed binomial or Poisson process). Attribute control charts are important in service or manufacturing environments when physical measurements are not appropriate. Subgroup size for attribute data may be large (e.g., over 100) depending on the rate of nonconformance. Because modern manufacturing processes may have very low nonconformance rates (e.g., .00001 or .0000001), even larger samples are needed.

Three Common Control Charts

For a sample mean, the control chart is called an $\bar{x}$ **chart**. For a sample range, it is called an **R chart**. For a sample proportion, it is called a **p chart**. These three charts are illustrated in Figure 17.4. Each chart plots a sample statistic over time, as well as upper and lower *control limits* that define the expected range of the sample statistic. In these illustrations, all samples fall within the control limits. Control limits are based on the sampling distribution of the statistic. While there are many others, the basic concepts of SPC and setting control limits can be illustrated with these three chart types.

FIGURE 17.4

Three Common Control Charts (from MINITAB)

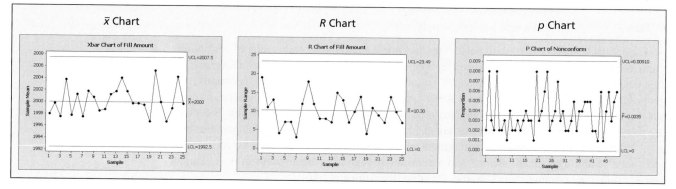

17.12 What is the difference between an attribute control chart and a variable control chart?

17.13 (a) What determines sampling frequency? (b) Why are variable samples often small? (c) Why are attribute samples often large?

x̄ Charts: Bottle-Filling Example

A bottling plant is filling 2-liter (2,000 ml) soft drink bottles. It is important that the equipment neither overfill nor underfill the bottle. The filling process is stable and in control with mean fill μ and standard deviation σ. The degree of variation depends on the process technology used in the plant. Every 10 minutes, n bottles are chosen at random and their fill is measured. The unit of measurement is milliliters. For a subgroup of size $n = 5$ the sample might look like this:

LO6

Make and interpret common control charts ($\bar{x}$, R, and p).

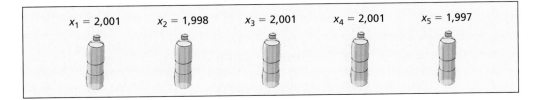

$x_1 = 2{,}001 \qquad x_2 = 1{,}998 \qquad x_3 = 2{,}001 \qquad x_4 = 2{,}001 \qquad x_5 = 1{,}997$

The mean fill for these five bottles is $\bar{x} = 1999.6$. Each time we take a sample of five bottles we expect a different value of the sample mean due to random variation inherent in the process. From previous chapters, we know that the sample mean is an unbiased estimator of the true process mean (i.e., its expected value is μ):

$$E(\bar{X}) = \mu \qquad (\bar{X} \text{ tends toward the true process mean}) \qquad \textbf{(17.1)}$$

The Central Limit Theorem says that the standard error of the sample mean is

$$\sigma_{\bar{X}} = \frac{\sigma}{\sqrt{n}} \qquad (\text{larger } n \text{ implies smaller variance of } \bar{X}) \qquad \textbf{(17.2)}$$

The sample mean follows a normal distribution if the population is normal, or if the sample is large enough to assure normality by the Central Limit Theorem.

Control Limits: Known μ and σ

Sample means from a process that is in control should be near the process mean μ, which is the *centerline* of the control chart. The **upper control limit (UCL)** and **lower control limit (LCL)** are set at ± 3 standard errors from the centerline, using the Empirical Rule, which says that almost all the sample means (actually 99.73 percent) will fall within "3-sigma" limits:

$$\text{UCL} = \mu + 3\frac{\sigma}{\sqrt{n}} \qquad (\text{upper control limit for } \bar{X}, \text{ known } \mu \text{ and } \sigma) \qquad \textbf{(17.3)}$$

$$\text{LCL} = \mu - 3\frac{\sigma}{\sqrt{n}} \qquad (\text{lower control limit for } \bar{X}, \text{ known } \mu \text{ and } \sigma) \qquad \textbf{(17.4)}$$

The $\bar{x}$ chart provides a kind of visual hypothesis test. Sample means will vary, sometimes above the centerline and sometimes below the centerline, but they should stay within the control limits and be symmetrically distributed on either side of the centerline. You will recognize the similarity between *control limits* and *confidence limits* covered in previous chapters. The idea is that if a sample mean falls outside these limits, we suspect that the sample may be from a different population from the one we have specified.

EXAMPLE

Bottle Filling

Table 17.3 shows 25 samples of size $n = 5$ from a bottling process with $\mu = 2000$ and $\sigma = 4$. For each sample, the mean and range are calculated. The control limits are:

$$\text{UCL} = \mu + 3\frac{\sigma}{\sqrt{n}} = 2000 + 3\frac{4}{\sqrt{5}} = 2000 + 5.367 = 2005.37$$

$$\text{LCL} = \mu - 3\frac{\sigma}{\sqrt{n}} = 2000 - 3\frac{4}{\sqrt{5}} = 2000 - 5.367 = 1994.63$$

TABLE 17.3   Twenty-Five Samples of Bottle Fill with $n = 5$ BottleFill

Sample	Bottle 1	Bottle 2	Bottle 3	Bottle 4	Bottle 5	Mean	Range
1	2001	1998	2001	2001	1997	1999.6	4
2	1997	2004	2001	2000	2002	2000.8	7
3	2001	2000	2003	1995	1994	1998.6	9
4	2007	2007	2001	2000	1997	2002.4	10
5	1999	2001	1998	2001	1996	1999.0	5
6	2002	2002	1988	1995	2004	1998.2	16
7	2003	1998	1998	1996	2001	1999.2	7
8	2005	2000	1991	1996	1996	1997.6	14
9	1999	1997	2006	1999	1999	2000.0	9
10	2005	1999	1998	2002	2000	2000.8	7
11	2001	1997	2002	2004	2007	2002.2	10
12	2002	1995	1995	1997	2000	1997.8	7
13	2006	2006	1997	1998	1994	2000.2	12
14	2003	1997	2000	2003	2004	2001.4	7
15	2003	2008	1994	1998	1999	2000.4	14
16	1998	1997	1999	2001	1994	1997.8	7
17	1988	1996	2001	2002	2002	1997.8	14
18	2003	2003	1997	1995	2001	1999.8	8
19	2003	2004	1998	1998	2006	2001.8	8
20	2005	2001	2005	2000	2004	2003.0	5
21	2004	1996	2003	2002	1993	1999.6	11
22	1998	1996	2005	1997	1999	1999.0	9
23	2002	2001	1995	2004	2007	2001.8	12
24	2002	2002	1997	1995	2002	1999.6	7
25	2002	1999	2001	1992	1993	1997.4	10
				Average over 25 samples of 5 bottles:		1999.832	9.160

FIGURE 17.5

MINITAB's $\bar{x}$ Chart with Known Control Limits

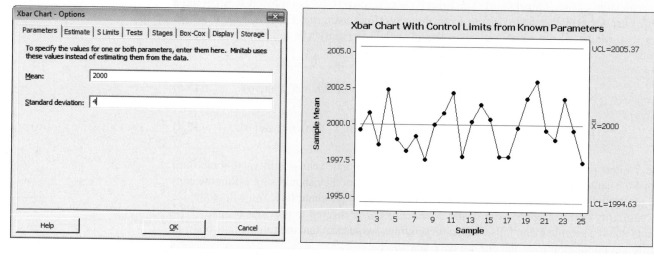

Figure 17.5 shows a MINITAB $\bar{x}$ chart for these 25 samples, with MINITAB's option to specify μ and σ instead of estimating them from the data. Because all the sample means lie within the control limits, this chart shows a process that is *in control*. If a sample mean exceeds UCL or is below LCL, we suspect that the process may be *out of control*. More rules for detecting an out-of-control process will be explained shortly.

Empirical Control Limits

When the process mean μ and standard deviation are unknown (as they often are) we can estimate them from sample data, replacing μ with $\bar{\bar{x}}$ (the average of the means of all samples) and replacing σ with the standard deviation s from a pooled sample of individual X-values. Generally, the centerline and control limits are based on *past* data, but are to be used on *future* data to monitor the process. It is desirable to set the control limits from samples taken independently, rather than using the same data to create the control limits and to plot the control chart. However, this is not always possible.

$$\text{UCL} = \bar{\bar{x}} + 3\frac{s}{\sqrt{n}} \qquad \text{(upper control limit for } \bar{X}, \text{ unknown } \mu \text{ and } \sigma) \qquad \textbf{(17.5)}$$

$$\text{LCL} = \bar{\bar{x}} - 3\frac{s}{\sqrt{n}} \qquad \text{(lower control limit for } \bar{X}, \text{ unknown } \mu \text{ and } \sigma) \qquad \textbf{(17.6)}$$

There are other ways to estimate the process standard deviation σ. For example, we could use $\bar{s}$, the mean of the standard deviations over many subgroups of size n, with an adjustment for bias. Or we could replace σ with an estimate $\bar{R}/d_2$ where $\bar{R}$ is the average range for many samples and d_2 is a control chart factor that depends on the subgroup size (see Table 17.4). If the number of samples is large enough, any of these methods should give reliable control limits. The $\bar{R}$ method is still common for historical reasons (easier to use prior to the advent of computers). If the $\bar{R}$ method is used, the formulas become:

$$\text{UCL} = \bar{\bar{x}} + 3\frac{\bar{R}}{d_2\sqrt{n}} \qquad \text{(upper control limit for } \bar{X}, \text{ unknown } \mu \text{ and } \sigma) \qquad \textbf{(17.7)}$$

$$\text{LCL} = \bar{\bar{x}} - 3\frac{\bar{R}}{d_2\sqrt{n}} \qquad \text{(lower control limit for } \bar{X}, \text{ unknown } \mu \text{ and } \sigma) \qquad \textbf{(17.8)}$$

Figure 17.6 shows MINITAB's menu options for estimating control limits from a sample. By default, MINITAB uses the pooled standard deviation, an attractive choice because it directly estimates σ. In Figure 17.6, using the $\bar{R}$ method, the $\bar{x}$ chart is similar to the chart in Figure 17.5, where σ was known, except that the LCL and UCL values are slightly different.

Control Chart Factors

Table 17.4 can be used to set up the control limits from sample data. We only need the first factor (d_2) for the $\bar{x}$ chart (the table also shows D_3 and D_4, which are used to construct control limits for an R chart, to be discussed shortly). The table only goes to $n = 9$ for purposes of illustration (larger tables are available in more specialized textbooks). These factors are built into MINITAB, MegaStat, Visual Statistics, and other computer packages.

Subgroup Size	d_2	D_3	D_4
2	1.128	0	3.267
3	1.693	0	2.574
4	2.059	0	2.282
5	2.326	0	2.114
6	2.534	0	2.004
7	2.704	0.076	1.924
8	2.847	0.136	1.864
9	2.970	0.184	1.816

TABLE 17.4

Control Chart Factors

See Laythe C. Alwan, *Statistical Process Analysis* (Irwin/McGraw-Hill, 2000), p. 740 for details of how these factors are derived.

FIGURE 17.6

MINITAB's $\bar{x}$ Chart with Estimated Control Limits

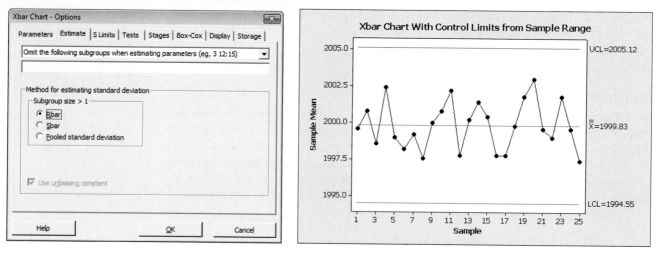

To calculate $\bar{\bar{x}}$ and $\bar{R}$ we use averages of 25 sample means and ranges (see Table 17.3):

$$(17.9) \quad \bar{\bar{x}} = \frac{\bar{x}_1 + \bar{x}_2 + \cdots + \bar{x}_{25}}{25} = \frac{1999.6 + 2000.8 + \cdots + 1997.4}{25} = 1999.832$$

$$(17.10) \quad \bar{R} = \frac{R_1 + R_2 + \cdots + R_{25}}{25} = \frac{4 + 7 + \cdots + 10}{25} = 9.160$$

Using the sample estimates $\bar{\bar{x}} = 1999.832$ and $\bar{R} = 9.160$, along with $d_2 = 2.326$ for $n = 5$ from Table 17.4, the estimated empirical control limits are

$$\text{UCL} = \bar{\bar{x}} + 3\frac{\bar{R}}{d_2\sqrt{n}} = 1999.832 + 3\frac{9.160}{2.326\sqrt{5}} = 2005.12$$

$$\text{LCL} = \bar{\bar{x}} - 3\frac{\bar{R}}{d_2\sqrt{n}} = 1999.832 - 3\frac{9.160}{2.326\sqrt{5}} = 1994.55$$

Note that these *empirical* control limits (2005.12 and 1994.55) differ somewhat from the *theoretical* control limits (2005.37 and 1994.63) that we obtained using $\mu = 2000$ and $\sigma = 4$, and the *empirical* centerline ($\bar{\bar{x}} = 1999.83$) differs from $\mu = 2000$. In practice, it would be necessary to take more than 25 samples to ensure a good estimate of the true process mean and standard deviation. Indeed, engineers may run a manufacturing process for days or weeks before its characteristics are well understood. Figure 17.7 shows MegaStat's $\bar{x}$ chart using the sample data to estimate the control limits. MegaStat *always* uses estimated control limits by the $\bar{R}$ method, and does not permit you to specify known parameters. Also, MegaStat expects the observed data to be arranged as a rectangle, with each subgroup's observations comprising a *row* (like Table 17.3). MegaStat's $\bar{x}$ chart is similar to MINITAB's except for details of scaling.

Detecting Abnormal Patterns

Sample means beyond the control limits are strong indicators of an out-of-control process. However, more subtle patterns can also indicate problems. Experts have developed many "rules of thumb" to check for patterns that might indicate an out-of-control process. Here are four of them (the "sigma" refers to the *standard error of the mean*):

- *Rule 1.* Single point outside 3 sigma.
- *Rule 2.* Two of three successive points outside 2 sigma on same side of centerline.
- *Rule 3.* Four of five successive points outside 1 sigma on same side of centerline.
- *Rule 4.* Nine successive points on same side of centerline.

FIGURE 17.7

MegaStat's x̄ Chart with Estimated Control Limits

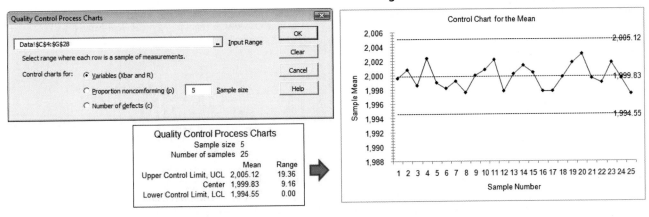

Violations of Rules 1 and 2 can usually be seen from "eyeball inspection" of control charts. Violations of the other rules are more subtle. A computer may be required to monitor a process to be sure that control chart violations are detected. Figure 17.8 illustrates these four rules, applied to a service organization (an HMO clinic conducting physical exams for babies).

Multiple rule violations are possible. Figure 17.9 shows a MINITAB x̄ chart with these four rules applied (note that MINITAB includes many other tests and uses a different numbering

FIGURE 17.8

Red Dots Indicate Rule Violations

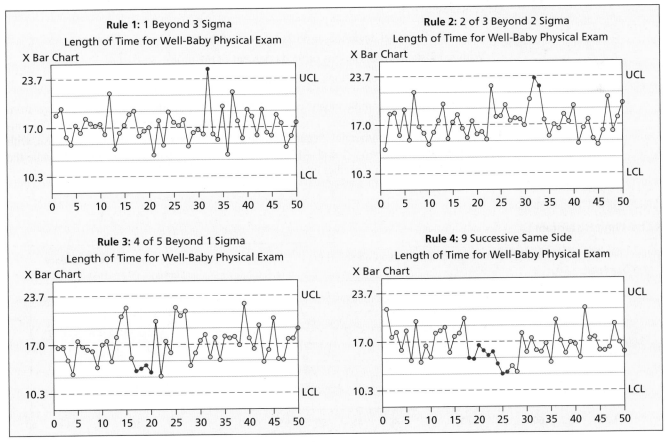

FIGURE 17.9

Violations of Rules of Thumb (from MINITAB)

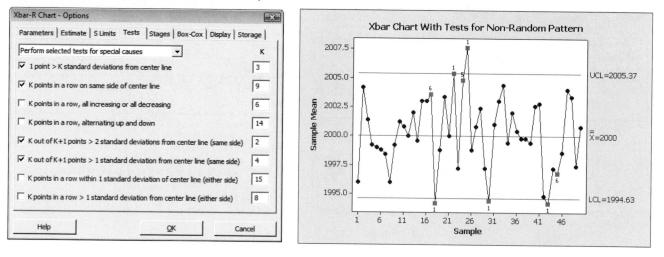

system for its rules). In this illustration, an out-of-control process is shown, with eight rule violations (each violation is numbered and highlighted in red).

Histograms

The normal curve is the reference point for variation inherent in the process or due to random sampling. UCL and LCL are set at ±3 standard errors from the mean, but we could (and should) also examine ±2 and ±1 standard error ranges to see whether the percentage of sample means follows the normal distribution. Recall that the expected percent of samples within various distances from the centerline can be stated as normal areas or percentages:

- Within ±1 standard deviation or 68.26 percent of the time.
- Within ±2 standard deviations or 95.44 percent of the time.
- Within ±3 standard deviations or 99.73 percent of the time.

The distribution of sample means can be scrutinized for symmetry and/or deviations from the expected normal percentages. Figure 17.10 shows an $\bar{x}$ chart and histogram for 100 samples of acidity for a commercial cleaning product. The histogram is roughly symmetric, with 60 sample means between −1 and +1 and 97 sample means between −2 and +2, while the normal distribution would predict 68 and 95, respectively.

FIGURE 17.10

$\bar{x}$ Chart and Histogram

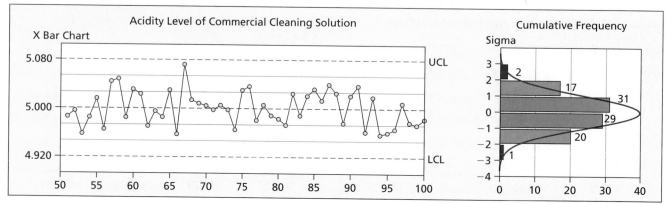

17.14 (a) To construct control limits for an $\bar{x}$ chart, name three ways to estimate σ empirically. (b) Why is the $\bar{R}$ method often used? (c) Why is the s method the default in MINITAB?

17.15 For an $\bar{x}$ chart, what percent of sample means should be (a) within 1 sigma of the centerline; (b) within 2 sigmas of the centerline; (c) within 3 sigmas of the centerline; (d) outside 2 sigmas of the centerline; (e) outside 3 sigmas of the centerline? *Note:* "sigma" denotes the standard error of the mean.

17.16 List four rules for detecting abnormal (special cause) observations in a control chart.

17.17 Set up control limits for an $\bar{x}$ chart, given $\bar{\bar{x}} = 12.50$, $\bar{R} = .42$, and $n = 5$.

17.18 Set up control limits for an $\bar{x}$ chart, given $\mu = 400$, $\sigma = 2$, and $n = 4$.

17.19 Time (in seconds) to serve an early-morning customer at a fast-food restaurant is normally distributed. Set up a control chart for the mean serving time, assuming that serving times were sampled in random subgroups of 4 customers. *Note:* Use this sample of 36 observations to estimate μ and σ. 🗀 **ServeTime**

Sample 1	Sample 2	Sample 3	Sample 4	Sample 5	Sample 6	Sample 7	Sample 8	Sample 9
65	56	84	69	75	87	87	99	102
51	87	67	81	80	84	90	61	61
94	84	71	59	76	80	65	84	88
79	70	85	75	88	52	61	79	78

17.20 To print 8.5 × 5.5 note pads, a copy shop uses standard 8.5 × 11 paper, glues the long edge, then cuts the pads in half so that the pad width is 5.5 inches. However, there is variation in the cutting process. Set up a control chart for the mean width of a note pad, assuming that, in the future, pads will be sampled in random subgroups of 5 pads. Use this sample of 40 observations (widths in inches) to estimate μ and σ. 🗀 **NotePads**

5.52	5.57	5.44	5.47	5.52	5.46	5.43	5.45
5.49	5.47	5.48	5.51	5.53	5.53	5.48	5.47
5.59	5.51	5.43	5.48	5.53	5.50	5.49	5.52
5.46	5.46	5.56	5.54	5.47	5.44	5.53	5.58
5.55	5.56	5.47	5.44	5.55	5.42	5.45	5.54

Mini Case   17.1

Control Limits for Jelly Beans 🗀 JellyBeans

The manufacture of jelly beans is a high-volume operation that is tricky to manage, with strict standards for food purity, worker safety, and environmental controls. Each bean's jelly core is soft and sticky, and must be coated with a harder sugar shell of the appropriate color. Hundreds of thousands of beans must be cooled and bagged, with approximately the desired color proportions. To meet consumer expectations, the surface finish of each bean and its weight must be as uniform as possible. Jelly beans are a low-priced item, and the market is highly competitive (i.e., there are many substitutes and many producers), so it is not cost-effective to spend millions to achieve the same level of precision that might be used, say, in manufacturing a prescription drug.

So, how do we measure jelly bean quality? One obvious metric is weight. To set control limits, we need estimates of μ and σ. From a local grocery, a bag of Brach's jelly beans was purchased (see Figure 17.11). Each bean was weighed on a precise scale. The resulting sample of 182 jelly beans weights showed a bell-shaped distribution, except for three high outliers, easily visible in Figure 17.12. Once the outliers are removed, the sample presents a satisfactory normal probability plot, shown in Figure 17.13. The sample mean and standard deviation ($\bar{x} = 3.352$ grams and $s = .3622$ grams) can now be used to set control limits.

FIGURE 17.11

The Data Set (*n* = 182)

FIGURE 17.12   **Dot Plot for All Data (*n* = 182)**

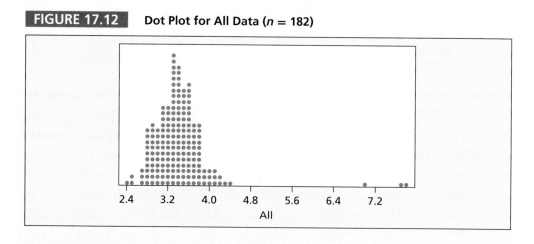

FIGURE 17.13   **Normal Plot for Trimmed Data (*n* = 179)**

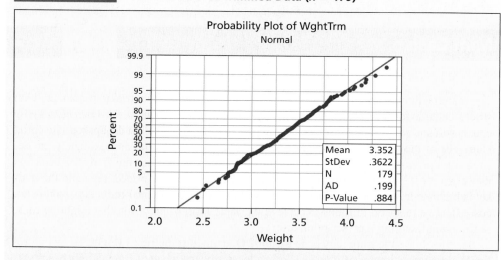

Referring back to Figure 17.11, some differences in size are visible. Can you spot the three oversized beans? Some consumers may regard "double" beans as a treat, rather than as a product defect. But manufacturers always strive for the most consistent product possible, subject to constraints of time, technology, and budget.

The $\bar{x}$ chart of sample means by itself is insufficient to tell whether a process is in control, because it reveals only *centrality*. We also should examine a chart showing *variation* around the mean. We could track the sample standard deviations (using an *s chart*), but it is more traditional to track the *sample range* (the difference between the largest and smallest item in each sample) using the *R chart*. The sample range is sensitive to extreme values. Nonetheless, its behavior can be predicted statistically, and control limits can be established. The *R* chart has asymmetric control limits, because the sample range is not a normally distributed statistic.

Control Limits for the Range

The centerline is obtained by calculating the average range $\bar{R}$ over many samples taken from the process. Estimation of $\bar{R}$ ideally would precede construction of the control chart, using a large number of independent samples, though this is not always possible in practice. Control limits based on samples may not be a good representation of the true process. It depends on the number of samples and the "luck of the draw." The control limits for the *R* chart can be set using either the average sample range $\bar{R}$ or an estimate $\hat{\sigma}$ of the process standard deviation:

$$\text{UCL} = D_4\bar{R} \quad \text{or} \quad \text{UCL} = D_4 d_2 \hat{\sigma} \qquad \text{(upper control limit of sample range)} \qquad \textbf{(17.11)}$$

$$\text{LCL} = D_3\bar{R} \quad \text{or} \quad \text{LCL} = D_3 d_2 \hat{\sigma} \qquad \text{(lower control limit of sample range)} \qquad \textbf{(17.12)}$$

The control limits depend upon factors which must be obtained from a table. For the bottle fill data with $n = 5$, we have $D_4 = 2.114$ and $D_3 = 0$ (from Table 17.4). Using $\bar{R} = 9.16$ from the 25 samples (from Table 17.3) the control limits are:

$$\bar{R} = 9.16 \qquad \text{(centerline for } R \text{ chart)}$$
$$\text{UCL} = D_4\bar{R} = (2.114)(9.160) = 19.36 \qquad \text{(upper control limit)}$$
$$\text{LCL} = D_3\bar{R} = (0)(9.160) = 0 \qquad \text{(lower control limit)}$$

Figure 17.14 shows MINITAB's *R* chart for the data in Table 17.3. Note that the *R* chart control limits could also be based on a pooled standard deviation. Using the Parameters tab, MINITAB also offers an option (not shown) to specify σ yourself (e.g., from historical experience). In this illustration, the process variation remains within the control limits.

Figure 17.15 shows MegaStat's *R* chart using the same data to estimate the control limits. The MINITAB and MegaStat charts are similar except for scaling. MegaStat always uses estimated control limits, whereas MINITAB gives you the option.

17.8 CONTROL CHARTS FOR A RANGE

LO6

Make and interpret common control charts ($\bar{x}$, *R*, and *p*).

EXAMPLE

Bottle Filling: R Chart

FIGURE 17.14

MINITAB's *R* Chart with Control Limits from Sample Data

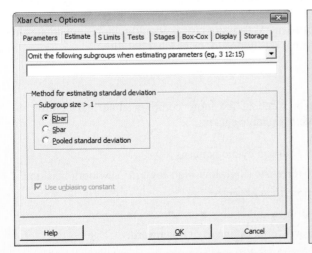

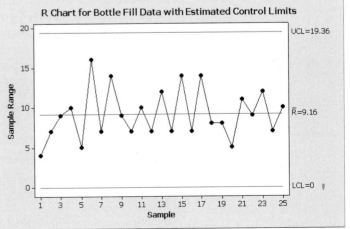

FIGURE 17.15

MegaStat R Chart with Estimated Control Limits

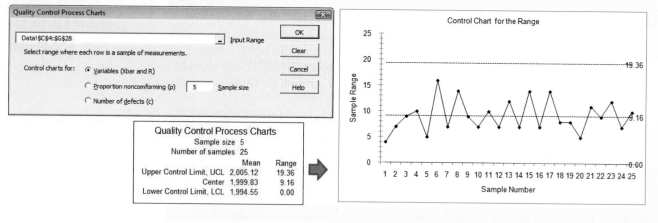

SECTION EXERCISES   **17.21** Set up limits for the R chart, given $\bar{R} = 0.82$ and $n = 6$.

17.22 Set up limits for the R chart, given $\bar{R} = 12$ and $n = 3$.

17.9
PATTERNS IN CONTROL CHARTS

The Overadjustment Problem

The $\bar{x}$ chart is a visual hypothesis test for μ, while the R chart is a visual hypothesis test for σ. In manufacturing, a control chart is used to guide decisions to continue the process or halt the process to make adjustments. *Overadjustment* or stopping to make unnecessary process corrections (Type I error) can lead to loss of production, downtime, unnecessary expense, forgone profit, delayed deliveries, stockout, or employee frustration. On the other hand, failing to make timely process corrections (Type II Error) can lead to poor quality, excess scrap, rework, customer dissatisfaction, adverse publicity or litigation, and employee cynicism.

Statistics allows managers to balance these Type I and II errors. It has been shown that, in the absence of statistical decision rules, manufacturing process operators tend toward over-adjustment, which will actually *increase* variation above the level the process is capable of attaining.

The actions to be taken when a control chart violation is detected will depend on the consequences of Type I and II error. For example, if a health insurer notices that processing times for claim payments are out of control (i.e., relative to target benchmarks), the only action may be an investigation into the problem, because the immediate consequences are not severe. But in car manufacturing, an out-of-control metal forming process could require immediate shutdown of the assembly process to prevent costly rework or product liability.

LO7

Recognize abnormal patterns in control charts and their potential causes.

Abnormal Patterns

Quality experts have given names to some of the more common abnormal control chart patterns, that is, patterns that indicate assignable causes:

- **Cycle**   Samples tend to follow a cyclic pattern.
- **Oscillation**   Samples tend to alternate (high-low-high-low) in "sawtooth" fashion.
- **Instability**   Samples vary more than expected.
- **Level shift**   Samples shift abruptly either above or below centerline.
- **Trend**   Samples drift slowly either upward or downward.
- **Mixture**   Samples come from two different populations (increased variation).

These names are intended to help you recognize symptoms that may be associated with known causes. These concepts extend to any time-series pattern (not just control charts).

Symptoms and Assignable Causes

Each $\bar{x}$ chart in Figure 17.16 displays 100 samples, which is a long enough run to show the patterns clearly. However, the $\bar{x}$ charts shown are exaggerated to emphasize the essential features of each pattern. Abnormal patterns like these would generate violations of Rules 1, 2, 3, or 4 (or multiple rule violations) so the process would actually have been stopped *before* the pattern developed to the degree shown in Figure 17.16. Although many patterns are discussed in terms of the $\bar{x}$ chart, the R chart and histogram of sample means may also reveal abnormal patterns. It may be impossible to identify a pattern or its assignable cause(s) if the period of observation is short. Table 17.5 summarizes the symptoms and likely underlying causes of abnormal patterns.

FIGURE 17.16

Common Abnormal Patterns

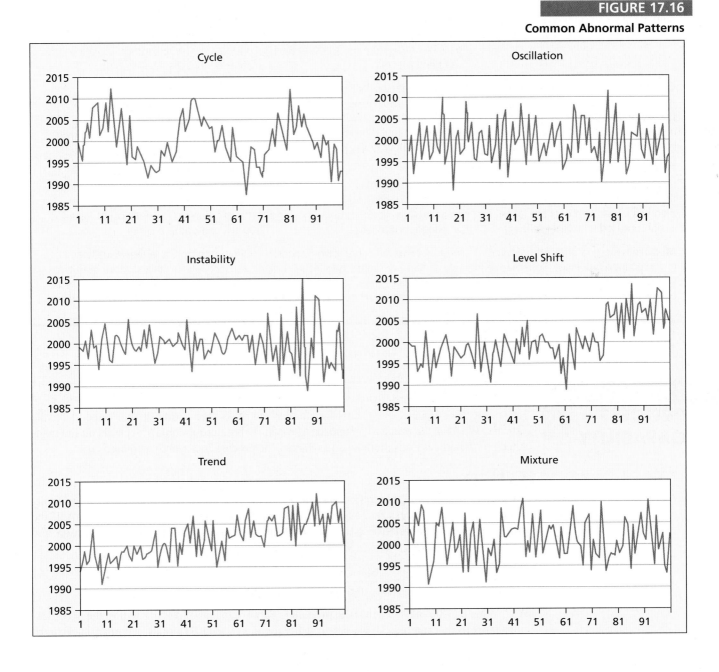

TABLE 17.5	Pattern Descriptions and Assignable Causes	
Pattern Description	*Likely Assignable Causes*	Detected How?
Cycle is a repeated series of high measurements followed by a series of low measurements (+ + + + − − − + + + − − − − + + + +, etc.) relative to the centerline. Equivalent to positive autocorrelation in regression residuals.	*Industry:* worn threads or gears, humidity or temperature fluctuations, operator fatigue, voltage changes, overadjustment. *Services:* duty rotations, employee fatigue, poor scheduling, periodic distractions.	May be detected visually (fewer than $m/2$ centerline crossings in m samples) or by a runs test (see Chapter 16) or higher-than-expected tail frequencies in a histogram. Look for violations of Rule 4.
Oscillation is a pattern of alternating high and low measurements (+ − +− + − + − +, etc.) relative to the centerline (a zigzag or sawtooth pattern). Equivalent to negative autocorrelation in regression residuals.	*Industry:* alternating sampling of two machines, two settings, two inspectors, or two gauges. *Services:* attempts to compensate for performance variation on the last task, alternating task between two workers.	May be detected visually (more than $m/2$ centerline crossings in m samples) or by a runs test (see Chapter 16). Process mean stays near the centerline, though process variance may increase. May not violate any rules.
Instability is a larger than normal amount of variation preceded by a period of normal, stable variation.	*Industry:* untrained operators, overadjustment, tool wear, defective material. *Services:* distractions, poor job design, untrained employees, flawed sampling process.	May be detectable on the $\bar{x}$ chart, but shows up most clearly on the R chart and in higher-than-expected frequencies in the tails of the histogram. Violations of Rules 1, 2, 3 are likely.
Level shift is a sudden change in measurements either above or below the centerline. It is a change in the actual process mean. Easily confused with trend.	*Industry:* new workers, change in equipment, new inspector, new machine setting, new lot of material. *Services:* changed environment, new supervisor, new work rules.	Center of the histogram shifts but with no change in variation. Violation of Rule 4 is likely, and perhaps others. May be too few centerline crossings (fewer than $m/2$).
Trend is a slow, continuous drifting of measurements either up or down from the chart centerline. Detectable visually if enough measurements are taken. Easily confused with level shift.	*Industry:* tool wear, inadequate maintenance, worker fatigue, gradual clogging (dirt, shavings, etc.), drying of lubricants. *Services:* inattention, rising workload, bottlenecks.	Process variance may be unchanged, but the histogram grows skewed in one tail. May be too few centerline crossings (fewer than $m/2$). Violation of Rule 4 is likely, and perhaps others.
Mixture is merged output from two or more separate processes. Both may be in control, but with different means, so the overall process variance is increased.	*Industry:* two machines, two gauges, two shifts (day, night), two inspectors, different lots of material. *Services:* different supervisors, two work teams, two shifts.	Difficult to detect, either visually or statistically, especially if more than two processes are mixed. Histogram may be bimodal. Use same tests as for instability.

17.10 PROCESS CAPABILITY

LO8

Assess the capability of a process.

A business must translate *customer requirements* into an **upper specification limit (USL)** and **lower specification limit (LSL)** of a quality metric. These limits do *not* depend on the process. Whether the process is *capable* of meeting these requirements depends on the magnitude of the process variation (σ) and whether the process is correctly centered (μ).

C_p Index

The *capability index* C_p is a ratio that compares the interval between the specification limits with the expected process range (defined as six times the process standard deviation). If the process range is small relative to the specification range, the capability index will be high, and conversely. A higher C_p index (a *more capable* process) is always better.

$$(17.13) \qquad C_p = \frac{USL - LSL}{6\sigma} \qquad \text{(process capability index } C_p\text{)}$$

A C_p value of 1.00 indicates that the process is barely capable of staying within the specifications *if* precisely centered. Managers typically require $C_p > 1.33$ (i.e., safety margin of 2σ) to allow flexibility in case the process drifts off center. A much higher capability index may be required in some applications.

Example 1: If USL − LSL = 6σ, then $C_p = \dfrac{6\sigma}{6\sigma} = 1.00$ (no safety margin).

Example 2: If USL − LSL = 8σ, then $C_p = \dfrac{8\sigma}{6\sigma} = 1.33$ (2σ safety margin).

Example 3: If USL − LSL = 10σ, then $C_p = \dfrac{10\sigma}{6\sigma} = 1.67$ (4σ safety margin).

C_{pk} Index

The index C_p is easy to understand, but fails to show whether the process is well-centered. A process with acceptable variation could be off-centerline and yet have a high C_p capability index. To remedy this weakness, we define another process capability index called C_{pk} which looks at each *separate* safety margin (the distance between each specification limit and the process centerline) as illustrated in Figure 17.17.

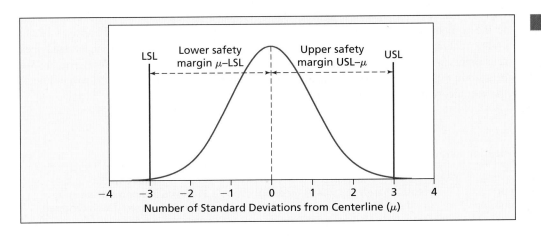

FIGURE 17.17

Individual Safety Margins for C_{pk} Index

The process capability index C_{pk} simply is the smaller of these two distances (USL $-\mu$ and $\mu -$ LSL) expressed as a fraction of the 3σ distance above or below μ:

$$C_{pk} = \frac{\min(\mu - \text{LSL}, \text{USL} - \mu)}{3\sigma} \qquad \text{(process capability index } C_{pk}) \qquad \textbf{(17.14)}$$

We are assuming that LSL lies below μ (the centerline) and USL lies above μ (the centerline) so that both distances are positive. If both safety margins $\mu -$ LSL and USL $-\mu$ are exactly 3σ, then $C_{pk} = 1.00$. A C_{pk} index of 1.00 is the minimum capability, but much higher values are preferred. If both safety margins ($\mu -$ LSL and USL $-\mu$) are the same, then C_{pk} will be identical to C_p. In contrast to the C_p index, the C_{pk} index imposes a penalty when the process is off-center.

A bakery is supposed to produce cookies whose average weight, after baking, is 31 grams. To meet quality requirements, it has been decided that USL = 35.0 grams and LSL = 28.0 grams. The process standard deviation is 0.8 grams and the process centerline is set at $\mu = 31$ grams. The company requires a capability index of at least 1.33.

EXAMPLE

Cookie Baking

C_p *index:*

$$C_p = \frac{\text{USL} - \text{LSL}}{6\sigma} = \frac{35.0 - 28.0}{(6)(.8)} = 1.46$$

C_{pk} *index:*

$$C_{pk} = \frac{\min(\mu - \text{LSL}, \text{USL} - \mu)}{3\sigma} = \frac{\min(31.0 - 28.0, 35.0 - 31.0)}{(3)(0.8)} = \frac{3.0}{2.4} = 1.25$$

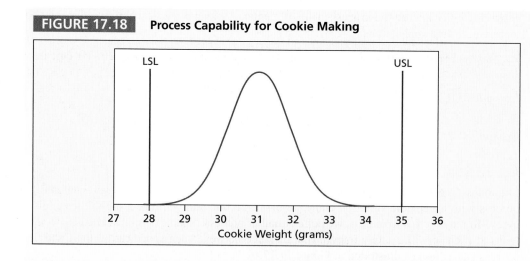

FIGURE 17.18   **Process Capability for Cookie Making**

According to the C_p index, the process capability is barely acceptable ($C_p = 1.46$), but using the C_{pk} index ($C_{pk} = 1.25$) the process capability is unacceptable. Actually, the process capability is doubtful regardless of index used, because both indexes are uncomfortably close to the company's chosen minimum (1.33). The situation is illustrated in Figure 17.18. In cookie making, management is less concerned about oversized cookies than undersized ones (customers will not complain if a cookie is too big) so the limits are not symmetric, as can be seen in Figure 17.18. Note that their process is correctly centered at $\mu = 31$, even though the specification limits are asymmetric.

FIGURE 17.19

Process Variation versus Specification Limits

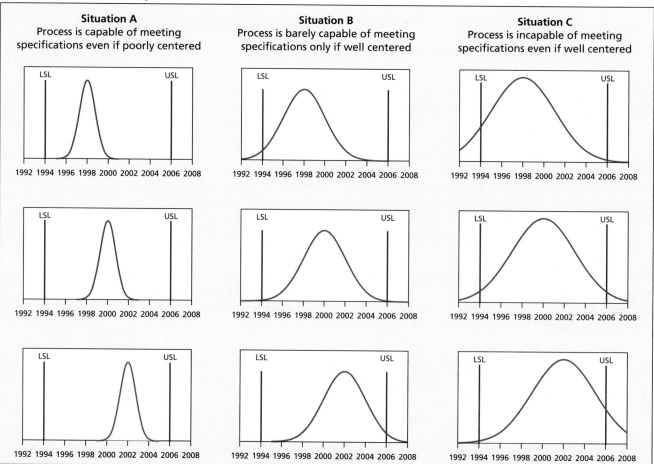

Bottle Filling Revisited

Figure 17.19 illustrates several possible situations, using the bottle filling scenario with symmetric specification limits LSL = 1994 and USL = 2006 and a target $\mu = 2000$. Remember that specification limits are based on customer demands (or engineering requirements) and not on the process itself. *There is no guarantee that the extant process is capable of meeting the requirements.* If it is not, there is no choice but to find ways to improve the process (i.e., by reducing σ) through improved technology, worker training, or capital investment.

17.23 Find the C_p and C_{pk} indexes for a process with $\mu = 720$, $\sigma = 1.0$, LSL = 715, USL = 725. How would you rate the capability of this process? Explain.

17.24 Find the C_p and C_{pk} indexes for a process with $\mu = 0.426$, $\sigma = 0.001$, LSL = 0.423, USL = 0.432. How would you rate the capability of this process? Explain.

17.25 Find the C_p and C_{pk} indexes for a process with $\mu = 55.4$, $\sigma = 0.1$, LSL = 55.2, USL = 55.9. How would you rate the capability of this process? Explain.

SECTION EXERCISES

Attribute Data: *p* Charts

17.11
OTHER CONTROL CHARTS

The *p chart* for attribute data plots the *proportion* of nonconforming items using the familiar sample proportion p:

$$p = \frac{\text{number of nonconforming items}}{\text{sample size}} = \frac{x}{n} \qquad \textbf{(17.15)}$$

LO6

Make and interpret common control charts ($\bar{x}$, R, and p).

In manufacturing, p used to be referred to as a "defect rate," but the term "nonconforming items" is preferred because it is more neutral and better adapted to applications outside manufacturing, such as service environments. For example, for a retailer, p might refer to the proportion of customers who return their purchases for a refund. For a bank, p might refer to the proportion of checking account customers who have insufficient funds to cover one or more checks. For Ticketmaster, p might refer to the proportion of customers who have to wait "on hold" more than 5 minutes to obtain concert tickets.

The number of nonconforming items in a sample of n items is a binomial random variable, so the control limits are constructed as a confidence interval for a population proportion using one of several methods to state the *population* nonconformance rate π:

- Use an assumed value of π (e.g., a target rate of nonconformance).
- Use an empirical estimate of π based on a large number of trials.
- Use an estimate p from the samples being tested (if no other choice).

If n is large enough to assume normality,* the control limits would be

$$\text{UCL} = \pi + 3\sqrt{\frac{\pi(1-\pi)}{n}} \qquad (\pi \text{ is the process centerline}) \qquad \textbf{(17.16)}$$

$$\text{LCL} = \pi - 3\sqrt{\frac{\pi(1-\pi)}{n}} \qquad (\pi \text{ is the process centerline}) \qquad \textbf{(17.17)}$$

The logic is similar to a two-tailed hypothesis test of a proportion. Approximately 99.73 percent of the time, we expect the sample proportion p to fall within 3 standard deviations of the assumed centerline (π). If the LCL is negative, it is assumed to be zero (since a proportion cannot be negative). In manufacturing, the rate of nonconformance is likely to be a very small fraction (e.g., .02 or even smaller) so it is quite likely that LCL will be zero.

---

*To assume normality, we want $n\pi \geq 10$ and $n(1-\pi) \geq 10$. If not, the binomial distribution may be used to set up control limits. MINITAB will handle this, although the resulting control limits may be quite wide.

EXAMPLE

Cell Phone Manufacture

A manufacturer of cell phones has a .002 historical rate of nonconformance to specifications (i.e., 2 nonconforming phones per 1,000). All phones are tested, and the nonconformance rates are plotted on a p chart, using an assumed value $\pi = .002$. Thus, the control limits are

$$\text{UCL} = .002 + 3\sqrt{\frac{(.002)(.998)}{n}} \quad \text{and} \quad \text{LCL} = .002 - 3\sqrt{\frac{(.002)(.998)}{n}}$$

Table 17.6 shows inspection data for 100 days of production. Each production run (n) is around 2,000 phones per day, but does vary. Hence, the control limits are not constant, as shown in the p chart in Figure 17.20.

TABLE 17.6   Nonconforming Cell Phones   CellPhones

Day	Nonconforming (x)	Production (n)	x/n
1	3	2,056	0.00146
2	1	1,939	0.00052
3	4	2,079	0.00192
4	5	2,079	0.00241
5	4	1,955	0.00205
⋮	⋮	⋮	⋮
96	4	1,967	0.00203
97	6	2,077	0.00289
98	3	2,075	0.00145
99	5	1,908	0.00262
100	2	2,045	0.00098

FIGURE 17.20   MINITAB p Chart for Cell Phones

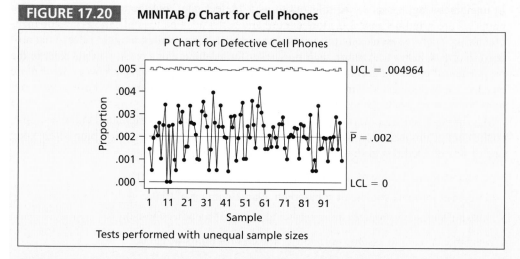

P Chart for Defective Cell Phones

Notice that p stays within the control limits although it touches the LCL twice (not a problem because zero defects is ideal). Although n varies, we can illustrate the control limit calculation by using $\pi = .002$ and $n = 2,000$:

$$\text{UCL} = .002 + 3\sqrt{\frac{(.002)(.998)}{2,000}} = .004997$$

$$\text{LCL} = .002 - 3\sqrt{\frac{(.002)(.998)}{2,000}} = -.000997$$

Because a negative proportion is impossible, we just set LCL = 0. You will notice that MINITAB's UCL is not quite the same as the calculation above, because MINITAB uses a binomial calculation rather than the normal approximation. The difference may be noticeable when $n\pi < 10$ (the criterion for a normal approximation to the binomial). In this example $n\pi = (.002)(2,000) = 4$, so the binomial method is preferred.

Application: Emergency Patients

Instead of being a rate of *nonconformance* to specifications, p could be a rate of *conformance* to specifications. Then

$$p = \frac{\text{number of conforming items}}{\text{sample size}} = \frac{x}{n} \qquad \textbf{(17.18)}$$

Ardmore Hospital's emergency facility advertises that its goal is to ensure that, on average, 90 percent of patients receive treatment within 30 minutes of arrival. Table 17.7 shows data from 100 days of emergency department records.

Day	Seen In 30 Minutes (x)	Patient Volume (n)	x/n
1	87	97	0.900
2	113	122	0.924
3	106	115	0.920
4	84	90	0.928
5	82	92	0.896
⋮	⋮	⋮	⋮
96	128	142	0.900
97	101	112	0.900
98	123	135	0.908
99	128	141	0.908
100	141	149	0.944

TABLE 17.7

Emergency Patients Seen within 30 Minutes
📁 ERPatients

The average number of patient arrivals per day is around 120, but there is considerable variation. Hence, the control limits are not constant, as shown in the p chart in Figure 17.21. Because the sample sizes are smaller than in the cell phone example, the LCL and UCL are more sensitive to the varying sample size, and hence appear more jagged. This process is in control.

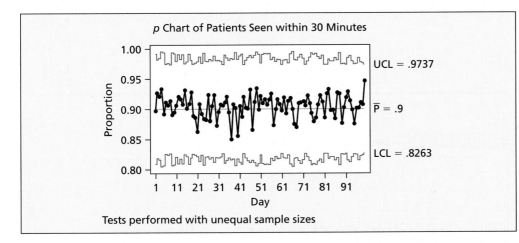

FIGURE 17.21

p Chart for ER Patients

The p chart is likely to be used in service operations (e.g., for benchmarking in health care delivery). Rules of thumb for detecting outliers, runs, and patterns apply to the p chart, just as for the $\bar{x}$ chart. However, tests for patterns are rarely seen outside manufacturing, except when service sector tasks are ongoing, repeatable, and easily sampled.

Other Control Charts (*s, c, np, I, MR*)

Other common types of control charts include:

- *I* **charts** (for individual numerical observations).
- *MR* **charts** (moving range for individual observations).
- *s* charts (for standard deviations).

- *c* charts (for Poisson events).
- *np* charts (for binomial totals).
- zone charts (using six regions based on σ).

The first two are used when *continuous inspection* is possible. When $n = 1$, there is no range, so a *moving range* is used. *I* chart control limits simply are $\mu \pm 3\sigma$ when $n = 1$. Mini Case 17.2 gives an illustration. Interpretation is the same as for any other control chart.

Mini Case   17.2

I-MR Charts for Jelly Beans 📁 **JellyBeans2**

Table 17.8 shows a sample of weights for 44 Brach's jelly beans (all black) from a randomly chosen bag of jelly beans. Is the weight of the jelly beans in control? To construct the control limits, we use the sample mean and standard deviation from the large trimmed sample in Mini Case 17.1 ($\bar{x} = 3.352$ grams and $s = .3622$ grams) with MINITAB's *I-MR* chart option with assumed parameters $\mu = 3.352$ and $\sigma = .3622$.

In Figure 17.22 the *I* chart (upper one) reveals that two jelly beans (the 4th and 43rd observations) are not within the control limits. There is also evidence of a problem in

TABLE 17.8	**Weights of 44 Black Brach's Jelly Beans**						
Obs	**Weight**	**Obs**	**Weight**	**Obs**	**Weight**	**Obs**	**Weight**
1	3.498	12	3.181	23	3.976	34	3.168
2	3.603	13	3.545	24	3.321	35	2.656
3	4.223	14	3.925	25	3.609	36	2.624
4	7.250	15	3.686	26	3.604	37	3.254
5	3.830	16	3.938	27	3.668	38	3.411
6	3.563	17	3.667	28	3.433	39	2.553
7	2.505	18	3.152	29	3.678	40	4.217
8	3.034	19	3.325	30	3.264	41	3.417
9	3.408	20	3.905	31	3.743	42	3.615
10	3.564	21	3.714	32	3.446	43	1.218
11	3.042	22	3.359	33	3.036	44	3.612

Note: Measurements taken using a Mettler DF360 Delta Range Scale.

FIGURE 17.22   **Before Outliers Removed**

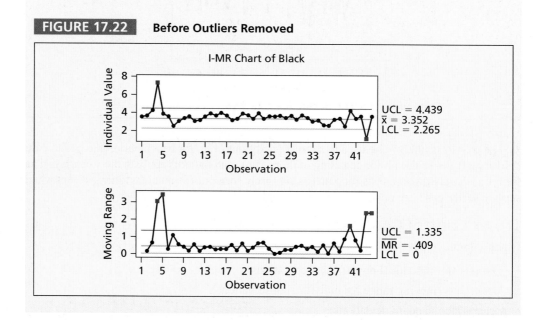

FIGURE 17.23   **After Outliers Removal**

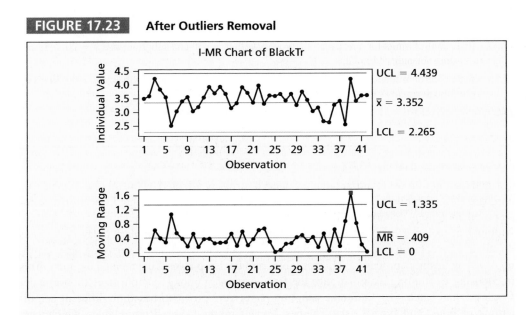

sample-to-sample variation in the *MR* chart (lower one). The explanation turned out to be rather clear. The 4th jelly bean was a "double-bean" (where two jelly beans got stuck together) and the 43rd jelly bean was a "mini-bean" (where the jelly bean was only partially formed). Figure 17.23 shows that, if we remove these outliers, the trimmed sample means stay within the control limits on the *I* chart (upper one), although the *MR* chart (lower one) still has one odd point. Improved quality control for a high-volume, low-cost item like jelly beans is cost-effective only up to a point. A business case would have to be made before spending money on better technology, taking into account consumer preferences and competitors' quality levels.

Ad Hoc Charts

We said earlier that any display of a quality metric over time is a kind of control chart. If we set aside the formalities of control chart theory, anyone can create a "control chart" to monitor something of importance. For example, Figure 17.24 is not a "classic" control chart, but it shows a quality metric (patient waiting time in an emergency department) plotted over time. A box plot showing the range and quartiles over time is an *ad hoc* chart, yet it's a useful one. Organizations must develop their own approaches to quality improvement. As long as they begin with measurement, charting, and analysis, they are heading in the right direction.

FIGURE 17.24

Box Plots over Time
 AdHoc

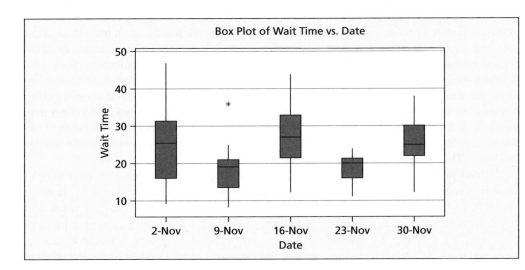

17.26 Create control limits for a p chart for a process with $\pi = .02$ and subgroup size $n = 500$. Is it safe to assume normality? Explain.

17.27 Create control limits for a p chart for a process with $\pi = .50$ and subgroup size $n = 20$. Is it safe to assume normality? Explain.

17.28 Create control limits for a p chart for a process with $\pi = .90$ and subgroup size $n = 40$. Is it safe to assume normality? Explain.

17.29 Why are p charts widely used in service applications like health care?

17.12 ADDITIONAL QUALITY TOPICS (OPTIONAL)

Acceptance Sampling

The end quality of most manufactured products is strongly affected by the quality of materials purchased from suppliers. Manufacturing firms relied on random sampling inspection of shipments of incoming material until the 1970s. This process is called **acceptance sampling**. Although acceptance sampling as a quality control tool is not commonplace today, companies do still use acceptance sampling plans when trying out a new vendor or verifying the capability of a new business process. Elaborate tables and decision rules were created to guide firms in choosing a sampling plan that gave the frequency of sampling, sample size, allowable defect level, and batch size. Different sampling plans were provided based on different combinations of Type I and Type II risks. The best-known are the Dodge-Romig tables, which were originally prepared for Bell Telephone.

In acceptance sampling, *the producer's risk* (α error) is the probability of rejecting material of some stated desirable quality level, while the *consumer's risk* (β error) is the probability of accepting material of some stated undesirable quality level. These two risks must be balanced, because there is a trade-off between α and β for a given sample size. In its simplest form, lot sampling is based on the hypergeometric distribution, in which samples of n items are taken from a lot of size N containing s nonconforming items. Power curves and operating characteristic curves can be developed to guide decisions about acceptance or rejection of shipments, based on the attribute of interest (usually the proportion of nonconforming items).

Single sampling means that the decision is based on only one random sample taken from a shipment. *Double sampling* means that a decision is postponed until a second sample has been taken, unless the results from the first sample are unambiguous. A second sample may not be needed if the first sample result is extremely clear-cut. The concept can be generalized to multiple sampling or sequential sampling using any number of samples. The techniques can also be generalized to include multiple attributes as well as more complex sampling methods such as stratified or cluster sampling.

Supply-Chain Management

The problem with acceptance sampling is that it places the firm in the awkward position of rejecting shipments of purchased material, which may be needed for production in the near future. This forces the firm to increase lead times and hold larger inventory to provide a buffer against defective material. It also strains relations with suppliers and creates incentives to cut corners on quality by accepting questionable shipments. Worst of all, it gives the firm no direct control over its suppliers, except the negative control of saying no to shipments.

Most firms believe that a more constructive approach is to reduce reliance on acceptance sampling, and instead to engage in direct dialogue with suppliers to ensure that their quality control is adequate to meet the buyer's expectations. The idea is to prevent problems, rather than merely spot them after they have occurred. If suppliers implement the TQM philosophy and utilize SPC to control and improve their processes, there is harmony of purpose between vendor and buyer. This is one principle behind ISO 9000, which will be discussed shortly.

But new problems arise from this supply-chain management approach. Suppliers may be smaller companies that lack the experience and resources needed to invest in training, research, and development, and there may be coordination problems between seller and buyer. Buyers may have to subsidize the process of implementing quality control at the supplier level, for example, by sponsoring training seminars, sharing their managerial experience, and working toward common database and decision support systems. Deming felt that suppliers should not be chosen solely on the basis of lowest cost. Rather, he thought buyers should develop long-term relationships with a small group of suppliers, and then nurture the links with those suppliers. Many firms have done this. But changing the supply-chain relationships can be difficult. Overseas outsourcing makes quality control even more complex. What does a U.S., Canadian, or European original equipment manufacturer do if its low-cost Chinese supplier delivers nonconforming or defective raw materials or parts? How do they work with a Chinese supplier to resolve the problem across thousands of miles and language and cultural barriers?

These nonstatistical problems illustrate why quality management in a global environment requires understanding of international business, as well as behavioral, financial, and supply-chain management. Engineers and technical specialists often find it helpful to study business management (and maybe Chinese). If you require a more detailed understanding of quality management, you will need further training (you can start with the Related Reading list).

Quality and Design

Quality is closely tied to design. A well-designed process, product, or service is more likely to yield better quality and more customer satisfaction, with less effort and for a longer time. A poorly designed process, product, or service is more likely to yield undesired outcomes, awkward or inconvenient working arrangements, employee frustration in trying to maintain quality, and more frequent problems, breakdowns, and dissatisfied customers.

Firms may know that their products and services could be designed in a better way, but it would take time and cost money. Customer needs must be met today, so they say, "We will nurse along the old design and do the best we can with it." The problem is that, in the longer run, the customers may not be there, as more dynamic competitors capture the market. One lesson of our time is that there is no such thing as a "safe job," even in a large organization. When we can see a better way to do it, change becomes an ally and inertia an enemy. The search for design improvement is an ongoing process, not something done once. If we improve the design tomorrow, even better solutions are likely to be found later on. Successful organizations try to create a climate in which employees are encouraged to suggest new ways of doing things.

Taguchi's Robust Design

The prominence of Japanese quality expert Genichi Taguchi is mainly due to his contributions in the field of *robust design,* which uses statistically planned experiments to identify process control parameter settings that reduce a process's sensitivity to manufacturing variation. In Taguchi's taxonomy, we identify the functional characteristics that measure the final product's performance, the control parameters that can be specified by process engineers, and the sources of noise that are expensive or impossible to control. By varying control parameters in a planned experiment, we can predict control parameter settings that would make the product's performance less sensitive to random variation. Parameter settings are first varied in a few experimental runs. Then, a fractional factorial experimental design is selected (see Chapter 11), using a balancing property to choose pairs of parameter settings. Finally, predictions of improved parameter settings are made and verified in a confirming experiment.

Taguchi's methods are especially useful in manufacturing situations with many process control parameters which imply complex experimental designs. Once the problem is defined, we rely on well-known experimental design methods. In addition, Taguchi is known for explicitly including in quality measures the total loss incurred from the time the product is shipped, using a quadratic loss penalty based on the squared difference between actual and target quality. His inclusion of customers in the model is considered a major innovation.

Six Sigma and Lean Six Sigma

Six Sigma is a broad philosophy to reduce cost, eliminate variability, and improve customer satisfaction through improved design and better management strategy. *Lean Six Sigma* integrates Six Sigma with supply-chain management to optimize resource flows, while also lowering cost and raising quality. Most of us have heard of the Six Sigma goal of 3.4 defects per million through reduced process variation (i.e., extremely high C_p and C_{pk} indexes) essentially using the tools outlined in this chapter and the DMAIC steps for process improvement. However, there is more to it than statistics, and Six Sigma experts must be certified (Green Belts, Black Belts, Master Black Belts) through advanced training. Six Sigma implementation varies according to the organization, with health care being perhaps the latest major application. Six-Sigma knowledge goes beyond the bounds of an introductory statistics class, but if you take a job that requires it, your company will give you advanced training.

ISO 9000

Since 1992, firms wishing to sell their products globally have had to comply with a series of ISO standards, first articulated in 1987 in Europe. These standards have continued to evolve. Now, **ISO 9000** and ISO audits (both internal and of suppliers) have become a de facto quality system standard for any company wanting to be a world-class competitor. ISO 9001 includes customer service as well as design of products and services (not just manufacturing). The broad scope of ISO 9000, ISO 14000, and QS 9000 requires special training that is not normally part of an introductory statistics class.

Malcolm Baldrige Award

To recognize the importance of achievement in attaining superior quality, in 1988 the U.S. initiated the *Malcolm Baldrige National Quality Award,* based on seven categories of quality: leadership, information/analysis, strategic planning, human resource development, process management, operational results, and customer satisfaction. The **Baldrige Award** is given by the president of the United States to firms (large or small, manufacturing or services) that have made notable achievements in design, manufacture, installation, sales, and service.

Advanced MINITAB Features

A glance at MINITAB's extensive menus will tell you that quality tools are one of its strengths. In addition to all types of control charts and cause-and-effect diagrams (fishbone or Ishikawa diagrams), MINITAB offers capability analysis, variable transformations to achieve normality, alternative distributions where the assumption of normality is inappropriate, and gage study for variables and attributes. If you want further study of statistical quality tools, you could do worse than to explore MINITAB's menus, help system, and data sets. Many other general-purpose software packages (e.g., SAS, SPSS) offer similar capabilities.

Future of Statistical Process Control

Automation, numerical control, and continuous process monitoring have changed the meaning of SPC in manufacturing. The integration of manufacturing and factory floor quality monitoring systems in manufacturing planning and control, materials requirements planning (MRP), computer-aided design and manufacturing (CAD/CAM), order entry, and financial, customer service, and support systems have continued to redefine the role of SPC. Automation has made 100 percent testing and inspection attainable in some applications where it was previously thought to be either impossible or uneconomical.

It may be that SPC itself will become part of the background that is built in to every manufacturing organization, allowing managers to focus on higher-level issues. As an analogy, consider that only a few decades ago chart-making required specialists who were skilled in drafting. Now, anyone with access to a computer can make excellent charts. In the service sector of the economy, quality improvement is still at an early level of implementation. In health care, financial services, and retailing, processes are harder to define and tasks are often not as repetitive or as standardized as in manufacturing. Thus, the role of SPC is still unfolding, and every business student needs to know its basic principles.

Mini Case 17.3 VAILRESORTS

ISO 9001/14001 Certification

Since 1992, firms wishing to compete globally have had to comply with a series of standards developed and maintained by the International Organization for Standardization (ISO). ISO 9000 standards address Quality Management Systems (QMS) within an organization. ISO 9001 certification means that an organization has a QMS in place to measure, achieve, and continually improve their customers' quality requirements, whether the organization provides products, services, or a combination of both. The ISO 14000 standards address Environmental Management Systems (EMS). ISO 14001 certification means that an organization is setting environmental objectives, identifying and controlling their environmental impact, and continually improving their environmental performance.

Vail Resorts Hospitality manages contracts within the Grand Teton National Park near Jackson, Wyoming, through the Grand Teton Lodge Company (GTLC). Grand Teton Lodge Company was one of the first Wyoming tourism entities to achieve ISO 14001 certification, a designation that also places them among an elite group of national park concessionaires that have received such certification. GTLC is also ISO 9001 certified, the only hospitality company in the United States to certify their quality management system.

Each year their commitment is verified through independent, third-party audits. Vail Resorts reports that the environmental management system has been successfully recertified each year, including several years with no adverse findings in this process. The GTLC EMS has achieved goals related to the environment such as annually diverting 300 tons of waste from landfills through recycling and reuse and working with their food vendors to develop a line of eco-friendly disposable food containers.

You can read more about the ISO certification process and Vail Resorts' quality and environmental efforts at the following Web sites: www.iso.org and www.vailresorts.com.

CHAPTER SUMMARY

Quality is measured by a set of attributes that affect **customer satisfaction. Quality improvement** is aimed at **variance reduction. Common cause** variation is normal and expected, while **special cause** variation is abnormal and requires action, such as adjusting the **process** for producing a good or service. Quality is affected by management, resources, technology, and human factors (e.g., training, employee involvement). **Statistical process control** (SPC) involves using **control charts** of key quality metrics to make sure that the processes are **in control**. The **upper control limit** (UCL) and **lower control limit** (LCL) define the range of allowable variation. These limits are usually set **empirically** by observing a process over time. Control charts are used to track the **mean** ($\bar{x}$ chart), **range** (R chart), **proportion** (p chart), and other statistics. Samples may be taken by **subgroups** of n items, or by continuous monitoring with **individual charts** (I charts) and **moving range** (MR charts). There are **rules of thumb** to identify out-of-control patterns (instability, trend, level shift, cycle, oscillation) and their likely causes. A **capable** process is one whose variability (σ) is small in relation to the **upper and lower specification limits** (USL and LSL) as reflected in the C_p and C_{pk} capability indexes. SPC concepts were first applied to manufacturing, but can be adapted to service environments such as finance, health care, and retailing. International **ISO standards** now guide companies selling in world markets, and Six Sigma techniques are widely used to improve quality in service organizations, as well as in manufacturing.

KEY TERMS

Commonly Used Formulas

Control limits for $\bar{x}$ chart (known or historical σ): $\mu \pm 3\dfrac{\sigma}{\sqrt{n}}$

Control limits for $\bar{x}$ chart (sample estimate of σ): $\bar{\bar{x}} \pm 3\dfrac{s}{\sqrt{n}}$

Control limits for $\bar{x}$ chart (using average range): $\bar{\bar{x}} \pm 3\dfrac{\bar{R}}{d_2\sqrt{n}}$

Control limits for R chart (using average range or sample standard deviation with control chart factors from a table):

$\text{UCL} = D_4\bar{R} \quad \text{or} \quad \text{UCL} = D_4 d_2 s$
$\text{LCL} = D_3\bar{R} \quad \text{or} \quad \text{LCL} = D_3 d_2 s$

Capability index (ignores centering): $C_p = \dfrac{\text{USL} - \text{LSL}}{6\sigma}$

Capability index (tests for centering): $C_{pk} = \dfrac{\min(\mu - \text{LSL}, \text{USL} - \mu)}{3\sigma}$

Control limits for p chart: $\pi \pm 3\sqrt{\dfrac{\pi(1 - \pi)}{n}}$

CHAPTER REVIEW

Note: Questions with * are based on optional material.

1. Define (a) quality, (b) process, and (c) productivity. Why are they hard to define?

2. List six general attributes of quality.

3. Distinguish between common cause and special cause variation.

4. In quality improvement, list three roles played by (a) statisticians and (b) managers.

5. Distinguish between (a) internal versus external customers, (b) assigning blame versus seeking solutions, and (c) employee involvement versus top-down decisions.

6. In chronological order, list important phases in the evolution of the quality movement in North America. What is the main change in emphasis over the last 100 years?

7. (a) Who was W. Edwards Deming and why is he remembered? (b) List three of Deming's major ideas and explain them in your own terms.

8. List three influential thinkers other than Deming who made contributions to the quality movement and state their contributions.

9. (a) Briefly explain each acronym: TQM, BPR, SQC, SPC, CQI, DMAIC. (b) List the steps in the continuous quality improvement model.

10. (a) What is shown on the $\bar{x}$ chart? (b) Name three ways to set the control limits on the $\bar{x}$ chart. (c) How can we obtain good empirical control limits for the $\bar{x}$ chart? (d) Why are quality control samples sometimes small?

11. Explain the four rules of thumb for identifying an out-of-control process.

12. (a) What is shown on the R chart? (b) How do we set control limits for the R chart?

13. Name the six abnormal control chart patterns and tell (a) how they may be recognized, and (b) what their likely causes might be.

14. (a) State the formulas for the two capability indexes C_p and C_{pk}. (b) Why isn't C_p alone sufficient? (c) What is considered an acceptable value for these indexes? (d) Why is an *in-control* process not necessarily *capable*?

15. (a) What is shown on the p chart? (b) How do we set control limits for the p chart? (c) Why might the p chart control limits vary from sample to sample?

*16. Briefly explain (a) the overadjustment problem, (b) *ad hoc* control charts, (c) acceptance sampling, (d) supply-chain management, (e) Taguchi's robust design, (f) the Six Sigma philosophy, (g) ISO 9000, and (h) the Malcolm Baldrige Award.

Instructions: You may use MINITAB, MegaStat, or similar software to assist you in the control chart questions. Data sets for the exercises are on the CD.

CHAPTER EXERCISES

connect

17.30 Explain each chart's purpose and the parameters that must be known or estimated to establish its control limits.

    a. $\bar{x}$ chart
    b. R chart
    c. p chart
    d. I chart

17.31 Define three possible quality metrics (not necessarily the ones actually used) to describe and monitor: (a) your performance in your college classes; (b) effectiveness of the professors in your college classes; (c) your effectiveness in managing your personal finances; (d) your textbook's effectiveness in helping you learn in a college statistics class.

17.32 Define three quality metrics that might be used to describe quality and performance for the following services: (a) your cellular phone service (e.g., Verizon); (b) your Internet service provider (e.g., AOL); (c) your dry cleaning and laundry service; (d) your physician's office; (e) your hairdresser; (f) your favorite fast-food restaurant. Do you think these data are actually collected or used? Why, or why not?

17.33 Define three quality metrics that might be used to describe quality and performance in the following consumer products: (a) your personal vehicle (e.g., car, SUV, truck, bicycle, motorcycle); (b) the printer on your computer; (c) the toilet in your bathroom; (d) a PDA (e.g., Palm Pilot); (e) an HDTV display screen; (f) a light bulb. Do you think these data are actually collected or used? Why, or why not?

17.34 Based on the cost of sampling and the presumed accuracy required, would sampling or 100 percent inspection be used to collect data on (a) the horsepower of each engine being installed in new cars; (b) the fuel consumption per seat mile of each Northwest Airlines flight; (c) the daily percent of customers who order low-carb menu items for each McDonald's restaurant; (d) the life in hours of each lithium ion battery installed in new laptop computers; (e) the number of medication errors per month in a large hospital.

17.35 Why are the control limits for an R chart asymmetric, while those of an $\bar{x}$ chart are symmetric?

17.36 Bob said, "We use the normal distribution to set the control limits for the $\bar{x}$ chart because samples from processes follow a normal distribution." Is Bob right? Explain.

17.37 Bob said, "They must not be using quality control in automobile manufacturing. Just look at the J.D. Power data showing that new cars all seem to have defects." (a) Discuss Bob's assertion, focusing on the concept of variation. (b) Can you think of processes where zero defects *could* be attained on a regular basis? Explain. (c) Can you think of processes where zero defects *cannot* be attained on a regular basis? *Hint:* Consider activities like pass completion by a football quarterback, 3-point shots by a college basketball player, or multiple-choice exams taken by a college student.

17.38 Use your favorite Internet search engine to look up any four of the following quality experts. Write a one-paragraph biographical sketch *in your own words* that lists his contributions to quality improvement.

    a. Walter A. Shewhart
    b. Harold F. Dodge
    c. Harry G. Romig
    d. Joseph M. Juran
    e. Genichi Taguchi
    f. Kaoru Ishikawa
    g. Armand V. Feigenbaum

17.39 Make a fishbone chart (cause-and-effect diagram) like the following for the reasons you have ever been (or could be) late to class. Use as many branches as necessary. Which factors are most important? Which are most easily controlled?

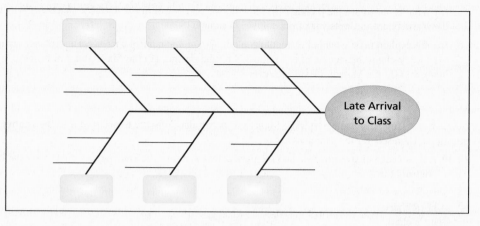

17.40 Make a fishbone chart (cause-and-effect diagram) for the reasons your end-of-month checkbook balance may not match your bank statement. Use as many branches as necessary. Which factors are most important? Which are most easily controlled?

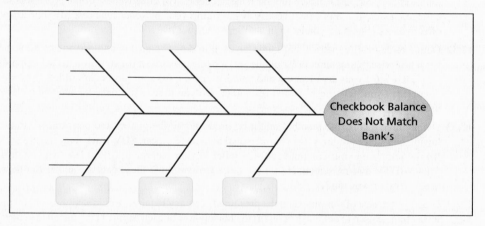

17.41 Make a fishbone chart (cause-and-effect diagram) for the reasons an airline flight might be late to arrive. Use as many branches as necessary. Which factors are most important? Which are most easily controlled?

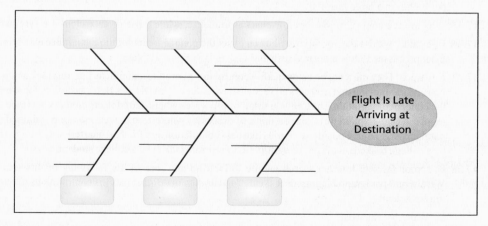

CAPABILITY

17.42 A process has specification limits of LSL = 540 and USL = 550. The process standard deviaton is $\sigma = 1.25$. Find the C_p and C_{pk} capability indexes if (a) the process mean is 545; (b) the process mean is 543. (c) What was the point of this exercise?

17.43 In painting an automobile, the thickness of the color coat has a lower specification limit of 0.80 mils and an upper specification limit of 1.20 mils. Find the C_p and C_{pk} capability indexes if (a) the process mean is 1.00 mils and the process standard deviation is .05 mils; and (b) the process mean is .90 mils and the process standard deviation is .05 mils. (c) What was the point of this exercise?

17.44 Moisture content per gram of a certain baked product has specification limits of 120 mg and 160 mg. Find the C_p and C_{pk} capability indexes if (a) the process mean is 140 mg and the process standard deviation is 5 mg; and (b) the process mean is 140 mg and the process standard deviation is 3 mg. (c) What was the point of this exercise?

x̄ CHARTS

17.45 The yield strength of a metal bolt has a mean of 6,050 pounds with a standard deviation of 100 pounds. Twenty samples of three bolts were tested, resulting in the means shown below. (a) Construct upper and lower control limits for the x̄ chart, using the given product parameters. (b) Plot the data on the control chart. (c) Is this process in control? Explain your reasoning. 🖻 **Bolts-M**

6,107	6,031	6,075	6,115	6,039	6,079	5,995	6,097	6,114	6,039
6,154	6,054	6,028	6,002	6,062	6,094	6,051	6,031	5,965	6,082

17.46 Refer to the bolt strength problem 17.45. Assume $\mu = 6,050$ and $\sigma = 100$. Use the following 32 *individual* bolt strength observations to answer the questions posed. (a) Prepare a histogram and/or normal probability plot for the sample. (b) Does the sample support the view that yield strength is a normally distributed random variable? (c) Are the sample mean and standard deviation about where they are expected to be? 🖻 **Bolts-I**

6,121	6,100	6,007	6,166	6,164	6,032	6,276	6,151
6,054	5,836	6,024	6,105	6,033	6,066	6,079	6,192
6,028	6,087	5,983	6,040	6,062	6,054	6,100	5,983

17.47 In painting an automobile at the factory, the thickness of the color coat has a process mean of 1.00 mils and a process standard deviation of .07 mils. Twenty samples of five cars were tested, resulting in the mean paint thicknesses shown below. (a) Construct upper and lower control limits for the x̄ chart, using the given process parameters. (b) Plot the data on the control chart. (c) Is this process in control? Explain your reasoning. 🖻 **Paint-M**

0.996	0.960	1.016	1.017	1.001	0.988	1.006	1.073	1.032	1.021
0.984	1.019	0.997	1.024	1.033	1.030	0.994	0.980	0.977	1.037

17.48 Refer to the paint thickness problem 17.47. Assume $\mu = 1.00$ and $\sigma = 0.07$. Use the following 35 *individual* observations on paint thickness to answer the questions posed. (a) Prepare a histogram and/or normal probability plot for the sample. (b) Does the sample support the view that paint thickness is a normally distributed random variable? (c) Are the mean and standard deviation about as expected? 🖻 **Paint-I**

1.026	0.949	1.069	1.105	0.995	0.955	1.080
0.932	1.014	0.899	1.031	1.042	1.022	1.082
1.111	0.995	1.005	1.004	0.964	1.065	0.909
0.912	0.978	1.037	0.992	1.010	0.974	0.977
0.905	1.008	0.971	0.951	1.200	1.065	0.972

17.49 The temperature control unit on a commercial freezer in a 24-hour grocery store is set to maintain a mean temperature of 23 degrees Fahrenheit. The temperature varies, because people are constantly opening the freezer door to remove items, but the thermostat is capable of maintaining temperature with a standard deviation of 2 degrees Fahrenheit. The desired range is 18 to 30 degrees Fahrenheit. (a) Find the C_p and C_{pk} capability indexes. (b) In words, how would you describe the process capability? (c) If improvement is desired, what might be some obstacles to increasing the capability?

17.50 Refer to the freezer problem 17.49 with $\mu = 23$ and $\sigma = 2$. Temperature measurements are recorded four times a day (at midnight, 0600, 1200, and 1800). Twenty samples of four observations are shown below. (a) Construct upper and lower control limits for the x̄ chart, using the given process parameters. (b) Plot the data on the control chart. (c) Is this process in control? Explain your reasoning. 📁 **Freezer**

Sample	Midnight	At 0600	At 1200	At 1800	Mean
1	25	26	23	23	24.25
2	22	23	28	22	23.75
3	20	24	25	21	22.50
4	21	25	22	23	22.75
5	21	23	21	23	22.00
6	26	25	27	26	26.00
7	21	23	25	20	22.25
8	25	23	22	25	23.75
9	22	24	24	22	23.00
10	27	23	26	25	25.25
11	24	23	20	21	22.00
12	25	21	23	20	22.25
13	26	21	21	23	22.75
14	26	22	26	22	24.00
15	21	24	20	19	21.00
16	23	26	23	23	23.75
17	23	21	24	21	22.25
18	25	22	22	23	23.00
19	24	20	21	22	21.75
20	24	21	23	21	22.25

17.51 Refer to the freezer data's 80 *individual* temperature observations in problem 17.50. (a) Prepare a histogram and/or normal probability plot for the sample. (b) Does the sample support the view that freezer temperature is a normally distributed random variable? (c) Are the sample mean and standard deviation about where they are expected to be? 📁 **Freezer**

17.52 A Nabisco Fig Newton has a process mean weight of 14.00 g with a standard deviation of 0.10 g. The lower specification limit is 13.40 g and the upper specification limit is 14.60 g. (a) Describe the capability of this process, using the techniques you have learned. (b) Would you think that further variance reduction efforts would be a good idea? Explain the pros and cons of such an effort. *Hint:* Use the economic concept of opportunity cost.

17.53 A new type of smoke detector battery is developed. From laboratory tests under standard conditions, the half-life (defined as less than 50 percent of full charge) of 20 batteries are shown below. (a) Make a histogram of the data and/or a probability plot. Do you think that battery half-life can be assumed normal? (b) The engineers say that the mean battery half-life will be 8,760 hours with a standard deviation of 200 hours. Using these parameters (not the sample), set up the centerline and control limits for the $\bar{x}$ chart for a subgroup size of $n = 5$ batteries to be sampled in future production runs. (c) Repeat the previous exercise, but this time, use the sample mean and standard deviation. (d) Do you think that the control limits from this sample would be reliable? Explain, and suggest alternatives. 📁 **Battery**

8,502	8,660	8,785	8,778	8,804	9,069	8,516	9,048	8,628	9,213
8,511	8,965	8,688	8,892	8,638	8,440	8,900	8,993	8,958	8,707

17.54 A box of Wheat Chex cereal is to be filled to a mean weight of 466 grams. The lower specification limit is 453 grams (the labeled weight is 453 grams) and the upper specification limit is 477 grams (so as not to overfill the box). The process standard deviation is 2 grams. (a) Find the C_p and C_{pk} capability indexes. (b) Assess the process capability. (c) Why might it be difficult to reduce the variance in this process to raise the capability indices? *Hint:* A single Wheat Chex weighs .3 g (30 mg).

17.55 Refer to the Wheat Chex problem 17.54 with $\mu = 465$ and $\sigma = 3$. During production, samples of three boxes are weighed every 5 minutes. (a) Find the upper and lower control limit for the $\bar{x}$ chart. (b) Plot the following 20 sample means on the chart. Is the process in control? 📁 **Chex-M**

465.7	463.7	466.0	466.3	463.0	468.3	465.0	463.3	462.0	463.0
465.7	467.0	463.3	466.0	465.3	465.3	463.0	466.7	466.3	466.3

17.56 Refer to the Wheat Chex box fill problem 17.54 with $\mu = 465$ and $\sigma = 3$. Below are 30 *individual* observations on box fill. (a) Prepare a histogram and/or normal probability plot for the sample. Does the sample support the view that box fill is a normally distributed random variable? Explain. (b) Is the mean of these 20 same means where it should be? 🖫 **Chex-I**

461	465	462	469	463	465	462	465	467	467
460	467	466	466	465	465	462	458	470	460
465	466	464	460	465	465	466	464	465	461

17.57 Each gum drop in two bags of Sathers Gum Drops was weighed (to the nearest .001 g) on a sensitive Mettler PE 360 Delta Range scale. After removing one outlier (to improve normality) there were 84 gum drops in the sample, yielding an overall mean $\bar{x} = 11.988$ g and a pooled standard deviation $s = .2208$ g. (a) Use these sample statistics to construct control limits for an $\bar{x}$ chart, using a subgroup size $n = 6$. (b) Plot the means shown below on your control chart. Is the process in control? (c) Prepare a histogram and/or normal probability plot for the pooled sample. Does the sample support the view that gum drop weight is a normally distributed random variable? Explain. 🖫 **GumDrops**

Sample	x_1	x_2	x_3	x_4	x_5	x_6	Mean
1	11.741	11.975	11.985	12.163	12.317	12.032	12.036
2	12.206	11.970	12.179	12.182	11.756	11.975	12.045
3	12.041	12.120	11.855	12.036	11.750	11.870	11.945
4	12.002	11.800	12.092	12.017	12.340	12.488	12.123
5	12.305	12.134	11.949	12.050	12.246	11.839	12.087
6	11.862	12.049	12.105	11.894	11.995	11.722	11.938
7	11.979	12.124	12.171	12.093	12.224	11.965	12.093
8	11.941	11.855	11.587	11.574	11.752	12.345	11.842
9	12.297	12.078	12.137	11.869	11.609	11.732	11.954
10	11.677	11.879	11.926	11.852	11.781	11.932	11.841
11	12.113	12.129	12.156	12.284	12.207	12.247	12.189
12	12.510	11.904	11.675	11.880	12.086	12.458	12.086
13	12.193	11.975	12.173	11.635	11.549	11.744	11.878
14	11.880	11.784	11.696	11.804	11.823	11.693	11.780

p CHARTS

17.58 Past experience indicates that the probability of a post-surgical complication in a certain procedure is 6 percent. A hospital typically performs 200 such surgeries per month. (a) Find the control limits for the monthly p chart. (b) Would it be reasonably safe to assume that the sample proportion x/n is normally distributed? Explain.

17.59 A large retail toy store finds that, on average, a certain cheap (under $20) electronic toy has a 5 percent damage rate during shipping. From each incoming shipment, a sample of 100 is inspected. (a) Find the control limits for a p chart. (b) Plot the 10 samples below on the p chart. Is the process in control? (c) Is the sample size large enough to assume normality of the sample proportion? Explain. 🖫 **Toys**

Sample	X	n	X/n
1	3	100	0.03
2	5	100	0.05
3	4	100	0.04
4	7	100	0.07
5	2	100	0.02
6	2	100	0.02
7	0	100	0.00
8	2	100	0.02
9	7	100	0.07
10	6	100	0.06

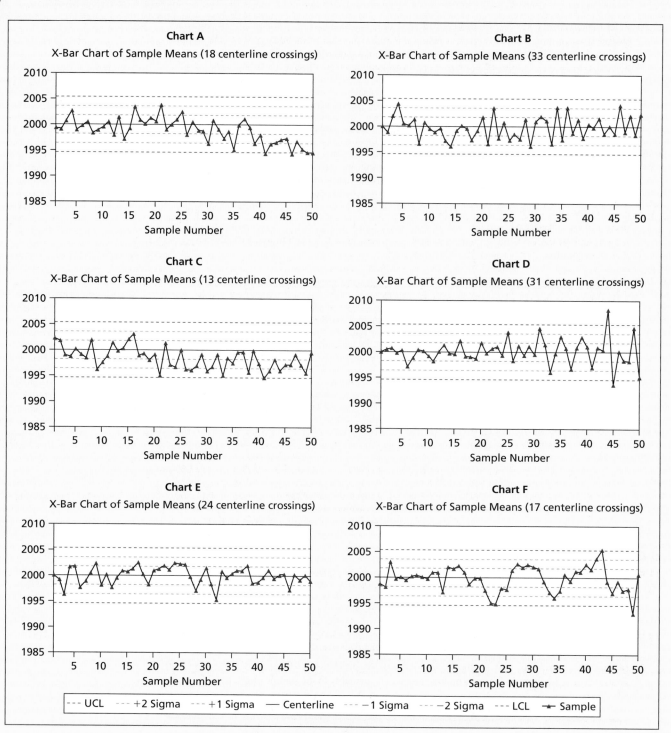

PATTERNS IN CONTROL CHARTS

17.60 Which abnormal pattern (cycle, instability, level shift, oscillation, trend, mixture), if any, exists in each of the $\bar{x}$ charts shown above? If you see none, say so. If you see more than one possibility, say so. Explain your reasoning.

17.61 Referring to Charts *A–F*, which Rules (1, 2, 3, 4) are violated in each chart? Make a photocopy and circle the points that violate each rule.

17.62 Refer to the bolt strength problem 17.45. Assuming $\mu = 6{,}050$ and $\sigma = 100$ with $n = 3$, then LCL = 5,876.8 and UCL = 6,223.2. Below are five sets of 20 sample means using $n = 3$. Test each set of means for the pattern suggested in the column heading. This is a visual judgment question, though you can apply Rules 1–4 if you wish. 📁 **Bolts-P**

Up Trend?	Down Trend?	Unstable?	Cycle?	Oscillate?
5,907	6,100	6,048	6,079	6,122
6,060	6,009	5,975	6,029	5,983
5,987	6,145	6,092	6,006	6,105
5,919	6,049	5,894	6,012	6,024
6,029	6,039	6,083	6,098	6,123
6,114	5,956	6,069	6,124	6,022
6,063	6,103	6,073	6,092	6,082
6,084	6,140	5,972	6,114	6,018
5,980	6,054	6,112	6,071	6,031
6,056	6,062	5,988	6,097	6,107
6,078	6,042	6,006	6,038	6,031
6,118	6,152	6,226	6,099	6,047
6,051	5,961	5,989	6,000	6,055
6,021	5,926	6,111	6,004	6,041
6,068	6,109	6,026	6,054	5,972
6,157	5,904	6,057	6,083	5,987
6,041	6,049	6,098	6,148	6,043
6,129	6,042	6,082	6,071	6,137
6,026	5,847	6,050	6,095	5,930
6,174	6,033	6,084	6,092	6,057

17.63 Refer to the paint problem 17.47 with $\mu = 1.00$ and $\sigma = .07$. With $n = 5$, LCL $= .906$ and UCL $= 1.094$. Below are five sets of 20 sample means using $n = 5$. Test each set of means for the pattern suggested in the column heading. This is a visual judgment question, though you can apply Rules 1–4 if you wish.   📂 **Paint-P**

No Pattern?	Up Trend?	Down Trend?	Unstable?	Cycle?
0.996	0.995	1.007	0.999	0.964
0.960	0.942	1.000	0.986	1.025
1.016	0.947	1.011	0.950	0.988
1.017	1.011	0.989	0.982	1.000
1.001	0.983	0.999	0.967	1.023
0.988	0.989	1.000	0.972	1.019
1.006	0.978	1.025	0.977	1.035
1.073	0.958	0.963	1.015	1.043
1.032	1.034	1.060	0.970	1.044
1.021	1.058	1.020	1.016	0.993
0.984	1.058	0.977	0.979	0.994
1.019	0.958	0.985	0.934	0.988
0.997	1.030	1.033	0.975	0.991
1.024	1.022	0.975	1.100	1.001
1.033	0.976	0.939	0.976	1.011
1.030	1.024	1.007	0.976	1.015
0.994	1.032	0.994	1.029	1.000
0.980	0.994	0.990	0.987	1.010
0.977	1.016	0.925	0.954	1.061
1.037	1.039	0.907	1.011	1.001

DO IT YOURSELF

17.64 Buy a bag of M&Ms. (a) As a measure of quality, take a sample of 100 M&Ms and count the number with incomplete or illegible "M" printed on them. (b) Calculate the sample proportion with defects. (c) What ambiguity (if any) did you encounter in this task? (d) Do you feel that your sample was large enough? Explain.

17.65 Examine a square meter (or another convenient unit) of paint on your car's driver door. Be sure the area is clean. (a) Tally the number of paint defects (scratch, abrasion, embedded dirt, chip, dent, rust, other). You may add your own defect categories. (b) Repeat, using a friend's car that is either older or newer than yours. (c) State your findings succinctly.

17.66 Buy a box of Cheerios (or your favorite breakfast cereal). (a) As a measure of quality, take a sample of 100 Cheerios, and count the number of Cheerios that are broken. (b) Calculate the sample proportion with defects. (c) What ambiguity (if any) did you encounter in this task? (d) Do you feel that your sample was truly random? Explain.

Web Data Sources

Source	Web Site
American Society for Quality (books, training, videos)	www.qualitypress.asq.org
Deming Society (philosophy, references)	www.deming.org
Quality Digest Magazine (current issues)	www.qualitydigest.com
Quality University (training videos)	www.qualityuniversity.com

RELATED READINGS

Besterfield, Dale H. *Quality Control*. 7th ed. Prentice-Hall, 2004.

Birkenstock, James M. *The ISO 9000 Quality System Checklist*. McGraw-Hill, 1997.

Boardman, Thomas J. "The Statistician Who Changed the World: W. Edwards Deming, 1900–1993." *The American Statistician* 48, no. 3 (August 1994), pp. 179–87.

Bossert, James L. *Supplier Management Handbook*. 6th ed. ASQC: 2004.

Brue, Greg. *Six Sigma for Managers*. McGraw-Hill, 2002.

Brussee, Warren. *Statistics for Six Sigma Made Easy*. McGraw-Hill, 2004.

Evans, James R., and William M. Lindsay. *Management and the Control of Quality*. South-Western, 2004.

George, Michael L.; David T. Rowlands; and Bill Kastle. *What Is Lean Six Sigma?* McGraw-Hill, 2003.

Gitlow, Howard S; Oppenheim, Oppenheim, and Levine. *Quality Management*. 3rd ed. McGraw-Hill, 2005.

Grant, Eugene, and Richard Leavenworth. *Statistical Quality Control*. 7th ed. McGraw-Hill, 1996.

Jonglekar, Anand M. *Statistical Methods for Six Sigma*. Wiley, 2003.

Kemp, Sid. *Quality Management Demystified*. McGraw-Hill, 2006.

Montgomery, Douglas C. *Introduction to Statistical Quality Control*. 6th ed. Wiley, 2008.

Norton, Mick. *A Quick Course in Statistical Process Control*. Pearson, 2005.

Pyzdek, Thomas. *The Six Sigma Handbook*. 3rd ed. McGraw-Hill, 2009.

Smith, Gerald M. *Statistical Process Control and Quality Improvement*. 5th ed. Prentice-Hall, 2004.

CHAPTER 17 Online Learning Resources

The Online Learning Center (OLC) at www.mhhe.com/doane3e has several *LearningStats* demonstrations to help you understand quality management. Your instructor may assign one or more of them, or you may decide to download the ones that sound interesting.

Topic	LearningStats Demonstrations
Quality overview	▣ Quality Overview ▣ Process Control Overview
Capability	▣ Capability Explained ▣ Capability Indexes ▣ Moving Range
Control chart patterns and rules	▣ Control Chart Patterns
Other	▣ What Is Six Sigma?

Key: ▣ = PowerPoint ▣ = Excel

BINOMIAL PROBABILITIES

Example: $P(X = 3 \mid n = 8, \pi = .50) = .2188$

This table shows $P(X = x)$.

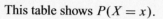

n	x	.01	.02	.05	.10	.15	.20	.30	.40	.50	.60	.70	.80	.85	.90	.95	.98	.99
2	0	.9801	.9604	.9025	.8100	.7225	.6400	.4900	.3600	.2500	.1600	.0900	.0400	.0225	.0100	.0025	.0004	.0001
	1	.0198	.0392	.0950	.1800	.2550	.3200	.4200	.4800	.5000	.4800	.4200	.3200	.2550	.1800	.0950	.0392	.0198
	2	.0001	.0004	.0025	.0100	.0225	.0400	.0900	.1600	.2500	.3600	.4900	.6400	.7225	.8100	.9025	.9604	.9801
3	0	.9703	.9412	.8574	.7290	.6141	.5120	.3430	.2160	.1250	.0640	.0270	.0080	.0034	.0010	.0001	—	—
	1	.0294	.0576	.1354	.2430	.3251	.3840	.4410	.4320	.3750	.2880	.1890	.0960	.0574	.0270	.0071	.0012	.0003
	2	.0003	.0012	.0071	.0270	.0574	.0960	.1890	.2880	.3750	.4320	.4410	.3840	.3251	.2430	.1354	.0576	.0294
	3	—	—	.0001	.0010	.0034	.0080	.0270	.0640	.1250	.2160	.3430	.5120	.6141	.7290	.8574	.9412	.9703
4	0	.9606	.9224	.8145	.6561	.5220	.4096	.2401	.1296	.0625	.0256	.0081	.0016	.0005	.0001	—	—	—
	1	.0388	.0753	.1715	.2916	.3685	.4096	.4116	.3456	.2500	.1536	.0756	.0256	.0115	.0036	.0005	—	—
	2	.0006	.0023	.0135	.0486	.0975	.1536	.2646	.3456	.3750	.3456	.2646	.1536	.0975	.0486	.0135	.0023	.0006
	3	—	—	.0005	.0036	.0115	.0256	.0756	.1536	.2500	.3456	.4116	.4096	.3685	.2916	.1715	.0753	.0388
	4	—	—	—	.0001	.0005	.0016	.0081	.0256	.0625	.1296	.2401	.4096	.5220	.6561	.8145	.9224	.9606
5	0	.9510	.9039	.7738	.5905	.4437	.3277	.1681	.0778	.0313	.0102	.0024	.0003	.0001	—	—	—	—
	1	.0480	.0922	.2036	.3281	.3915	.4096	.3602	.2592	.1563	.0768	.0284	.0064	.0022	.0005	—	—	—
	2	.0010	.0038	.0214	.0729	.1382	.2048	.3087	.3456	.3125	.2304	.1323	.0512	.0244	.0081	.0011	.0001	—
	3	—	.0001	.0011	.0081	.0244	.0512	.1323	.2304	.3125	.3456	.3087	.2048	.1382	.0729	.0214	.0038	.0010
	4	—	—	—	.0005	.0022	.0064	.0284	.0768	.1563	.2592	.3602	.4096	.3915	.3281	.2036	.0922	.0480
	5	—	—	—	—	.0001	.0003	.0024	.0102	.0313	.0778	.1681	.3277	.4437	.5905	.7738	.9039	.9510
6	0	.9415	.8858	.7351	.5314	.3771	.2621	.1176	.0467	.0156	.0041	.0007	.0001	—	—	—	—	—
	1	.0571	.1085	.2321	.3543	.3993	.3932	.3025	.1866	.0938	.0369	.0102	.0015	.0004	.0001	—	—	—
	2	.0014	.0055	.0305	.0984	.1762	.2458	.3241	.3110	.2344	.1382	.0595	.0154	.0055	.0012	.0001	—	—
	3	—	.0002	.0021	.0146	.0415	.0819	.1852	.2765	.3125	.2765	.1852	.0819	.0415	.0146	.0021	.0002	—
	4	—	—	.0001	.0012	.0055	.0154	.0595	.1382	.2344	.3110	.3241	.2458	.1762	.0984	.0305	.0055	.0014
	5	—	—	—	.0001	.0004	.0015	.0102	.0369	.0938	.1866	.3025	.3932	.3993	.3543	.2321	.1085	.0571
	6	—	—	—	—	—	.0001	.0007	.0041	.0156	.0467	.1176	.2621	.3771	.5314	.7351	.8858	.9415
7	0	.9321	.8681	.6983	.4783	.3206	.2097	.0824	.0280	.0078	.0016	.0002	—	—	—	—	—	—
	1	.0659	.1240	.2573	.3720	.3960	.3670	.2471	.1306	.0547	.0172	.0036	.0004	.0001	—	—	—	—
	2	.0020	.0076	.0406	.1240	.2097	.2753	.3177	.2613	.1641	.0774	.0250	.0043	.0012	.0002	—	—	—
	3	—	.0003	.0036	.0230	.0617	.1147	.2269	.2903	.2734	.1935	.0972	.0287	.0109	.0026	.0002	—	—
	4	—	—	.0002	.0026	.0109	.0287	.0972	.1935	.2734	.2903	.2269	.1147	.0617	.0230	.0036	.0003	—
	5	—	—	—	.0002	.0012	.0043	.0250	.0774	.1641	.2613	.3177	.2753	.2097	.1240	.0406	.0076	.0020
	6	—	—	—	—	.0001	.0004	.0036	.0172	.0547	.1306	.2471	.3670	.3960	.3720	.2573	.1240	.0659
	7	—	—	—	—	—	—	.0002	.0016	.0078	.0280	.0824	.2097	.3206	.4783	.6983	.8681	.9321
8	0	.9227	.8508	.6634	.4305	.2725	.1678	.0576	.0168	.0039	.0007	.0001	—	—	—	—	—	—
	1	.0746	.1389	.2793	.3826	.3847	.3355	.1977	.0896	.0313	.0079	.0012	.0001	—	—	—	—	—
	2	.0026	.0099	.0515	.1488	.2376	.2936	.2965	.2090	.1094	.0413	.0100	.0011	.0002	—	—	—	—
	3	.0001	.0004	.0054	.0331	.0839	.1468	.2541	.2787	.2188	.1239	.0467	.0092	.0026	.0004	—	—	—
	4	—	—	.0004	.0046	.0185	.0459	.1361	.2322	.2734	.2322	.1361	.0459	.0185	.0046	.0004	—	—
	5	—	—	—	.0004	.0026	.0092	.0467	.1239	.2188	.2787	.2541	.1468	.0839	.0331	.0054	.0004	.0001
	6	—	—	—	—	.0002	.0011	.0100	.0413	.1094	.2090	.2965	.2936	.2376	.1488	.0515	.0099	.0026
	7	—	—	—	—	—	.0001	.0012	.0079	.0313	.0896	.1977	.3355	.3847	.3826	.2793	.1389	.0746
	8	—	—	—	—	—	—	.0001	.0007	.0039	.0168	.0576	.1678	.2725	.4305	.6634	.8508	.9227
9	0	.9135	.8337	.6302	.3874	.2316	.1342	.0404	.0101	.0020	.0003	—	—	—	—	—	—	—
	1	.0830	.1531	.2985	.3874	.3679	.3020	.1556	.0605	.0176	.0035	.0004	—	—	—	—	—	—
	2	.0034	.0125	.0629	.1722	.2597	.3020	.2668	.1612	.0703	.0212	.0039	.0003	—	—	—	—	—
	3	.0001	.0006	.0077	.0446	.1069	.1762	.2668	.2508	.1641	.0743	.0210	.0028	.0006	.0001	—	—	—
	4	—	—	.0006	.0074	.0283	.0661	.1715	.2508	.2461	.1672	.0735	.0165	.0050	.0008	—	—	—
	5	—	—	—	.0008	.0050	.0165	.0735	.1672	.2461	.2508	.1715	.0661	.0283	.0074	.0006	—	—
	6	—	—	—	.0001	.0006	.0028	.0210	.0743	.1641	.2508	.2668	.1762	.1069	.0446	.0077	.0006	.0001
	7	—	—	—	—	—	.0003	.0039	.0212	.0703	.1612	.2668	.3020	.2597	.1722	.0629	.0125	.0034
	8	—	—	—	—	—	—	.0004	.0035	.0176	.0605	.1556	.3020	.3679	.3874	.2985	.1531	.0830
	9	—	—	—	—	—	—	—	.0003	.0020	.0101	.0404	.1342	.2316	.3874	.6302	.8337	.9135

π

n	x	.01	.02	.05	.10	.15	.20	.30	.40	.50	.60	.70	.80	.85	.90	.95	.98	.99
10	0	.9044	.8171	.5987	.3487	.1969	.1074	.0282	.0060	.0010	.0001	—	—	—	—	—	—	—
	1	.0914	.1667	.3151	.3874	.3474	.2684	.1211	.0403	.0098	.0016	.0001	—	—	—	—	—	—
	2	.0042	.0153	.0746	.1937	.2759	.3020	.2335	.1209	.0439	.0106	.0014	.0001	—	—	—	—	—
	3	.0001	.0008	.0105	.0574	.1298	.2013	.2668	.2150	.1172	.0425	.0090	.0008	.0001	—	—	—	—
	4	—	—	.0010	.0112	.0401	.0881	.2001	.2508	.2051	.1115	.0368	.0055	.0012	.0001	—	—	—
	5	—	—	.0001	.0015	.0085	.0264	.1029	.2007	.2461	.2007	.1029	.0264	.0085	.0015	.0001	—	—
	6	—	—	—	.0001	.0012	.0055	.0368	.1115	.2051	.2508	.2001	.0881	.0401	.0112	.0010	—	—
	7	—	—	—	—	.0001	.0008	.0090	.0425	.1172	.2150	.2668	.2013	.1298	.0574	.0105	.0008	.0001
	8	—	—	—	—	—	.0001	.0014	.0106	.0439	.1209	.2335	.3020	.2759	.1937	.0746	.0153	.0042
	9	—	—	—	—	—	—	.0001	.0016	.0098	.0403	.1211	.2684	.3474	.3874	.3151	.1667	.0914
	10	—	—	—	—	—	—	—	.0001	.0010	.0060	.0282	.1074	.1969	.3487	.5987	.8171	.9044
12	0	.8864	.7847	.5404	.2824	.1422	.0687	.0138	.0022	.0002	—	—	—	—	—	—	—	—
	1	.1074	.1922	.3413	.3766	.3012	.2062	.0712	.0174	.0029	.0003	—	—	—	—	—	—	—
	2	.0060	.0216	.0988	.2301	.2924	.2835	.1678	.0639	.0161	.0025	.0002	—	—	—	—	—	—
	3	.0002	.0015	.0173	.0852	.1720	.2362	.2397	.1419	.0537	.0125	.0015	.0001	—	—	—	—	—
	4	—	.0001	.0021	.0213	.0683	.1329	.2311	.2128	.1208	.0420	.0078	.0005	.0001	—	—	—	—
	5	—	—	.0002	.0038	.0193	.0532	.1585	.2270	.1934	.1009	.0291	.0033	.0006	—	—	—	—
	6	—	—	—	.0005	.0040	.0155	.0792	.1766	.2256	.1766	.0792	.0155	.0040	.0005	—	—	—
	7	—	—	—	—	.0006	.0033	.0291	.1009	.1934	.2270	.1585	.0532	.0193	.0038	.0002	—	—
	8	—	—	—	—	.0001	.0005	.0078	.0420	.1208	.2128	.2311	.1329	.0683	.0213	.0021	.0001	—
	9	—	—	—	—	—	.0001	.0015	.0125	.0537	.1419	.2397	.2362	.1720	.0852	.0173	.0015	.0002
	10	—	—	—	—	—	—	.0002	.0025	.0161	.0639	.1678	.2835	.2924	.2301	.0988	.0216	.0060
	11	—	—	—	—	—	—	—	.0003	.0029	.0174	.0712	.2062	.3012	.3766	.3413	.1922	.1074
	12	—	—	—	—	—	—	—	—	.0002	.0022	.0138	.0687	.1422	.2824	.5404	.7847	.8864
14	0	.8687	.7536	.4877	.2288	.1028	.0440	.0068	.0008	.0001	—	—	—	—	—	—	—	—
	1	.1229	.2153	.3593	.3559	.2539	.1539	.0407	.0073	.0009	.0001	—	—	—	—	—	—	—
	2	.0081	.0286	.1229	.2570	.2912	.2501	.1134	.0317	.0056	.0005	—	—	—	—	—	—	—
	3	.0003	.0023	.0259	.1142	.2056	.2501	.1943	.0845	.0222	.0033	.0002	—	—	—	—	—	—
	4	—	.0001	.0037	.0349	.0998	.1720	.2290	.1549	.0611	.0136	.0014	—	—	—	—	—	—
	5	—	—	.0004	.0078	.0352	.0860	.1963	.2066	.1222	.0408	.0066	.0003	—	—	—	—	—
	6	—	—	—	.0013	.0093	.0322	.1262	.2066	.1833	.0918	.0232	.0020	.0003	—	—	—	—
	7	—	—	—	.0002	.0019	.0092	.0618	.1574	.2095	.1574	.0618	.0092	.0019	.0002	—	—	—
	8	—	—	—	—	.0003	.0020	.0232	.0918	.1833	.2066	.1262	.0322	.0093	.0013	—	—	—
	9	—	—	—	—	—	.0003	.0066	.0408	.1222	.2066	.1963	.0860	.0352	.0078	.0004	—	—
	10	—	—	—	—	—	—	.0014	.0136	.0611	.1549	.2290	.1720	.0998	.0349	.0037	.0001	—
	11	—	—	—	—	—	—	.0002	.0033	.0222	.0845	.1943	.2501	.2056	.1142	.0259	.0023	.0003
	12	—	—	—	—	—	—	—	.0005	.0056	.0317	.1134	.2501	.2912	.2570	.1229	.0286	.0081
	13	—	—	—	—	—	—	—	.0001	.0009	.0073	.0407	.1539	.2539	.3559	.3593	.2153	.1229
	14	—	—	—	—	—	—	—	—	.0001	.0008	.0068	.0440	.1028	.2288	.4877	.7536	.8687
16	0	.8515	.7238	.4401	.1853	.0743	.0281	.0033	.0003	—	—	—	—	—	—	—	—	—
	1	.1376	.2363	.3706	.3294	.2097	.1126	.0228	.0030	.0002	—	—	—	—	—	—	—	—
	2	.0104	.0362	.1463	.2745	.2775	.2111	.0732	.0150	.0018	.0001	—	—	—	—	—	—	—
	3	.0005	.0034	.0359	.1423	.2285	.2463	.1465	.0468	.0085	.0008	—	—	—	—	—	—	—
	4	—	.0002	.0061	.0514	.1311	.2001	.2040	.1014	.0278	.0040	.0002	—	—	—	—	—	—
	5	—	—	.0008	.0137	.0555	.1201	.2099	.1623	.0667	.0142	.0013	—	—	—	—	—	—
	6	—	—	.0001	.0028	.0180	.0550	.1649	.1983	.1222	.0392	.0056	.0002	—	—	—	—	—
	7	—	—	—	.0004	.0045	.0197	.1010	.1889	.1746	.0840	.0185	.0012	.0001	—	—	—	—
	8	—	—	—	.0001	.0009	.0055	.0487	.1417	.1964	.1417	.0487	.0055	.0009	.0001	—	—	—
	9	—	—	—	—	.0001	.0012	.0185	.0840	.1746	.1889	.1010	.0197	.0045	.0004	—	—	—
	10	—	—	—	—	—	.0002	.0056	.0392	.1222	.1983	.1649	.0550	.0180	.0028	.0001	—	—
	11	—	—	—	—	—	—	.0013	.0142	.0667	.1623	.2099	.1201	.0555	.0137	.0008	—	—
	12	—	—	—	—	—	—	.0002	.0040	.0278	.1014	.2040	.2001	.1311	.0514	.0061	.0002	—
	13	—	—	—	—	—	—	—	.0008	.0085	.0468	.1465	.2463	.2285	.1423	.0359	.0034	.0005
	14	—	—	—	—	—	—	—	.0001	.0018	.0150	.0732	.2111	.2775	.2745	.1463	.0362	.0104
	15	—	—	—	—	—	—	—	—	.0002	.0030	.0228	.1126	.2097	.3294	.3706	.2363	.1376
	16	—	—	—	—	—	—	—	—	—	.0003	.0033	.0281	.0743	.1853	.4401	.7238	.8515

APPENDIX

B

POISSON PROBABILITIES

Example: $P(X = 3 | \lambda = 2.3) = .2033$

This table shows $P(X = x)$.

															λ
x	0.1	0.2	0.3	0.4	0.5	0.6	0.7	0.8	0.9	1.0	1.1	1.2	1.3	1.4	1.5
0	.9048	.8187	.7408	.6703	.6065	.5488	.4966	.4493	.4066	.3679	.3329	.3012	.2725	.2466	.2231
1	.0905	.1637	.2222	.2681	.3033	.3293	.3476	.3595	.3659	.3679	.3662	.3614	.3543	.3452	.3347
2	.0045	.0164	.0333	.0536	.0758	.0988	.1217	.1438	.1647	.1839	.2014	.2169	.2303	.2417	.2510
3	.0002	.0011	.0033	.0072	.0126	.0198	.0284	.0383	.0494	.0613	.0738	.0867	.0998	.1128	.1255
4	—	.0001	.0003	.0007	.0016	.0030	.0050	.0077	.0111	.0153	.0203	.0260	.0324	.0395	.0471
5	—	—	—	.0001	.0002	.0004	.0007	.0012	.0020	.0031	.0045	.0062	.0084	.0111	.0141
6	—	—	—	—	—	—	.0001	.0002	.0003	.0005	.0008	.0012	.0018	.0026	.0035
7	—	—	—	—	—	—	—	—	—	.0001	.0001	.0002	.0003	.0005	.0008
8	—	—	—	—	—	—	—	—	—	—	—	—	.0001	.0001	.0001

															λ
x	1.6	1.7	1.8	1.9	2.0	2.1	2.2	2.3	2.4	2.5	2.6	2.7	2.8	2.9	3.0
0	.2019	.1827	.1653	.1496	.1353	.1225	.1108	.1003	.0907	.0821	.0743	.0672	.0608	.0550	.0498
1	.3230	.3106	.2975	.2842	.2707	.2572	.2438	.2306	.2177	.2052	.1931	.1815	.1703	.1596	.1494
2	.2584	.2640	.2678	.2700	.2707	.2700	.2681	.2652	.2613	.2565	.2510	.2450	.2384	.2314	.2240
3	.1378	.1496	.1607	.1710	.1804	.1890	.1966	.2033	.2090	.2138	.2176	.2205	.2225	.2237	.2240
4	.0551	.0636	.0723	.0812	.0902	.0992	.1082	.1169	.1254	.1336	.1414	.1488	.1557	.1622	.1680
5	.0176	.0216	.0260	.0309	.0361	.0417	.0476	.0538	.0602	.0668	.0735	.0804	.0872	.0940	.1008
6	.0047	.0061	.0078	.0098	.0120	.0146	.0174	.0206	.0241	.0278	.0319	.0362	.0407	.0455	.0504
7	.0011	.0015	.0020	.0027	.0034	.0044	.0055	.0068	.0083	.0099	.0118	.0139	.0163	.0188	.0216
8	.0002	.0003	.0005	.0006	.0009	.0011	.0015	.0019	.0025	.0031	.0038	.0047	.0057	.0068	.0081
9	—	.0001	.0001	.0001	.0002	.0003	.0004	.0005	.0007	.0009	.0011	.0014	.0018	.0022	.0027
10	—	—	—	—	—	.0001	.0001	.0001	.0002	.0002	.0003	.0004	.0005	.0006	.0008
11	—	—	—	—	—	—	—	—	—	—	.0001	.0001	.0001	.0002	.0002
12	—	—	—	—	—	—	—	—	—	—	—	—	—	—	.0001

															λ
x	3.1	3.2	3.3	3.4	3.5	3.6	3.7	3.8	3.9	4.0	4.1	4.2	4.3	4.4	4.5
0	.0450	.0408	.0369	.0334	.0302	.0273	.0247	.0224	.0202	.0183	.0166	.0150	.0136	.0123	.0111
1	.1397	.1304	.1217	.1135	.1057	.0984	.0915	.0850	.0789	.0733	.0679	.0630	.0583	.0540	.0500
2	.2165	.2087	.2008	.1929	.1850	.1771	.1692	.1615	.1539	.1465	.1393	.1323	.1254	.1188	.1125
3	.2237	.2226	.2209	.2186	.2158	.2125	.2087	.2046	.2001	.1954	.1904	.1852	.1798	.1743	.1687
4	.1733	.1781	.1823	.1858	.1888	.1912	.1931	.1944	.1951	.1954	.1951	.1944	.1933	.1917	.1898
5	.1075	.1140	.1203	.1264	.1322	.1377	.1429	.1477	.1522	.1563	.1600	.1633	.1662	.1687	.1708
6	.0555	.0608	.0662	.0716	.0771	.0826	.0881	.0936	.0989	.1042	.1093	.1143	.1191	.1237	.1281
7	.0246	.0278	.0312	.0348	.0385	.0425	.0466	.0508	.0551	.0595	.0640	.0686	.0732	.0778	.0824
8	.0095	.0111	.0129	.0148	.0169	.0191	.0215	.0241	.0269	.0298	.0328	.0360	.0393	.0428	.0463
9	.0033	.0040	.0047	.0056	.0066	.0076	.0089	.0102	.0116	.0132	.0150	.0168	.0188	.0209	.0232
10	.0010	.0013	.0016	.0019	.0023	.0028	.0033	.0039	.0045	.0053	.0061	.0071	.0081	.0092	.0104
11	.0003	.0004	.0005	.0006	.0007	.0009	.0011	.0013	.0016	.0019	.0023	.0027	.0032	.0037	.0043
12	.0001	.0001	.0001	.0002	.0002	.0003	.0003	.0004	.0005	.0006	.0008	.0009	.0011	.0013	.0016
13	—	—	—	—	.0001	.0001	.0001	.0001	.0002	.0002	.0002	.0003	.0004	.0005	.0006
14	—	—	—	—	—	—	—	—	—	.0001	.0001	.0001	.0001	.0001	.0002
15	—	—	—	—	—	—	—	—	—	—	—	—	—	—	.0001

λ

x	4.6	4.7	4.8	4.9	5.0	5.1	5.2	5.3	5.4	5.5	5.6	5.7	5.8	5.9	6.0
0	.0101	.0091	.0082	.0074	.0067	.0061	.0055	.0050	.0045	.0041	.0037	.0033	.0030	.0027	.0025
1	.0462	.0427	.0395	.0365	.0337	.0311	.0287	.0265	.0244	.0225	.0207	.0191	.0176	.0162	.0149
2	.1063	.1005	.0948	.0894	.0842	.0793	.0746	.0701	.0659	.0618	.0580	.0544	.0509	.0477	.0446
3	.1631	.1574	.1517	.1460	.1404	.1348	.1293	.1239	.1185	.1133	.1082	.1033	.0985	.0938	.0892
4	.1875	.1849	.1820	.1789	.1755	.1719	.1681	.1641	.1600	.1558	.1515	.1472	.1428	.1383	.1339
5	.1725	.1738	.1747	.1753	.1755	.1753	.1748	.1740	.1728	.1714	.1697	.1678	.1656	.1632	.1606
6	.1323	.1362	.1398	.1432	.1462	.1490	.1515	.1537	.1555	.1571	.1584	.1594	.1601	.1605	.1606
7	.0869	.0914	.0959	.1002	.1044	.1086	.1125	.1163	.1200	.1234	.1267	.1298	.1326	.1353	.1377
8	.0500	.0537	.0575	.0614	.0653	.0692	.0731	.0771	.0810	.0849	.0887	.0925	.0962	.0998	.1033
9	.0255	.0281	.0307	.0334	.0363	.0392	.0423	.0454	.0486	.0519	.0552	.0586	.0620	.0654	.0688
10	.0118	.0132	.0147	.0164	.0181	.0200	.0220	.0241	.0262	.0285	.0309	.0334	.0359	.0386	.0413
11	.0049	.0056	.0064	.0073	.0082	.0093	.0104	.0116	.0129	.0143	.0157	.0173	.0190	.0207	.0225
12	.0019	.0022	.0026	.0030	.0034	.0039	.0045	.0051	.0058	.0065	.0073	.0082	.0092	.0102	.0113
13	.0007	.0008	.0009	.0011	.0013	.0015	.0018	.0021	.0024	.0028	.0032	.0036	.0041	.0046	.0052
14	.0002	.0003	.0003	.0004	.0005	.0006	.0007	.0008	.0009	.0011	.0013	.0015	.0017	.0019	.0022
15	.0001	.0001	.0001	.0001	.0002	.0002	.0002	.0003	.0003	.0004	.0005	.0006	.0007	.0008	.0009
16	—	—	—	—	—	.0001	.0001	.0001	.0001	.0001	.0002	.0002	.0002	.0003	.0003
17	—	—	—	—	—	—	—	—	—	—	.0001	.0001	.0001	.0001	.0001

λ

x	6.1	6.2	6.3	6.4	6.5	6.6	6.7	6.8	6.9	7.0	7.1	7.2	7.3	7.4	7.5
0	.0022	.0020	.0018	.0017	.0015	.0014	.0012	.0011	.0010	.0009	.0008	.0007	.0007	.0006	.0006
1	.0137	.0126	.0116	.0106	.0098	.0090	.0082	.0076	.0070	.0064	.0059	.0054	.0049	.0045	.0041
2	.0417	.0390	.0364	.0340	.0318	.0296	.0276	.0258	.0240	.0223	.0208	.0194	.0180	.0167	.0156
3	.0848	.0806	.0765	.0726	.0688	.0652	.0617	.0584	.0552	.0521	.0492	.0464	.0438	.0413	.0389
4	.1294	.1249	.1205	.1162	.1118	.1076	.1034	.0992	.0952	.0912	.0874	.0836	.0799	.0764	.0729
5	.1579	.1549	.1519	.1487	.1454	.1420	.1385	.1349	.1314	.1277	.1241	.1204	.1167	.1130	.1094
6	.1605	.1601	.1595	.1586	.1575	.1562	.1546	.1529	.1511	.1490	.1468	.1445	.1420	.1394	.1367
7	.1399	.1418	.1435	.1450	.1462	.1472	.1480	.1486	.1489	.1490	.1489	.1486	.1481	.1474	.1465
8	.1066	.1099	.1130	.1160	.1188	.1215	.1240	.1263	.1284	.1304	.1321	.1337	.1351	.1363	.1373
9	.0723	.0757	.0791	.0825	.0858	.0891	.0923	.0954	.0985	.1014	.1042	.1070	.1096	.1121	.1144
10	.0441	.0469	.0498	.0528	.0558	.0588	.0618	.0649	.0679	.0710	.0740	.0770	.0800	.0829	.0858
11	.0244	.0265	.0285	.0307	.0330	.0353	.0377	.0401	.0426	.0452	.0478	.0504	.0531	.0558	.0585
12	.0124	.0137	.0150	.0164	.0179	.0194	.0210	.0227	.0245	.0263	.0283	.0303	.0323	.0344	.0366
13	.0058	.0065	.0073	.0081	.0089	.0099	.0108	.0119	.0130	.0142	.0154	.0168	.0181	.0196	.0211
14	.0025	.0029	.0033	.0037	.0041	.0046	.0052	.0058	.0064	.0071	.0078	.0086	.0095	.0104	.0113
15	.0010	.0012	.0014	.0016	.0018	.0020	.0023	.0026	.0029	.0033	.0037	.0041	.0046	.0051	.0057
16	.0004	.0005	.0005	.0006	.0007	.0008	.0010	.0011	.0013	.0014	.0016	.0019	.0021	.0024	.0026
17	.0001	.0002	.0002	.0002	.0003	.0003	.0004	.0004	.0005	.0006	.0007	.0008	.0009	.0010	.0012
18	—	.0001	.0001	.0001	.0001	.0001	.0001	.0002	.0002	.0002	.0003	.0003	.0004	.0004	.0005
19	—	—	—	—	—	—	.0001	.0001	.0001	.0001	.0001	.0001	.0001	.0002	.0002
20	—	—	—	—	—	—	—	—	—	—	—	—	.0001	.0001	.0001

								λ							
x	8.0	8.5	9.0	9.5	10.0	11.0	12.0	13.0	14.0	15.0	16.0	17.0	18.0	19.0	20.0
0	.0003	.0002	.0001	.0001	—	—	—	—	—	—	—	—	—	—	—
1	.0027	.0017	.0011	.0007	.0005	.0002	.0001	—	—	—	—	—	—	—	—
2	.0107	.0074	.0050	.0034	.0023	.0010	.0004	.0002	.0001	—	—	—	—	—	—
3	.0286	.0208	.0150	.0107	.0076	.0037	.0018	.0008	.0004	.0002	.0001	—	—	—	—
4	.0573	.0443	.0337	.0254	.0189	.0102	.0053	.0027	.0013	.0006	.0003	.0001	.0001	—	—
5	.0916	.0752	.0607	.0483	.0378	.0224	.0127	.0070	.0037	.0019	.0010	.0005	.0002	.0001	.0001
6	.1221	.1066	.0911	.0764	.0631	.0411	.0255	.0152	.0087	.0048	.0026	.0014	.0007	.0004	.0002
7	.1396	.1294	.1171	.1037	.0901	.0646	.0437	.0281	.0174	.0104	.0060	.0034	.0019	.0010	.0005
8	.1396	.1375	.1318	.1232	.1126	.0888	.0655	.0457	.0304	.0194	.0120	.0072	.0042	.0024	.0013
9	.1241	.1299	.1318	.1300	.1251	.1085	.0874	.0661	.0473	.0324	.0213	.0135	.0083	.0050	.0029
10	.0993	.1104	.1186	.1235	.1251	.1194	.1048	.0859	.0663	.0486	.0341	.0230	.0150	.0095	.0058
11	.0722	.0853	.0970	.1067	.1137	.1194	.1144	.1015	.0844	.0663	.0496	.0355	.0245	.0164	.0106
12	.0481	.0604	.0728	.0844	.0948	.1094	.1144	.1099	.0984	.0829	.0661	.0504	.0368	.0259	.0176
13	.0296	.0395	.0504	.0617	.0729	.0926	.1056	.1099	.1060	.0956	.0814	.0658	.0509	.0378	.0271
14	.0169	.0240	.0324	.0419	.0521	.0728	.0905	.1021	.1060	.1024	.0930	.0800	.0655	.0514	.0387
15	.0090	.0136	.0194	.0265	.0347	.0534	.0724	.0885	.0989	.1024	.0992	.0906	.0786	.0650	.0516
16	.0045	.0072	.0109	.0157	.0217	.0367	.0543	.0719	.0866	.0960	.0992	.0963	.0884	.0772	.0646
17	.0021	.0036	.0058	.0088	.0128	.0237	.0383	.0550	.0713	.0847	.0934	.0963	.0936	.0863	.0760
18	.0009	.0017	.0029	.0046	.0071	.0145	.0255	.0397	.0554	.0706	.0830	.0909	.0936	.0911	.0844
19	.0004	.0008	.0014	.0023	.0037	.0084	.0161	.0272	.0409	.0557	.0699	.0814	.0887	.0911	.0888
20	.0002	.0003	.0006	.0011	.0019	.0046	.0097	.0177	.0286	.0418	.0559	.0692	.0798	.0866	.0888
21	.0001	.0001	.0003	.0005	.0009	.0024	.0055	.0109	.0191	.0299	.0426	.0560	.0684	.0783	.0846
22	—	.0001	.0001	.0002	.0004	.0012	.0030	.0065	.0121	.0204	.0310	.0433	.0560	.0676	.0769
23	—	—	—	.0001	.0002	.0006	.0016	.0037	.0074	.0133	.0216	.0320	.0438	.0559	.0669
24	—	—	—	—	.0001	.0003	.0008	.0020	.0043	.0083	.0144	.0226	.0328	.0442	.0557
25	—	—	—	—	—	.0001	.0004	.0010	.0024	.0050	.0092	.0154	.0237	.0336	.0446
26	—	—	—	—	—	—	.0002	.0005	.0013	.0029	.0057	.0101	.0164	.0246	.0343
27	—	—	—	—	—	—	.0001	.0002	.0007	.0016	.0034	.0063	.0109	.0173	.0254
28	—	—	—	—	—	—	—	.0001	.0003	.0009	.0019	.0038	.0070	.0117	.0181
29	—	—	—	—	—	—	—	.0001	.0002	.0004	.0011	.0023	.0044	.0077	.0125
30	—	—	—	—	—	—	—	—	.0001	.0002	.0006	.0013	.0026	.0049	.0083
31	—	—	—	—	—	—	—	—	—	.0001	.0003	.0007	.0015	.0030	.0054
32	—	—	—	—	—	—	—	—	—	.0001	.0001	.0004	.0009	.0018	.0034
33	—	—	—	—	—	—	—	—	—	—	.0001	.0002	.0005	.0010	.0020
34	—	—	—	—	—	—	—	—	—	—	—	.0001	.0002	.0006	.0012
35	—	—	—	—	—	—	—	—	—	—	—	—	.0001	.0003	.0007
36	—	—	—	—	—	—	—	—	—	—	—	—	.0001	.0002	.0004
37	—	—	—	—	—	—	—	—	—	—	—	—	—	.0001	.0002
38	—	—	—	—	—	—	—	—	—	—	—	—	—	—	.0001
39	—	—	—	—	—	—	—	—	—	—	—	—	—	—	.0001

APPENDIX

STANDARD NORMAL AREAS

Example: $P(0 < z < 1.96) = .4750$

This table shows the normal area between 0 and z.

z	.00	.01	.02	.03	.04	.05	.06	.07	.08	.09
0.0	.0000	.0040	.0080	.0120	.0160	.0199	.0239	.0279	.0319	.0359
0.1	.0398	.0438	.0478	.0517	.0557	.0596	.0636	.0675	.0714	.0753
0.2	.0793	.0832	.0871	.0910	.0948	.0987	.1026	.1064	.1103	.1141
0.3	.1179	.1217	.1255	.1293	.1331	.1368	.1406	.1443	.1480	.1517
0.4	.1554	.1591	.1628	.1664	.1700	.1736	.1772	.1808	.1844	.1879
0.5	.1915	.1950	.1985	.2019	.2054	.2088	.2123	.2157	.2190	.2224
0.6	.2257	.2291	.2324	.2357	.2389	.2422	.2454	.2486	.2517	.2549
0.7	.2580	.2611	.2642	.2673	.2704	.2734	.2764	.2794	.2823	.2852
0.8	.2881	.2910	.2939	.2967	.2995	.3023	.3051	.3078	.3106	.3133
0.9	.3159	.3186	.3212	.3238	.3264	.3289	.3315	.3340	.3365	.3389
1.0	.3413	.3438	.3461	.3485	.3508	.3531	.3554	.3577	.3599	.3621
1.1	.3643	.3665	.3686	.3708	.3729	.3749	.3770	.3790	.3810	.3830
1.2	.3849	.3869	.3888	.3907	.3925	.3944	.3962	.3980	.3997	.4015
1.3	.4032	.4049	.4066	.4082	.4099	.4115	.4131	.4147	.4162	.4177
1.4	.4192	.4207	.4222	.4236	.4251	.4265	.4279	.4292	.4306	.4319
1.5	.4332	.4345	.4357	.4370	.4382	.4394	.4406	.4418	.4429	.4441
1.6	.4452	.4463	.4474	.4484	.4495	.4505	.4515	.4525	.4535	.4545
1.7	.4554	.4564	.4573	.4582	.4591	.4599	.4608	.4616	.4625	.4633
1.8	.4641	.4649	.4656	.4664	.4671	.4678	.4686	.4693	.4699	.4706
1.9	.4713	.4719	.4726	.4732	.4738	.4744	.4750	.4756	.4761	.4767
2.0	.4772	.4778	.4783	.4788	.4793	.4798	.4803	.4808	.4812	.4817
2.1	.4821	.4826	.4830	.4834	.4838	.4842	.4846	.4850	.4854	.4857
2.2	.4861	.4864	.4868	.4871	.4875	.4878	.4881	.4884	.4887	.4890
2.3	.4893	.4896	.4898	.4901	.4904	.4906	.4909	.4911	.4913	.4916
2.4	.4918	.4920	.4922	.4925	.4927	.4929	.4931	.4932	.4934	.4936
2.5	.4938	.4940	.4941	.4943	.4945	.4946	.4948	.4949	.4951	.4952
2.6	.4953	.4955	.4956	.4957	.4959	.4960	.4961	.4962	.4963	.4964
2.7	.4965	.4966	.4967	.4968	.4969	.4970	.4971	.4972	.4973	.4974
2.8	.4974	.4975	.4976	.4977	.4977	.4978	.4979	.4979	.4980	.4981
2.9	.4981	.4982	.4982	.4983	.4984	.4984	.4985	.4985	.4986	.4986
3.0	.49865	.49869	.49874	.49878	.49882	.49886	.49889	.49893	.49896	.49900
3.1	.49903	.49906	.49910	.49913	.49916	.49918	.49921	.49924	.49926	.49929
3.2	.49931	.49934	.49936	.49938	.49940	.49942	.49944	.49946	.49948	.49950
3.3	.49952	.49953	.49955	.49957	.49958	.49960	.49961	.49962	.49964	.49965
3.4	.49966	.49968	.49969	.49970	.49971	.49972	.49973	.49974	.49975	.49976
3.5	.49977	.49978	.49978	.49979	.49980	.49981	.49981	.49982	.49983	.49983
3.6	.49984	.49985	.49985	.49986	.49986	.49987	.49987	.49988	.49988	.49989
3.7	.49989	.49990	.49990	.49990	.49991	.49991	.49992	.49992	.49992	.49992

APPENDIX

CUMULATIVE STANDARD NORMAL DISTRIBUTION

Example: $P(z < -1.96) = .0250$

This table shows the normal area less than z.

z	.00	.01	.02	.03	.04	.05	.06	.07	.08	.09
−3.7	.00011	.00010	.00010	.00010	.00009	.00009	.00008	.00008	.00008	.00008
−3.6	.00016	.00015	.00015	.00014	.00014	.00013	.00013	.00012	.00012	.00011
−3.5	.00023	.00022	.00022	.00021	.00020	.00019	.00019	.00018	.00017	.00017
−3.4	.00034	.00032	.00031	.00030	.00029	.00028	.00027	.00026	.00025	.00024
−3.3	.00048	.00047	.00045	.00043	.00042	.00040	.00039	.00038	.00036	.00035
−3.2	.00069	.00066	.00064	.00062	.00060	.00058	.00056	.00054	.00052	.00050
−3.1	.00097	.00094	.00090	.00087	.00084	.00082	.00079	.00076	.00074	.00071
−3.0	.00135	.00131	.00126	.00122	.00118	.00114	.00111	.00107	.00104	.00100
−2.9	.0019	.0018	.0018	.0017	.0016	.0016	.0015	.0015	.0014	.0014
−2.8	.0026	.0025	.0024	.0023	.0023	.0022	.0021	.0021	.0020	.0019
−2.7	.0035	.0034	.0033	.0032	.0031	.0030	.0029	.0028	.0027	.0026
−2.6	.0047	.0045	.0044	.0043	.0041	.0040	.0039	.0038	.0037	.0036
−2.5	.0062	.0060	.0059	.0057	.0055	.0054	.0052	.0051	.0049	.0048
−2.4	.0082	.0080	.0078	.0075	.0073	.0071	.0069	.0068	.0066	.0064
−2.3	.0107	.0104	.0102	.0099	.0096	.0094	.0091	.0089	.0087	.0084
−2.2	.0139	.0136	.0132	.0129	.0125	.0122	.0119	.0116	.0113	.0110
−2.1	.0179	.0174	.0170	.0166	.0162	.0158	.0154	.0150	.0146	.0143
−2.0	.0228	.0222	.0217	.0212	.0207	.0202	.0197	.0192	.0188	.0183
−1.9	.0287	.0281	.0274	.0268	.0262	.0256	.0250	.0244	.0239	.0233
−1.8	.0359	.0351	.0344	.0336	.0329	.0322	.0314	.0307	.0301	.0294
−1.7	.0446	.0436	.0427	.0418	.0409	.0401	.0392	.0384	.0375	.0367
−1.6	.0548	.0537	.0526	.0516	.0505	.0495	.0485	.0475	.0465	.0455
−1.5	.0668	.0655	.0643	.0630	.0618	.0606	.0594	.0582	.0571	.0559
−1.4	.0808	.0793	.0778	.0764	.0749	.0735	.0721	.0708	.0694	.0681
−1.3	.0968	.0951	.0934	.0918	.0901	.0885	.0869	.0853	.0838	.0823
−1.2	.1151	.1131	.1112	.1093	.1075	.1056	.1038	.1020	.1003	.0985
−1.1	.1357	.1335	.1314	.1292	.1271	.1251	.1230	.1210	.1190	.1170
−1.0	.1587	.1562	.1539	.1515	.1492	.1469	.1446	.1423	.1401	.1379
−0.9	.1841	.1814	.1788	.1762	.1736	.1711	.1685	.1660	.1635	.1611
−0.8	.2119	.2090	.2061	.2033	.2005	.1977	.1949	.1922	.1894	.1867
−0.7	.2420	.2389	.2358	.2327	.2296	.2266	.2236	.2206	.2177	.2148
−0.6	.2743	.2709	.2676	.2643	.2611	.2578	.2546	.2514	.2483	.2451
−0.5	.3085	.3050	.3015	.2981	.2946	.2912	.2877	.2843	.2810	.2776
−0.4	.3446	.3409	.3372	.3336	.3300	.3264	.3228	.3192	.3156	.3121
−0.3	.3821	.3783	.3745	.3707	.3669	.3632	.3594	.3557	.3520	.3483
−0.2	.4207	.4168	.4129	.4090	.4052	.4013	.3974	.3936	.3897	.3859
−0.1	.4602	.4562	.4522	.4483	.4443	.4404	.4364	.4325	.4286	.4247
−0.0	.5000	.4960	.4920	.4880	.4841	.4801	.4761	.4721	.4681	.4641

This table shows the normal area less than *z*.

z	.00	.01	.02	.03	.04	.05	.06	.07	.08	.09
0.0	.5000	.5040	.5080	.5120	.5160	.5199	.5239	.5279	.5319	.5359
0.1	.5398	.5438	.5478	.5517	.5557	.5596	.5636	.5675	.5714	.5753
0.2	.5793	.5832	.5871	.5910	.5948	.5987	.6026	.6064	.6103	.6141
0.3	.6179	.6217	.6255	.6293	.6331	.6368	.6406	.6443	.6480	.6517
0.4	.6554	.6591	.6628	.6664	.6700	.6736	.6772	.6808	.6844	.6879
0.5	.6915	.6950	.6985	.7019	.7054	.7088	.7123	.7157	.7190	.7224
0.6	.7257	.7291	.7324	.7357	.7389	.7422	.7454	.7486	.7517	.7549
0.7	.7580	.7611	.7642	.7673	.7704	.7734	.7764	.7794	.7823	.7852
0.8	.7881	.7910	.7939	.7967	.7995	.8023	.8051	.8078	.8106	.8133
0.9	.8159	.8186	.8212	.8238	.8264	.8289	.8315	.8340	.8365	.8389
1.0	.8413	.8438	.8461	.8485	.8508	.8531	.8554	.8577	.8599	.8621
1.1	.8643	.8665	.8686	.8708	.8729	.8749	.8770	.8790	.8810	.8830
1.2	.8849	.8869	.8888	.8907	.8925	.8944	.8962	.8980	.8997	.9015
1.3	.9032	.9049	.9066	.9082	.9099	.9115	.9131	.9147	.9162	.9177
1.4	.9192	.9207	.9222	.9236	.9251	.9265	.9279	.9292	.9306	.9319
1.5	.9332	.9345	.9357	.9370	.9382	.9394	.9406	.9418	.9429	.9441
1.6	.9452	.9463	.9474	.9484	.9495	.9505	.9515	.9525	.9535	.9545
1.7	.9554	.9564	.9573	.9582	.9591	.9599	.9608	.9616	.9625	.9633
1.8	.9641	.9649	.9656	.9664	.9671	.9678	.9686	.9693	.9699	.9706
1.9	.9713	.9719	.9726	.9732	.9738	.9744	.9750	.9756	.9761	.9767
2.0	.9772	.9778	.9783	.9788	.9793	.9798	.9803	.9808	.9812	.9817
2.1	.9821	.9826	.9830	.9834	.9838	.9842	.9846	.9850	.9854	.9857
2.2	.9861	.9864	.9868	.9871	.9875	.9878	.9881	.9884	.9887	.9890
2.3	.9893	.9896	.9898	.9901	.9904	.9906	.9909	.9911	.9913	.9916
2.4	.9918	.9920	.9922	.9925	.9927	.9929	.9931	.9932	.9934	.9936
2.5	.9938	.9940	.9941	.9943	.9945	.9946	.9948	.9949	.9951	.9952
2.6	.9953	.9955	.9956	.9957	.9959	.9960	.9961	.9962	.9963	.9964
2.7	.9965	.9966	.9967	.9968	.9969	.9970	.9971	.9972	.9973	.9974
2.8	.9974	.9975	.9976	.9977	.9977	.9978	.9979	.9979	.9980	.9981
2.9	.9981	.9982	.9982	.9983	.9984	.9984	.9985	.9985	.9986	.9986
3.0	.99865	.99869	.99874	.99878	.99882	.99886	.99889	.99893	.99896	.99900
3.1	.99903	.99906	.99910	.99913	.99916	.99918	.99921	.99924	.99926	.99929
3.2	.99931	.99934	.99936	.99938	.99940	.99942	.99944	.99946	.99948	.99950
3.3	.99952	.99953	.99955	.99957	.99958	.99960	.99961	.99962	.99964	.99965
3.4	.99966	.99968	.99969	.99970	.99971	.99972	.99973	.99974	.99975	.99976
3.5	.99977	.99978	.99978	.99979	.99980	.99981	.99981	.99982	.99983	.99983
3.6	.99984	.99985	.99985	.99986	.99986	.99987	.99987	.99988	.99988	.99989
3.7	.99989	.99990	.99990	.99990	.99991	.99991	.99992	.99992	.99992	.99992

STUDENT'S *t* CRITICAL VALUES

This table shows the *t*-value that defines the area for the stated degrees of freedom (*d.f.*).

	Confidence Level						Confidence Level			
	.80	.90	.95	.98	.99		.80	.90	.95	.98	.99
	Significance Level for Two-Tailed Test						Significance Level for Two-Tailed Test			
	.20	.10	.05	.02	.01		.20	.10	.05	.02	.01
	Significance Level for One-Tailed Test						Significance Level for One-Tailed Test			
d.f.	.10	.05	.025	.01	.005	*d.f.*	.10	.05	.025	.01	.005
1	3.078	6.314	12.706	31.821	63.656	36	1.306	1.688	2.028	2.434	2.719
2	1.886	2.920	4.303	6.965	9.925	37	1.305	1.687	2.026	2.431	2.715
3	1.638	2.353	3.182	4.541	5.841	38	1.304	1.686	2.024	2.429	2.712
4	1.533	2.132	2.776	3.747	4.604	39	1.304	1.685	2.023	2.426	2.708
5	1.476	2.015	2.571	3.365	4.032	40	1.303	1.684	2.021	2.423	2.704
6	1.440	1.943	2.447	3.143	3.707	41	1.303	1.683	2.020	2.421	2.701
7	1.415	1.895	2.365	2.998	3.499	42	1.302	1.682	2.018	2.418	2.698
8	1.397	1.860	2.306	2.896	3.355	43	1.302	1.681	2.017	2.416	2.695
9	1.383	1.833	2.262	2.821	3.250	44	1.301	1.680	2.015	2.414	2.692
10	1.372	1.812	2.228	2.764	3.169	45	1.301	1.679	2.014	2.412	2.690
11	1.363	1.796	2.201	2.718	3.106	46	1.300	1.679	2.013	2.410	2.687
12	1.356	1.782	2.179	2.681	3.055	47	1.300	1.678	2.012	2.408	2.685
13	1.350	1.771	2.160	2.650	3.012	48	1.299	1.677	2.011	2.407	2.682
14	1.345	1.761	2.145	2.624	2.977	49	1.299	1.677	2.010	2.405	2.680
15	1.341	1.753	2.131	2.602	2.947	50	1.299	1.676	2.009	2.403	2.678
16	1.337	1.746	2.120	2.583	2.921	55	1.297	1.673	2.004	2.396	2.668
17	1.333	1.740	2.110	2.567	2.898	60	1.296	1.671	2.000	2.390	2.660
18	1.330	1.734	2.101	2.552	2.878	65	1.295	1.669	1.997	2.385	2.654
19	1.328	1.729	2.093	2.539	2.861	70	1.294	1.667	1.994	2.381	2.648
20	1.325	1.725	2.086	2.528	2.845	75	1.293	1.665	1.992	2.377	2.643
21	1.323	1.721	2.080	2.518	2.831	80	1.292	1.664	1.990	2.374	2.639
22	1.321	1.717	2.074	2.508	2.819	85	1.292	1.663	1.988	2.371	2.635
23	1.319	1.714	2.069	2.500	2.807	90	1.291	1.662	1.987	2.368	2.632
24	1.318	1.711	2.064	2.492	2.797	95	1.291	1.661	1.985	2.366	2.629
25	1.316	1.708	2.060	2.485	2.787	100	1.290	1.660	1.984	2.364	2.626
26	1.315	1.706	2.056	2.479	2.779	110	1.289	1.659	1.982	2.361	2.621
27	1.314	1.703	2.052	2.473	2.771	120	1.289	1.658	1.980	2.358	2.617
28	1.313	1.701	2.048	2.467	2.763	130	1.288	1.657	1.978	2.355	2.614
29	1.311	1.699	2.045	2.462	2.756	140	1.288	1.656	1.977	2.353	2.611
30	1.310	1.697	2.042	2.457	2.750	150	1.287	1.655	1.976	2.351	2.609
31	1.309	1.696	2.040	2.453	2.744	∞	1.282	1.645	1.960	2.326	2.576
32	1.309	1.694	2.037	2.449	2.738						
33	1.308	1.692	2.035	2.445	2.733						
34	1.307	1.691	2.032	2.441	2.728						
35	1.306	1.690	2.030	2.438	2.724						

Note: As *n* increases, critical values of Student's *t* approach the *z*-values in the last line of this table. A common rule of thumb is to use *z* when *n* > 30, but that is *not* conservative.

APPENDIX

E

CHI-SQUARE CRITICAL VALUES

Example for *d.f.* = 4

.05

0   9.488

This table shows the critical value of chi-square for each desired right-tail area and degrees of freedom (*d.f.*).

					Area in Upper Tail					
d.f.	.995	.990	.975	.95	.90	.10	.05	.025	.01	.005
1	0.000	0.000	0.001	0.004	0.016	2.706	3.841	5.024	6.635	7.879
2	0.010	0.020	0.051	0.103	0.211	4.605	5.991	7.378	9.210	10.60
3	0.072	0.115	0.216	0.352	0.584	6.251	7.815	9.348	11.34	12.84
4	0.207	0.297	0.484	0.711	1.064	7.779	9.488	11.14	13.28	14.86
5	0.412	0.554	0.831	1.145	1.610	9.236	11.07	12.83	15.09	16.75
6	0.676	0.872	1.237	1.635	2.204	10.64	12.59	14.45	16.81	18.55
7	0.989	1.239	1.690	2.167	2.833	12.02	14.07	16.01	18.48	20.28
8	1.344	1.646	2.180	2.733	3.490	13.36	15.51	17.53	20.09	21.95
9	1.735	2.088	2.700	3.325	4.168	14.68	16.92	19.02	21.67	23.59
10	2.156	2.558	3.247	3.940	4.865	15.99	18.31	20.48	23.21	25.19
11	2.603	3.053	3.816	4.575	5.578	17.28	19.68	21.92	24.72	26.76
12	3.074	3.571	4.404	5.226	6.304	18.55	21.03	23.34	26.22	28.30
13	3.565	4.107	5.009	5.892	7.042	19.81	22.36	24.74	27.69	29.82
14	4.075	4.660	5.629	6.571	7.790	21.06	23.68	26.12	29.14	31.32
15	4.601	5.229	6.262	7.261	8.547	22.31	25.00	27.49	30.58	32.80
16	5.142	5.812	6.908	7.962	9.312	23.54	26.30	28.85	32.00	34.27
17	5.697	6.408	7.564	8.672	10.09	24.77	27.59	30.19	33.41	35.72
18	6.265	7.015	8.231	9.390	10.86	25.99	28.87	31.53	34.81	37.16
19	6.844	7.633	8.907	10.12	11.65	27.20	30.14	32.85	36.19	38.58
20	7.434	8.260	9.591	10.85	12.44	28.41	31.41	34.17	37.57	40.00
21	8.034	8.897	10.28	11.59	13.24	29.62	32.67	35.48	38.93	41.40
22	8.643	9.542	10.98	12.34	14.04	30.81	33.92	36.78	40.29	42.80
23	9.260	10.20	11.69	13.09	14.85	32.01	35.17	38.08	41.64	44.18
24	9.886	10.86	12.40	13.85	15.66	33.20	36.42	39.36	42.98	45.56
25	10.52	11.52	13.12	14.61	16.47	34.38	37.65	40.65	44.31	46.93
26	11.16	12.20	13.84	15.38	17.29	35.56	38.89	41.92	45.64	48.29
27	11.81	12.88	14.57	16.15	18.11	36.74	40.11	43.19	46.96	49.64
28	12.46	13.56	15.31	16.93	18.94	37.92	41.34	44.46	48.28	50.99
29	13.12	14.26	16.05	17.71	19.77	39.09	42.56	45.72	49.59	52.34
30	13.79	14.95	16.79	18.49	20.60	40.26	43.77	46.98	50.89	53.67
31	14.46	15.66	17.54	19.28	21.43	41.42	44.99	48.23	52.19	55.00
32	15.13	16.36	18.29	20.07	22.27	42.58	46.19	49.48	53.49	56.33
33	15.82	17.07	19.05	20.87	23.11	43.75	47.40	50.73	54.78	57.65
34	16.50	17.79	19.81	21.66	23.95	44.90	48.60	51.97	56.06	58.96
35	17.19	18.51	20.57	22.47	24.80	46.06	49.80	53.20	57.34	60.27
36	17.89	19.23	21.34	23.27	25.64	47.21	51.00	54.44	58.62	61.58
37	18.59	19.96	22.11	24.07	26.49	48.36	52.19	55.67	59.89	62.88
38	19.29	20.69	22.88	24.88	27.34	49.51	53.38	56.90	61.16	64.18
39	20.00	21.43	23.65	25.70	28.20	50.66	54.57	58.12	62.43	65.48
40	20.71	22.16	24.43	26.51	29.05	51.81	55.76	59.34	63.69	66.77
50	27.99	29.71	32.36	34.76	37.69	63.17	67.50	71.42	76.15	79.49
60	35.53	37.48	40.48	43.19	46.46	74.40	79.08	83.30	88.38	91.95
70	43.28	45.44	48.76	51.74	55.33	85.53	90.53	95.02	100.4	104.2
80	51.17	53.54	57.15	60.39	64.28	96.58	101.9	106.6	112.3	116.3
90	59.20	61.75	65.65	69.13	73.29	107.6	113.1	118.1	124.1	128.3
100	67.33	70.06	74.22	77.93	82.36	118.5	124.3	129.6	135.8	140.2

APPENDIX

CRITICAL VALUES OF $F_{.10}$

This table shows the 10 percent right-tail critical values of F for the stated degrees of freedom ($d.f.$).

Denominator Degrees of Freedom (df_2)	Numerator Degrees of Freedom (df_1)										
	1	2	3	4	5	6	7	8	9	10	12
1	39.86	49.50	53.59	55.83	57.24	58.20	58.91	59.44	59.86	60.19	60.71
2	8.53	9.00	9.16	9.24	9.29	9.33	9.35	9.37	9.38	9.39	9.41
3	5.54	5.46	5.39	5.34	5.31	5.28	5.27	5.25	5.24	5.23	5.22
4	4.54	4.32	4.19	4.11	4.05	4.01	3.98	3.95	3.94	3.92	3.90
5	4.06	3.78	3.62	3.52	3.45	3.40	3.37	3.34	3.32	3.30	3.27
6	3.78	3.46	3.29	3.18	3.11	3.05	3.01	2.98	2.96	2.94	2.90
7	3.59	3.26	3.07	2.96	2.88	2.83	2.78	2.75	2.72	2.70	2.67
8	3.46	3.11	2.92	2.81	2.73	2.67	2.62	2.59	2.56	2.54	2.50
9	3.36	3.01	2.81	2.69	2.61	2.55	2.51	2.47	2.44	2.42	2.38
10	3.29	2.92	2.73	2.61	2.52	2.46	2.41	2.38	2.35	2.32	2.28
11	3.23	2.86	2.66	2.54	2.45	2.39	2.34	2.30	2.27	2.25	2.21
12	3.18	2.81	2.61	2.48	2.39	2.33	2.28	2.24	2.21	2.19	2.15
13	3.14	2.76	2.56	2.43	2.35	2.28	2.23	2.20	2.16	2.14	2.10
14	3.10	2.73	2.52	2.39	2.31	2.24	2.19	2.15	2.12	2.10	2.05
15	3.07	2.70	2.49	2.36	2.27	2.21	2.16	2.12	2.09	2.06	2.02
16	3.05	2.67	2.46	2.33	2.24	2.18	2.13	2.09	2.06	2.03	1.99
17	3.03	2.64	2.44	2.31	2.22	2.15	2.10	2.06	2.03	2.00	1.96
18	3.01	2.62	2.42	2.29	2.20	2.13	2.08	2.04	2.00	1.98	1.93
19	2.99	2.61	2.40	2.27	2.18	2.11	2.06	2.02	1.98	1.96	1.91
20	2.97	2.59	2.38	2.25	2.16	2.09	2.04	2.00	1.96	1.94	1.89
21	2.96	2.57	2.36	2.23	2.14	2.08	2.02	1.98	1.95	1.92	1.87
22	2.95	2.56	2.35	2.22	2.13	2.06	2.01	1.97	1.93	1.90	1.86
23	2.94	2.55	2.34	2.21	2.11	2.05	1.99	1.95	1.92	1.89	1.84
24	2.93	2.54	2.33	2.19	2.10	2.04	1.98	1.94	1.91	1.88	1.83
25	2.92	2.53	2.32	2.18	2.09	2.02	1.97	1.93	1.89	1.87	1.82
26	2.91	2.52	2.31	2.17	2.08	2.01	1.96	1.92	1.88	1.86	1.81
27	2.90	2.51	2.30	2.17	2.07	2.00	1.95	1.91	1.87	1.85	1.80
28	2.89	2.50	2.29	2.16	2.06	2.00	1.94	1.90	1.87	1.84	1.79
29	2.89	2.50	2.28	2.15	2.06	1.99	1.93	1.89	1.86	1.83	1.78
30	2.88	2.49	2.28	2.14	2.05	1.98	1.93	1.88	1.85	1.82	1.77
40	2.84	2.44	2.23	2.09	2.00	1.93	1.87	1.83	1.79	1.76	1.71
50	2.81	2.41	2.20	2.06	1.97	1.90	1.84	1.80	1.76	1.73	1.68
60	2.79	2.39	2.18	2.04	1.95	1.87	1.82	1.77	1.74	1.71	1.66
120	2.75	2.35	2.13	1.99	1.90	1.82	1.77	1.72	1.68	1.65	1.60
200	2.73	2.33	2.11	1.97	1.88	1.80	1.75	1.70	1.66	1.63	1.58
∞	2.71	2.30	2.08	1.94	1.85	1.77	1.72	1.67	1.63	1.60	1.55

Denominator Degrees of Freedom (df_2)	Numerator Degrees of Freedom (df_1)										
	15	20	25	30	35	40	50	60	120	200	∞
1	61.22	61.74	62.05	62.26	62.42	62.53	62.69	62.79	63.06	63.17	63.32
2	9.42	9.44	9.45	9.46	9.46	9.47	9.47	9.47	9.48	9.49	9.49
3	5.20	5.18	5.17	5.17	5.16	5.16	5.15	5.15	5.14	5.14	5.13
4	3.87	3.84	3.83	3.82	3.81	3.80	3.80	3.79	3.78	3.77	3.76
5	3.24	3.21	3.19	3.17	3.16	3.16	3.15	3.14	3.12	3.12	3.11
6	2.87	2.84	2.81	2.80	2.79	2.78	2.77	2.76	2.74	2.73	2.72
7	2.63	2.59	2.57	2.56	2.54	2.54	2.52	2.51	2.49	2.48	2.47
8	2.46	2.42	2.40	2.38	2.37	2.36	2.35	2.34	2.32	2.31	2.29
9	2.34	2.30	2.27	2.25	2.24	2.23	2.22	2.21	2.18	2.17	2.16
10	2.24	2.20	2.17	2.16	2.14	2.13	2.12	2.11	2.08	2.07	2.06
11	2.17	2.12	2.10	2.08	2.06	2.05	2.04	2.03	2.00	1.99	1.97
12	2.10	2.06	2.03	2.01	2.00	1.99	1.97	1.96	1.93	1.92	1.90
13	2.05	2.01	1.98	1.96	1.94	1.93	1.92	1.90	1.88	1.86	1.85
14	2.01	1.96	1.93	1.91	1.90	1.89	1.87	1.86	1.83	1.82	1.80
15	1.97	1.92	1.89	1.87	1.86	1.85	1.83	1.82	1.79	1.77	1.76
16	1.94	1.89	1.86	1.84	1.82	1.81	1.79	1.78	1.75	1.74	1.72
17	1.91	1.86	1.83	1.81	1.79	1.78	1.76	1.75	1.72	1.71	1.69
18	1.89	1.84	1.80	1.78	1.77	1.75	1.74	1.72	1.69	1.68	1.66
19	1.86	1.81	1.78	1.76	1.74	1.73	1.71	1.70	1.67	1.65	1.63
20	1.84	1.79	1.76	1.74	1.72	1.71	1.69	1.68	1.64	1.63	1.61
21	1.83	1.78	1.74	1.72	1.70	1.69	1.67	1.66	1.62	1.61	1.59
22	1.81	1.76	1.73	1.70	1.68	1.67	1.65	1.64	1.60	1.59	1.57
23	1.80	1.74	1.71	1.69	1.67	1.66	1.64	1.62	1.59	1.57	1.55
24	1.78	1.73	1.70	1.67	1.65	1.64	1.62	1.61	1.57	1.56	1.53
25	1.77	1.72	1.68	1.66	1.64	1.63	1.61	1.59	1.56	1.54	1.52
26	1.76	1.71	1.67	1.65	1.63	1.61	1.59	1.58	1.54	1.53	1.50
27	1.75	1.70	1.66	1.64	1.62	1.60	1.58	1.57	1.53	1.52	1.49
28	1.74	1.69	1.65	1.63	1.61	1.59	1.57	1.56	1.52	1.50	1.48
29	1.73	1.68	1.64	1.62	1.60	1.58	1.56	1.55	1.51	1.49	1.47
30	1.72	1.67	1.63	1.61	1.59	1.57	1.55	1.54	1.50	1.48	1.46
40	1.66	1.61	1.57	1.54	1.52	1.51	1.48	1.47	1.42	1.41	1.38
50	1.63	1.57	1.53	1.50	1.48	1.46	1.44	1.42	1.38	1.36	1.33
60	1.60	1.54	1.50	1.48	1.45	1.44	1.41	1.40	1.35	1.33	1.29
120	1.55	1.48	1.44	1.41	1.39	1.37	1.34	1.32	1.26	1.24	1.19
200	1.52	1.46	1.41	1.38	1.36	1.34	1.31	1.29	1.23	1.20	1.15
∞	1.49	1.42	1.38	1.34	1.32	1.30	1.26	1.24	1.17	1.13	1.00

CRITICAL VALUES OF $F_{.05}$

This table shows the 5 percent right-tail critical values of F for the stated degrees of freedom (d.f.).

Denominator Degrees of Freedom (df_2)	Numerator Degrees of Freedom (df_1)										
	1	2	3	4	5	6	7	8	9	10	12
1	161.4	199.5	215.7	224.6	230.2	234.0	236.8	238.9	240.5	241.9	243.9
2	18.51	19.00	19.16	19.25	19.30	19.33	19.35	19.37	19.38	19.40	19.41
3	10.13	9.55	9.28	9.12	9.01	8.94	8.89	8.85	8.81	8.79	8.74
4	7.71	6.94	6.59	6.39	6.26	6.16	6.09	6.04	6.00	5.96	5.91
5	6.61	5.79	5.41	5.19	5.05	4.95	4.88	4.82	4.77	4.74	4.68
6	5.99	5.14	4.76	4.53	4.39	4.28	4.21	4.15	4.10	4.06	4.00
7	5.59	4.74	4.35	4.12	3.97	3.87	3.79	3.73	3.68	3.64	3.57
8	5.32	4.46	4.07	3.84	3.69	3.58	3.50	3.44	3.39	3.35	3.28
9	5.12	4.26	3.86	3.63	3.48	3.37	3.29	3.23	3.18	3.14	3.07
10	4.96	4.10	3.71	3.48	3.33	3.22	3.14	3.07	3.02	2.98	2.91
11	4.84	3.98	3.59	3.36	3.20	3.09	3.01	2.95	2.90	2.85	2.79
12	4.75	3.89	3.49	3.26	3.11	3.00	2.91	2.85	2.80	2.75	2.69
13	4.67	3.81	3.41	3.18	3.03	2.92	2.83	2.77	2.71	2.67	2.60
14	4.60	3.74	3.34	3.11	2.96	2.85	2.76	2.70	2.65	2.60	2.53
15	4.54	3.68	3.29	3.06	2.90	2.79	2.71	2.64	2.59	2.54	2.48
16	4.49	3.63	3.24	3.01	2.85	2.74	2.66	2.59	2.54	2.49	2.42
17	4.45	3.59	3.20	2.96	2.81	2.70	2.61	2.55	2.49	2.45	2.38
18	4.41	3.55	3.16	2.93	2.77	2.66	2.58	2.51	2.46	2.41	2.34
19	4.38	3.52	3.13	2.90	2.74	2.63	2.54	2.48	2.42	2.38	2.31
20	4.35	3.49	3.10	2.87	2.71	2.60	2.51	2.45	2.39	2.35	2.28
21	4.32	3.47	3.07	2.84	2.68	2.57	2.49	2.42	2.37	2.32	2.25
22	4.30	3.44	3.05	2.82	2.66	2.55	2.46	2.40	2.34	2.30	2.23
23	4.28	3.42	3.03	2.80	2.64	2.53	2.44	2.37	2.32	2.27	2.20
24	4.26	3.40	3.01	2.78	2.62	2.51	2.42	2.36	2.30	2.25	2.18
25	4.24	3.39	2.99	2.76	2.60	2.49	2.40	2.34	2.28	2.24	2.16
26	4.23	3.37	2.98	2.74	2.59	2.47	2.39	2.32	2.27	2.22	2.15
27	4.21	3.35	2.96	2.73	2.57	2.46	2.37	2.31	2.25	2.20	2.13
28	4.20	3.34	2.95	2.71	2.56	2.45	2.36	2.29	2.24	2.19	2.12
29	4.18	3.33	2.93	2.70	2.55	2.43	2.35	2.28	2.22	2.18	2.10
30	4.17	3.32	2.92	2.69	2.53	2.42	2.33	2.27	2.21	2.16	2.09
40	4.08	3.23	2.84	2.61	2.45	2.34	2.25	2.18	2.12	2.08	2.00
50	4.03	3.18	2.79	2.56	2.40	2.29	2.20	2.13	2.07	2.03	1.95
60	4.00	3.15	2.76	2.53	2.37	2.25	2.17	2.10	2.04	1.99	1.92
120	3.92	3.07	2.68	2.45	2.29	2.18	2.09	2.02	1.96	1.91	1.83
200	3.89	3.04	2.65	2.42	2.26	2.14	2.06	1.98	1.93	1.88	1.80
∞	3.84	3.00	2.60	2.37	2.21	2.10	2.01	1.94	1.88	1.83	1.75

Denominator Degrees of Freedom (df_2)	Numerator Degrees of Freedom (df_1)										
	15	20	25	30	35	40	50	60	120	200	∞
1	245.9	248.0	249.3	250.1	250.7	251.1	251.8	252.2	253.3	253.7	254.3
2	19.43	19.45	19.46	19.46	19.47	19.47	19.48	19.48	19.49	19.49	19.50
3	8.70	8.66	8.63	8.62	8.60	8.59	8.58	8.57	8.55	8.54	8.53
4	5.86	5.80	5.77	5.75	5.73	5.72	5.70	5.69	5.66	5.65	5.63
5	4.62	4.56	4.52	4.50	4.48	4.46	4.44	4.43	4.40	4.39	4.37
6	3.94	3.87	3.83	3.81	3.79	3.77	3.75	3.74	3.70	3.69	3.67
7	3.51	3.44	3.40	3.38	3.36	3.34	3.32	3.30	3.27	3.25	3.23
8	3.22	3.15	3.11	3.08	3.06	3.04	3.02	3.01	2.97	2.95	2.93
9	3.01	2.94	2.89	2.86	2.84	2.83	2.80	2.79	2.75	2.73	2.71
10	2.85	2.77	2.73	2.70	2.68	2.66	2.64	2.62	2.58	2.56	2.54
11	2.72	2.65	2.60	2.57	2.55	2.53	2.51	2.49	2.45	2.43	2.41
12	2.62	2.54	2.50	2.47	2.44	2.43	2.40	2.38	2.34	2.32	2.30
13	2.53	2.46	2.41	2.38	2.36	2.34	2.31	2.30	2.25	2.23	2.21
14	2.46	2.39	2.34	2.31	2.28	2.27	2.24	2.22	2.18	2.16	2.13
15	2.40	2.33	2.28	2.25	2.22	2.20	2.18	2.16	2.11	2.10	2.07
16	2.35	2.28	2.23	2.19	2.17	2.15	2.12	2.11	2.06	2.04	2.01
17	2.31	2.23	2.18	2.15	2.12	2.10	2.08	2.06	2.01	1.99	1.96
18	2.27	2.19	2.14	2.11	2.08	2.06	2.04	2.02	1.97	1.95	1.92
19	2.23	2.16	2.11	2.07	2.05	2.03	2.00	1.98	1.93	1.91	1.88
20	2.20	2.12	2.07	2.04	2.01	1.99	1.97	1.95	1.90	1.88	1.84
21	2.18	2.10	2.05	2.01	1.98	1.96	1.94	1.92	1.87	1.84	1.81
22	2.15	2.07	2.02	1.98	1.96	1.94	1.91	1.89	1.84	1.82	1.78
23	2.13	2.05	2.00	1.96	1.93	1.91	1.88	1.86	1.81	1.79	1.76
24	2.11	2.03	1.97	1.94	1.91	1.89	1.86	1.84	1.79	1.77	1.73
25	2.09	2.01	1.96	1.92	1.89	1.87	1.84	1.82	1.77	1.75	1.71
26	2.07	1.99	1.94	1.90	1.87	1.85	1.82	1.80	1.75	1.73	1.69
27	2.06	1.97	1.92	1.88	1.86	1.84	1.81	1.79	1.73	1.71	1.67
28	2.04	1.96	1.91	1.87	1.84	1.82	1.79	1.77	1.71	1.69	1.66
29	2.03	1.94	1.89	1.85	1.83	1.81	1.77	1.75	1.70	1.67	1.64
30	2.01	1.93	1.88	1.84	1.81	1.79	1.76	1.74	1.68	1.66	1.62
40	1.92	1.84	1.78	1.74	1.72	1.69	1.66	1.64	1.58	1.55	1.51
50	1.87	1.78	1.73	1.69	1.66	1.63	1.60	1.58	1.51	1.48	1.44
60	1.84	1.75	1.69	1.65	1.62	1.59	1.56	1.53	1.47	1.44	1.39
120	1.75	1.66	1.60	1.55	1.52	1.50	1.46	1.43	1.35	1.32	1.26
200	1.72	1.62	1.56	1.52	1.48	1.46	1.41	1.39	1.30	1.26	1.19
∞	1.67	1.57	1.51	1.46	1.42	1.39	1.35	1.32	1.22	1.17	1.00

CRITICAL VALUES OF $F_{.025}$

This table shows the 2.5 percent right-tail critical values of F for the stated degrees of freedom (d.f.).

Denominator Degrees of Freedom (df_2)	Numerator Degrees of Freedom (df_1)										
	1	2	3	4	5	6	7	8	9	10	12
1	647.8	799.5	864.2	899.6	921.8	937.1	948.2	956.6	963.3	968.6	976.7
2	38.51	39.00	39.17	39.25	39.30	39.33	39.36	39.37	39.39	39.40	39.41
3	17.44	16.04	15.44	15.10	14.88	14.73	14.62	14.54	14.47	14.42	14.34
4	12.22	10.65	9.98	9.60	9.36	9.20	9.07	8.98	8.90	8.84	8.75
5	10.01	8.43	7.76	7.39	7.15	6.98	6.85	6.76	6.68	6.62	6.52
6	8.81	7.26	6.60	6.23	5.99	5.82	5.70	5.60	5.52	5.46	5.37
7	8.07	6.54	5.89	5.52	5.29	5.12	4.99	4.90	4.82	4.76	4.67
8	7.57	6.06	5.42	5.05	4.82	4.65	4.53	4.43	4.36	4.30	4.20
9	7.21	5.71	5.08	4.72	4.48	4.32	4.20	4.10	4.03	3.96	3.87
10	6.94	5.46	4.83	4.47	4.24	4.07	3.95	3.85	3.78	3.72	3.62
11	6.72	5.26	4.63	4.28	4.04	3.88	3.76	3.66	3.59	3.53	3.43
12	6.55	5.10	4.47	4.12	3.89	3.73	3.61	3.51	3.44	3.37	3.28
13	6.41	4.97	4.35	4.00	3.77	3.60	3.48	3.39	3.31	3.25	3.15
14	6.30	4.86	4.24	3.89	3.66	3.50	3.38	3.29	3.21	3.15	3.05
15	6.20	4.77	4.15	3.80	3.58	3.41	3.29	3.20	3.12	3.06	2.96
16	6.12	4.69	4.08	3.73	3.50	3.34	3.22	3.12	3.05	2.99	2.89
17	6.04	4.62	4.01	3.66	3.44	3.28	3.16	3.06	2.98	2.92	2.82
18	5.98	4.56	3.95	3.61	3.38	3.22	3.10	3.01	2.93	2.87	2.77
19	5.92	4.51	3.90	3.56	3.33	3.17	3.05	2.96	2.88	2.82	2.72
20	5.87	4.46	3.86	3.51	3.29	3.13	3.01	2.91	2.84	2.77	2.68
21	5.83	4.42	3.82	3.48	3.25	3.09	2.97	2.87	2.80	2.73	2.64
22	5.79	4.38	3.78	3.44	3.22	3.05	2.93	2.84	2.76	2.70	2.60
23	5.75	4.35	3.75	3.41	3.18	3.02	2.90	2.81	2.73	2.67	2.57
24	5.72	4.32	3.72	3.38	3.15	2.99	2.87	2.78	2.70	2.64	2.54
25	5.69	4.29	3.69	3.35	3.13	2.97	2.85	2.75	2.68	2.61	2.51
26	5.66	4.27	3.67	3.33	3.10	2.94	2.82	2.73	2.65	2.59	2.49
27	5.63	4.24	3.65	3.31	3.08	2.92	2.80	2.71	2.63	2.57	2.47
28	5.61	4.22	3.63	3.29	3.06	2.90	2.78	2.69	2.61	2.55	2.45
29	5.59	4.20	3.61	3.27	3.04	2.88	2.76	2.67	2.59	2.53	2.43
30	5.57	4.18	3.59	3.25	3.03	2.87	2.75	2.65	2.57	2.51	2.41
40	5.42	4.05	3.46	3.13	2.90	2.74	2.62	2.53	2.45	2.39	2.29
50	5.34	3.97	3.39	3.05	2.83	2.67	2.55	2.46	2.38	2.32	2.22
60	5.29	3.93	3.34	3.01	2.79	2.63	2.51	2.41	2.33	2.27	2.17
120	5.15	3.80	3.23	2.89	2.67	2.52	2.39	2.30	2.22	2.16	2.05
200	5.10	3.76	3.18	2.85	2.63	2.47	2.35	2.26	2.18	2.11	2.01
∞	5.02	3.69	3.12	2.79	2.57	2.41	2.29	2.19	2.11	2.05	1.94

Denominator Degrees of Freedom (df_2)	Numerator Degrees of Freedom (df_1)										
	15	20	25	30	35	40	50	60	120	200	∞
1	984.9	993.1	998.1	1001	1004	1006	1008	1010	1014	1016	1018
2	39.43	39.45	39.46	39.46	39.47	39.47	39.48	39.48	39.49	39.49	39.50
3	14.25	14.17	14.12	14.08	14.06	14.04	14.01	13.99	13.95	13.93	13.90
4	8.66	8.56	8.50	8.46	8.43	8.41	8.38	8.36	8.31	8.29	8.26
5	6.43	6.33	6.27	6.23	6.20	6.18	6.14	6.12	6.07	6.05	6.02
6	5.27	5.17	5.11	5.07	5.04	5.01	4.98	4.96	4.90	4.88	4.85
7	4.57	4.47	4.40	4.36	4.33	4.31	4.28	4.25	4.20	4.18	4.14
8	4.10	4.00	3.94	3.89	3.86	3.84	3.81	3.78	3.73	3.70	3.67
9	3.77	3.67	3.60	3.56	3.53	3.51	3.47	3.45	3.39	3.37	3.33
10	3.52	3.42	3.35	3.31	3.28	3.26	3.22	3.20	3.14	3.12	3.08
11	3.33	3.23	3.16	3.12	3.09	3.06	3.03	3.00	2.94	2.92	2.88
12	3.18	3.07	3.01	2.96	2.93	2.91	2.87	2.85	2.79	2.76	2.73
13	3.05	2.95	2.88	2.84	2.80	2.78	2.74	2.72	2.66	2.63	2.60
14	2.95	2.84	2.78	2.73	2.70	2.67	2.64	2.61	2.55	2.53	2.49
15	2.86	2.76	2.69	2.64	2.61	2.59	2.55	2.52	2.46	2.44	2.40
16	2.79	2.68	2.61	2.57	2.53	2.51	2.47	2.45	2.38	2.36	2.32
17	2.72	2.62	2.55	2.50	2.47	2.44	2.41	2.38	2.32	2.29	2.25
18	2.67	2.56	2.49	2.44	2.41	2.38	2.35	2.32	2.26	2.23	2.19
19	2.62	2.51	2.44	2.39	2.36	2.33	2.30	2.27	2.20	2.18	2.13
20	2.57	2.46	2.40	2.35	2.31	2.29	2.25	2.22	2.16	2.13	2.09
21	2.53	2.42	2.36	2.31	2.27	2.25	2.21	2.18	2.11	2.09	2.04
22	2.50	2.39	2.32	2.27	2.24	2.21	2.17	2.14	2.08	2.05	2.01
23	2.47	2.36	2.29	2.24	2.20	2.18	2.14	2.11	2.04	2.01	1.97
24	2.44	2.33	2.26	2.21	2.17	2.15	2.11	2.08	2.01	1.98	1.94
25	2.41	2.30	2.23	2.18	2.15	2.12	2.08	2.05	1.98	1.95	1.91
26	2.39	2.28	2.21	2.16	2.12	2.09	2.05	2.03	1.95	1.92	1.88
27	2.36	2.25	2.18	2.13	2.10	2.07	2.03	2.00	1.93	1.90	1.85
28	2.34	2.23	2.16	2.11	2.08	2.05	2.01	1.98	1.91	1.88	1.83
29	2.32	2.21	2.14	2.09	2.06	2.03	1.99	1.96	1.89	1.86	1.81
30	2.31	2.20	2.12	2.07	2.04	2.01	1.97	1.94	1.87	1.84	1.79
40	2.18	2.07	1.99	1.94	1.90	1.88	1.83	1.80	1.72	1.69	1.64
50	2.11	1.99	1.92	1.87	1.83	1.80	1.75	1.72	1.64	1.60	1.55
60	2.06	1.94	1.87	1.82	1.78	1.74	1.70	1.67	1.58	1.54	1.48
120	1.94	1.82	1.75	1.69	1.65	1.61	1.56	1.53	1.43	1.39	1.31
200	1.90	1.78	1.70	1.64	1.60	1.56	1.51	1.47	1.37	1.32	1.23
∞	1.83	1.71	1.63	1.57	1.52	1.48	1.43	1.39	1.27	1.21	1.00

CRITICAL VALUES OF $F_{.01}$

This table shows the 1 percent right-tail critical values of F for the stated degrees of freedom (d.f.).

| Denominator Degrees of Freedom (df_2) | Numerator Degrees of Freedom (df_1) | | | | | | | | | | |
	1	2	3	4	5	6	7	8	9	10	12
1	4052	4999	5404	5624	5764	5859	5928	5981	6022	6056	6107
2	98.50	99.00	99.16	99.25	99.30	99.33	99.36	99.38	99.39	99.40	99.42
3	34.12	30.82	29.46	28.71	28.24	27.91	27.67	27.49	27.34	27.23	27.05
4	21.20	18.00	16.69	15.98	15.52	15.21	14.98	14.80	14.66	14.55	14.37
5	16.26	13.27	12.06	11.39	10.97	10.67	10.46	10.29	10.16	10.05	9.89
6	13.75	10.92	9.78	9.15	8.75	8.47	8.26	8.10	7.98	7.87	7.72
7	12.25	9.55	8.45	7.85	7.46	7.19	6.99	6.84	6.72	6.62	6.47
8	11.26	8.65	7.59	7.01	6.63	6.37	6.18	6.03	5.91	5.81	5.67
9	10.56	8.02	6.99	6.42	6.06	5.80	5.61	5.47	5.35	5.26	5.11
10	10.04	7.56	6.55	5.99	5.64	5.39	5.20	5.06	4.94	4.85	4.71
11	9.65	7.21	6.22	5.67	5.32	5.07	4.89	4.74	4.63	4.54	4.40
12	9.33	6.93	5.95	5.41	5.06	4.82	4.64	4.50	4.39	4.30	4.16
13	9.07	6.70	5.74	5.21	4.86	4.62	4.44	4.30	4.19	4.10	3.96
14	8.86	6.51	5.56	5.04	4.69	4.46	4.28	4.14	4.03	3.94	3.80
15	8.68	6.36	5.42	4.89	4.56	4.32	4.14	4.00	3.89	3.80	3.67
16	8.53	6.23	5.29	4.77	4.44	4.20	4.03	3.89	3.78	3.69	3.55
17	8.40	6.11	5.19	4.67	4.34	4.10	3.93	3.79	3.68	3.59	3.46
18	8.29	6.01	5.09	4.58	4.25	4.01	3.84	3.71	3.60	3.51	3.37
19	8.18	5.93	5.01	4.50	4.17	3.94	3.77	3.63	3.52	3.43	3.30
20	8.10	5.85	4.94	4.43	4.10	3.87	3.70	3.56	3.46	3.37	3.23
21	8.02	5.78	4.87	4.37	4.04	3.81	3.64	3.51	3.40	3.31	3.17
22	7.95	5.72	4.82	4.31	3.99	3.76	3.59	3.45	3.35	3.26	3.12
23	7.88	5.66	4.76	4.26	3.94	3.71	3.54	3.41	3.30	3.21	3.07
24	7.82	5.61	4.72	4.22	3.90	3.67	3.50	3.36	3.26	3.17	3.03
25	7.77	5.57	4.68	4.18	3.85	3.63	3.46	3.32	3.22	3.13	2.99
26	7.72	5.53	4.64	4.14	3.82	3.59	3.42	3.29	3.18	3.09	2.96
27	7.68	5.49	4.60	4.11	3.78	3.56	3.39	3.26	3.15	3.06	2.93
28	7.64	5.45	4.57	4.07	3.75	3.53	3.36	3.23	3.12	3.03	2.90
29	7.60	5.42	4.54	4.04	3.73	3.50	3.33	3.20	3.09	3.00	2.87
30	7.56	5.39	4.51	4.02	3.70	3.47	3.30	3.17	3.07	2.98	2.84
40	7.31	5.18	4.31	3.83	3.51	3.29	3.12	2.99	2.89	2.80	2.66
50	7.17	5.06	4.20	3.72	3.41	3.19	3.02	2.89	2.78	2.70	2.56
60	7.08	4.98	4.13	3.65	3.34	3.12	2.95	2.82	2.72	2.63	2.50
120	6.85	4.79	3.95	3.48	3.17	2.96	2.79	2.66	2.56	2.47	2.34
200	6.76	4.71	3.88	3.41	3.11	2.89	2.73	2.60	2.50	2.41	2.27
∞	6.63	4.61	3.78	3.32	3.02	2.80	2.64	2.51	2.41	2.32	2.18

Denominator Degrees of Freedom (df_2)	Numerator Degrees of Freedom (df_1)										
	15	20	25	30	35	40	50	60	120	200	∞
1	6157	6209	6240	6260	6275	6286	6302	6313	6340	6350	6366
2	99.43	99.45	99.46	99.47	99.47	99.48	99.48	99.48	99.49	99.49	99.50
3	26.87	26.69	26.58	26.50	26.45	26.41	26.35	26.32	26.22	26.18	26.13
4	14.20	14.02	13.91	13.84	13.79	13.75	13.69	13.65	13.56	13.52	13.47
5	9.72	9.55	9.45	9.38	9.33	9.29	9.24	9.20	9.11	9.08	9.02
6	7.56	7.40	7.30	7.23	7.18	7.14	7.09	7.06	6.97	6.93	6.88
7	6.31	6.16	6.06	5.99	5.94	5.91	5.86	5.82	5.74	5.70	5.65
8	5.52	5.36	5.26	5.20	5.15	5.12	5.07	5.03	4.95	4.91	4.86
9	4.96	4.81	4.71	4.65	4.60	4.57	4.52	4.48	4.40	4.36	4.31
10	4.56	4.41	4.31	4.25	4.20	4.17	4.12	4.08	4.00	3.96	3.91
11	4.25	4.10	4.01	3.94	3.89	3.86	3.81	3.78	3.69	3.66	3.60
12	4.01	3.86	3.76	3.70	3.65	3.62	3.57	3.54	3.45	3.41	3.36
13	3.82	3.66	3.57	3.51	3.46	3.43	3.38	3.34	3.25	3.22	3.17
14	3.66	3.51	3.41	3.35	3.30	3.27	3.22	3.18	3.09	3.06	3.01
15	3.52	3.37	3.28	3.21	3.17	3.13	3.08	3.05	2.96	2.92	2.87
16	3.41	3.26	3.16	3.10	3.05	3.02	2.97	2.93	2.84	2.81	2.76
17	3.31	3.16	3.07	3.00	2.96	2.92	2.87	2.83	2.75	2.71	2.66
18	3.23	3.08	2.98	2.92	2.87	2.84	2.78	2.75	2.66	2.62	2.57
19	3.15	3.00	2.91	2.84	2.80	2.76	2.71	2.67	2.58	2.55	2.49
20	3.09	2.94	2.84	2.78	2.73	2.69	2.64	2.61	2.52	2.48	2.42
21	3.03	2.88	2.79	2.72	2.67	2.64	2.58	2.55	2.46	2.42	2.36
22	2.98	2.83	2.73	2.67	2.62	2.58	2.53	2.50	2.40	2.36	2.31
23	2.93	2.78	2.69	2.62	2.57	2.54	2.48	2.45	2.35	2.32	2.26
24	2.89	2.74	2.64	2.58	2.53	2.49	2.44	2.40	2.31	2.27	2.21
25	2.85	2.70	2.60	2.54	2.49	2.45	2.40	2.36	2.27	2.23	2.17
26	2.81	2.66	2.57	2.50	2.45	2.42	2.36	2.33	2.23	2.19	2.13
27	2.78	2.63	2.54	2.47	2.42	2.38	2.33	2.29	2.20	2.16	2.10
28	2.75	2.60	2.51	2.44	2.39	2.35	2.30	2.26	2.17	2.13	2.07
29	2.73	2.57	2.48	2.41	2.36	2.33	2.27	2.23	2.14	2.10	2.04
30	2.70	2.55	2.45	2.39	2.34	2.30	2.25	2.21	2.11	2.07	2.01
40	2.52	2.37	2.27	2.20	2.15	2.11	2.06	2.02	1.92	1.87	1.81
50	2.42	2.27	2.17	2.10	2.05	2.01	1.95	1.91	1.80	1.76	1.69
60	2.35	2.20	2.10	2.03	1.98	1.94	1.88	1.84	1.73	1.68	1.60
120	2.19	2.03	1.93	1.86	1.81	1.76	1.70	1.66	1.53	1.48	1.38
200	2.13	1.97	1.87	1.79	1.74	1.69	1.63	1.58	1.45	1.39	1.28
∞	2.04	1.88	1.77	1.70	1.64	1.59	1.52	1.47	1.32	1.25	1.00

APPENDIX G

Solutions to Odd-Numbered Exercises

CHAPTER 1

1.5 a. Statistics summarizes data.
  b. Statistics tells us how large a sample to take.
1.9 No, association does not imply causation. See Pitfall 5.
1.11 a. All combinations have same chance of winning so method did not "work."
  b. No, same as any other six numbers.
1.13 A reduction of .2% may not seem important to the individual customer, but from the company's perspective it could be significant depending on how many customers they have.
1.15 Disagree. The difference is practically important. 0.9% of 231,164 is 2,080 patients.
1.19 a. Analyze the 80 responses but make no conclusions about nonrespondents.
  b. No, study seems too flawed.
  c. Suggest a new well-designed survey with response incentive.
1.23 a. Attendance, study time, ability level, interest level, instructor's ability, prerequisites.
  b. Reverse causation? Good students make better decisions about their health.
  c. No, causation is not shown.
1.25 A major problem is that we don't know number of students in each major.
  a. Likely fewer philosophy majors to begin with.
  b. Likely more engineers want an MBA, so they take it.
  c. Causation not shown. Physics may differ from marketing majors (e.g., math skills).
  d. The GMAT is just an indicator of academic skills.
1.27 a. Most would prefer the graph, but both are clear.
  b. The number of salads sold reached a maximum in May and decreased steadily toward the end of 2005.

CHAPTER 2

2.1 a. categorical   b. categorical   c. discrete numerical
2.3 a. continuous numerical
  b. continuous numerical (often reported as an integer)
  c. categorical   d. categorical
2.5 a. ratio   b. ordinal   c. nominal   d. interval
  e. ratio   f. ordinal
2.9 a. Interval, assuming intervals are equal.
  b. Yes (assuming interval data).
  c. 10-point scale might give too many points and make it hard for guests to choose between.

2.11 a. cross-sectional   b. time series
  c. time series   d. cross-sectional
2.13 a. time series   b. cross-sectional
  c. time series   d. cross-sectional
2.15 a. Census   b. Sample or census   c. Sample
  d. Census
2.17 a. Parameter   b. Parameter   c. Statistic
  d. Statistic
2.19 a. Convenience   b. Systematic   c. Judgment or biased
2.25 a. Telephone or Web.   b. Direct observation.
  c. Interview, Web, or mail.   d. Interview or Web.
2.27 Version 1: Most would say yes. Version 2: More varied responses.
2.29 a. Continuous numerical   b. Categorical
  c. Discrete numerical   d. Discrete numerical
  e. Continuous numerical
2.33 Q1 Categorical, nominal   Q2 Continuous, ratio
  Q3 Continuous, ratio   Q4 Discrete, ratio
  Q5 Categorical, ordinal   Q6 Categorical, ordinal
  Q7 Discrete, ratio   Q8 Continuous, ratio
  Q9 Discrete, ratio   Q10 Categorical, ordinal
  Q11 Continuous, ratio   Q12 Discrete, ratio
  Q13 Categorical, ordinal   Q14 Categorical, nominal
  Q15 Categorical, ordinal
2.35 a. time series   b. cross-sectional   c. cross-sectional
  d. time series
2.37 a. statistic   b. parameter
  c. statistic   d. parameter
2.39 a. No, census costly, perhaps impossible.
  b. Cluster sample, by Web or mail.
2.41 Use mail or telephone. Census not possible.
2.43 a. Cluster sampling   b. Yes, but costly
2.45 a. Cluster sampling or convenience
2.47 a. Census   b. Sample   c. Sample   d. Census
2.49 a. Internet Survey.   b. Telephone Survey.
  c. Random Sample of tax returns.   d. Statistic based on sales, not a sample.   e. Cluster sample.
2.51 a. Cluster sampling, neighborhoods are natural clusters.
  b. Impractical if potential gain is small.
  c. Picking a day near a holiday with light trash.
2.53 a. systematic.   b. simple random sample.
  c. systematic or simple random sample.
  d. simple random sample or systematic.   e. stratified.
2.55 a. Income, store type   b. Simple random sample

2.57 a. Yes, 11,000/18 > 20.   b. 1/39

2.59 Convenience. Cost and Time.

2.61 Education and income could affect who uses the no-call list.

    a. They won't reach those who purchase such services. Same response for b and c.

Surveys and Scales

2.63 a. Ordinal.   b. Intervals are equal.

2.65 a. Rate the effectiveness of this professor. 1—Excellent to 5—Poor.

    b. Rate your satisfaction with the President's economic policy. 1—Very Satisfied to 5—Very dissatisfied.

    c. How long did you wait to see your doctor? Less than 15 minutes, between 15 and 30 minutes, between 30 minutes and 1 hour, more than 1 hour.

2.67 a. Likert

CHAPTER 3

3.1 Approximately symmetric with typical values around 25.

3.3 Sarah's calls are shorter.

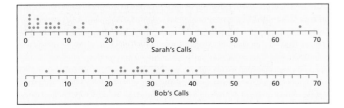

3.5 Sturges' Rule suggests about 6 bins. Slight right skew.

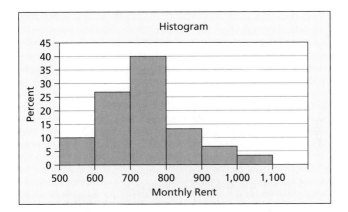

3.7 a. 7 bins, width = 5, Sturges' Rule = 6 bins

    b. 8 bins, width = 10, Sturges' Rule = 6 or 7 bins

    c. 10 bins, width = 0.15, Sturges' Rule = 9 bins

    d. 8 bins, width = 0.01, Sturges' Rule = 8 bins

3.9 a.

    b. Increasing trend until 2005, then sharp decrease.

3.11 Declining at a declining rate.

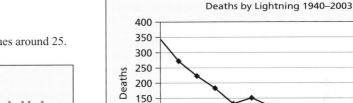

3.13 a. Line chart is clear but not attention-getting.

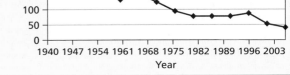

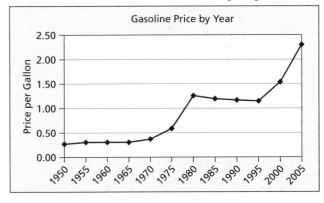

    b. Bar chart displays a more dramatic increase.

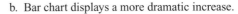

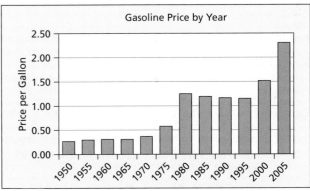

3.15 a.

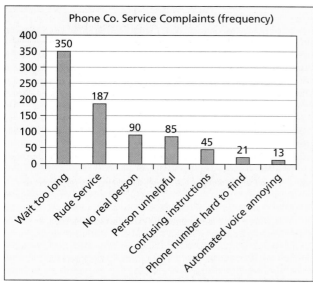

b. Wait too long, Rude service, No real person on line
c. Wait too long

3.17 a. To show more detail, you could start the graph at (20,20).
b. There is a moderate positive linear relationship.

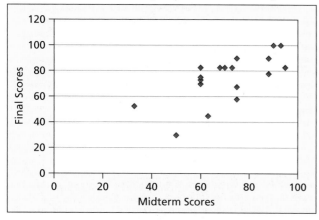

3.19 a. To show more detail, you could start the graph at (.80,100).
b. There is a moderate negative linear relationship.

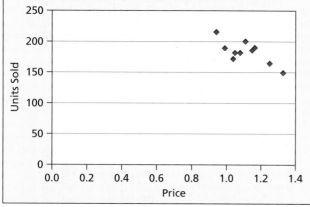

3.21 a. Default pie is clear, but rather small (can be dragged larger).
b. Visually strong, but harder to read due to rotation.
c. Clear, easy to read.

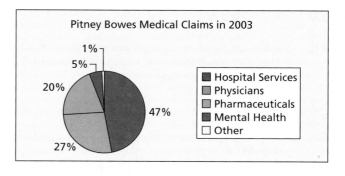

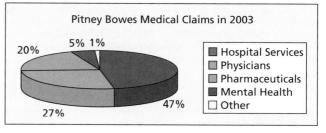

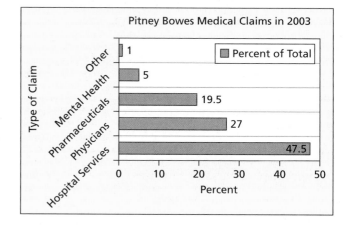

3.23 a.

b.

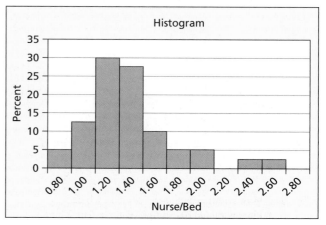

c. Skewed to the right. Half of the data values are between 1.2 and 1.6.

3.25 a. MegaStat's dotplot.

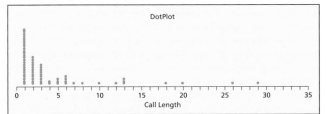

b. MegaStat's histogram.

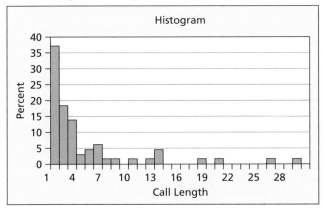

c. Heavily skewed to the right. Central tendency approximately 3 minutes.

3.27

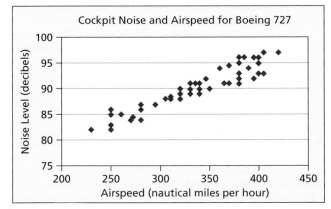

3.29 a.

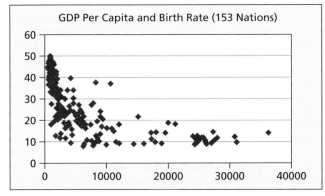

b. Negative, Nonlinear, Moderate relationship.

3.31 a. Horizontal bar chart with 3D visual effect.

b. Strengths: Good proportions and no distracting pictures. Weaknesses: No labels on X and Y axes, title unclear, 3D effect does not add to presentation.

c. Vertical bar chart without visual effect and label on X axis.

3.33 a. Exploded pie chart.

b. Strengths: Information complete, colorful. Weaknesses: Hard to assess differences in size of pie slices.

c. Sorted column chart with OPEC and non-OPEC countries color coded.

3.35 a. Pie chart.

b. Strengths: Source identified, answers the question posed. Weaknesses: "Other" category quite large.

c. Might change title: Distribution of Advertising Dollars in the United States, 2001. Some might prefer a column chart.

3.37 a. Pictograph.

b. Pictures distracting, implies irresponsibility, does show source of data.

c. Take out pictures, show a simple line chart.

3.39 a.

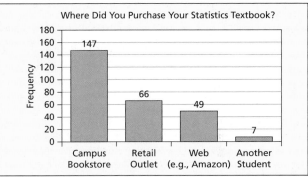

b. Yes, pie chart could be used.

3.41 a.

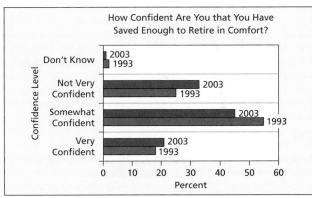

b. Yes, a vertical column chart would also work.

3.43 a.

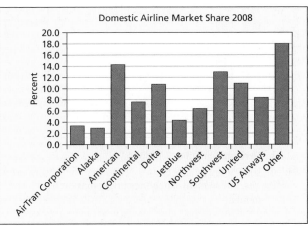

b. Yes, a pie chart could be used.

3.45 a.

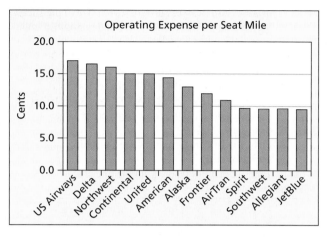

b. Yes, a bar chart could be used. But a table may be clearest, because the large quantity of data tends to clutter the graphs.

3.47 a.

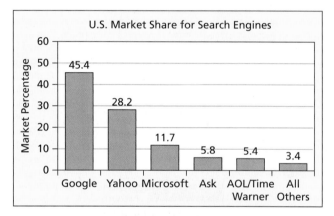

b. Yes, a pie chart would work.

3.49 a.

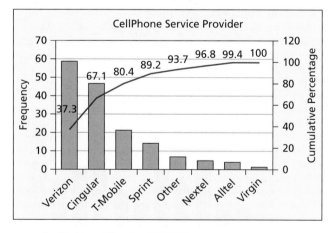

b. Verizon, Cingular, T-Mobile.

3.51 a. Bar chart.

b. Yes, but so many categories might make it hard to read.

CHAPTER 4

4.1 a. mean = 2.833, median = 1.5, mode = 0.

b. mean = 68.33, median = 72, mode = 40.

c. mean = 3.044, median = 3.03, no mode.

4.3 a. Continuous data, skewed right, no mode. Median best choice.

b. Mostly one rider, mode best choice.

c. Symmetric distribution, mean and median the same, and two modes. Mean best choice.

4.5 a. $\bar{x} = 27.34$, median = 26, mode = 26.

b. No, $\bar{x}$ is greater than the median and mode.

d. Slightly skewed right.

4.7 b. $\bar{x} = 4.48$, median = 2, mode = 1.

c. No, $\bar{x} >$ median > mode.

d. Skewed right.

4.9 a. TRIMMEAN(A1:A50,.2). b. 5. c. 10.

4.11 a. $\bar{x} = 27.34$, midrange = 25.50, geometric mean = 26.08, 10% trimmed mean = 27.46.

b. The measures are all close, especially the mean and trimmed mean.

4.13 a. $\bar{x} = 4.48$, midrange = 15.0, geometric mean = 2.6, 10% trimmed mean = 3.13.

b. No, the midrange is much greater than the other three measures.

c. The data is skewed right.

d. Mean and trimmed mean describe the central tendency better than the other two, but they are also affected by skewness.

4.15 a. Sample A: $\bar{x} = 7$, $s = 1$. Sample B: $\bar{x} = 62$, $s = 1$. Sample C: $\bar{x} = 1001$, $s = 1$.

b. The standard deviation is not a function of the mean.

4.17 a. Stock A: $CV = 21.43\%$. Stock B: $CV = 8.32\%$. Stock C: $CV = 36.17\%$.

b. Stock C

c. Directly comparing standard deviation would not be helpful in this case because the means have different magnitudes.

4.19 a. $\bar{x}_A = 6.857$, $s_A = 1.497$, $\bar{x}_B = 7.243$, $s_B = 1.209$.

b. $CV_A = 0.218$, $CV_B = 0.167$.

c. Consumers preferred sauce B.

4.21 a. $z = 2.4$. b. $z = 1$. c. $z = 0.6$.

4.23 a. Bob's GPA = 3.5956.

b. Sarah's weekly work hours = 29.978.

c. Dave's bowling score = 96.

4.25 b. 18 ($z = 2.30$) and 20 ($z = 2.64$) are unusual observations. 26 ($z = 3.67$) and 29 ($z = 4.18$) are outliers.

c. 87.7% lie within 1 standard deviation and 93.8% lie within 2 standard deviations. 87.7% is much greater than the 68% specified by the empirical rule. The distribution does not appear normal.

4.27 b. Strongly skewed right.

4.29 a. $Q_1 = 1$, $Q_3 = 5$. The middle 50% of the calls last between 1 and 5 minutes.

b. *Midhinge* = 3. Calls typically last 3 minutes.

c. The data are heavily skewed to the right.

4.31

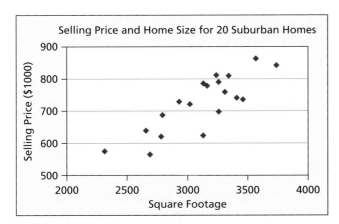

Selling Price and Home Size for 20 Suburban Homes

b. $r = .8338$
c. Yes, there is a strong positive linear relationship.

4.33 Using Chebyshev's Theorem, at least 88.9%.

4.35 a. Allison's final exam = 90.1.
b. Jim's weekly grocery bill = $35.60.
c. Eric's daily video game time = 3.09 hours.

4.37 a. Standard deviation = 2.
b. Assumed a normal distribution.

4.39 a.

The distribution is heavily skewed right.
b. $\bar{x} = 26.71$, median = 14.5, mode = 11, and midrange = 124.5.
c. $Q_1 = 7.75$, $Q_3 = 20.25$, *Midhinge* = 14.
d. The geometric mean is only valid for data greater than zero.
e. The median because the data is quantitative and heavily skewed right.

4.41 a. Stock funds: $\bar{x} = 1.329$, median = 1.22. Bond funds: $\bar{x} = 0.875$, median = 0.85.
b. The central tendency of stock fund expense ratios is higher than bond funds.
c. Stock funds: $s = 0.5933$, $CV = 44.65\%$. Bond funds: $s = 0.4489$, $CV = 51.32\%$.
d. The stock funds have less variability relative to the mean.

4.43 a. mean = 6807, median = 6,646.
b. Not skewed.
c. There is no mode.

4.45 a.

The dot plot shows that most of the data are centered around 6500 yards. The distribution is skewed to the left.
b. $\bar{x} = 6{,}335.52$, median = 6,400.0, mode = 6,500.0, and midrange = 6,361.5.

c. Best: Median because data is quantitative and skewed left. Worst: Mode worst because the data is quantitative and very few values repeat themselves.
d. This data is not highly skewed. The geometric mean works well for skewed data.

4.47 b. Yes, height percentiles do change. The population is slowly increasing in height.

4.49 a. $\bar{x} = 3012.44$, median = 2,550.5.
b. The typical cricket club's income is approximately £2.5 million.

4.51 a.

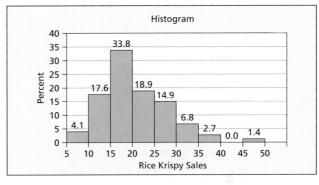

b. Skewed right.
c. Mean = 20.12, standard deviation = 7.64.
d. One possible outlier at 49 (store 22).

4.53 a. Tuition Plans: $CV = 42.86\%$, S&P 500: $CV = 122.48\%$.
b. The *CV* shows *relative* risk for each investment.
c. While the tuition plans have a lower return, there is less risk of losing your investment than if you had invested in stocks.

4.55 a. Midrange = 0.855.
b. Standard deviation = .0217.

4.57 a. The distribution is skewed to the right.
b. This makes sense, most patrons would keep books about 10 days with a few keeping them much longer.

4.59 a. Reasonable to expect the distribution is skewed right.
b. Median < mean.

4.61 a. Would expect mean to be close in value to the median, or slightly higher.   b. Life span would have normal distribution. If skewed, more likely skewed right than left. Life span is bounded below by zero, but is unbounded in the positive direction.

4.63 a. It is the midrange, not the median.
b. The midrange is influenced by outliers. Salaries tend to be skewed to the right. Community should use the median.

4.65 a. and c.

	Week 1	Week 2	Week 3	Week 4
mean	50.00	50.00	50.00	50.00
sample standard deviation	10.61	10.61	10.61	10.61
median	50.00	52.00	56.00	47.00

b. Based on the mean and standard deviation, it appears that the distributions are the same.

d.

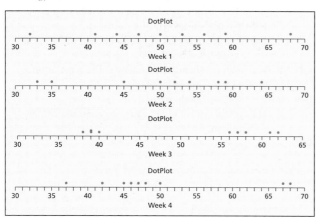

e. Based on the medians and dotplots, distributions are quite different.

4.67 a. 1990: $\bar{x} = 3.98$, $s = 1.93$, $CV = 48.5\%$.
   2000: $\bar{x} = 3.47$, $s = 1.83$, $CV = 52.6\%$.
   b. The average fertility rate is approximately 4 children per women with standard deviation 1.9. Stayed fairly constant from 1990 to 2000.
   d. Frequency table makes it easier to see distribution and create a histogram.

4.69 a. $\bar{x} = 60.2$, $s = 8.54$, $CV = 14.2\%$.
   b. No. The class widths increase as the data values get more spread out.

4.73 a.

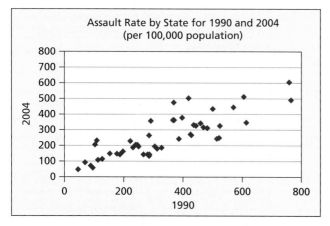

b. $r = .8332$.
c. The rates are positively correlated.
d. 1990: mean = 331.92, median = 3.7, mode = 286.
   2004: mean = 256.6, median = 232, mode = 143.

CHAPTER 5

5.1 a. $S = \{(V,B), (V,E), (V,O), (M,B), (M,E), (M,O), (A,B), (A,E), (A,O)\}$
   b. Events are not equally likely. Border's probably carries more books than other merchandise.

5.3 a. $S = \{(L,B), (L,B'), (R,B), (R,B')\}$
   b. Events are not equally likely. More right handed people than left handed people.

5.5 a. Empirical.
   b. From historical data of IPOs.

5.7 a. Empirical.   b. Historical data of past launches.

5.9 a. Subjective.   b. Expert judgment by NASA.

5.11 a. Empirical.   b. Based on past attempts.

5.13 a. Not mutually exclusive.
   b. Mutually exclusive.
   c. Not mutually exclusive.

5.15 a. $P(A \cup B) = .4 + .5 - .05 = .85$.
   b. $P(A \mid B) = .05/.50 = .10$.
   c. $P(B \mid A) = .05/.4 = .125$.

5.17 a. $P(S) = .217$.   b. $P(S') = .783$.
   c. Odds in favor of S: $.217/.783 = .277$.
   d. Odds against S: $.783/.217 = 3.61$

5.19 a. $X = 1$ if the drug is approved, 0 otherwise.
   b. $X = 1$ if batter gets a hit, 0 otherwise.
   c. $X = 1$ if breast cancer detected, 0 otherwise.

5.21 a. $P(S') = 1 - .246$. There is a 75.4% chance that a female aged 18–24 is a nonsmoker.
   b. $P(S \cup C) = .246 + .830 - .232 = .844$. There is an 84.4% chance that a female aged 18–24 is a smoker or is Caucasian.
   c. $P(S \mid C) = .232/.830 = .2795$. Given that the female aged 18–24 is a Caucasian, there is a 27.95% chance that they are a smoker.
   d. $P(S \cap C') = P(S) - P(S \cap C) = .246 - .232 = .014$. $P(S \mid C') = .014/.17 = .0824$. Given that the female aged 18–24 is *not* Caucasian, there is an 8.24% chance that she smokes.

5.23 $P(A \mid B) = P(A \cap B)/P(B) = .05/.50 = .10$ No, A and B are not independent because $P(A \mid B) \neq P(A)$.

5.25 a. $P(V \cup M) = .73 + .18 - .03 = .88$.
   b. $P(V \cap M) \neq P(V)P(M)$ therefore V and M are not independent.

5.27 "Five nines" reliability means $P(not\ failing) = .99999$. $P(power\ system\ failure) = 1 - (.05)^3 = .999875$. The system does not meet the test.

5.29 Ordering a soft drink is independent of ordering a square pizza. $P(ordering\ a\ soft\ drink) \times P(ordering\ a\ square\ pizza) = .5(.8) = .4$. This is equal to $P(ordering\ both\ a\ soft\ drink\ and\ a\ square\ pizza)$.

5.31 a. $P(Recycles) = .34$.
   b. $P(Don't\ Recycle \mid Lives\ in\ Deposit\ Law\ State) = .30$.
   c. $P(Recycle\ and\ Live\ in\ Deposit\ Law\ State) = .154$.
   d. $P(Recycle \mid Lives\ in\ Deposit\ Law\ State) = .70$.

5.33 a. $P(D) = .5064$.   b. $P(R) = .1410$.
   c. $P(D \cap R) = .0513$.   d. $P(D \cup R) = .5962$.
   e. $P(R \mid D) = .1013$.   f. $P(R \mid P) = .1628$.

5.35 *Gender* and *Major* are not independent. For example, $P(A \cap F) = .22$. $P(A)P(F) = .245$. Because the values are not equal, the events are not independent.

5.37

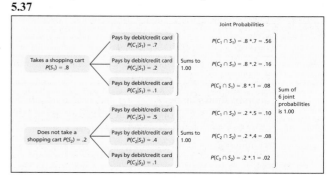

5.39 Let A = using the drug. $P(A) = .04$. $P(A') = .96$. Let T be a positive result. False positive: $P(T \mid A') = .05$. False negative: $P(T' \mid A) = .10$. $P(T \mid A) = 1 - .10 = .90$. $P(T) = (.04)(.90) + (.05)(.96) = .084$. $P(A \mid T) = (.9)(.04)/.084 = .4286$.

5.41 Let W = suitcase contains a weapon. $P(W) = .001$. $P(W') = .999$. Let A be the alarm trigger. False positive: $P(A \mid W') = .02$. False negative: $P(A' \mid W) = .02$. $P(A \mid W) = 1 - .02 = .98$. $P(A) = (.001)(.98) + (.02)(.999) = .02096$. $P(W \mid A) = (.98)(.001)/.02096 = .04676$.

5.43 $_{20}C_5 = 15{,}504$.

5.45 a. $26^6 = 308{,}915{,}776$.
b. $36^6 = 2{,}176{,}782{,}336$.
c. $32^6 = 1{,}073{,}741{,}824$.

5.47 a. $10^6 = 1{,}000{,}000$.
b. $10^5 = 100{,}000$.
c. $10^6 = 1{,}000{,}000$.

5.49 a. $7! = 5{,}040$ ways.   b. No, too many!

5.51 a. $_8C_3 = 56$.   b. $_8C_5 = 56$.
c. $_8C_1 = 8$.   d. $_8C_8 = 1$.

5.57 Empirical.

5.59 a. An empirical probability using response frequencies from the survey.
b. Odds for failure: $.44/.56 = .786$ or 11 to 14.

5.61 No, the law of large numbers says that the larger the sample, the closer our sample results will be to the true value. If Tom Brookens increases his times "at bat" he'll get closer and closer to his true batting average, which is probably close to .176.

5.63 a. Empirical or subjective.
b. Most likely estimated by interviewing ER doctors.

5.65 a. Subjective.
b. Simulated experiment using a computer model.

5.67 a. Empirical or subjective.
b. Observation or survey.

5.71 Odds against an Acura Integra being stolen $= .987/.013 = 76$ to 1.

5.73 P(Detroit Wins) $= 1/51 = .0196$. P(New Jersey Wins) $= 1/6 = .1667$.

5.75 a. $26^3 10^3 = 17{,}576{,}000$.
b. $36^6 = 2{,}176{,}782{,}336$.
c. 0 and 1 might be disallowed because they are similar in appearance to letters like O and I.
d. Yes, 2.2 billion unique plates should be enough.
e. $34^6 = 1{,}544{,}804{,}416$.

5.77 Order does not matter. $_7C_3 = 35$.

5.79 a. P(Two aces) $= (4/52)(3/51) = 0.00452$.
b. P(Two red cards) $= (26/52)(25/51) = 0.245098$.
c. P(Two red aces) $= (2/52)(1/51) = 0.000754$.
d. P(Two honor cards) $= (20/52)(19/51) = 0.143288$.

5.81 No, $P(A)P(B) \neq .05$.

5.83 a. Having independent back up power for computers might have eliminated delayed flights.
b. If the cost due to delayed/cancelled flights, weighted by the risk of a power outage, is greater than \$100,000, then the airline can justify the expenditure.

5.85 Assuming independence, P(3 cases won out of next 3) $= .7^3 = .343$.

5.87* Assuming independence, P(4 adults say yes) $= .56^4 = 0.0983$.

5.89* See the Excel Spreadsheet in *Learning Stats:* 05-13 Birthday Problem.xls.
For 2 riders: P(no match) $= .9973$.
For 10 riders: P(no match) $= 0.8831$.
For 20 riders: P(no match) $= 0.5886$.
For 50 riders: P(no match) $= 0.0296$.

5.91* a. i. .4825 ii. .25 iii. .115 iv. .19 v. .64 vi. .3316 vii. .09 viii. .015 ix. .0325.
b. Yes, the vehicle type and mall location are dependent.

5.93 a. i. .5588 ii. .5294 iii. .3684 iv. .4000 v. .1765 vi. .2059.
b. No, P(A−) $= .4705$ and P(A− | F−) $= .3684$. Interest rates moved down 47% of the time and yet the forecasters predictions of a decline showed a 37% accuracy rate.

5.95*

	Cancer	No Cancer	Totals
Positive Test	4	500	504
Negative Test	0	9496	9496
Totals	4	9996	10000

P(Cancer | Positive Test) $= 4/504 = 0.00794$.

5.97* Let D = applicant uses drugs and T = applicant has positive test result.

$$P(D \mid T) = \frac{P(T \mid D)P(D)}{P(T \mid D)P(D) + P(T \mid D')P(D')} = \frac{.036}{.036 + .144}$$

CHAPTER 6

6.1 Only A is a PDF because $P(x)$ sum to 1.

6.3 $E(X) = 2.25$, $V(X) = 1.6875$, $\sigma = 1.299$, right-skewed.

6.5 $E(X) = 1000(.01) + (0)(.999) = \$10$, add \$25, charges \$35.

6.7 $E(X) = 250(.3) + 950(.3) + 0(.4) = \$360$ million.

6.9 a. $\mu = (20 + 60)/2 = 40$,
$\sigma = \sqrt{[(60 - 20 + 1)^2 - 1]/12} = 11.83$.
b. $P(X \geq 40) = .5122$, $P(X \geq 30) = .7561$.

6.11 Answers may vary.
a. 1 = correct, 0 = incorrect.
b. 1 = insured, 0 = uninsured.
c. 1 = busy, 0 = not busy.
d. 1 = lost weight, 0 no weight loss.

6.13 a. $X = 0, 1$, or 2.
b. $X = 4, 5, 6$, or 7.
c. $X = 4, 5, 6, 7, 8, 9$, or 10.

6.15 a. $\mu = 0.8$, $\sigma = 0.8485$ b. $\mu = 4$, $\sigma = 1.5492$
c. $\mu = 6$, $\sigma = 1.7321$ d. $\mu = 27$, $\sigma = 1.6432$
e. $\mu = 56$, $\sigma = 4.0988$ f. $\mu = 16$, $\sigma = 1.7888$

6.17 a. $P(X \leq 3) = .9437$
b. $P(X > 7) = 1 - P(X \leq 7) = .0547$
c. $P(X < 3) = P(X \leq 2) = .0705$
d. $P(X \leq 10) = .00417$

6.19 a. $P(X = 0) = .10737$
b. $P(X \geq 2) = .62419$
c. $P(X < 3) = .67780$
d. $\mu = n\pi = (10)(.2) = 2$
e. $\sigma = \sqrt{(10)(.2)(1 - .2)} = 1.2649$ g. Skewed right.

6.21 a. $P(X = 0) = .0916$.   b. $P(X \geq 2) = .6276$.
c. $P(X < 4) = .9274$.   d. $P(X = 5) = .0079$.

6.23 a. $P(X = 16) = .0033$.
   b. $P(X < 10) = .1753$.
   c. $P(X \geq 10) = .8247$.

6.25 a. $\lambda = 1, \mu = 1.0, \sigma = 1$
   b. $\lambda = 2, \mu = 2.0, \sigma = 1.414$
   c. $\lambda = 4, \mu = 4.0, \sigma = 2.0$ d. $\lambda = 9, \mu = 9.0, \sigma = 3$
   e. $\lambda = 12, \mu = 12.0, \sigma = 3.464$

6.27 a. $\lambda = 4.3, P(X \leq 3) = .37715$
   b. $\lambda = 5.2, P(X > 7) = .15508$
   c. $\lambda = 2.7, P(X < 3) = .49362$
   d. $\lambda = 11.0, P(X \leq 10) = .45989$

6.29 a. $P(X \geq 1) = .8173$.   b. $P(X = 0) = .1827$.
   c. $P(X > 3) = .0932$.

6.31 a. Add-ons are ordered independently.
   b. $P(X \geq 2) = .4082$.   c. $P(X = 0) = .2466$.

6.33* Let $\lambda = n\pi = (500)(.003) = 1.5$
   a. $P(X \geq 2) = 1 - .55783 = .44217$
   b. $P(X \leq 4) = .93436$ c. Large n and small π.
   d. Yes, $n \geq 20$ and $\pi \leq .05$

6.35* a. Set $\lambda = \mu = (200)(.03) = 6$
   b. $\sigma = \sqrt{(200)(.03)(1 - .03)} = 2.412$
   c. $P(X \geq 10) = 1 - .91608 = .08392$
   d. $P(X \leq 4) = .28506$
   e. n is too large without Excel.
   f. Yes, $n \geq 20$ and $\pi \leq .05$.

6.37* a. $E(X) = 2.3$.
   b. $P(X = 0) \approx .1003, P(X > 2) = .4040$.

6.39 Distribution is symmetric with small range.

6.41 a. $X =$ number of incorrect vouchers in sample.
   b. $P(X = 0) = .06726$ c. $P(X = 1) = .25869$
   d. $P(X \geq 3) = 1 - .69003 = .30997$
   e. Fairly symmetric

6.43* a. $3/100 < .05$, OK.   b. $10/200 > .05$, not OK.
   c. $12/160 > .05$, not OK.   d. $7/500 < .05$, OK.

6.45* a. $P(X = 0) = 0.34868$ (B) or $.34516$ (H).
   b. $P(X \geq 2) = .26390$ (B) or $.26350$ (H).
   c. $P(X < 4) = .98720$ (B) or $.98814$ (H).
   d. $n/N = 10/500 = .02$, so set $\pi = s/N = 50/500 = .1$.

6.47* a. $P(X = 5) = .03125$ when $\pi = .50$
   b. $P(X = 3) = .14063$ when $\pi = .25$
   c. $P(X = 4) = .03840$ when $\pi = .60$

6.49* a. $\mu = 1/\pi = 1/(.50) = 2$
   b. $P(X > 10) = (.50)^{10} = .00098$

6.51* a. $\mu = 9500 + 7400 + 8600 = \$25,500$ (Rule 3), $\sigma^2 = 1250 + 1425 + 1610 = 4285$ (Rule 4), $\sigma = 65.4599$.
   b. Rule 4 assumes independent monthly sales (unlikely).

6.53* a. If $Y =$ Bob's point total then $\mu_Y = 400, \sigma_Y = 11.18$.
   b. No, 450 is more than 3 standard deviations from the mean.

6.55 $E(\text{loss}) = \$0(.98) + \$250(.02)$
       $= \$5. E(\text{loss}) >$ Insurance
       so purchase insurance.

6.57 a. $\pi = .80$ (answers will vary).
   b. $\pi = .300$ (answers will vary).
   c. $\pi = .50$ (answers will vary).
   d. $\pi = .80$ (answers will vary).
   e. One trial may influence the next.

6.59 a. $P(X = 5) = .59049$ b. $P(X = 4) = .32805$
   c. Strongly right-skewed

6.61 a. $P(X = 0) = .06250$
   b. $P(X \geq 2) = 1 - .31250 = .68750$
   c. $P(X \leq 2) = .68750$ d. Symmetric.

6.63 a. =BINOMDIST(3,20,0.3,0)
   b. =BINOMDIST(7,50,0.1,0)
   c. =BINOMDIST(6,80,0.05,1)
   d. =1−BINOMDIST(29,120,0.2,1)

6.65 a. $P(X = 0) = .48398$
   b. $P(X \geq 3) = 1 - P(X \leq 2) = 1 - .97166 = .02834$
   c. $\mu = n\pi = (10)(.07) = 0.7$ defaults

6.67 Binomial with $n = 16, \pi = .8$:
   a. $P(X \geq 10) = 1 - P(X \leq 9) = 1 - .02666 = .97334$.
   b. $P(X < 8) = P(X \leq 7) = .00148$.

6.69 Let $X =$ number of no shows. Then:
   a. If $n = 10$ and $\pi = .10$, then $P(X = 0) = .34868$.
   b. If $n = 11$ and $\pi = .10$, then $P(X \geq 1) = 1 - P(X = 0) = 1 - .31381 = .68619$.
   c. If they sell 11 seats, not more than 1 will be bumped.
   d. If $X =$ number who show ($\pi = .90$). Using $= 1 -$ BINOMDIST(9, n, .9,TRUE) we find that $n = 13$ will ensure that $P(X \geq 10) \geq .95$.

6.71 a. Because calls to a fire station within a minute are most likely all about the same fire, the calls are not independent.
   b. Answers will vary.

6.73 a. $P(X = 5) = .0872$.   b. $P(X \leq 5) = .9349$.
   c. $\lambda = 14$ arrivals/5 min interval.   d. Independence.

6.75 a. $P(X = 0) = .7408$.   b. $P(X \geq 2) = .0369$.

6.77 a. Assume independent cancellations.
   b. $P(X = 0) = .22313$ c. $P(X = 1) = .33470$
   d. $P(X > 2) = 1 - .80885 = .19115$
   e. $P(X \geq 5) = 1 - .98142 = .01858$

6.79 a. Assume independent defects with $\lambda = 2.4$.
   b. $P(X = 0) = .09072$ c. $P(X = 1) = .21772$
   d. $P(X \leq 1) = .30844$

6.81* $P(\text{at least one rogue wave in 5 days}) = 1 - P(X = 0) = .9892$.

6.83 a. Assume independent crashes.
   b. $P(X \geq 1) = 1 - .13534 = .86466$
   c. $P(X < 5) = P(X \leq 4) = .94735$
   d. Skewed right.

6.85* a. Set $\lambda = n\pi = (200)(.02) = 4$.
   b. $P(X = 0) = .01832$ c. $P(X = 1) = .07326$
   d. $P(X = 0) = .01759$ from =BINOMDIST(0,200,0.02,0)
      $P(X = 1) = .07179$ from =BINOMDIST(1,200,0.02,0)
   e. Yes, $n \geq 20$ and $\pi \leq .05$.

6.87* a. $E(X) = 6.4$. b. $P(X < 10) = .8858, P(X > 5) = .6163$.

6.89* a. $P(X \geq 4) = 1 - P(X \leq 3) = .5182$.
   b. Assume calls are independent.

6.91* a. $\mu = 1/.25 = 4$.   b. $P(X \leq 6) = .8220$.

6.93* a. $\mu = 1/\pi = 1/(.08) = 12.5$ cars
   b. $P(X \leq 5) = 1 - (1 - .08)^5 = .3409$

6.95* a. $\mu = 1/\pi = 1/(.05) = 20$
   b. $P(X \leq 29) = 1 - (1 - .05)^{29} = 1 - .2259 = .7741$

6.97* a. $(233.1)(0.4536) = 105.734$ kg
   b. $(34.95)(0.4536) = 15.8533$ kg
   c. Rule 1 for the μ, Rule 2 for σ.

6.101*Rule 1, $\mu_{vQ+F} = v\mu_Q + F = (2225)(7) + 500 = \$16,075$
       Rule 2, $\sigma_{vQ+F} = v\sigma_Q = (2225)(2) = \$4,450$
       Rule 1, $E(PQ) = P\mu_Q = (2850)(7) = \$19,950$
       $E(TR) - E(TC) = 19,950 - 16,075 = \$3,875$

6.103*a. $\mu_{X+Y} = \$70 + \$200 = \$270$.
   b. $\sigma_{X+Y} = \sqrt{10^2 + 30^2 + 2 \times 400} = \$42.43$.
   c. The variance of the total is greater than either of the individual variances.

CHAPTER 7

Note: Using Appendix C or Excel will lead to somewhat different answers.

7.1   a. D   b. C   c. C

7.3   a. Area $= bh = (1)(.25) = .25$, so not a PDF (area is not 1).
   b. Area $= bh = (4)(.25) = 1$, so could be a PDF (area is 1).
   c. Area $= \frac{1}{2}bh = \frac{1}{2}(2)(2) = 2$, so not a PDF (area is not 1).

7.5   a. $\mu = (0 + 10)/2 = 5, \sigma = \sqrt{\dfrac{(10 - 0)^2}{12}} = 2.886751$.

   b. $\mu = (200 + 100)/2 = 150, \sigma = \sqrt{\dfrac{(200 - 100)^2}{12}} = 28.86751$.

   c. $\mu = (1 + 99)/2 = 50, \sigma = \sqrt{\dfrac{(99 - 1)^2}{12}} = 28.29016$.

7.7   A point has no area in a continuous distribution so $<$ or $\leq$ yields the same result.

7.9   Means and standard deviations differ (X axis scales are different) and so do $f(x)$ heights.

7.11   For samples from a *normal distribution* we expect about 68.26% within $\mu \pm 1\,\sigma$, about 95.44% within $\mu \pm 2\,\sigma$, and about 99.73% within $\mu \pm 3\,\sigma$.

7.13   Using Appendix C-1:
   a. $P(0 < Z < 0.50) = .1915$
   b. $P(-0.50 < Z < 0) = P(0 < Z < 0.50) = .1915$.
   c. $P(Z > 0) = .5000$.   d. Probability of any point is 0.

7.15   Using Appendix C-2:
   a. $P(Z < 2.15) - P(Z < -1.22) = .9842 - .1112 = .8730$
   b. $P(Z < 2.00) - P(Z < -3.00) = .9772 - .00135 = .97585$
   c. $P(Z < 2.00) = .9772$
   d. Probability of any point is 0.

7.17   Using Appendix C-2:
   a. $P(Z < -1.28) = .1003$.   b. $P(Z > 1.28) = .1003$.
   c. $P(Z < 1.96) - P(Z < -1.96) = .975 - .025 = .95$.
   d. $P(Z < 1.65) - P(Z < -1.65) = .9505 - .0485 = .902$.

7.19   Using Appendix C-2:
   a. $z = -1.555$ (the area .06 is halfway between .0606 and .0594).
   b. $z = .25$ (the closest area to .6 is .5987).
   c. $z = -1.48$ (closest area is .0694).

7.21   Using Appendix C-2:
   a. $-0.84 < Z < 0.84$ (the closest area is .2995).
   b. $z = 2.05$ (closest area is .9798).
   c. $-1.96 < Z < 1.96$.

7.23   a. $P(X < 300) = P(Z < 0.71) = .7611$
   b. $P(X > 250) = 1 - P(Z < -2.86) = .9979$
   c. $P(275 < X < 310) = P(Z < 1.43) - P(Z < -1.07) = .9236 - .1423 = .7813$

7.25 $P(X \geq 24) = P(Z \geq 1.92) = 1 - .9726 = .0274$.

7.27   a. $Z = 1.282, X = 13.85$.   b. $Z = 0, X = 10.00$.
   c. $Z = 1.645, X = 14.94$.   d. $Z = -0.842, X = 7.47$.
   e. $Z = -1.282, X = 6.15$.
   f. $Z = \pm 0.675, X = 7.98, 12.03$.
   g. $Z = 1.476, X = 14.43$.
   h. $Z = \pm 1.960, X = 4.12, 15.88$.
   i. $Z = -1.476, X = 5.572$.

7.29   a. $Z = (8.0 - 6.9)/1.2 = 0.92$, so $P(Z < 0.92) = .8212$ (82 percentile).
   b. $Z = 1.282, X = 8.44$ lbs
   c. $Z = \pm 1.960, X = 4.55$ lbs to 9.25 lbs

7.31 $P(X \leq X_L) = .25$ and $P(X \geq X_U) = .25$. Solve for X_L and X_U using $z = \pm 0.67$. $X_L = 18$ and $X_U = 21$. The middle 50% of occupied beds falls between 18 and 21.

7.33   Using Appendix C-2: Use $z = 0.52$ (closest area is .6985). Solve the following for σ:
   $0.52 = (\$171 - \$157)/\sigma, \sigma = \$26.92$.

7.35   a. NORMDIST(110,100,15,TRUE) $-$ NORMDIST(80,100,15,TRUE) $= .6563$
   b. NORMDIST(2,0,1,TRUE) $-$ NORMDIST(1.5,0,1,TRUE) $= .0441$
   c. NORMDIST(7000,6000,1000,TRUE) $-$ NORMDIST(4500,6000,1000,TRUE) $= .7745$
   d. NORMDIST(450,600,100,TRUE) $-$ NORMDIST(225,600,100,TRUE) $= .0667$

7.37   a. $1 -$ NORMDIST(60,40,28,TRUE) $= 0.2375$
   b. NORMDIST(20,40,28,TRUE) $= 0.2375$
   c. $1 -$ NORMDIST(10,40,28,TRUE) $= 0.8580$

7.39   Normality OK because $n\pi = (1000)(.07) = 70 \geq 10$, $n(1 - \pi) = (1000)(.93) = 930 \geq 10$. Set $\mu = n\pi = 70$ and $\sigma = \sqrt{n\pi(1 - \pi)} = 8.0684571$.
   a. $P(X < 50) = P(Z < -2.54) = .0055$ (using $X = 49.5$)
   b. $P(X > 100) = P(Z > 3.78) = 1 - P(Z \leq 3.78) = 1 - .99992 = .00008$ (using $X = 100.5$)

7.41   Normality OK. Set $\mu = 180, \sigma = 4.242641$.
   a. $P(X \geq 175) = P(Z \geq -1.30) = 1 - P(Z \leq 1.30) = 1 - .0968 = .9032$ (using $X = 174.5$)
   b. $P(X < 190) = P(Z \leq 2.24) = .9875$ (using $X = 189.5$)

7.43   Set $\mu = \lambda = 28$ and $\sigma = \sqrt{28} = 5.2915$.
   a. $P(X > 35) = 1 - P(Z \leq 1.42) = 1 - .9222 = .0788$ (using $X = 35.5$)
   b. $P(X < 25) = P(Z \leq -0.66) = .2546$ (using $X = 24.5$)
   c. $\lambda = 28 \geq 10$, so OK to use normal.
   d. .0823 and .2599. Yes, it is good.

7.45   a. $P(X > 7) = e^{-\lambda x} = e^{-(0.3)(7)} = e^{-2.1} = .1225$
   b. $P(X < 2) = 1 - e^{-\lambda x} = 1 - e^{-(0.3)(2)} = 1 - e^{-0.6} = 1 - .5488 = .4512$

7.47 $\lambda = 2.1$ alarms/minute or $\lambda = .035$ alarms/second
   a. $P(X < 60 \text{ seconds}) = 1 - e^{-\lambda x} = 1 - e^{(-0.035)(60)} = 1 - .1225 = .8775$
   b. $P(X > 30 \text{ seconds}) = e^{-\lambda x} = e^{(-0.035)(30)} = .3499$
   c. $P(X > 45 \text{ seconds}) = e^{-\lambda x} = e^{(-0.035)(45)} = .2070$

7.49   a. $P(X > 30 \text{ sec}) = .2466$.   b. $P(X \leq 15 \text{ sec}) = .5034$.
   c. $P(X > 1 \text{ min}) = .0608$.

7.51 $\lambda = 4.2$ orders/hour or $\lambda = .07$ orders/minute.
   a. Set $e^{-\lambda x} = .50$, take logs, $x = 0.165035$ hr (9.9 min).
   b. Set $e^{-\lambda x} = .25$, take logs, $x = 0.33007$ hr (19.8 min).
   c. Set $e^{-\lambda x} = .10$, take logs, $x = 0.548235$ hr (32.89 min).

7.53   MTBE $= 20$ min/order so $\lambda = 1/$MTBE $= 1/20$ orders/min.
   a. Set $e^{-\lambda x} = .50$, take logs, $x = 13.86$ min.
   b. Distribution is very right-skewed.
   c. Set $e^{-\lambda x} = .25$, take logs, $x = 27.7$ min.

7.55   a. $\mu = (0 + 25 + 75)/3 = 33.3333$
   b.
   $$\sigma = \sqrt{\dfrac{0^2 + 75^2 + 25^2 - (0)(75) - (0)(25) - (75)(25)}{18}} = 15.5902$$
   c. $P(X < 25) = (25 - 0)^2/((75 - 0)*(25 - 0)) = .3333$

d. Shaded area represents the probability.

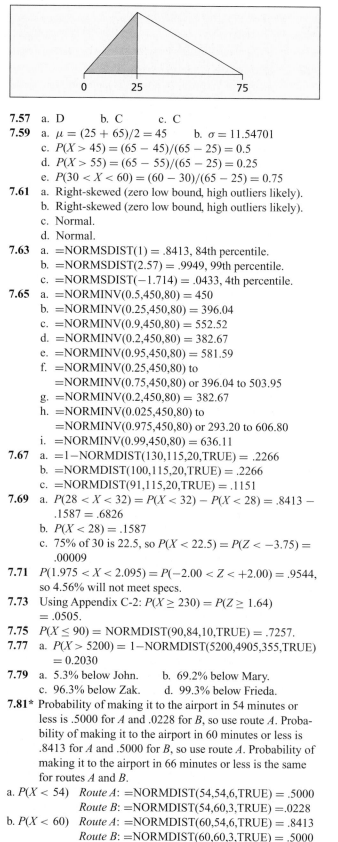

7.57 a. D b. C c. C

7.59 a. $\mu = (25 + 65)/2 = 45$ b. $\sigma = 11.54701$
 c. $P(X > 45) = (65 - 45)/(65 - 25) = 0.5$
 d. $P(X > 55) = (65 - 55)/(65 - 25) = 0.25$
 e. $P(30 < X < 60) = (60 - 30)/(65 - 25) = 0.75$

7.61 a. Right-skewed (zero low bound, high outliers likely).
 b. Right-skewed (zero low bound, high outliers likely).
 c. Normal.
 d. Normal.

7.63 a. =NORMSDIST(1) = .8413, 84th percentile.
 b. =NORMSDIST(2.57) = .9949, 99th percentile.
 c. =NORMSDIST(−1.714) = .0433, 4th percentile.

7.65 a. =NORMINV(0.5,450,80) = 450
 b. =NORMINV(0.25,450,80) = 396.04
 c. =NORMINV(0.9,450,80) = 552.52
 d. =NORMINV(0.2,450,80) = 382.67
 e. =NORMINV(0.95,450,80) = 581.59
 f. =NORMINV(0.25,450,80) to
  =NORMINV(0.75,450,80) or 396.04 to 503.95
 g. =NORMINV(0.2,450,80) = 382.67
 h. =NORMINV(0.025,450,80) to
  =NORMINV(0.975,450,80) or 293.20 to 606.80
 i. =NORMINV(0.99,450,80) = 636.11

7.67 a. =1−NORMDIST(130,115,20,TRUE) = .2266
 b. =NORMDIST(100,115,20,TRUE) = .2266
 c. =NORMDIST(91,115,20,TRUE) = .1151

7.69 a. $P(28 < X < 32) = P(X < 32) - P(X < 28) = .8413 - .1587 = .6826$
 b. $P(X < 28) = .1587$
 c. 75% of 30 is 22.5, so $P(X < 22.5) = P(Z < -3.75) = .00009$

7.71 $P(1.975 < X < 2.095) = P(-2.00 < Z < +2.00) = .9544$, so 4.56% will not meet specs.

7.73 Using Appendix C-2: $P(X \geq 230) = P(Z \geq 1.64) = .0505$.

7.75 $P(X \leq 90) = $ NORMDIST(90,84,10,TRUE) = .7257.

7.77 a. $P(X > 5200) = 1-$NORMDIST(5200,4905,355,TRUE) $= 0.2030$

7.79 a. 5.3% below John. b. 69.2% below Mary.
 c. 96.3% below Zak. d. 99.3% below Frieda.

7.81* Probability of making it to the airport in 54 minutes or less is .5000 for A and .0228 for B, so use route A. Probability of making it to the airport in 60 minutes or less is .8413 for A and .5000 for B, so use route A. Probability of making it to the airport in 66 minutes or less is the same for routes A and B.

a. $P(X < 54)$ *Route A*: =NORMDIST(54,54,6,TRUE) = .5000
     Route B: =NORMDIST(54,60,3,TRUE) =.0228
b. $P(X < 60)$ *Route A*: =NORMDIST(60,54,6,TRUE) = .8413
     Route B: =NORMDIST(60,60,3,TRUE) = .5000
c. $P(X < 66)$ *Route A*: =NORMDIST(66,54,6,TRUE) = .9772
     Route B: =NORMDIST(66,60,3,TRUE) = .9772

7.83 =NORMINV(.20) = −0.842, so $x = \mu + z\sigma = 12.5 + (-0.842)(1.2) = 11.49$ inches

7.85 For any normal distribution, $P(X > \mu) = .5$ or $P(X < \mu) = .5$. Assuming independent events:
 a. Probability that both exceed the mean is $(.5)(.5) = .25$
 b. Probability that both are less than the mean is $(.5)(.5) = .25$
 c. Probability that one is above and one is less than the mean is $(.5)(.5) = .25$ but there are two combinations that yield this, so the likelihood is: $.25 + .25 = .50$.
 d. $P(X = \mu) = 0$ for any continuous random variable.

7.87 Normality OK because $n\pi \geq 10$ and $n(1 - \pi) \geq 10$. Set $\mu = n\pi = (.25)(100) = 25$ and $\sigma = $ SQRT(.25*100* $(1 - .25)) = 4.3301$. Then $P(X < 19.5) =$NORMDIST$(19.5,25,4.3301,1) = .1020$.

7.89 Set $\mu = n\pi = (.25)(100) = 25$ and $\sigma = $ SQRT(.25*100* $(1 - .25)) = 4.3301$.
 a. $z = $ NORMSINV(.95) $= 1.645$ so $x = \mu + z\sigma = 25 + 1.645(4.3301) = 32.12$
 b. $z = $ NORMSINV(.99) $= 2.326$ so $x = \mu + z\sigma = 25 + 2.326(4.3301) = 35.07$
 c. Q1 = NORMINV(0.25,25,4.3301) = 22.08
  Q2 = NORMINV(0.5, 25,4.3301) = 25.00
  Q3 = NORMINV(0.75, 25,4.3301) = 27.92

7.91 Set $\mu = n\pi = (.02)(1500) = 30$ and $\sigma = $ SQRT(.02* $1500*(1 - .02)) = 5.4222$. Then
 a. $P(X > 24.5) = 1 - P(X < 24.5) = 1-$NORMDIST(24.5,30,5.4222,1) = .8448
 b. $P(X > 40.5) = 1 - P(X < 40.5) = 1-$NORMDIST(40.5, 30,5.4222,1) = .0264

7.93 a. $P(X > 100,000$ hrs.) $= .2397$.
 b. $P(X \leq 50,000$ hrs.) $= .5105$.
 c. $P(50,000 \leq X \leq 80,000) = .6811 - .5105 = .1706$.

7.95 a. $P(X \leq 3$ min) $= .6321$.
 b. The distribution is skewed right so the mean is greater than the median.

7.97* a. $\mu = (300 + 350 + 490)/3 = 380$
 b.
$$\sigma = \sqrt{\frac{300^2 + 350^2 + 490^2 - (300)(350) - (300)(490) - (350)(490)}{18}}$$
$$= 40.21$$
 c. $P(X > 400) = (490 - 400)^2/((490 - 300)(490 - 350)) = .3045$

7.99* a. $\mu = (500 + 700 + 2100)/3 = 1100$
 b.
$$\sigma = \sqrt{\frac{500^2 + 700^2 + 2100^2 - (500)(700) - (500)(2100) - (700)(2100)}{18}}$$
$$= 355.90$$
 c. $P(X > 750) = (2100 - 750)^2/((2100 - 500)(2100 - 700)) = .8136$
 d. Shaded area represents the probability.

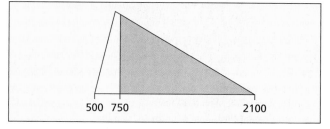

CHAPTER 8

8.1   a. 16   b. 8   c. 4

8.3   a. (4.0252, 4.0448).

b. (4.0330, 4.0370).

c. Both are outside expected range.

8.5   a. $\sigma_{\bar{X}} = \sigma/\sqrt{n} = 0.25/\sqrt{10} = 0.0791$.

b. (3.345, 3.655).

8.7   a. (11.06, 16.94)   b. (33.68, 40.33)

c. (115.12, 126.88)

8.9   a. (254.32, 285.68).   b. (258.91, 281.09).

c. (262.16, 277.84).   d. Width decreases as n increases.

8.11 (20.225, 21.775).

8.15 a. 2.262, 2.2622

b. 2.602, 2.6025

c. 1.678, 1.6779

8.17 a. $d.f. = 9$, $t = 2.262$, (255.6939, 284.3061).

b. $d.f. = 19$, $t = 2.093$, (260.6398, 279.3602).

c. $d.f. = 39$, $t = 2.023$, (263.6027, 276.3973).

8.19 a. (33.01, 58.31)

b. Increase n or decrease 95%.

8.21 a. (742.20, 882.80)

8.23 a. (81.87, 88.13) for Exam 1, (82.79, 94.41) for Exam 2, (73.34, 78.66) for Exam 3.

b. Exams 1 and 2 overlap.   c. Unknown σ.

8.25 a. Yes   b. Yes   c. No, $.08 \times 100 = 8 < 10$.

8.27 a. .062   b. .0877   c. .1216

8.29 a. (.2556, .4752)   b. Yes, normal.

8.31 a. (.013, .083)   b. Yes, normal.

8.33 a. (.1416, .3290)   b. Yes, normal.

8.35 25

8.37 43, $\sigma = R/6 = 16.67$

8.39 385

8.41 a. $\sigma = R/6 = (21 - 16)/6 = 0.833$ b. 31

8.43 a. 1692   b. Stratify (e.g., income)

8.45 a. 2401   b. Stratify (e.g., age)

8.47 a. 125   b. Conduct inspection of a sample of 125. AA fleet size is much larger.

8.49 (1.01338, 1.94627)

8.51 (5.88, 10.91)

8.53 a. Uneven wear.   b. (0.8332, 0.8355)

c. Normality.   d. 95

8.55 a. (29.443, 39.634)   b. Varying methods

c. Raisin clumps

8.57 a. (19.245, 20.69)   b. Small n.

8.59 a. (33.013, 58.315)   b. 119   c.* (21. 26, 40.14)

8.61 a. (29.078, 29.982)   b. 116

8.63 (4.38, 6.30), $\chi^2_L = 17.71$, $\chi^2_U = 42.56$

8.65 a. (48.515, 56.965)   b. Outliers   c. 75

8.67 a. (.125, .255)   b. Yes   c. 463

8.69 136

8.71 a. (.258, .322)   b. Yes

8.73 (.595, .733)

8.75 a. margin of error $= .035$ for 95% CI

b. Greater

8.77 a. (.393, .527)   b. Yes

8.79 a. No   b. (.0044, .0405)

8.81 a. (.914, 1.006)   b. Use binomial.

c. (.863, .995) from MINITAB

8.83 .04 for 95% CI.

8.85 a. 385

b. n would increase to 1537

CHAPTER 9

9.1   a. 50   b. 10   c. 1

9.3   a. H_0: Employee not using drugs.

H_1: Employee is using drugs.

b. Type I error: Test positive for drugs when not using.

Type II error: Test negative for drugs when using.

c. Employees fear Type I, while employers fear both for legal reasons.

9.5 H_0: $\mu = 2.5$ mg vs. H_1: $\mu \neq 2.5$ mg.

9.7 H_0: $\mu \leq 4$ min vs. H_1: $\mu > 4$ min.

9.9   a. Reject in lower tail.   b. Reject in both tails.

c. Reject in upper tail.

9.11 a. $z_{calc} = 2.98$.   b. $z_{calc} = -1.58$.

c. $z_{calc} = 2.22$.

9.13 a. H_0: $\mu \leq 3.5$ mg vs. H_1: $\mu > 3.5$ mg.

b. $z_{calc} = 2.50$.

c. Yes, $z_{crit} = 2.33$ and $2.50 > 2.33$.

d. p-value $= .0062$.

9.15 a. $z = 1.50$, p-value $= .1336$.

b. $z = -2.0$, p-value $= .0228$.

c. $z = 3.75$, p-value $= .0001$.

9.17 p-value $= .0062$. The mean weight is heavier than it should be.

9.19 a. Reject H_0 if $z > 1.96$ or $z < -1.96$.

b. $z = 0.78$. Fail to reject H_0.

9.21 $z = 3.26$, p-value $= .0006$.

9.23 a. Using $d.f. = 20$, $t_{.05} = 1.725$.

b. Using $d.f. = 8$, $t_{.01} = 2.896$.

c. Using $d.f. = 27$, $t_{.05} = -1.703$.

9.25 a. p-value $= .0836$.   b. p-value $= .0316$.

c. p-value $= .0391$.

9.27 a. $t = 1.5$, p-value $= .1544$.

b. $t = -2.0$, p-value $= .0285$.

c. $t = 3.75$, p-value $= .0003$.

9.29 H_0: $\mu \geq 400$ H_1: $\mu < 400$. Reject H_0 if p-value is less than .10. The p-value $= 0.0525$, therefore reject H_0. Decision is close at $\alpha = 0.05$, could be important to a large contractor.

9.31 a. H_0: $\mu \geq \$216$ vs. H_1: $\mu < \$216$. Reject H_0 if $t_{calc} < -1.729$. $t_{calc} = -2.408$ so reject H_0.

b. p-value $= .0132$.

9.33 H_0: $\mu \leq 1.6$ vs. H_1: $\mu > 1.6$, $t_{calc} = 1.14$, p-value $= .1306$. Fail to reject H_0.

9.35 a. p-value $= .1079$. Fail to reject H_0.

b. (3.226, 3.474) includes 3.25

9.37 a. $z = 2.0$, p-value $= .046$.

b. $z = 1.90$, p-value $= .029$.

c. $z = 1.14$, p-value $= .127$.

9.39 a. No.   b. No.   c. Yes.

9.41 a. H_0: $\pi = .997$ versus H_1: $\pi < .997$. Reject H_0 if the p-value is less than 0.05.

b. Yes.

c. Type I error: Throw away a good syringe.

Type II error: Keep a bad syringe.

d. p-value $= .1401$ ($z = -1.08$)

e. Type II increases.

9.43 a. H_0: $\pi \geq .50$ versus H_1: $\pi < 0.50$. If the p-value is less than .05, reject H_0.

b. p-value $= .0228$.

c. Yes, cost could be high if call volume is large.

9.45 p-value ≈ 0. More than half support the ban.

9.47 a. p-value $= .143$. Standard is being met.

b. Less than five defects observed, cannot assume normality.

9.49 a. .4622

b. .7974

c. .9459

9.51 a. .0924

b. .3721

c. .7497

9.53 No, p-value $= .2233$

9.55 p-value $= .0465$. Reject H_0.

9.57 p-value $= .6202$. Fail to reject H_0.

9.59 a. P(Type I error) $= 0$.

b. You increase the P(Type II error).

9.61 a. H_0: User is authorized.

H_1: User is unauthorized.

b. Type I error: Scanner fails to admit an authorized user.

Type II error: Scanner admits an unauthorized user.

c. Type II is feared by the public.

9.63 H_0: $\pi \leq .02$ vs. H_1: $\pi > .02$.

9.65 P(Type I error) $= 0$.

9.67 a. Type I: deny access to authorized user, Type II: allow access to an unauthorized user.

b. The consequences of a false rejection are less serious than a false authorization.

9.69 a. H_0: $\mu \leq 20$ min vs. H_1: $\mu > 20$ min.   b. $t_{calc} = 2.545$.

c. Yes. Using $d.f. = 14$, $t_{.05} = 1.761$, $2.545 < 1.761$.

d. p-value $= .0117 < .05$. Yes.

9.71 a. A two-tailed test.

b. Overfill is unnecessary while underfill is illegal.

c. Normal (known σ).

d. Reject if $z > 2.576$ or if $z < -2.576$.

9.73 a. H_0: $\mu \geq 90$

H_1: $\mu < 90$

b. Student's t.

c. $t = -0.92$. Fail to reject H_0.

d. At least a symmetric population.

e. p-value $= .1936$.

9.75 a. H_0: $\mu \geq 2.268$

H_1: $\mu < 2.268$

If the p-value is less than .05 reject H_0.

p-value $= .0478$. Reject H_0.

b. Usage wears them down.

9.77 p-value $= .0228$. Reject H_0.

9.79 p-value $= .0258$. Fail to reject (close decision) H_0.

9.81 p-value $= .1327$. Fail to reject H_0.

9.83 p-value $= .0193$. Reject H_0. Important to players and universities.

9.85 Yes, $t_{calc} = -3.35$, p-value $= .0004$.

9.87 a. Yes, $z = 1.95$, p-value $= .0253$.   b. Yes.

9.91 p-value $= .0794$. Fail to reject H_0.

9.93 H_0: $\pi = .50$ vs. H_1: $\pi > .50$. P$(X \geq 10 \mid n = 16, \pi = .5) = .2272$. Fail to reject H_0.

9.95 a. $(0, .0125)$ b. $np < 10$.

c. Goal is being achieved.

9.97 $\beta = 1 - $ power. The power values are:

$n = 4$: .2085, .5087, .8038, .9543

$n = 16$: .5087, .9543, .9996, 1.0000

9.99 a. H_0: $\mu \leq 106$ vs. H_1: $\mu > 106$. $t_{calc} = 131.04$ so reject the null hypothesis.

b. H_0: $\sigma^2 \geq .0025$ vs. H_1: $\sigma^2 < .0025$. $\chi^2 = 12.77$ therefore we would fail to reject the null hypothesis.

CHAPTER 10

Note: Results from Excel except as noted (may not agree with Appendix C, D, or E due to rounding or use of exact $d.f.$).

10.1 a. H_0: $\mu_1 - \mu_2 \geq 0$ vs. H_1: $\mu_1 - \mu_2 < 0$, $t = -2.148$, $d.f. = 28$, $t_{.025} = -2.048$, p-value $= .0202$, so reject H_0.

b. H_0: $\mu_1 - \mu_2 = 0$ vs. H_1: $\mu_1 - \mu_2 \neq 0$, $t = -1.595$, $d.f. = 39$, $t_{.05} = \pm 2.023$, p-value $= .1188$, so can't reject H_0.

c. H_0: $\mu_1 - \mu_2 \leq 0$ vs. H_1: $\mu_1 - \mu_2 > 0$, $t = 1.935$, $d.f. = 27$, $t_{.05} = 1.703$, p-value $= .0318$, so reject H_0.

10.3 a. H_0: $\mu_1 - \mu_2 = 0$ vs. H_1: $\mu_1 - \mu_2 \neq 0$. Using $d.f. = 190$, $t_{.005} = 2.602$. $t_{calc} = -6.184 < -2.602$. Reject H_0.

b. Using $d.f. = 190$, p-value $= 3.713E-09$.

10.5 a. H_0: $\mu_1 - \mu_2 \leq 0$ vs. H_1: $\mu_1 - \mu_2 > 0$, $t = 1.902$, $d.f. = 29$, $t_{.01} = 2.462$, can't reject H_0.

b. p-value $= .0336$. Would be significant at $\alpha = .05$.

10.7 H_0: $\mu_1 - \mu_2 = 0$ vs. H_1: $\mu_1 - \mu_2 \neq 0$. $t = -3.55$, $d.f. = 11$, p-value $= .0045$. Reject H_0.

10.9 a. $(-1.16302, 0.80302)$

b. $(-1.15081, 0.79081)$

c. Overlap

d. Same means

10.11 H_0: $\mu_d \leq 0$, H_1: $\mu_d > 0$, $t = 1.93$, $d.f. = 6$, and p-value $= .0509$, so can't quite reject H_0 at $\alpha = .05$.

10.13 H_0: $\mu_d \leq 0$, H_1: $\mu_d > 0$, $t = 2.86$, $d.f. = 9$, and p-value $= .0094$, so reject H_0 at $\alpha = .10$.

10.15 H_0: $\mu_d = 0$, H_1: $\mu_d \neq 0$, $t = -1.71$, $d.f. = 7$, and p-value $= .1307$, so can't reject H_0 at $\alpha = .01$.

10.17 a. H_0: $\pi_1 - \pi_2 \geq 0$ vs. H_1: $\pi_1 - \pi_2 < 0$, $\bar{p} = .4200$, $z = -2.431$, $z_{.01} = -2.326$, p-value $= .0075$, so reject at $\alpha = .01$.

b. H_0: $\pi_1 - \pi_2 = 0$ vs. H_1: $\pi_1 - \pi_2 \neq 0$, $\bar{p} = .37500$, $z = 2.263$, $z_{.05} = \pm 1.645$, p-value $= .0237$, reject at $\alpha = .10$.

c. H_0: $\pi_1 - \pi_2 \geq 0$ vs. H_1: $\pi_1 - \pi_2 < 0$, $\bar{p} = .25806$, $z = -1.706$, $z_{.05} = -1.645$, p-value $= .0440$, reject at $\alpha = .05$.

10.19 a. H_0: $\pi_1 - \pi_2 \geq 0$ vs. H_1: $\pi_1 - \pi_2 < 0$, $\bar{p} = .26000$, $z = -2.280$.

b. $z_{.01} = -2.326$, can't reject at $\alpha = .01$ (close decision).

c. p-value $= .0113$

d. Normality OK because $n_1 p_1 = 42$, $n_2 p_2 = 62$, both exceed 10.

10.21 H_0: $\pi_1 - \pi_2 = 0$ vs. H_1: $\pi_1 - \pi_2 \neq 0$, $\bar{p} = .11$, $z = 2.021$, $z_{.025} = \pm 1.960$ ($p = .0432$) so reject at $\alpha = .05$ (close decision).

10.23 a. H_0: $\pi_1 - \pi_2 = 0$ vs. H_1: $\pi_1 - \pi_2 \neq 0$, $p_1 = .07778$, $p_2 = .10448$, $\bar{p} = .08502$, $z = -0.669$, critical value is $z_{.025} = 1.960$, and p-value $= .5036$, so cannot reject at $\alpha = .05$.

b. Normality not OK because $n_1 p_1 = 14$ but $n_2 p_2 = 7$.

10.25 a. H_0: $\pi_1 - \pi_2 \leq .10$, H_1: $\pi_1 - \pi_2 > .10$, $p_1 = .28125$, $p_2 = .14583$, $\bar{p} = .22321$, $z = 0.66$, and critical value is $z_{.05} = 1.645$.

b. p-value $= .2546$, cannot reject at $\alpha = .05$

10.27 $(-.1584, .1184)$

10.29 $(.0063, .1937)$

10.31 a. H_0: $\sigma_1^2 = \sigma_2^2$ versus $\sigma_1^2 \neq \sigma_2^2$. Reject H_0 if $F > 4.76$ or $F < .253$. ($df_1 = 10$, $df_2 = 7$.) $F = 2.54$ so we fail to reject the null hypothesis.

b. H_0: $\sigma_1^2 = \sigma_2^2$ versus $\sigma_1^2 < \sigma_2^2$. Reject H_0 if $F < .264$ ($df_1 = 7$, $df_2 = 7$). $F = .247$ so we reject the null hypothesis.

c. H_0: $\sigma_1^2 = \sigma_2^2$ versus $\sigma_1^2 > \sigma_2^2$. Reject H_0 if $F > 2.80$ ($df_1 = 9$, $df_2 = 12$). $F = 19.95$ so we reject the null hypothesis.

10.33 H_0: $\sigma_1^2 = \sigma_2^2$ versus $\sigma_1^2 < \sigma_2^2$. Reject H_0 if $F < .355$ ($df_1 = 11$, $df_2 = 11$). $F = .103$ so we reject the null hypothesis. The new drill has a reduced variance.

10.35 a. H_0: $\pi_M - \pi_W = 0$ vs. H_1: $\pi_M - \pi_W \neq 0$. Reject the null hypothesis if $z < -1.645$ or $z > 1.645$.

b. $p_M = .60$ and $p_W = .6875$.

c. $z = -.69$, p-value $= .492$. The sample does not show a significant difference in proportions.

d. Normality can be assumed because both $n_1 p_1 \geq 10$ and $n_2 p_2 \geq 10$.

10.37 a. H_0: $\pi_1 - \pi_2 \leq 0$ vs. H_1: $\pi_1 - \pi_2 > 0$.

b. Reject if $z > z_{.05} = 1.645$.

c. $p_1 = .98000$, $p_2 = .93514$, $\bar{p} = .95912$, $z = 4.507$.

d. Reject at $\alpha = .05$.   e. p-value $= .0000$.

f. Normality is OK because $n_1(1 - \pi_1) = 17$ and $n_2(1 - \pi_2) = 48$ both > 10.

10.39 a. H_0: $\pi_1 - \pi_2 = 0$ vs. H_1: $\pi_1 - \pi_2 \neq 0$.

b. $p_1 = .17822$, $p_2 = .14300$, $\bar{p} = .14895$, $z = 1.282$, p-value $= .2000$. Because z is within ± 1.960 for a two-tail test at $\alpha = .05$ and p-value exceeds .05, we fail to reject H_0.

10.41 a. H_0: $\pi_1 - \pi_2 = 0$ vs. H_1: $\pi_1 - \pi_2 \neq 0$, $p_1 = .38492$, $p_2 = .48830$, $\bar{p} = .44444$, $z = -2.506$. Because z does not exceed ± 2.576, we cannot reject H_0.

b. Two-tailed p-value $= .0122$.

c. Normality OK because $n_1 p_1 = 97$, $n_2 p_2 = 167$ both exceed 10.

d. Gender interests may imply different marketing strategies.

10.43 a. H_0: $\pi_1 - \pi_2 \geq 0$ vs. H_1: $\pi_1 - \pi_2 < 0$, $p_1 = .14914$, $p_2 = .57143$, $\bar{p} = .21086$, $z = -8.003$. Because $z < -2.326$, we conclude that pilots are more likely to approve of night-flying without non-instrument rating.

b. Left-tailed p-value $= .0000$.

c. Normality assumption OK because $n_1 p_1 = 61$, $n_2(1 - p_2) = 30$ both exceed 10.

10.45 a. H_0: $\pi_1 - \pi_2 \leq 0$ vs. H_1: $\pi_1 - \pi_2 > 0$, $p_1 = .02950$, $p_2 = .02229$, $\bar{p} = .02589$, $z = 2.932$. Reject H_0 because $z > 2.326$.

b. Right-tailed p-value $= .0017$.

c. Normality OK because $n_1 p_1 = 245$, $n_2 p_2 = 185$ both exceed 10.

d. Not a large difference, but life is important.

e. Were smoking, diet, exercise, etc. considered?

10.47 a. H_0: $\pi_1 - \pi_2 \geq 0$ vs. H_1: $\pi_1 - \pi_2 < 0$. Reject the null hypothesis if $z < -1.645$ or p-value $< .05$. p-value $= .0914$, fail to reject H_0.

b. Yes, normality is met.

10.49 a. H_0: $\mu_1 - \mu_2 \leq 0$ vs. H_1: $\mu_1 - \mu_2 > 0$. Assuming equal variances, $t = 4.089$ with $d.f. = 84$. Because the p-value is .0000, reject H_0 at $\alpha = .01$.

10.51 a. H_0: $\pi_1 - \pi_2 \geq 0$ vs. H_1: $\pi_1 - \pi_2 < 0$, $p_1 = .1402$, $p_2 = .2000$, $\bar{p} = .16396$.

b. $z = -2.777$ and left-tailed p-value $= .0027$. Because $z < -2.326$, reject H_0.

c. Normality OK because $n_1 p_1 = 104$, $n_2 p_2 = 98$ both exceed 10.

d. Many people can't afford them or lack insurance to pay for them.

10.53 a. H_0: $\mu_1 - \mu_2 \leq 0$ vs. H_1: $\mu_1 - \mu_2 > 0$. Assuming unequal variances, $t = 1.718$ with $d.f. = 16$ (using Welch's adjustment). Because the p-value is .0525, we fail to reject H_0 at $\alpha = .05$.

b. If we had looked at the same firm in each year, the test would have more power.

10.55 a. Dot plots suggest that the new bumper has less down-time, but variation is similar.

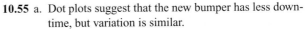

b. H_0: $\mu_1 - \mu_2 \leq 0$ vs. H_1: $\mu_1 - \mu_2 > 0$.

c. Assuming equal variances, reject H_0 if $t < -1.729$ with $d.f. = 19$.

d. $\bar{x}_1 = 5.917$, $s_1 = 3.423$, $\bar{x}_2 = 8.889$, $s_2 = 4.961$, $s_p^2 = 17.148$, $t = 1.63$, p-value $= .0600$, so fail to reject H_0 at $\alpha = .05$.

10.57 a. H_0: $\mu_1 - \mu_2 \leq 0$ vs. H_1: $\mu_1 - \mu_2 > 0$, $t = 7.08$, $d.f. = 28$, p-value ≈ 0. Reject H_0.

b. H_0: $\sigma_1^2 = \sigma_2^2$ versus $\sigma_1^2 \neq \sigma_2^2$. Reject H_0 if $F < .3357$ or $F > 2.9786$ ($df_1 = 14$, $df_2 = 14$). $F = 2.778$ so we fail to reject the null hypothesis.

10.59 a. Dot plots suggest that the means differ and variances differ (outlier in men's salaries).

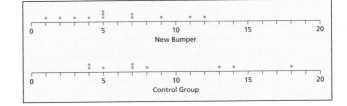

b. H_0: $\mu_1 - \mu_2 \leq 0$ vs. H_1: $\mu_1 - \mu_2 > 0$.

c. Reject H_0 if $t > 2.438$ with $d.f. = 35$.

d. $\bar{x}_1 = 117,853$, $s_1 = 10,115$, $\bar{x}_2 = 98,554$, $s_2 = 14,541$, $s_p^2 = 152,192,286$, $t = 4.742$.

e. Reject H_0 at $\alpha = .01$. Men are paid significantly more.

f. p-value $= .0000$. Unlikely result if H_0 is true.

g. Yes, the large difference suggests gender discrimination.

10.61 a. Dot plots show strong skewness, but means could be similar.

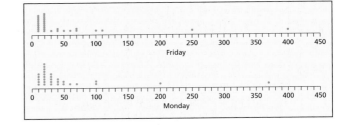

b. $H_0: \mu_1 - \mu_2 = 0$ vs. $H_1: \mu_1 - \mu_2 \neq 0$. Assume equal variances.

c. Reject H_0 if $t > 2.663$ or if $t < -2.663$ with $d.f. = 58$.

d. $\bar{x}_1 = 50.333$, $s_1 = 81.684$, $\bar{x}_2 = 50.000$, $s_2 = 71.631$, $s_p^2 = 5,901.667$. Because $t = .017$ we cannot reject H_0.

e. p-value $= .9866$. Sample result well within chance range.

10.63 a. $H_0: \mu_1 - \mu_2 = 0$ vs. $H_1: \mu_1 - \mu_2 \neq 0$.

b. For equal variances, $d.f. = 55$, reject H_0 if $t < -2.004$.

c. Because $t = -3.162$ ($p = .0025$) we reject H_0 at $\alpha = .05$. Mean sales are lower on the east side.

10.65 $H_0: \sigma_1^2 = \sigma_2^2$, $H_1: \sigma_1^2 \neq \sigma_2^2$, $df_1 = 30$, $df_2 = 29$. For $\alpha/2 = .025$ $F_R = F_{30,29} = 2.09$, and $F_L = 1/F_{29,30} \cong 1/F_{25,30} = 1/2.12 = .47$. Test statistic is $F = (13.482)^2/(15.427)^2 = 0.76$, so we can't reject H_0.

10.67 $H_0: \mu_d = 0$ vs. $H_1: \mu_d \neq 0$. $t = -0.87$. p-value $= .4154$ (from MegaStat). Fail to reject the null hypothesis.

10.69 a. $H_0: \mu_1 - \mu_2 = 0$ vs. $H_1: \mu_1 - \mu_2 \neq 0$, $t = -1.10$, $d.f. = 22$, p-value $= .2839$. Fail to reject H_0.

b. $H_0: \sigma_1^2 = \sigma_2^2$ versus $\sigma_1^2 \neq \sigma_2^2$. Reject H_0 if $F < 0.224$ or $F > 4.46$ ($df_1 = 11$, $df_2 = 11$). $F = 2.59$ so we fail to reject the null hypothesis.

10.71 a. $H_0: \sigma_1^2 \leq \sigma_2^2$, $H_1: \sigma_1^2 > \sigma_2^2$, $df_1 = 11$, $df_2 = 11$. For a right-tail test at $\alpha = .025$, Appendix F gives $F_R = F_{11,11} \cong F_{10,11} = 3.53$. The test statistic is $F = (2.9386)^2/(0.9359)^2 = 9.86$, so conclude that Portfolio A has a greater variance than Portfolio B.

b. These are independent samples. $H_0: \mu_1 - \mu_2 = 0$ vs. $H_1: \mu_1 - \mu_2 \neq 0$. $\bar{x}_1 = 8.5358$, $s_1 = 2.9386$, $\bar{x}_2 = 8.1000$, $s_2 = .9359$, Assuming unequal variances with $d.f. = 13$ (with Welch's adjustment) we get $t = 0.49$ with p-value $= .6326$, so we cannot reject H_0 at $\alpha = .025$.

10.73 $(-.0153, .2553)$. Yes, the interval includes zero.

10.75 a. $(-2.51, 0.11)$. b. No.

10.77 a. $(-.4431, -.0569)$.   b. Normality is not met.

10.79 a. $(-28.119, -15.686)$.

b. Yes there is a difference. The interval does not include zero.

CHAPTER 11

11.1 a. $H_0: \mu_A = \mu_B = \mu_C$, H_1: Not all means are equal.

b. One-factor, $F = 5.31$, p-value $= .0223$.

c. Reject H_0 at $\alpha = .05$.

d. Plant B mean likely higher, Plant C lower.

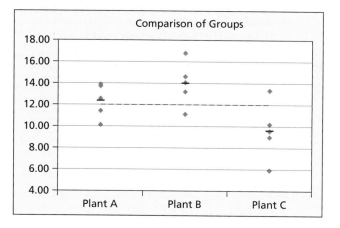

11.3 a. $H_0: \mu_1 = \mu_2 = \mu_3 = \mu_4$, H_1: Not all equal.

b. One-factor $F = 3.52$, p-value $= .0304$.

c. Reject H_0 at $\alpha = .05$. GPAs not the same.

d. Marketing and HR likely higher, accounting and finance lower.

11.5 Only Plant B and Plant C differ at $\alpha = .05$ ($t = 3.23$) using MegaStat Tukey test.

11.7 Only marketing and accounting differ at $\alpha = .05$ (Tukey $t = 3.00$).

11.9 $H_{calc} = 7.027/2.475 = 2.839$. Critical value from Table 11.5 $= 15.5$ ($df_1 = c = 3$, $df_2 = n/c - 1 = 4$). Fail to reject equal variances.

11.11 $H_{calc} = 8.097$. Critical value from Table 11.5 $= 10.4$ ($df_1 = c = 4$, $df_2 = n/c - 1 = 6$). Fail to reject null.

11.13 a. H_0: Mean absenteeism same in all four plants, H_1: Mean absenteeism not the same in all four plants.

b. ANOVA table: Two factor without replication.

c. Plant means differ, $F = 41.19$ ($p = .0002$). Blocking factor $F = 8.62$ ($p = .0172$) also significant.

d. Plant 1, 2 below overall mean, Plant 3, 4 above.

ANOVA table: Two factor without replication

Source	SS	df	MS	F	p-value
Treatments (plant)	216.25	3	72.083	41.19	.0002
Blocks (date)	30.17	2	15.083	8.62	.0172
Error	10.50	6	1.750		
Total	256.92	11			

Mean	n	Std. Dev	Factor Level
20.333	3	1.528	Plant 1
18.000	3	2.000	Plant 2
29.000	3	2.646	Plant 3
25.000	3	2.646	Plant 4
21.500	4	4.041	04-Mar-05
25.250	4	5.377	11-Mar-05
22.50	4	5.508	18-Mar-05

11.15 a. H_0: Mean scores same for all five professors, H_1: Mean scores are not the same.

c. For "professor effect" ambiguous, $F = 3.26$ ($p = .0500$), blocking factor not significant.

d. Clagmire above overall mean; Ennuyeux slightly below; plots suggest no strong differences.

11.17 a. *Rows:* H_0: Year means the same, H_1: Year means differ. *Columns:* H_0: portfolio type means the same, H_1: portfolio type means differ. *Interaction*(Year × Type): H_0: no interaction, H_1 There is an interaction effect.

b. ANOVA table: Two factor with replication (5 observations per cell).

c. Year ($F = 66.82$, $p < .0001$) is highly significant. Portfolio ($F = 5.48$, $p = .0026$) differ significantly, and significant interaction ($F = 4.96$, $p = .0005$).

d. p-values are very small, indicating significant effects at $\alpha = .05$. Year is strongest result.

e. Interacton plot lines do cross and support the interaction found and reported above.

ANOVA table: Two factor with replication (5 observations per cell)

Source	SS	df	MS	F	p-value
Factor 1 (portfolio)	1,191.584	2	595.7922	66.82	<.0001
Factor 2 (year)	146.553	3	48.8511	5.48	.0026
Interaction	265.192	6	44.1986	4.96	.0005
Error	427.980	48	8.9162		
Total	2,031.309	59			

11.19 a. *Rows: H_0*: Age group means same, H_1: Age group means differ

Columns: H_0: Region means same, H_1: Region means differ

Interaction (Age $\times$ Region): H_0: no interaction, H_1: interaction

b. ANOVA table: Two factor with replication (5 observations per cell).

c. Age group means ($F = 36.96$, $p < .0001$) differ dramatically. Region means ($F = 0.5$, $p = .6493$) don't differ significantly. Significant interaction ($F = 3.66$, $p = .0010$).

d. Age group p-value indicates very strong result, interaction is significant at $\alpha = .05$.

e. Interaction plot lines do cross and support the interaction found and reported above.

11.21 a. $H_0: \mu_1 = \mu_2 = \mu_3 = \mu_4$, H_1: Not all the means are equal.

b. Graph shows mean Freshmen GPA is lower than overall mean.

c. $F = 2.36$ ($p = .1000$), fail to reject H_0 at $\alpha = .05$, No significant difference among GPAs.

d. Reject H_0 if $F > F_{3,21} = 3.07$.

e. Differences in mean grades large enough (.4 to .7) to matter, but not significant, so cannot be considered important.

f. Large variances within groups and small samples rob the test of power, suggests larger sample within each group.

g. Tukey confirms no significant difference in any pairs of means.

h. $H_{calc} = (0.6265)^2/(0.2826)^2 = 4.91$ which is less than Hartley's critical value 13.7 with $df_1 = c = 4$ and $df_2 = n/c - 1 = 5$, so conclude equal variances.

11.23 a. $H_0: \mu_1 = \mu_2 = \mu_3$, H_1: Not all means are equal.

b. Graph suggests Type B a bit lower, C higher than the overall mean.

c. $F = 9.44$ ($p = .0022$) so there is a significant difference in mean cell outputs.

d. Reject H_0 if $F > F_{2,15} = 3.68$.

e. Small differences in means, but could be important in a large solar cell array.

f. Sounds like a controlled experiment and variances are small, so a small sample suffices.

g. Tukey test shows that C differs from B at $\alpha = .01$ and from A at $\alpha = .05$.

h. $H_{calc} = (4.57)^2/(4.00)^2 = 1.31$, less than Hartley's 10.8 with $df_1 = c = 3$ and $df_2 = n/c - 1 = 5$, conclude equal variances.

11.25 a. $H_0: \mu_1 = \mu_2 = \mu_3 = \mu_4$, H_1: Not all means equal.

b. Graph shows B higher, D lower.

c. $F = 1.79$ ($p = .1857$) so at $\alpha = .05$ no significant difference in mean waiting times.

d. Reject H_0 if $F > F_{3,18} = 3.16$.

e. Differences in means might matter to patient, but not significant so can't be considered important.

f. Variances large, samples small, so test has low power.

g. Tukey test shows no significant differences in pairs of means.

h. $H_{calc} = (11.90)^2/(6.74)^2 = 3.121 = .142$, less than the Hartley's 20.6 with $df_1 = c = 4$ and $df_2 = n/c - 1 = 4$ so conclude equal variances.

11.27 a. *Columns: H_0*: Surface has no effect on mean braking distance, H_1: Surface does effect distance

Rows: H_0: Pumping method has no effect on mean braking distance, H_1: Pumping method does effect distance

b. Graph suggests differences (ice is greater than the other two).

c. Surface: $F = 134.39$ ($p = .0002$), reject H_0. Surface has a significant effect on mean stopping distance. Braking method: $F = 0.72$ ($p = .5387$), cannot reject H_0. Braking method has no significant effect on stopping distance.

d. Reject H_0 if $F > F_{2,4} = 6.94$.

e. For surface, differences large enough to be very importance in preventing accidents.

f. Replication would be desirable, if tests are not too costly.

g. Tukey test shows a difference between ice and the other two surfaces.

11.29 a. $H_0: \mu_1 = \mu_2 = \mu_3 = \mu_4 = \mu_5$; H_1: Not all means equal.

b. Graph suggests that Chalmers is higher and Ulysses is lower.

c. $F_{calc} = 6.19$ ($p = .0019$) so reject H_0. There are significant differences in means.

d. Reject H_0 if $F_{calc} > F_{4,21} = 2.84$ at $\alpha = .05$.

e. Significant and probably important to clients.

f. Sample may be limited by number of clinics in each town.

g. Chalmers differs from all except Villa Nueve, while other means do not differ significantly.

h. $H_{calc} = (11.171)^2/(6.850)^2 = 2.659$ does not exceed Hartley's $H_{crit} = 25.2$ with $df_1 = c = 5$ and $df_2 = n/c - 1 = 26/5 - 1 = 4$ so conclude equal variances.

11.31 a. $H_0: \mu_1 = \mu_2 = \mu_3 = \mu_4 = \mu_5$, H_1: Not all means equal.

b. Graph shows no differences in means.

c. $F = 0.39$ ($p = .8166$), cannot reject H_0. No significant difference in the mean dropout rates.

d. Reject H_0 if $F > F_{4,45} = 2.61$.

e. Differences not significant, not important.

f. Could look at a different year. But sample is already fairly large.

g. Tukey shows no significant differences in pairs.

h. $H_{calc} = (10.585)^2/(3.759)^2 = 7.93$, exceeds Hartley's 7.11 with $df_1 = c = 5$ and $df_2 = n/c - 1 = 9$ so conclude unequal variances.

11.33 In this replicated two-factor ANOVA, the response (days until expiration) is significantly related to *Brand* (row factor, $F_{calc} = 3.39$, $p = .0284$) and strongly related to *Store* (column factor, $F_{calc} = 7.36$, $p = .0021$). Freshness is important to customers. Sample sizes could be increased because bag inspection is not difficult.

11.35 In this two-factor ANOVA without replication (randomized block), the response (trucks produced per shift) is weakly related to *Plant* (row factor, $F_{\text{calc}} = 2.72$, $p = .0912$) and strongly related to *Day* (column factor, $F_{\text{calc}} = 9.18$, $p = .0012$). Productivity is important to car companies. Sample sizes could be increased because daily production is routinely recorded for each shift.

11.37 a. Two Factor ANOVA
b. Instructor gender *p*-value ($p = .43$) exceeds $\alpha = .10$, instructor gender means do not differ. Student gender *p*-value ($p = .24$) exceeds $\alpha = .10$, student gender means do not differ (*p*-value $> \alpha = .10$). For interaction, the *p*-value ($p = .03$) suggests significant interaction effect (at $\alpha = .05$).
c. Unlikely that a gender effect was overlooked due to sample size, test should have very good power.

11.39 a. $F_{\text{calc}} = (1069.17)/(12270.28) = 0.0871$
b. *p*-value $= .9666$
c. $F_{3,36} = 2.87$
d. No significant difference in means.

11.41 a. Two-factor ANOVA without replication (randomized block).
b. 4 rows, 4 columns, 1 observation per cell.
c. At $\alpha = .05$, plant location is not significant ($p = .1200$) while noise level is quite significant ($p = .0093$).

11.43 a. Two factor, either factor could be of research interest.
b. Pollution affected freeway ($F = 24.90$, $p = .0000$) and by time of day ($F = 21.51$, $p = .0000$).
c. Variances for freeway 2926.7 to 14333.7, for time of day 872.9 to 14333.6. Ratios are large (4.90 and 16.42), suggesting possibly unequal variances.
d. For freeway, $df_1 = c = 4$ and $df_2 = n/c - 1 = 20/4 - 1 = 4$, Hartley's critical value 20.6, so conclude equal variances. Time of day, $df_1 = c = 5$ and $df_2 = n/c - 1 = 20/5 - 1 = 3$, so Hartley's critical value is 50.7 so conclude equal variances.

11.45 a. One factor.
b. Between Groups $df_1 = 4$ and $df_1 = c - 1$ so $c = 5$ bowlers.
c. *p*-value 0.000, reject null, conclude at least two samples are significantly different.
d. Sample variances 83.66 to 200.797, $F_{\text{max}} = 200.797/83.66 = 2.40$. Hartley's test, $df_1 = c = 5$ and $df_2 = n/c - 1 = 67/5 - 1 = 12$, critical value is 5.30. Not enough variation to reject null hypothesis of homogeneity.

CHAPTER 12

12.1 For each sample: H_0: $\rho = 0$ vs. H_1: $\rho \neq 0$

Sample	df	r	t	t_α	Decision
a	18	.45	2.138	2.101	Reject
b	28	−.35	−1.977	1.701	Reject
c	5	.6	1.677	2.015	Fail to reject
d	59	−.3	−2.416	2.39	Reject

12.3 b. −.7328   c. $t_{.025} = 3.182$
d. $t = -1.865$, Fail to reject.   e. *p*-value $= .159$

12.5 b. .531   c. 2.131   d. 2.429   e. Yes, reject.

12.7 a. Each additional *Sq Ft* increases price $150.
b. $425,000.   c. No, *SquareFeet* cannot be zero.

12.9 a. For each additional year in median age there is an average of 35.3 fewer cars stolen per 100,000 people.
b. 255 cars per 100,000 people.
c. No, median age cannot be zero.

12.11 a. Earning an extra $1,000 raises home price by $2610.
b. No.   c. $181,800, $312,300.

12.13 a. Blazer: Each year reduces price by $1050. Silverado: each year reduces price by $1339.
b. Intercept could indicate price of new car.
c. $10,939.
d. $15,896.

12.15 a. $\hat{y} = 14.42$, $e = 3.58$, underestimate.
b. $\hat{y} = 13.3$, $e = -7.3$, overestimate.

12.17 b. *Wait Time* $= 458 - 18.5$ *Operators*.
d. $R^2 = .5369$.

12.19 $\hat{y} = 0.458x + 1.155$, $R^2 = .2823$.

12.21 b. H_0: $\beta_1 = 0$ vs. H_0: $\beta_1 \neq 0$.   c. *p*-value $= .0269$, (1.3192, 10.8522).   d. Slope is significantly different from zero because the *p*-value is less than .05.

12.23 a. $\hat{y} = 557.45 + 3.00x$ b. (1.2034, 4.806)
c. H_0: $\beta_1 \geq 0$ vs. H_1: $\beta_1 < 0$, *p*-value $= .0019$, Reject H_0.

12.25 a. $\hat{y} = 1.8064 + .0039x$
b. intercept: $1.8064/.6116 = 2.954$, slope: $.0039/.0014 = 2.786$ (may be off due to rounding).
c. *d.f.* $= 10$, $t_{.025} = \pm 2.228$.

12.27 a. $\hat{y} = 6.9609 - 0.053x$
b. (−0.1946, 0.0886). Interval does contain zero, slope is not significantly different from zero.
c. *t* test *p*-value $= .4133$. Conclusion: slope is not significantly different from zero.
d. *F* statistic *p*-value $= .4133$. Conclusion: No significant relationship between variables.
e. $0.74 = (-0.863)^2$

12.29 a. $\hat{y} = -31.1895 + 4.9322x$.   b. (2.502, 7.362). Interval does not contain zero, the slope is greater than zero.   c. *t* test *p*-value is 0.0011. Conclusion: the slope is positive.   d. *F* statistic *p*-value $= .0011$. Conclusion: significant relationship between variables.
e. $(4.523)^2 = 20.46$.

12.31 b. 95% confidence interval: (0.3671, 1.1477), 95% prediction interval: (−0.4662, 1.9810).
c. 95% confidence interval for μ_Y: (−0.205, 1.4603).
d. The second interval is much wider.

12.49 $t_{\text{critical}} = 2.3069$ (from Excel). From sample: $t = 2.3256$. Reject H_0.

12.51 a. 1515.2.
b. No.
c. (1406.03, 1624.37).

12.53 a. $y = 1743.57 - 1.2163x$.   b. *d.f.* $= 13$. $t_{\text{critical}} = 2.160$.
c. Slope is significantly different from zero.
d. (−2.1671, −0.2656). Interval indicates slope is significantly less than zero.
e. $7.64 = (-2.764)^2$

12.55 a. $r = .6771$
b. From sample: $t = 5.8193$. For a two-tailed test, $t_{.005} = 2.704$. Reject H_0.

12.57 b. $r = .749$
c. *d.f.* $= 13$. For a two-tailed test, $t_{.025} = 2.160$, $t_{\text{calc}} = 4.076$. Reject H_0.

12.61 b. $y = -4.2896 + 0.171x$, $R^2 = .2474$. Fit is poor.

12.63 a. No significant relationship between variables.
(p-value $= .774$).
  b. No, study time and class level could be predictors.
  (Answers will vary.)

12.65 a. The negative slope means that as age increases, price decreases.
  b. Intercepts could be asking price of a new car.
  c. The fit is good for the Explorer, Pickup, and Taurus.
  d. Additional predictors: condition of car, mileage.

CHAPTER 13

13.1 a. $Net\ Revenue = 4.31 - 0.082ShipCost + 2.265\ PrintAds + 2.498WebAds + 16.7Rebate\%$
  b. Positive coefficients indicate an increase in net revenue; negative coefficients indicate a decrease in net revenue.
  c. The intercept is meaningless.
  d. $467,111.

13.3 a. $Ovalue = 2.8931 + 0.1542LiftWait + 0.2495AmountGroomed + 0.0539SkiPatrolVisibility - 0.1196FriendlinessHosts$.
  b. Overall satisfaction increases with an increase in satisfaction for each coefficient except for friendliness of hosts. This counterintuitive result could be due to an interaction effect.
  c. No.
  d. 4.5831.

13.5 a. $df_1 = 4$ (numerator) and $df_2 = 45$ (denominator).
  b. $F_{.05} = 2.61$. Using $df_1 = 4$ and $df_2 = 40$.
  c. $F = 12.997$. Yes, overall regression is significant.
  d. $R^2 = .536$. $R^2_{adj} = .495$.

13.7 a. $df_1 = 4$, $df_2 = 497$.
  b. Using App F, $df_1 = 4$ and $df_2 = 200$, $F_{.05} = 2.42$.
  c. $F_{calc} = 12.923$. Yes, overall regression is significant.
  d. $R^2 = .0942$, $R^2_{adj} = .0869$.

13.9 a. and c. See Table.

Predictor	Coef	std error coef	t-value	p-value
Intercept	4.31	70.82	0.0608585	0.9517414
ShipCost	−0.082	4.678	−0.0175289	0.9860922
PrintAds	2.265	1.05	2.1571429	0.0363725
WebAds	2.498	0.8457	2.9537661	0.0049772
Rebate%	16.697	3.57	4.6770308	.0003

  b. $t_{critical} = 2.69$. WebAds and Rebate% differ significantly from zero.

13.11 a. and c.

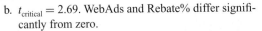

Predictor	Coef	std error coef	t-value	p-value
Intercept	2.8931	0.3680	7.8617	2.37E-14
LiftWait	0.1542	0.0440	3.5045	.0005
AmountGroomed	0.2495	0.0529	4.7164	3.07E-06
SkiPatrolVisibility	0.0539	0.0443	1.2167	.2245
FriendlinessHosts	−0.1196	0.0623	−1.9197	.0557

  b. $t_{.005} = 2.586$. LiftWait and AmountGroomed differ significantly from zero.

13.13 $\hat{y}_i \pm 2.032(3620)$: $\hat{y}_i \pm 7355.84$.
  Quick Rule $\hat{y}_i \pm 2s$: $\hat{y}_i \pm 7240$.

13.15 a. Number of nights needed and number of bedrooms.
  b. Two: $SwimPool = 1$ if there is a swimming pool and $ParkGarage = 1$ if there is a parking garage.

  c. $CondoPrice = \beta_0 + \beta_1\ NumNights + \beta_2\ NumBedrooms + \beta_3\ SwimPool + \beta_4\ ParkGarage$.

13.17 a. $ln(Price) = 5.4841 - 0.0733SalePrice + 1.1196Sub\text{-}Zero + 0.0696Capacity + 0.04662DoorFzBot - 0.34322DoorFzTop - 0.70961DoorFz - 0.88201DoorNoFz$.
  b. $SalePrice$: p-value $= .0019$, $Sub\text{-}Zero$: p-value $= 2.24E\text{-}14$, $Capacity$: p-value $= 2.71E\text{-}31$, $2DoorFzBot$: p-value $= .5650$, $2DoorFzTop$: p-value $= 3.68E\text{-}19$, $1DoorFz$: p-value $= 1.19E\text{-}07$, $1DoorNoFz$: p-value $= 8.59E\text{-}09$.
  c. 0.3432.
  d. Side Freezer.

13.19 a. $LiftOps$ and $Scanners$ ($r = .635$), $Crowds$ and $LiftWait$ ($r = .577$), $AmountGroomed$ and $TrailGr$ ($r = .531$), $SkiSafe$ and $SkiPatrolVisibility$ ($r = .488$)
  b. All VIFs are less than 2. No cause for concern.

13.39 There are no quantitative predictor variables and the sample size is too small relative to number of predictors.

13.41 Overall regression not significant (F statistic p-value $= .371$), $R^2 = 0.117$ indicates poor fit. Conclusion: No apparent relationship between cost per load and predictors type of washer and type of detergent used.

13.43 a. Coefficients make sense, except for TrnOvr, which would be expected to be negative.
  b. No.
  c. With 6 predictors, should have minimum of 30 observations. We have only 23 so sample is small.
  d. Rebounds and points highly correlated.

13.45 a. Experience lowers the predicted finish time.
  b. No.
  c. If the relationship is not strictly linear, it can make sense to include a squared predictor, such as seen here.

13.47 The first three predictors ($Income$, $Unem$, $Pupil/Tea$) are significant at $\alpha = .05$, but adding the fourth predictor ($Divorce$) yields a weak p-value (.1987) and R^2 and R^2_{adj} barely improve when $Divorce$ is added.

CHAPTER 14

14.1 a.

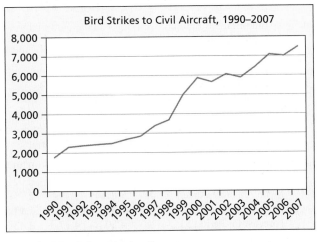

  b. More planes in the air.
  c. Linear: $y_t = 1008.5 + 361.51t$ ($R^2 = .9503$); quadratic: $y_t = 1277.8 + 280.73t + 4.2515t^2$ ($R^2 = .9531$); exponential: $y_t = 1724.4e^{.0886t}$ ($R^2 = .9489$).

d. Linear is simplest, exponential increases too rapidly.

e. Linear: 7877, 8239, 8600; quadratic: 8146, 8593, 9048; exponential: 9284, 10,144, 11,084.

14.3 a. Declining but leveling off (erratic pattern).

b. Erosion of unskilled jobs, globalization, tougher bargaining.

c. Linear: $y_t = 340.4 - 29.018t$ ($R^2 = .4061$); quadratic: $y_t = 426.65 - 72.143t + 3.9205t^2$ ($R^2 = .4535$); exponential: $y_t = 304.1e^{-0.1426\,t}$ ($R^2 = .3160$).

d. Linear predicts negative strikes (impossible). Quadratic has best fit but predicts a rise. Exponential has worse fit but gives believable predictions.

e. Either exponential or quadratic give defensible forecasts.

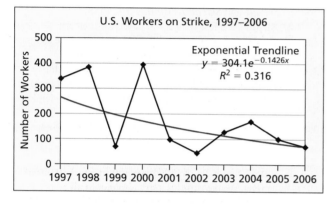

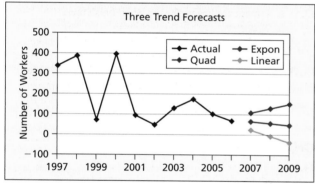

14.5 a. Linear ($R^2 = .8667$).

b. More healthy diet choices.

c. $y_t = 596.79 + 19.95t$.

d. Increased capacity needed for production and distribution.

e. Using $t = 7$, $y_7 = 596.79 + 19.95(7) = 736$.

14.7 Graph shows negative trend and cyclical pattern. Fit improves as α increases (i.e., as we give more weight to recent data). Forecasts are similar for each value of α.

Alpha	.10	.20	0.30
Mean Squared Error	0.039	0.028	0.021
Mean Absolute Percent Error	3.8%	3.1%	2.7%
Percent Positive Errors	42.3%	46.2%	51.9%
Forecast for Period 53	4.30	4.37	4.43

14.9 a. Seasonality exists, but not much trend. Spike in October, 2001 (perhaps a 9-11 reaction).

b. Fit is not very good ($R^2 = .282$, $R^2_{adj} = .036$), and only April ($t = 2.296$, $p = .0278$) shows significant season-

ality at $\alpha = .05$. Reasonable, because spring might cause a spike in Corvette sales.

c. Forecasts for 2004:

Period	Forecast	Period	Forecast
January	1,781.46	July	1,916.21
February	2,427.21	August	2,442.21
March	2,532.96	September	2,563.96
April	3,313.96	October	2,866.71
May	2,540.46	November	2,036.21
June	2,284.71	December	1,941.46

14.11 a. Dual scale graph is needed due to differing magnitudes.

b. Electronic sales are large, but have a declining trend ($y_t = 31,578 - 1615.7t$, $R^2 = .9449$). Mechanical sales are small, but with a rising trend ($y_t = 2467 + 40.543t$, $R^2 = .7456$).

c. Electronic sales are falling at 6.27% ($y_t = 32091e^{-0.0627t}$, $R^2 = .9413$) while mechanical are rising at 1.54% ($y_t = 2470.6e^{0.0154t}$, $R^2 = .7465$).

d. Fascination with electronic gadgets may be waning and/or competitors may be moving in on the Swiss watch industry. They may have stronger specialty niche.

e. Linear forecast for electronic is 20,268, mechanical is 2,750.

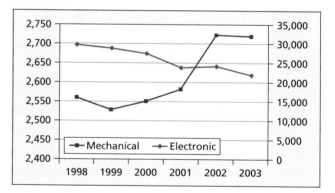

14.13 a. High 1960 (Kennedy v. Nixon), low 1996 (Clinton v. Dole).

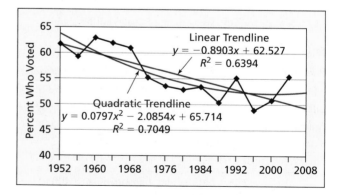

b. Downward trend but issues may energize voters (e.g., Iraq war in 2004).

c. Linear: $y_t = 62.527 - 0.8903t$ ($R^2 = .6394$); quadratic: $y_t = 65.714 - 2.0854t + 0.0797t^2$ ($R^2 = .7049$); exponential: $y_t = 62.687e^{-0.0158t}$ ($R^2 = .6342$).

d. Last four elections suggest a judgment forecast in the range 50–55.

e. Answers may vary. Linear is $y_t = 62.527 - 0.8903(15) = 49.2$.

14.15 a. Total credit is growing linearly.

b. Trend is consistently upward.

c. *Total*: $y_t = 1630.9 + 113.26t$ ($R^2 = .9950$); *Revolving*: $y_t = 658.13 + 28.486t$ ($R^2 = .9966$); *Nonrevolving*: $y_t = 972.33 + 84.857t$ ($R^2 = .9940$).

d. Using linear model with $t = 7$, *Total*: $y_7 = 2424$; *Revolving*: $y_7 = 858$; *Nonrevolving*: $y_7 = 1566$.

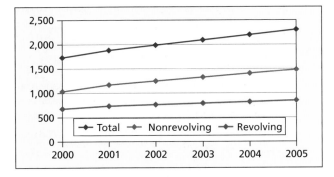

14.17 a. Graphs will vary.

b. Whole milk down, low-fat milk up. Both diet and regular carbonated drinks up. Fruit juices up slightly, beer and wine level or down slightly. Hard liquor is down sharply.

c–d. Answers will vary, but defend using specific criteria (past fit, recent fit, believability, Occam's Razor).

e. Answers will vary.

14.19 a.

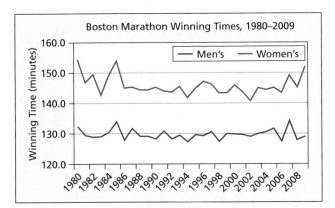

b. It is unlikely.

d. Yes, a moving average would make sense. There is not much of a decreasing trend.

14.21 a. Spike in 2001 (due to 2001 terror attacks), otherwise no clear trend.

b. No trend ($R^2 = .00003$)

c. Fitted trend would not help.

d. Use average = 136.

14.23 a.

b. Yes, a linear trend would work.

c. Using the linear trend: $y_{07-08} = 56.933$ million.

14.25 a. Steady upward trend.

b. Growing population, bigger cars, rising world demand.

c. Linear: $y_t = 39.667 + 441.59t$ ($R^2 = .9188$); Exponential $y_t = 667.17e^{0.2067t}$ ($R^2 = 0.9108$)

d. Forecast for 2010: Linear: $y_{11} = 4897$, exponential $y_{11} = 6482$. Believable, given continued role of oil in the U.S. economy.

e. Consumers, producers, government, refiners (i.e., all of us).

14.27 a. Rate declines, then increases.

b. The following graph shows $\alpha = .20$. Other graphs similar.

c. For this data $\alpha = .20$ seems to track the recent data well, yet provides enough smoothing to iron out the "blips." It gives enough weight to recent data to bring its forecasts above 1.80 (lagging but reflecting the recent rise in rates). In contrast, $\alpha = .05$ or $\alpha = .10$ provide too much smoothing, so they give a forecast below 1.80. While $\alpha = .50$ gives a good "fit" it does not smooth the data very much.

d. Smoothing methods are useful since there is no single, consistent trend.

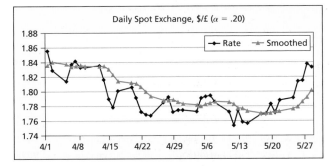

14.29 a. Upward trend with seasonal pattern.

b. Yes (make a bar chart to see this clearly).

c. MegaStat's indexes are adjusted so they sum to 12.000. The average monthly index is 1.000.

Month	Index	Month	Index
Jan	0.7976	Jul	1.3630
Feb	0.7943	Aug	1.2422
Mar	0.9843	Sep	0.9347
Apr	0.8057	Oct	0.9246
May	1.0755	Nov	0.9305
Jun	1.2470	Dec	0.9006

d. Highest: summer (June, July, August); Lowest: winter (January, February).

e. MegaStat trend after deseasonalizing: $y_t = 21469 + 382.11t$ ($R^2 = .6200$).

14.31 a. Trend is upward (weakened in 2003 but stronger in 2004) with seasonal fluctuations.

b. The average month's index is 1.000. Indexes are adjusted so they sum to 12.000.

Month	Index	Month	Index
Jan	1.0235	Jul	0.9767
Feb	1.0064	Aug	0.9857
Mar	0.9861	Sep	0.9771
Apr	0.9916	Oct	0.9761
May	0.9977	Nov	1.0320
Jun	0.9852	Dec	1.0617

c. Highest: December, November, January. Lowest: October, September, July.

d. Yes, this is logical. Credit increases due to the Christmas buying season, drops off during the month of July (vacation) and September and October, kids back to school, waiting for Christmas spending season. Equation is $y = 1.4874x + 210.72$. $R^2 = 0.8344$

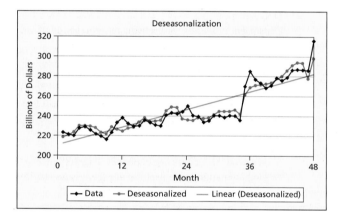

14.33 a. Upward trend with slight seasonal pattern.

b. Yes (make a bar chart to see this clearly).

c. MegaStat's indexes are adjusted to they sum to 12.000. The average monthly index is 1.000.

Month	Index	Month	Index
Jan	0.9971	Jul	0.9993
Feb	0.9889	Aug	0.9970
Mar	1.0055	Sep	0.9978
Apr	1.0058	Oct	0.9925
May	0.9988	Nov	0.9961
Jun	1.0029	Dec	1.0183

d. Highest: December; Lowest: February.

e. MegaStat trend after deseasonalizing: $y_t = 1078.9 + 4.2079t$ ($R^2 = .9317$).

14.35 a. Positive time trend is significant. Using January as a base month (omitted) the seasonal binary t-values show that summer months (Jun, Jul, Aug) are significantly higher and winter months (Nov, Dec) are significantly lower. The fitted regression is *Permits* = 4491 + 7.89 *Time* − 219 *Feb* + 95 *Mar* − 210 *Apr* + 206 *May* +

969 *Jun* + 1256 *Jul* + 1823 *Aug* + 514 *Sep* + 126 *Oct* − 793 *Nov* − 1832 *Dec.*

Variable	Coef	Std Err	t	p
Intercept	4490.9	221.5	20.27	0.000
Time	7.886	2.859	2.76	0.008
Feb	−219.1	287.1	−0.76	0.448
Mar	95.4	287.1	0.33	0.741
Apr	−210.0	287.2	−0.73	0.468
May	206.1	287.3	0.72	0.476
Jun	969.2	287.4	3.37	0.001
Jul	1255.7	287.6	4.37	0.000
Aug	1822.6	287.8	6.33	0.000
Sep	514.4	288.0	1.79	0.079
Oct	126.0	288.2	0.44	0.664
Nov	−793.2	288.5	−2.75	0.008
Dec	−1832.4	288.8	−6.35	0.000

$S = 497.229$ R-Sq = 80.6%   R-Sq(adj) = 76.7%

b. Forecasts for 2006 are obtained from the fitted regression using *Time* = 73, 74, . . . , 84 and the binary predictors from the spreadsheet. MegaStat gives these predictions:

Month	Forecast	Month	Forecast
Jan	5,067	Jul	6,370
Feb	4,855	Aug	6,944
Mar	5,178	Sep	5,644
Apr	4,880	Oct	5,264
May	5,304	Nov	4,352
Jun	6,075	Dec	3,321

14.37* To convert a fitted models of the form $y_t = y_0(1 + r)^t$ to Excel's equivalent exponential form $y_t = a\,e^{bt}$, we use the same intercept but set $b = \ln(1 + r)$. This converts the model to a continuously compounded rate of growth (if $b > 0$) or decline (if $b < 0$).

a. $y_t = 123(1.089)^t$ so we set $b = \ln(1.089) = .08525$ and thus $y_t = 123e^{.08525t}$.

b. $y_t = 654(1.217)^t$ so we set $b = \ln(1.217) = .19639$ and thus $y_t = 654e^{.19639t}$.

c. $y_t = 308(0.942)^t$ so we set $b = \ln(.942) = -.05975$ and thus $y_t = 308e^{-.05975t}$.

CHAPTER 15

15.1 a. H_0: *Earnings* are independent of *Approach*

b. Degrees of Freedom = $(r − 1)(c − 1) = (4 − 1)(3 − 1) = 6$

c. CHIINV(.01,6) = 16.81

d. Test statistic is 127.57 (p-value = .0000) so reject null at $\alpha = .01$.

e. *No Clear Effect* and *Business Combinations* contributes the most.

f. All expected frequencies exceed 5.

g. p-value is near zero (observed difference not due to chance).

15.3 a. H_0: *Verbal* and *Quantitative* are independent

b. Degrees of Freedom = $(r − 1)(c − 1) = (3 − 1)(3 − 1) = 4$

c. CHIINV(.005,4) = 14.86

d. Test statistic is 55.88 (p-value = .0000), reject null at $\alpha = .005$.

e. *Under 25* and *Under 25* contributes the most.

f. Expected frequency is less than 5 in two cells.

g. *p*-value is nearly zero (observed difference not due to chance).

15.5 a. H_0: *Return Rate* and *Notification* are independent

b. Degrees of Freedom $= (r - 1)(c - 1) = (2 - 1)(2 - 1) = 1$

c. CHIINV(.025,1) = 5.024

d. Test statistic is 5.42 (*p*-value = .0199), reject null at $\alpha = .025$.

e. *Returned* and *No* contribute the most.

f. All expected frequencies exceed 5.

g. *p*-value is less than .025 (observed difference did not arise by chance).

h. $z = 2.33$ (*p*-value = .0199 for two-tailed test).

15.7 a. Bars are similar in length. Vanilla and Mocha are the leading flavors.

b. If uniform, $e_j = 84/4 = 21$ for each flavor.

c. Test statistic is 0.86 with $d.f. = 4 - 1 = 3$ (*p*-value = .8358). Chi-square critical value for $\alpha = .05$ is 7.815, so sample does not contradict the hypothesis that sales are the same for each beverage.

15.9 Expected frequency is $56/7 = 8$ for each age group. Test statistic is 10.000 (*p*-value = .1247). At $\alpha = .05$, critical value for $d.f. = 7 - 1 = 6$ is 12.59. Cannot reject the hypothesis that movie goers are from a uniform population.

Age Class	Obs	Exp	O−E	$(O−E)^2/E$
10 < 20	5	8.000	−3.000	1.125
20 < 30	6	8.000	−2.000	0.500
30 < 40	10	8.000	2.000	0.500
40 < 50	3	8.000	−5.000	3.125
50 < 60	14	8.000	6.000	4.500
60 < 70	9	8.000	1.000	0.125
70 < 80	9	8.000	1.000	0.125
Total	56	56.000	0.000	10.000

15.11 Sample mean $\lambda = 4.948717949$, test statistic 3.483 (*p*-value = .4805) with $d.f. = 6 - 1 - 1 = 4$. The critical value for $\alpha = .05$ is 9.488, cannot reject the hypothesis of a Poisson distribution.

X	P(X)	Obs	Exp	O−E	$(O−E)^2/E$
2 or Less	0.12904	3	5.032	−2.032	0.821
3	0.14326	5	5.587	−0.587	0.062
4	0.17724	9	6.912	2.088	0.631
5	0.17542	10	6.841	3.159	1.458
6	0.14468	5	5.643	−0.643	0.073
7 or More	0.23036	7	8.984	−1.984	0.438
	1.00000	39	39.000	0.000	3.483

15.13 From sample, $\bar{x} = 75.375$, $s = 8.943376$. Set $e_j = 40/8 = 5$. Test statistic is 6.000 (*p*-value = .306) using $d.f. = 8 - 2 - 1 = 5$. Critical value for $\alpha = .05$ is 11.07, cannot reject the hypothesis of a normal distribution.

Score	Obs	Exp	Obs−Exp	Chi-Square
Under 65.09	5	5.000	0.000	0.000
65.09 < 69.34	3	5.000	−2.000	0.800
69.34 < 72.53	5	5.000	0.000	0.000
72.53 < 75.38	3	5.000	−2.000	0.800
75.38 < 78.22	9	5.000	4.000	3.200
78.22 < 81.41	7	5.000	2.000	0.800
81.41 < 85.66	4	5.000	−1.000	0.200
85.66 or more	4	5.000	−1.000	0.200
Total	40	40.000	0.000	6.000

15.15* The probability plot looks linear, but *p*-value (.033) for the Anderson-Darling test is less than $\alpha = .05$. This tends to contradict the chi-square test used in Exercise 15.13. However, the Kolmogorov-Smirnov test ($D_{Max} = .158$) = does not reject normality (*p*-value > .20). Data are a borderline case, having some characteristics of a normal distribution. If we have to choose one test, the A-D is the most powerful.

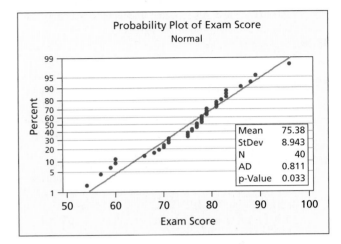

Probability Plot of Exam Score
Normal

Mean	75.38
StDev	8.943
N	40
AD	0.811
p-Value	0.033

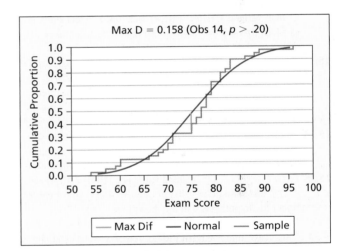

Max D = 0.158 (Obs 14, *p* > .20)

— Max Dif — Normal — Sample

15.17 Is *Satisfaction* independent of *Pay Category*? For $d.f. = (r - 1)(c - 1) = (3 - 1)(2 - 1) = 2$, critical value is CHIINV(.05,2) = 5.991. Test statistic is 4.54 (*p*-value = .1032), cannot reject the null at $\alpha = .05$. *Salaried* and *Dissatisfied* contributes the most. All expected frequencies exceed 5. The *p*-value suggests that observed difference would arise by chance 103 times in 1,000 samples if the two variables really were independent, which is not very convincing.

15.19 Is *Grade* independent of *Hand-In Order*? For $d.f. = (r - 1)(c - 1) = (2 - 1)(2 - 1) = 1$, critical value CHIINV(.10,1) = 2.706. Test statistic is 0.23 (*p*-value = .6284) so cannot reject the null at $\alpha = .10$. *"B" or Better* and *Later Hand-In* contributes the most. All expected frequencies exceed 5. For a two-tailed test of proportions, $p_1 = .4000$, $p_2 = .3333$, $\bar{p} = .3673$, $z = 0.48$ (*p*-value = .6284) which agrees with the chi-square test.

15.21 a. Is *Reading* independent of *Language*? For $d.f. = (r - 1)(c - 1) = (3 - 1)(4 - 1) = 6$ the critical value is CHIINV (.10,6) = 10.64. Test statistic is 4.14 (*p*-value = .6577) so we cannot reject the null at

$\alpha = .10$. Four cells (each corner) have expected frequencies below 5.

15.23 Is *Smoking* independent of *Race?* For $d.f. = (r-1)(c-1) = (2-1)(2-1) = 1$, critical value is CHIINV(.005,1) = 7.879. For males, test statistic is 5.84 (p-value = .0157), can't reject the null at $\alpha = .005$. For females, test statistic is 14.79 (p-value = .0001) so reject the null at $\alpha = .005$. *Black* and *Smoker* contributes the most in each test. All expected frequencies exceed 5. The two-tailed test of proportions agrees.

15.25 For $d.f. = (r-1)(c-1) = (2-1)(2-1) = 1$, critical value CHIINV(.10,1) = 2.706, test statistic is 1.80 (p-value = .1792) so fail to reject the null at $\alpha = .10$. The lower left cell contributes most. All expected frequencies exceed 5. The two-tailed test of proportions ($z = 1.342$) agrees with the chi-square test. Interestingly, the relationship seems to be inverse (i.e., rates tend to rise when they are predicted to fall).

15.27 For the 2×2 table, $d.f. = 1$, critical value is CHIINV(.05,1) = 3.841, test statistic is 7.15 (p-value = .0075) so reject null at $\alpha = .05$. For the 3×3 table, $d.f. = 4$, critical value is CHIINV(.05,4) = 13.28, test statistic is 12.30 (p-value = .0153), so reject null at $\alpha = .05$. All expected frequencies exceed 5.

15.29 With $d.f. = (r-1)(c-1) = (3-1)(3-1) = 4$, the critical value is CHIINV(.01,4) = 2.706. The test statistic is 54.18 (p-value = .0000) so we reject the null at $\alpha = .01$. All expected frequencies exceed 5.

15.31 If uniform, all expected frequencies would be 9. For $d.f. = 4 - 1 = 3$, critical value is CHIINV(.10,3) = 6.251, test statistic is 1.556 (p-value = .6695) so cannot reject the hypothesis of a uniform (it is logical to expect no pattern).

15.33 For $d.f. = 4 - 1 = 3$, critical value is CHIINV(.05,3) = 7.815, test statistic is 6.045 (p-value = .1095) so we cannot reject hypothesis that Oxnard follows U.S. distribution.

15.35 For $d.f. = 6 - 1 = 5$, critical value is CHIINV(.10,5) = 9.236, test statistic is 4.40 (p-value = .4934) so we can't reject the hypothesis that the die is fair.

15.37 Estimated mean is $\lambda = 1.06666667$. For $d.f. = 4 - 1 - 1 = 2$, critical value is CHIINV(.025,2) = 7.378, test statistic is 4.947 (p-value = .0843) so can't reject the hypothesis of a Poisson distribution.

X	f_j	$P(X)$	e_j	$f_j - e_j$	$(f_j - e_j)^2/e_j$
0	25	0.344154	20.64923	4.35077	0.917
1	18	0.367097	22.02584	-4.02584	0.736
2	8	0.195785	11.74712	-3.74712	1.195
3 or more	9	0.092964	5.57781	3.42219	2.100
Total	60	1.000000	60.00000	0.00000	4.947

15.39 Mean is $\lambda = 0.702479339$ runs/inning. For $d.f. = 4 - 1 - 1 = 2$, critical value is CHIINV(.05,2) = 5.991, test statistic is 95.51 (p-value = .0000) so reject hypothesis that runs per inning are Poisson. In hockey, goals are independent events, while in baseball they are not.

15.41* Answers will vary, but most should confirm the normal distribution and intended μ and σ.

15.43* Answers will vary, but most should confirm the Poisson distribution and intended λ.

CHAPTER 16

16.1 $R = 14$, $z = -0.133$ (p-value = .8942). Fail to reject H_0.

16.3 $R = 15$, $z = 0.697$ (p-value = .4858). Results are random.

16.5 a. Sample median = 53.75. $W = 234.5$, $z = 0.7174$, p-value = .48. Median is not significantly different from 50.
b. Close to a normal distribution. Parametric t test could be justified.

16.7 a. $z = 1.319$, p-value = .1872. No difference in medians.
b. $t = 1.62$, p-value = .0606 (assuming equal variances). Same decision but p-value closer to .05.

16.9 a. $H = 5.724$, p-value = .1258. No difference in medians.
b. Yes, $F = 2.71$, p-value = .055.
c. Can assume normality for Energy and Retail. Health and Leisure are less obvious.

16.11 $\chi^2 = 4.950$, p-value = .2925. No difference in median ratings.

16.13 a.

2004	2005	2004	2005
6	7	17	20
5	5	16	16
10	10	4	4
13	14	14	19
15	15	11	13
19	18	1	1
3	3	20	17
7	6	2	2
8	8	18	12
12	11	9	9

b. $r_s = .9338$.   c. Yes, $r_{.01} = .561$.
e. Pearson: $r = .996$.
f. Nonnormal data justifies use of Spearman rank correlation.

16.15 $R = 28$, $z = 0.775$ (p-value = .4383). Results are random.

16.17 $R = 22$, $z = 1.419$ (p-value = .1559). Results are random.

16.19 $R = 9$, $z = -1.647$ (p-value = .0996). Results are random.

16.21 $z = -1.039$, p-value = .2988. No difference in medians.

16.23 From MegaStat Wilcoxon – Signed-Rank Paired Data Test: $z = -1.481$, p-value = .1386. Medians do not differ.

16.25 $z = -3.086$, p-value = .0020. The medians differ.

16.27 $H = 1.46$, p-value = .4819. No difference in medians.

16.29 $H = 9.026$, p-value = .0110. The medians differ.

16.31 $F_{calc} = 2.731$, p-value = .6038. No difference in median waiting times by day of week.

16.33 $r_s = .812$, $r_{.05} = .514$. Significant rank correlation.

16.35 $r_s = .813$, $r_{.05} = .413$. Significant rank correlation.

16.37 $r_s = .812$, $r_{.05} = .444$. Significant rank correlation.

CHAPTER 17

17.1 a. See text, Section 17.1.   b. See text, Section 17.1.
c. See text, Section 17.1.

17.3 Zero variation is not achievable.

17.5 Answers will vary. Use Likert scales for service attributes.
a. Cleanliness of vehicle, full gas tank, waiting time for sales help.
b. Length of queues, friendliness of staff (Likert), interest paid on accounts.
c. Price, seat comfort, picture quality (Likert scale for all).

17.7 Deming felt most workers want to do a good job, but are often hampered by the work environment, management policies, and fear of reprisal.

17.9 See text, Section 17.4.

17.11 See text, Section 17.4.

17.13 a. Sampling frequency depends on cost and physical possibility of sampling.

b. For normal data, small samples may suffice for a mean (Central Limit Theorem).

c. Large samples may be needed for a proportion to get sufficient precision.

17.15 Expect 68.26 percent, 95.44 percent, 99.73 percent respectively.

17.17 $\text{UCL} = \bar{\bar{x}} + 3\dfrac{\bar{R}}{d_2\sqrt{n}} = 12.5 + 3\dfrac{.42}{2.326\sqrt{5}} = 12.742$

$\text{LCL} = \bar{\bar{x}} - 3\dfrac{\bar{R}}{d_2\sqrt{n}} = 12.5 - 3\dfrac{.42}{2.326\sqrt{5}} = 12.258$

17.19 Estimated σ is $\bar{R}/d_2 = 30/2.059 = 14.572$, UCL $=$ 98.37, LCL $=$ 54.63

$$\bar{\bar{x}} = \frac{\bar{x}_1 + \bar{x}_2 + \cdots + \bar{x}_9}{9}$$

$$= \frac{72.25 + 74.25 + \cdots + 82.25}{9} = 76.5$$

$$\bar{R} = \frac{R_1 + R_2 + \cdots + R_9}{9}$$

$$= \frac{43 + 31 + \cdots + 41}{9} = 30$$

17.21 $\bar{R} = .82$ (centerline)

$\text{UCL} = D_4\bar{R} = (2.004)(.82) = 1.64328$

$\text{LCL} = D_3\bar{R} = (0)(.82) = 0$

17.23 By either criterion, process is within acceptable standard ($C_p = 1.67$, $C_{pk} = 1.67$).

17.25 Fails both criteria, especially C_{pk} due to bad centering ($C_p = 1.17$, $C_{pk} = 0.67$).

17.27 Yes, safe to assume normality. UCL $= .8354$, LCL $= .1646$.

17.29 Services are often assessed using percent conforming or acceptable quality, so we use p charts.

17.31 Answers will vary. Examples:

a. GPA, number of classes retaken, faculty recommendation letters (Likert).

b. Knowledge of material, enthusiasm, organization, fairness (Likert scales for all).

c. Number of bounced checks, size of monthly bank balance errors, unpaid Visa balance.

d. Number of print errors, clarity of graphs, useful case studies (Likert scales for last two).

17.33 Answers will vary. Examples:

a. MPG, repair cost.

b. Frequency of jams, ink cost.

c. Frequency of re-flushes, water consumption.

d. Battery life, ease of use (Likert scale).

e. Cost, useful life, image sharpness (Likert scale).

f. Cost, useful life, watts per lumen.

17.35 $\bar{x}$ is normally distributed from the Central Limit Theorem for sufficiently large values of n (i.e., symmetric distribution) while the range and standard deviation are not.

17.37 a. Variation and chance defects are inevitable in all human endeavors.

b. Some processes have very *few* defects (maybe zero in short run, but not in long run).

c. Quarterbacks cannot complete all their passes, etc.

17.39 Answers will vary (e.g., forgot to set clock, clock set incorrectly, couldn't find backpack, stopped to charge cell phone, had to shovel snow, clock didn't go off, traffic, car won't start, can't find parking).

17.41 Answers will vary (e.g., weather, union slowdown, pilot arrived late, crew change required, deicing planes, traffic congestion at takeoff, no arrival gate available).

17.43 a. $C_p = 1.33$, $C_{pk} = 1.33$ b. $C_p = 1.33$, $C_{pk} = 0.67$

c. Example shows why we need more than just the C_p index. A change in the process mean can reduce the C_{pk} index, even though the C_p index is unaffected.

17.45 a. UCL $= 6223$, LCL $= 5877$.

b. Chart violates no rules. c. Process is in control.

17.47 a. UCL $= 1.0939$, LCL $= 0.9061$

b. Chart violates no rules. c. Process is in control.

17.49 a. $C_p = 1.00$, $C_{pk} = 0.83$.

b. Process well below capability standards (both indices less than 1.33).

c. Technology, cost, door not closed tightly, frequency of door opening.

17.51 Sample mean of 23.025 and standard deviation of 2.006 are very close to the process values ($\mu = 23$, $\sigma = 2$). Histogram is symmetric, but perhaps platykurtic (chi-square or Anderson-Darling test needed).

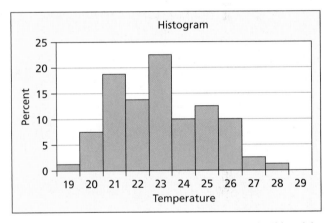

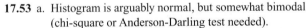

17.53 a. Histogram is arguably normal, but somewhat bimodal (chi-square or Anderson-Darling test needed).

b. $\mu = 8760$, $\sigma = 200$, UCL $= 9028$, LCL $= 8492$

c. $\bar{x} = 8785$, $s = 216.14$, UCL $= 9075$, LCL $= 8495$

d. Sample is small, may have unreliable estimates of μ and σ.

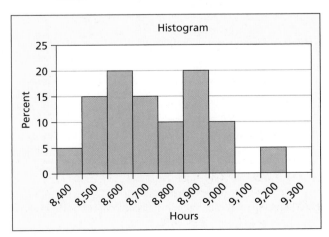

17.55 a. UCL = 470.2, LCL = 459.8.
 b. No rules violated. Process in control.
17.57 a. UCL = 12.22095, LCL = 11.75569, centerline = 11.98832.
 b. Sample 7 hits the LCL.
 c. Histogram approximates normal distribution.
17.59 a. UCL = .1154, LCL = 0.
 b. Sample 7 hits the LCL, otherwise in control.
 c. Samples are too small to assume normality ($n\pi = 5$). (Better to use MINITAB's binomial option.)

17.61 Chart A: Rule 4.
 Chart B: No rules violated.
 Chart C: Rule 4.
 Chart D: Rules 1, 4.
 Chart E: No rules violated.
 Chart F: Rules 1, 2.
17.63 Each pattern is clearly evident, except possibly instability in third series.

APPENDIX H

Answers to Exam Review Questions

CHAPTERS 1–4

1. a. inferential; b. descriptive; c. inferential
2. c. independent judgment is needed
3. b. anecdotal data ($n = 1$)
4. a. numerical; b. categorical; c. numerical
5. a. ratio (true zero); b. ordinal; c. nominal
6. a. continuous; b. continuous; c. discrete
7. a. convenience; b. simple random; c. systematic
8. c. Computer software makes it easy, and inexpensive, to generate random numbers.
9. a. Likert only if distances have meaning
10. a. sampling error cannot be eliminated
11. Skewed right, no outliers, Sturges $k \cong 6$
12. c. range is $-1 \le r \le +1$
13. a. small n and sum to 100%
14. $\bar{x} = 12$, $s = 5.701$, CV $= 47.5\%$
15. $\bar{x} = 59.3$, median $= 58.5$, modes 55, 58, 62 (not unique), mean or median best
16. a. slight positive correlation;
    b. $r = 0.5656$ (not very linear)

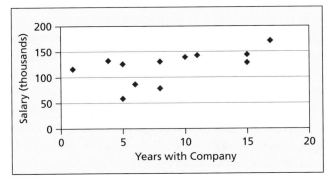

17. b. GEOMEAN(Data) requires all $x_i > 0$
18. a. $z = (x - \mu)/\sigma = (81 - 52)/15 = 1.93$ (not an outlier)
19. b. log scales are less familiar to most

CHAPTERS 5–7

1. a. empirical; b. subjective; c. classical
2. a. $40/200 = .20$; b. $50/90 = .5556$;
   c. $100/200 = .50$
3. no, since $P(A)P(B) = (.30)(.70) = .21 \ne$
   $P(A \cap B) = .25$
4. b. would be true if $P(A \cap B) = 0$

5. c. $U(a, b)$ has two parameters
6. c. $.60(1000) + .30(2000) + .10(5000) = 1700$
7. a. .2565; b. .4562; c. .7576;
   d. Poisson, $\lambda = 2.5$
8. a. .1468; b. .0563; c. .7969;
   d. binomial, $n = 8$, $\pi = .20$
9. a. $\mu = n\pi = (50)(.30) = 15$;
   b. $\sigma = \sqrt{n\pi(1 - \pi)} = \sqrt{(50)(.30)(.70)} = 3.24$
10. a. binomial ($n = 8$ trials, π unknown)
    b. Poisson (arrivals, λ unknown);
    c. discrete uniform ($a = 0$, $b = 9$)
11. c. $X =$ trials until first success in geometric
12. a. points have no area, hence no probability
13. a. Normal PDF is always symmetric about the mean
14. Using Appendix C:
    a. $P(Z > 1.14) = .1271$;
    b. $P(-.71 < Z < +0.71) = .5222$;
    c. $P(Z < 0) = .5000$.
    Using Excel:
    a. .1265; b. .5249; c. .5000
15. Using Table 7.9:
    a. $\mu + 1.645\sigma = 70 + 1.645(7) = 81.52$;
    b. $\mu - 1.282\sigma = 70 - 1.282(7) = 61.04$;
    c. $\mu + 0.675\sigma = 70 + 0.675(7) = 74.73$
16. a. gives cumulative left tail area
17. Using $\lambda = 1.2$:
    a. $P(X < 1.5) = 1 - e^{-\lambda x} = 1 - e^{(-1.2)(1.5)} = .8347$;
    b. $P(X > 0.5) = e^{-\lambda x} = e^{(-1.2)(0.5)} = .5488$;
    c. $P(X > 1) - P(X > 2) = e^{(-1.2)(1)} - e^{(-1.2)(2)} = .3012 - .0907 = .2105$ (if X is expressed in minutes)
18. Using $\lambda = 1.2$:
    a. Solve $e^{-\lambda x} = .05$ to get $x = 2.496$ min (149.8 sec);
    b. Solve $e^{-\lambda x} = .75$ to get $x = 0.2397$ min (14.38 sec);
    c. MTBE $= 1/\lambda = (1/1.2) = 0.83$ min (50 sec)
19. a. This is a correct rule of thumb (set $\mu = \lambda$ and $\sigma = \sqrt{\lambda}$)
20. c. Triangular is skewed unless b is halfway between a and c.

CHAPTERS 8–10

1. a. CLT applies to $\bar{X}$. Sample *data* may not be normal.
2. a. consistent; b. efficient;
   c. unbiased
3. b. It is conservative to use t *whenever* σ is unknown, regardless of n.

4. a. d.f. $= n - 1 = 8$, $t_{.025} = 2.306$, so $\bar{x} \pm t \frac{s}{\sqrt{n}}$
  gives $13.14 < \mu < 16.36$;

 b. Unknown σ.

5. a. $n = 200$, $z = 1.96$, $p = 28/200 = .14$,
  so $p \pm z \sqrt{\frac{p(1-p)}{n}}$ gives $.092 < \pi < .188$;

 b. $np = 28 > 10$;

 c. Using $z = 1.645$ and $E = \pm.03$ the formula
  $n = \left(\frac{z}{E}\right)^2 \pi(1 - \pi)$ gives $n = 363$ (using $p = .14$ for π
  from preliminary sample) or $n = 752$ (using $\pi = .50$ if
  we want to be very conservative)

6. c. Normality OK since $np = 17.5 > 10$.

7. b. Type I error is rejecting a true H_0.

8. b. $z_{.025} = \pm 1.960$

9. a. $H_0 : \mu \geq 56$, $H_1 : \mu < 56$;

 b. Using $\bar{x} = 55.82$, $\sigma = 0.75$ (known), and $n = 49$, we get
  $z_{\text{calc}} = \frac{\bar{x} - \mu_0}{\sigma/\sqrt{n}} = -1.636$;

 c. $z_{.05} = -1.645$;

 d. fail to reject (but a very close decision)

10. a. $H_0 : \mu \leq 60$, $H_1 : \mu > 60$;

 b. Using $\bar{x} = 67$, $s = 12$, and $n = 16$, we get $t_{\text{calc}} = \frac{\bar{x} - \mu_0}{s/\sqrt{n}}$
  $= 2.333$;

 c. For d.f. $= n - 1 = 15$, $t_{.025} = 2.131$;   d. reject

11. a. $\alpha = P(\text{reject } H_0 \mid H_0 \text{ is true})$

12. a. $H_0 : \pi \leq .85$, $H_1 : \pi > .85$, $p = 435/500 = .87$,
  $z_{\text{calc}} = \frac{p - \pi_0}{\sqrt{\frac{\pi_0(1-\pi_0)}{n}}} = 1.252$, $z_{.05} = 1.645$, not a
  significant increase;

 b. $n\pi_0 = (500)(.85) = 425 > 10$ and
  $n(1 - \pi_0) = (500)(.15) = 75 > 10$

13. a. independent samples, unknown variances, $t_{\text{calc}} = -2.034$
  (regardless whether equal or unequal variances assumed);

 b. two-tailed test, $t_{.025} = \pm 1.717$ (if equal variances
  assumed, d.f. $= 22$) or $t_{.025} = \pm 1.721$ (if unequal
  variances assumed, d.f. $= 21$);

 c. reject $H_0 : \mu_1 = \mu_2$ in favor of $H_1 : \mu_1 \neq \mu_2$.

14. a. $H_0 : \pi_1 \leq \pi_2$, $H_1 : \pi_1 > \pi_2$, $p_1 = 150/200 = .75$,
  $p_2 = 140/200 = .70$, $\bar{p} = .725$,
  $z_{\text{calc}} = 1.120$, $z_{.025} = 1.96$
  Colorado not significantly greater

15. a. paired t-test;

 b. d.f. $= n - 1 = 5 - 1 = 4$, left-tailed test, $t_{.10} = -1.533$

 c. $t_{\text{calc}} = -1.251$, fail to reject, second exam not significantly greater

16. a. Reject if *small p-value*

17. a. $F_{\text{calc}} = s_1^2/s_2^2 = (14^2)/(7^2) = 4.00$;

 b. $\alpha/2 = .05/2 = .025$, $F_L = 1/(5.12) = 0.195$
  (d.f. $= 6, 7$) and $F_R = 5.70$ (d.f. $= 7, 6$) or folded
  F-test, $F_{.025} = 5.70$, fail to reject $H_0 : \sigma_1^2 = \sigma_2^2$.

CHAPTERS 11–13

1. a. In ANOVA, each population is assumed normal.

2. b. Hartley's F_{max} test compares variances (not means).

3. $F_{\text{calc}} = (744/4)/(751.5/15) = 3.71$, $F_{4,15} = 3.06$

4. a. 3;

 b. 210;

 c. No, p-value $= .9055 > .05$;

 d. No, p-value $= .3740 > .05$

5. Two-tailed test, $t_{\text{calc}} = 2.127$, d.f. $= 28$, $t_{.005} = 2.763$, fail
  to reject.

6. b. In correlation analysis, neither variable is assumed
  dependent.

7. a. $R^2 = \text{SSR/SST} = (158.3268)/(317.4074) = .4988$.

8. b. d.f. $= n - 2 = 25$, $t_{.025} = 2.060$

9. a, c. Both formulas give the same t_{calc}.

10. a. false (residual is within $\pm 1 s_{yx}$);

 b. true;

 c. true

11. a. Evans' Rule suggests $n/k \geq 10$.

12. b. $R_{\text{adj}}^2 \leq R^2$ always, big difference would suggest weak
  predictors

13. a. because their 95% CIs do not include zero.

14. c. p-value $< .05$ for X_3 (clearly) and X_4 (barely)

15. d.f. $= 38$, $t_{.005} = \pm 2.712$, so only X_3 is significant
  ($t_{\text{calc}} = -5.378$)

Writing and Presenting Reports

Business recruiters say that written and oral communication skills are critical for success in business. Susan R. Meisinger, president and CEO of the Society for Human Resource Management, says that "In a knowledge-based economy a talented workforce with communication and critical thinking skills is necessary for organizations and the United States to be successful." Yet a survey of 431 human-resource officials in corporate America found a need for improvement in writing (www.conference-board.org). Table I.1 lists the key business skills needed for *initial* and *long-range* success, as well as some common *weaknesses.*

For Initial Job Success	For Long-Range Job Success	Common Weaknesses
Report writing	Managerial accounting	Communication skills
Accounting principles	Managerial economics	Writing skills
Mathematics	Managerial finance	Immaturity
Statistics	Oral communication	Unrealistic expectations

TABLE I.1

**Skills Needed for
Success in Business**

Mini Case I.1

Can You Read a Company Annual Report?

Many people say that company annual reports are hard to read. To investigate this claim, Prof. Feng Li of the University of Michigan's Ross School of Business analyzed the readability of more than 50,000 annual reports. One of his readability measures was the Gunning-Fog Index (GFI) which estimates how many years of formal education would be needed in order to read and understand a block of text. For company annual reports, the average GFI was 19.4. Since a college graduate will have 16 years of education, almost a Ph.D. level of education is apparently required to read a typical firm's annual report. Li also found that annual reports of firms with lower earnings were harder to read. (See http://accounting.smartpros.com/x53453.xml; and *Detroit Free Press,* June 7, 2006, p. E1.)

Rules for "Power" Writing

Why is writing so important? Because someone may mention your report on warranty repairs during a meeting of department heads, and your boss may say "OK, make copies of that report so we can all see it." Next thing you know, the CEO is looking at it! Wish you'd taken more care in writing it? To avoid this awkward situation, set aside 25 percent of your allotted project time to *write* the report. You should always outline the report *before* you begin. Then complete the report in sections. Finally, ask trusted peers to review the report, and make revisions as necessary. Keep in mind that you may need to revise more than once. If you have trouble getting started, consult a good reference on technical report-writing.

While you may have creative latitude in how to organize the flow of ideas in the report, it is essential to answer the assigned question succinctly. Describe what you did and what conclusions you reached, listing the most important results first.

Use section headings to group related material and avoid lengthy paragraphs. Your report is your legacy to others who may rely on it. They will find it instructive to know about difficulties you encountered. Provide clear data so others will not need to waste time checking your data and sources. Consider placing technical details in an appendix to keep the main report simple.

If you are writing the report as part of a team, an "editor-in-chief" must be empowered to edit the material so that it is stylistically consistent, has a common voice, and flows together. Allow enough lead time so that all team members can read the final report and give their comments and corrections to the editor-in-chief.

Avoid Jargon   Experts use jargon to talk to one another, but outsiders may find it obscure or even annoying. Technical concepts must be presented so that others can understand them. If you can't communicate the importance of your work, your potential for advancement will be limited. Even if your ideas are good and hundreds of hours went into your analysis, readers up the food chain will toss your report aside if it contains too many cryptic references like SSE, MAPE, or 3-Sigma Limits.

Make It Attractive   Reports should have a title page, descriptive title, date, and author names. It's a good idea to use footers with page numbers and dates (e.g., Page 7 of 23—Draft of 10/8/06) to distinguish revised drafts.

Use wide margins so readers can take notes or write comments. Select an appropriate typeface and point size. Times Roman, Garamond, and Arial are widely accepted.

Call attention to your main points by using subheadings, bullets, **boldfaced type,** *italics,* large fonts, or color, but use special effects sparingly.

Watch Your Spelling and Grammar   To an educated reader, incorrect grammar or spelling errors are conspicuous signs of sloppy work. You don't recognize your errors—that's why you make them. Get someone you trust to red-pencil your work. Study your errors until you're sure you won't repeat them. Your best bet? Keep a dictionary handy! You can refer to it for both proper spelling and grammatical usage. Remember that Microsoft specializes in software, not English, so don't rely on spelling and grammar checkers. Here are some examples from student papers that passed the spell-checker, but each contains two errors. Can you spot them quickly?

Original	*Correction*
• "It's effects will transcend our nation's boarders."	(its, borders)
• "We cannot except this shipment on principal."	(accept, principle)
• "They seceded despite there faults."	(succeeded, their)
• "This plan won't fair well because it's to rigid."	(fare, too)
• "The amount of unhappy employees is raising."	(number, rising)

Organizing a Technical Report

Report formats vary, but a business report usually begins with an *executive summary* limited to a *single page*. Attach the full report containing discussion, explanations, tables, graphs, interpretations, and (if needed) footnotes and appendices. Use appendices for backup material. Paste your graphs and tables *into the main report* where you refer to them, and format them nicely. Each table or graph needs a title and a number. A common beginner's error is to attach a bunch of Excel printouts and graphs at the end of a technical report; most readers won't take the time to flip pages to look at them. Worse, if you put all your tables and graphs at the end, you may be tempted not to spend time formatting them nicely. There is no single acceptable style for a business report but the following would be typical:

- Executive Summary (1 page maximum)
- Introduction (1 to 3 paragraphs)
  - Statement of the problem
  - Data sources and definitions
  - Methods utilized
- Body of the Report (as long as necessary)
  - Break it into sections
  - Each section has a descriptive heading
  - Use subsection headings as necessary
  - Discuss, explain, interpret everything
  - Tables and graphs, as needed
- Conclusions (1 to 3 paragraphs)
  - Restatement of findings
  - Limitations of your analysis
  - Future research suggestions
- Bibliography and Sources
- Appendices (if needed for lengthy or technical material)

General tips:

- Avoid huge paragraphs (break them up).
- Include page numbers to help the reader take notes.
- Check spelling and grammar. Ask others to proofread the report.

Writing an Executive Summary

The goal of an **executive summary** is to permit a busy decision maker to understand what you did and what you found out *without reading the rest of the report*. In a statistical report, the executive summary *briefly* describes the task and goals, data and data sources, methods that were used, main findings of the analysis, and (if necessary) any limitations of the analysis. The main findings will occupy most of the space in the executive summary. Each other item may only rate a sentence or two. The executive summary is limited to a single page (maybe only two or three paragraphs) and should avoid technical language.

   An excellent way to evaluate your executive summary is to hand it to a peer. Ask him/her to read it and then tell you what you did and what you found out. If the peer cannot answer precisely, then your summary is deficient. The executive summary must make it *impossible to miss your main findings*. Your boss may judge you and your team by the executive summary alone. S/he may merely leaf through the report to examine key tables or graphs, or may assign someone to review your full report.

Rules for Presenting Oral Reports

The goals of an oral report are *not the same* as those of a written report. Your oral presentation must only *highlight* the main points. If your presentation does not provide the answer to an audience question, you can say, "Good question. We don't have time to discuss that further here, but it's covered in the full report. I'll be happy to talk to you about it at the end of the presentation." Or, give a brief answer so they know you did consider the matter. Keep these tips in mind while preparing your oral presentation:

- Select just a few key points you most want to convey.
- Use simple charts and diagrams to get the point across.
- Use **color** and ***fonts*** creatively to **emphasize a point.**

- Levity is nice on occasion, but avoid gratuitous jokes.
- Have backup slides or transparencies just in case.
- Rehearse to get the timing right (don't go too long).
- Refer the audience to the written report for details.
- Imagine yourself in the audience. Don't bore yourself!

The Three Ps

Pace   Many presenters speak too rapidly—partly because they are nervous and partly because they think it makes them look smarter.

FIGURE I.1

Pictures Help Make the Point

Source: Copyright © 2005 Stuart Rojstaczer. Used with permission.

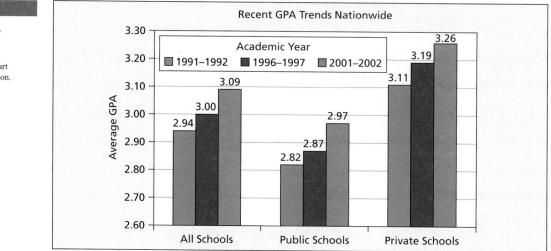

Slow down! Take a little time to introduce yourself, introduce your data, and explain what you are trying to do. If you skip the basic background and definitions, many members of the audience will not be able to follow the presentation and will have only a vague idea what you are talking about.

Planning   Create an outline to organize the ideas you want to discuss. Remember to keep it simple! You'll also need to prepare a verbal "executive summary" to tell your audience what your talk is about. Before you choose your planned opening words, *"Our team correlated robbery with income,"* you should ask yourself:

- Is the audience familiar with correlation analysis?
- Should I explain that our data came from the FBI and the 2010 U.S. Census?
- Will they know that our observations are averages for the 50 U.S. states?
- Will they know that we are talking about per capita robbery rates (not total robberies)?
- Will they know that we are using per capita personal income (not median family income)?
- Should I show them a few data values to help them visualize the data?

Don't bury them in detail, but make the first minute count. If you ran into problems or made errors in your analysis, it's OK to say so. The audience will sympathize.

Check the raw data carefully—you may be called on to answer questions. It's hard to defend yourself when you failed to catch serious errors or didn't understand a key definition.

Practice   Rehearse the oral presentation to get the timing right. Maybe your employer will send you to training classes to bolster your presentation skills. Otherwise consider videotaping yourself or practicing in front of a few peers for valuable feedback. Technical presentations may demand skills different from the ones you used in English class, so don't panic if you have a few problems.

I.1 Use your favorite Web search engine to search for each key term, and print one or two excerpts from Web sites that you found particularly interesting or useful. (a) "technical writing"; (b) "scientific reports"; (c) "presentation tips."

I.2 Go to the McGraw-Hill *OnLine Learning Center* (OLC) Web site www.mhhe.com/doane3e and select the folder called Appendix I—Business Reports. Download the document Executive Summaries.docx that contains actual executive summaries from project reports by 16 student teams. There were three introductory statistics students on each team. Their assignment was to forecast the annual revenue for a company of their choice and to write a report. The project instructions are shown in the document. Choose *three* of their executive summaries and grade them (A, A–, B+, B, B–, C+ and so on). List specific strengths and weaknesses, using the criteria for an effective executive summary in Appendix I. Write the same kinds of comments that you would think an instructor would write.

I.3 Go to the McGraw-Hill *OnLine Learning Center* (OLC) Web site www.mhhe.com/doane3e and select the folder called Appendix I—Business Reports. Download the document Oral Presentation Tips.docx. (a) Think of an oral presentation you have heard recently. After reading these tips, write three suggestions that would have helped the speaker improve. (b) Which of these tips seem most relevant for you? Why?

I.4 Go to the McGraw-Hill *OnLine Learning Center* (OLC) Web site www.mhhe.com/doane3e and select the folder called Appendix I—Business Reports. Download the document Fog Index Project.docx. (a) Follow the instructions for calculating the *Fog Index* from samples of 100 words from each of three types of publications (company annual report, business magazine, scholarly journal). (b) Report your results in the indicated table format. (c) Do the Fog Index results support your prior expectations about the degree of writing complexity in these three types of publications?

PHOTO CREDITS

INDEX

Page numbers followed by *n* refer to notes.

STUDENT'S *t* CRITICAL VALUES

This table shows the *t*-value that defines the area for the stated degrees of freedom (*d.f.*).

	Confidence Level						Confidence Level			
	.80	.90	.95	.98	.99		.80	.90	.95	.98	.99
	Significance Level for Two-Tailed Test						Significance Level for Two-Tailed Test				
	.20	.10	.05	.02	.01		.20	.10	.05	.02	.01
	Significance Level for One-Tailed Test						Significance Level for One-Tailed Test				
d.f.	.10	.05	.025	.01	.005	*d.f.*	.10	.05	.025	.01	.005
1	3.078	6.314	12.706	31.821	63.656	36	1.306	1.688	2.028	2.434	2.719
2	1.886	2.920	4.303	6.965	9.925	37	1.305	1.687	2.026	2.431	2.715
3	1.638	2.353	3.182	4.541	5.841	38	1.304	1.686	2.024	2.429	2.712
4	1.533	2.132	2.776	3.747	4.604	39	1.304	1.685	2.023	2.426	2.708
5	1.476	2.015	2.571	3.365	4.032	40	1.303	1.684	2.021	2.423	2.704
6	1.440	1.943	2.447	3.143	3.707	41	1.303	1.683	2.020	2.421	2.701
7	1.415	1.895	2.365	2.998	3.499	42	1.302	1.682	2.018	2.418	2.698
8	1.397	1.860	2.306	2.896	3.355	43	1.302	1.681	2.017	2.416	2.695
9	1.383	1.833	2.262	2.821	3.250	44	1.301	1.680	2.015	2.414	2.692
10	1.372	1.812	2.228	2.764	3.169	45	1.301	1.679	2.014	2.412	2.690
11	1.363	1.796	2.201	2.718	3.106	46	1.300	1.679	2.013	2.410	2.687
12	1.356	1.782	2.179	2.681	3.055	47	1.300	1.678	2.012	2.408	2.685
13	1.350	1.771	2.160	2.650	3.012	48	1.299	1.677	2.011	2.407	2.682
14	1.345	1.761	2.145	2.624	2.977	49	1.299	1.677	2.010	2.405	2.680
15	1.341	1.753	2.131	2.602	2.947	50	1.299	1.676	2.009	2.403	2.678
16	1.337	1.746	2.120	2.583	2.921	55	1.297	1.673	2.004	2.396	2.668
17	1.333	1.740	2.110	2.567	2.898	60	1.296	1.671	2.000	2.390	2.660
18	1.330	1.734	2.101	2.552	2.878	65	1.295	1.669	1.997	2.385	2.654
19	1.328	1.729	2.093	2.539	2.861	70	1.294	1.667	1.994	2.381	2.648
20	1.325	1.725	2.086	2.528	2.845	75	1.293	1.665	1.992	2.377	2.643
21	1.323	1.721	2.080	2.518	2.831	80	1.292	1.664	1.990	2.374	2.639
22	1.321	1.717	2.074	2.508	2.819	85	1.292	1.663	1.988	2.371	2.635
23	1.319	1.714	2.069	2.500	2.807	90	1.291	1.662	1.987	2.368	2.632
24	1.318	1.711	2.064	2.492	2.797	95	1.291	1.661	1.985	2.366	2.629
25	1.316	1.708	2.060	2.485	2.787	100	1.290	1.660	1.984	2.364	2.626
26	1.315	1.706	2.056	2.479	2.779	110	1.289	1.659	1.982	2.361	2.621
27	1.314	1.703	2.052	2.473	2.771	120	1.289	1.658	1.980	2.358	2.617
28	1.313	1.701	2.048	2.467	2.763	130	1.288	1.657	1.978	2.355	2.614
29	1.311	1.699	2.045	2.462	2.756	140	1.288	1.656	1.977	2.353	2.611
30	1.310	1.697	2.042	2.457	2.750	150	1.287	1.655	1.976	2.351	2.609
31	1.309	1.696	2.040	2.453	2.744	∞	1.282	1.645	1.960	2.326	2.576
32	1.309	1.694	2.037	2.449	2.738						
33	1.308	1.692	2.035	2.445	2.733						
34	1.307	1.691	2.032	2.441	2.728						
35	1.306	1.690	2.030	2.438	2.724						

Note: As *n* increases, critical values of Student's *t* approach the *z*-values in the last line of this table. A common rule of thumb is to use *z* when *n* > 30, but that is *not* conservative.

STANDARD NORMAL AREAS

This table shows the normal area between 0 and z. Example: $P(0 < z < 1.96) = .4750$

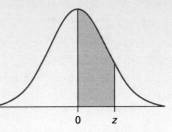

z	.00	.01	.02	.03	.04	.05	**.06**	.07	.08	.09
0.0	.0000	.0040	.0080	.0120	.0160	.0199	.0239	.0279	.0319	.0359
0.1	.0398	.0438	.0478	.0517	.0557	.0596	.0636	.0675	.0714	.0753
0.2	.0793	.0832	.0871	.0910	.0948	.0987	.1026	.1064	.1103	.1141
0.3	.1179	.1217	.1255	.1293	.1331	.1368	.1406	.1443	.1480	.1517
0.4	.1554	.1591	.1628	.1664	.1700	.1736	.1772	.1808	.1844	.1879
0.5	.1915	.1950	.1985	.2019	.2054	.2088	.2123	.2157	.2190	.2224
0.6	.2257	.2291	.2324	.2357	.2389	.2422	.2454	.2486	.2517	.2549
0.7	.2580	.2611	.2642	.2673	.2704	.2734	.2764	.2794	.2823	.2852
0.8	.2881	.2910	.2939	.2967	.2995	.3023	.3051	.3078	.3106	.3133
0.9	.3159	.3186	.3212	.3238	.3264	.3289	.3315	.3340	.3365	.3389
1.0	.3413	.3438	.3461	.3485	.3508	.3531	.3554	.3577	.3599	.3621
1.1	.3643	.3665	.3686	.3708	.3729	.3749	.3770	.3790	.3810	.3830
1.2	.3849	.3869	.3888	.3907	.3925	.3944	.3962	.3980	.3997	.4015
1.3	.4032	.4049	.4066	.4082	.4099	.4115	.4131	.4147	.4162	.4177
1.4	.4192	.4207	.4222	.4236	.4251	.4265	.4279	.4292	.4306	.4319
1.5	.4332	.4345	.4357	.4370	.4382	.4394	.4406	.4418	.4429	.4441
1.6	.4452	.4463	.4474	.4484	.4495	.4505	.4515	.4525	.4535	.4545
1.7	.4554	.4564	.4573	.4582	.4591	.4599	.4608	.4616	.4625	.4633
1.8	.4641	.4649	.4656	.4664	.4671	.4678	.4686	.4693	.4699	.4706
1.9	.4713	.4719	.4726	.4732	.4738	.4744	**.4750**	.4756	.4761	.4767
2.0	.4772	.4778	.4783	.4788	.4793	.4798	.4803	.4808	.4812	.4817
2.1	.4821	.4826	.4830	.4834	.4838	.4842	.4846	.4850	.4854	.4857
2.2	.4861	.4864	.4868	.4871	.4875	.4878	.4881	.4884	.4887	.4890
2.3	.4893	.4896	.4898	.4901	.4904	.4906	.4909	.4911	.4913	.4916
2.4	.4918	.4920	.4922	.4925	.4927	.4929	.4931	.4932	.4934	.4936
2.5	.4938	.4940	.4941	.4943	.4945	.4946	.4948	.4949	.4951	.4952
2.6	.4953	.4955	.4956	.4957	.4959	.4960	.4961	.4962	.4963	.4964
2.7	.4965	.4966	.4967	.4968	.4969	.4970	.4971	.4972	.4973	.4974
2.8	.4974	.4975	.4976	.4977	.4977	.4978	.4979	.4979	.4980	.4981
2.9	.4981	.4982	.4982	.4983	.4984	.4984	.4985	.4985	.4986	.4986
3.0	.49865	.49869	.49874	.49878	.49882	.49886	.49889	.49893	.49896	.49900
3.1	.49903	.49906	.49910	.49913	.49916	.49918	.49921	.49924	.49926	.49929
3.2	.49931	.49934	.49936	.49938	.49940	.49942	.49944	.49946	.49948	.49950
3.3	.49952	.49953	.49955	.49957	.49958	.49960	.49961	.49962	.49964	.49965
3.4	.49966	.49968	.49969	.49970	.49971	.49972	.49973	.49974	.49975	.49976
3.5	.49977	.49978	.49978	.49979	.49980	.49981	.49981	.49982	.49983	.49983
3.6	.49984	.49985	.49985	.49986	.49986	.49987	.49987	.49988	.49988	.49989
3.7	.49989	.49990	.49990	.49990	.49991	.49991	.49992	.49992	.49992	.49992

CUMULATIVE STANDARD NORMAL DISTRIBUTION

This table shows the normal area less than z. Example: $P(z < -1.96) = .0250$

z	.00	.01	.02	.03	.04	.05	**.06**	.07	.08	.09
−3.7	.00011	.00010	.00010	.00010	.00009	.00009	.00008	.00008	.00008	.00008
−3.6	.00016	.00015	.00015	.00014	.00014	.00013	.00013	.00012	.00012	.00011
−3.5	.00023	.00022	.00022	.00021	.00020	.00019	.00019	.00018	.00017	.00017
−3.4	.00034	.00032	.00031	.00030	.00029	.00028	.00027	.00026	.00025	.00024
−3.3	.00048	.00047	.00045	.00043	.00042	.00040	.00039	.00038	.00036	.00035
−3.2	.00069	.00066	.00064	.00062	.00060	.00058	.00056	.00054	.00052	.00050
−3.1	.00097	.00094	.00090	.00087	.00084	.00082	.00079	.00076	.00074	.00071
−3.0	.00135	.00131	.00126	.00122	.00118	.00114	.00111	.00107	.00104	.00100
−2.9	.0019	.0018	.0018	.0017	.0016	.0016	.0015	.0015	.0014	.0014
−2.8	.0026	.0025	.0024	.0023	.0023	.0022	.0021	.0021	.0020	.0019
−2.7	.0035	.0034	.0033	.0032	.0031	.0030	.0029	.0028	.0027	.0026
−2.6	.0047	.0045	.0044	.0043	.0041	.0040	.0039	.0038	.0037	.0036
−2.5	.0062	.0060	.0059	.0057	.0055	.0054	.0052	.0051	.0049	.0048
−2.4	.0082	.0080	.0078	.0075	.0073	.0071	.0069	.0068	.0066	.0064
−2.3	.0107	.0104	.0102	.0099	.0096	.0094	.0091	.0089	.0087	.0084
−2.2	.0139	.0136	.0132	.0129	.0125	.0122	.0119	.0116	.0113	.0110
−2.1	.0179	.0174	.0170	.0166	.0162	.0158	.0154	.0150	.0146	.0143
−2.0	.0228	.0222	.0217	.0212	.0207	.0202	.0197	.0192	.0188	.0183
−1.9	.0287	.0281	.0274	.0268	.0262	.0256	**.0250**	.0244	.0239	.0233
−1.8	.0359	.0351	.0344	.0336	.0329	.0322	.0314	.0307	.0301	.0294
−1.7	.0446	.0436	.0427	.0418	.0409	.0401	.0392	.0384	.0375	.0367
−1.6	.0548	.0537	.0526	.0516	.0505	.0495	.0485	.0475	.0465	.0455
−1.5	.0668	.0655	.0643	.0630	.0618	.0606	.0594	.0582	.0571	.0559
−1.4	.0808	.0793	.0778	.0764	.0749	.0735	.0721	.0708	.0694	.0681
−1.3	.0968	.0951	.0934	.0918	.0901	.0885	.0869	.0853	.0838	.0823
−1.2	.1151	.1131	.1112	.1093	.1075	.1056	.1038	.1020	.1003	.0985
−1.1	.1357	.1335	.1314	.1292	.1271	.1251	.1230	.1210	.1190	.1170
−1.0	.1587	.1562	.1539	.1515	.1492	.1469	.1446	.1423	.1401	.1379
−0.9	.1841	.1814	.1788	.1762	.1736	.1711	.1685	.1660	.1635	.1611
−0.8	.2119	.2090	.2061	.2033	.2005	.1977	.1949	.1922	.1894	.1867
−0.7	.2420	.2389	.2358	.2327	.2296	.2266	.2236	.2206	.2177	.2148
−0.6	.2743	.2709	.2676	.2643	.2611	.2578	.2546	.2514	.2483	.2451
−0.5	.3085	.3050	.3015	.2981	.2946	.2912	.2877	.2843	.2810	.2776
−0.4	.3446	.3409	.3372	.3336	.3300	.3264	.3228	.3192	.3156	.3121
−0.3	.3821	.3783	.3745	.3707	.3669	.3632	.3594	.3557	.3520	.3483
−0.2	.4207	.4168	.4129	.4090	.4052	.4013	.3974	.3936	.3897	.3859
−0.1	.4602	.4562	.4522	.4483	.4443	.4404	.4364	.4325	.4286	.4247
−0.0	.5000	.4960	.4920	.4880	.4841	.4801	.4761	.4721	.4681	.4641

This table shows the normal area less than z. Example: $P(z < 1.96) = .9750$

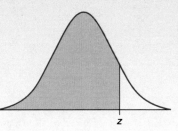

z	.00	.01	.02	.03	.04	.05	**.06**	.07	.08	.09
0.0	.5000	.5040	.5080	.5120	.5160	.5199	.5239	.5279	.5319	.5359
0.1	.5398	.5438	.5478	.5517	.5557	.5596	.5636	.5675	.5714	.5753
0.2	.5793	.5832	.5871	.5910	.5948	.5987	.6026	.6064	.6103	.6141
0.3	.6179	.6217	.6255	.6293	.6331	.6368	.6406	.6443	.6480	.6517
0.4	.6554	.6591	.6628	.6664	.6700	.6736	.6772	.6808	.6844	.6879
0.5	.6915	.6950	.6985	.7019	.7054	.7088	.7123	.7157	.7190	.7224
0.6	.7257	.7291	.7324	.7357	.7389	.7422	.7454	.7486	.7517	.7549
0.7	.7580	.7611	.7642	.7673	.7704	.7734	.7764	.7794	.7823	.7852
0.8	.7881	.7910	.7939	.7967	.7995	.8023	.8051	.8078	.8106	.8133
0.9	.8159	.8186	.8212	.8238	.8264	.8289	.8315	.8340	.8365	.8389
1.0	.8413	.8438	.8461	.8485	.8508	.8531	.8554	.8577	.8599	.8621
1.1	.8643	.8665	.8686	.8708	.8729	.8749	.8770	.8790	.8810	.8830
1.2	.8849	.8869	.8888	.8907	.8925	.8944	.8962	.8980	.8997	.9015
1.3	.9032	.9049	.9066	.9082	.9099	.9115	.9131	.9147	.9162	.9177
1.4	.9192	.9207	.9222	.9236	.9251	.9265	.9279	.9292	.9306	.9319
1.5	.9332	.9345	.9357	.9370	.9382	.9394	.9406	.9418	.9429	.9441
1.6	.9452	.9463	.9474	.9484	.9495	.9505	.9515	.9525	.9535	.9545
1.7	.9554	.9564	.9573	.9582	.9591	.9599	.9608	.9616	.9625	.9633
1.8	.9641	.9649	.9656	.9664	.9671	.9678	.9686	.9693	.9699	.9706
1.9	.9713	.9719	.9726	.9732	.9738	.9744	**.9750**	.9756	.9761	.9767
2.0	.9772	.9778	.9783	.9788	.9793	.9798	.9803	.9808	.9812	.9817
2.1	.9821	.9826	.9830	.9834	.9838	.9842	.9846	.9850	.9854	.9857
2.2	.9861	.9864	.9868	.9871	.9875	.9878	.9881	.9884	.9887	.9890
2.3	.9893	.9896	.9898	.9901	.9904	.9906	.9909	.9911	.9913	.9916
2.4	.9918	.9920	.9922	.9925	.9927	.9929	.9931	.9932	.9934	.9936
2.5	.9938	.9940	.9941	.9943	.9945	.9946	.9948	.9949	.9951	.9952
2.6	.9953	.9955	.9956	.9957	.9959	.9960	.9961	.9962	.9963	.9964
2.7	.9965	.9966	.9967	.9968	.9969	.9970	.9971	.9972	.9973	.9974
2.8	.9974	.9975	.9976	.9977	.9977	.9978	.9979	.9979	.9980	.9981
2.9	.9981	.9982	.9982	.9983	.9984	.9984	.9985	.9985	.9986	.9986
3.0	.99865	.99869	.99874	.99878	.99882	.99886	.99889	.99893	.99896	.99900
3.1	.99903	.99906	.99910	.99913	.99916	.99918	.99921	.99924	.99926	.99929
3.2	.99931	.99934	.99936	.99938	.99940	.99942	.99944	.99946	.99948	.99950
3.3	.99952	.99953	.99955	.99957	.99958	.99960	.99961	.99962	.99964	.99965
3.4	.99966	.99968	.99969	.99970	.99971	.99972	.99973	.99974	.99975	.99976
3.5	.99977	.99978	.99978	.99979	.99980	.99981	.99981	.99982	.99983	.99983
3.6	.99984	.99985	.99985	.99986	.99986	.99987	.99987	.99988	.99988	.99989
3.7	.99989	.99990	.99990	.99990	.99991	.99991	.99992	.99992	.99992	.99992